OUTLINES OF DAIRY TECHNOLOGY

OUTLINES OF
DAIRY TECHNOLOGY

SUKUMAR DE

Former Professor and Head of the Department of Dairy Technology,
Bidhan Chandra Krishi Viswa Vidyalaya,
West Bengal

OXFORD
UNIVERSITY PRESS

OXFORD
UNIVERSITY PRESS

YMCA Library Building, Jai Singh Road, New Delhi 110001

Oxford University Press is a department of the University of Oxford.
It furthers the University's objective of excellence in research, scholarship,
and education by publishing worldwide in

Oxford   New York
Auckland   Cape Town   Dar es Salaam   Hong Kong   Karachi
Kuala Lumpur   Madrid   Melbourne   Mexico City   Nairobi
New Delhi   Shanghai   Taipei   Toronto

With offices in
Argentina   Austria   Brazil   Chile   Czech Republic   France   Greece
Guatemala   Hungary   Italy   Japan   Poland   Portugal   Singapore
South Korea   Switzerland   Thailand   Turkey   Ukraine   Vietnam

Oxford is a registered trade mark of Oxford University Press
in the UK and in certain other countries.

Published in India
by Oxford University Press

© Department of English, University of Delhi 1991

The moral rights of the author/s have been asserted.

Database right Oxford University Press (maker)

First published 1991
Nineteenth impression 2005

ISBN 0-19-561194-2

Printed in India by Ram Book Binding House, Delhi 110020
and published by Manzar Khan, Oxford University Press
YMCA Library Building, Jai Singh Road, New Delhi 110001

This book is dedicated to
my wife Shailaja,
without whose encouragement,
inspiration and moral support,
it would never have been
written.

CONTENTS

CHAPTER

FOREWORD

A competent teacher of dairy technology who has had a succession of undergraduates to handle, is bound to know how to present the 'basics' and 'essentials' of his subject to students of varying calibre and receptivity. As a research worker, who also guides students doing postgraduate work, he has to remain in close touch with recent advances made in his field. Professor Sukumar De, the author of this work, is such a person and is, in addition, a proven pioneer in his field who has contributed to our knowledge of the peculiarities and problems which dairying in India presents. Given this background, his special qualifications to write a textbook on dairy technology cannot be in doubt.

Ever since I first met him in 1946 as an esteemed colleague, Professor Sukumar De has been both a teacher and a researcher. This, together with his membership for more than three decades of the staff of an institution of unquestionable pre-eminence—the National Dairy Research Institute, Karnal—has provided Professor De with a rich background for writing this book.

A perusal of *Outlines of Dairy Technology* amply fulfils the specialist's expectations. Its treatment of the subject-matter of each chapter, and its special attention to the Indian context, is in the best traditions of scholarship. In its five hundred odd pages, divided into twelve chapters and five appendices, every aspect of dairy technology conforming to the approved diploma/degree syllabus has been discussed with skill and in a manner at once succinct and economic in expression. The sequence of treatment is well thought-out and appropriate.

The impetus given to the development of dairying in India, especially during the last quarter of a century, encouraging enquiries, information and research, has also found a place in the book, in sufficient detail to contribute to the knowledge of students/fellow professionals, while at the same time arousing their interest and curiosity to read beyond it.

I feel certain that the book will be keenly sought after not only by students of dairying in India (and other developing countries) but also by teachers, researchers, plant managers and extension workers who need a dependable reference book at hand.

S. C. RAY

PREFACE

The Indian Dairy Industry has made rapid progress since Independence. A large number of modern milk plants and product factories have since been established. These organized dairies have been successfully engaged in the routine commercial production of pasteurized bottled milk and various Western and Indian dairy products. Most of the supervisory and technical personnel in these dairies have had their dairy education in this country, although a few have been trained abroad as well. The author has had the privilege of sharing his knowledge of dairy technology with many of these persons during the past two or three decades. Lately there has been a persistent demand from these and other sources that I write a book on Dairy Technology for the benefit of students and industry alike.

Although standard books dealing with dairy products have been published in the West, their expense and non-availability on easy terms makes it rather difficult for Indian students to procure them. It was, therefore, considered desirable to compile in one volume the salient aspects of the processing and manufacture of various types of milks and milk products. This book has been written in clear and concise language, the text-matter supplemented with tables, illustrative problems and their solutions, and photographs of some of the equipment used in the dairy industry. Moreover, enough current scientific information has been included in it to justify its publication. A chapter on Indian Dairy Products is a special feature. I am sure it will not only serve as a textbook on Dairy Technology for Indian students but also as a reference book for our dairy factory supervisors.

The book has been divided into twelve chapters, viz., Market Milk, Special Milks, Cream, Butter, Butteroil, Ice Cream, Cheese, Condensed Milks, Dried Milks, Dried Milk Products, Indian Dairy Products and dairy By-products. At the end, there are five appendices and a list of books recommended for further reading.

I am indebted to the authors, editors and publishers of various scientific books, periodicals and pamphlets from which most of the information presented here has been gathered. In particular, I have freely consulted the following:

1. *Market Milk* by H. H. Sommer
2. *The Butter Maker's Manual* by F. H. McDowall
3. *Ice Cream* by W. S. Arbuckle
4. *Cheese* by J. G. Davis
5. *Condensed Milk and Milk Powder* by O. F. Hunziker
6. *Drying of Milk and Milk Products* by C. W. Hall and T. I. Hedrick
7. *By-Products from Milk* by B. H. Webb and E. O. Whittier
8. *Judging Dairy Products* by J. A. Nelson and G. M. Trout
9. *Indian Dairy Products* by K. S. Rangappa and K. T. Achaya
10. *Milk Products of India* by M. R. Srinivasan and C. P. Anantakrishnan
11. *Indian Dairyman* and *Indian Journal of Dairy Science*
12. *Indian Standards*

I am indeed grateful to Sri Mohindra Singh Saini, stenographer in Dairy Technology Division, N.D.R.I., Karnal, for typing the manuscript diligently and accurately. Thanks are due to all my students (past and present), friends and well-wishers for their continued support in this endeavour.

I would like to express my deep gratitude to Dr S. C. Ray, President, Indian Dairy Association, for not only writing the Foreword, but also for offering invaluable suggestions regarding the text. I am highly indebted to Dr D. Sundaresan, Director, N.D.R.I., Karnal, for issuing me a letter of recommendation. I record my grateful thanks to the National Book Trust, India, for their generous financial assistance which has made the book easily accessible to students. Lastly, to Oxford University Press, New Delhi, to whom I am most indebted, since without their kind co-operation this book would not have seen the light of day.

September 1977   SUKUMAR DE

GENERAL INTRODUCTION

A dairy is a place for handling milk and milk products. Technology refers to the application of scientific knowledge for practical purposes. Dairy technology has been defined as that branch of dairy science which deals with the processing of milk and the manufacture of milk products on an industrial scale. In developed dairying countries such as the U.S.A., the year 1850 is seen as the dividing line between farm and factory-scale production. Various factors contributed to this change in these countries, viz. concentration of population in cities where jobs were plentiful, rapid industrialization, improvement of transportation facilities, development of machines, etc. Whereas the rural areas were identified for milk production, the urban centres were selected for the location of milk processing plants and product manufacturing factories. These plants and factories were rapidly expanded and modernized with improved machinery and equipment to secure the various advantages of large-scale production. This heralded the advent of dairy technology in these countries.

In India, dairying has been practised as a rural cottage industry since the remote past. Semi-commercial dairying started with the establishment of military dairy farms and co-operative milk unions throughout the country towards the end of the nineteenth century. However, market milk technology may be considered to have commenced in 1950, with the functioning of the Central Dairy of Aarey Milk Colony, and milk product technology in 1956 with the establishment of AMUL Dairy, Anand.

In this book, *Outlines of Dairy Technology*, the main principles of the production of various types of milks and milk products, both Western and Indian, have been discussed in sufficient detail to meet normal requirements. A few books, some of a general nature, and others dealing with specific products, have been recommended for supplementary information.

OUTLINES OF DAIRY TECHNOLOGY

1 MARKET MILK

1.1 Introduction

As a major enterprise, the market milk industry is of comparatively recent origin even in developed dairying countries (such as the U.S.A.). Though ancient written records report milk as an important food, its processing and distribution as a separate commercial business did not develop in those countries until the concentration of population in the cities reached a high level in the middle of the nineteenth century.

During the earlier years, each household in those countries maintained its 'family cow' or secured milk from its neighbour who supplied those living close by. As the urban population increased, fewer households could keep a cow for private use. The high cost of milk production, problems of sanitation (which led to sanitary regulations by Public Health Authorities), etc., restricted the practice; and gradually the family cow in the city was eliminated and city cattle were all sent back to the rural areas.

Gradually farmers within easy driving distance began delivering milk over regular routes in the cities. This was the beginning of the fluid milk-sheds which surround the large cities of today. Prior to the 1850s most milk was necessarily produced within a short distance of the place of consumption because of lack of suitable means of transportation and refrigeration.

With modern knowledge of the protection of milk during transportation, it became possible to locate dairies where land was less expensive and crops could be grown more economically. The milk supply of the large cities of the U.S.A. now comes largely from 80–160 kms or more away.

Nearly all the milk in the U.S.A. before 1900 was delivered as raw (natural) milk. Once pasteurization was introduced, it caught on rapidly. Mechanical refrigeration contributed to the rapid development of the factory system of market milk distribution.

In India, the market milk industry may be said to have started in 1950–1 when the Central Dairy of Aarey Milk Colony was commissioned and went into stream. The industry is still in its infancy and barely 10 per cent of our total milk production undergoes organized handling.

1.2 Definition

The term 'market milk' refers to fluid whole milk that is sold to individuals usually for direct consumption. It excludes milk consumed on the farm and that used for the manufacture of dairy products.

Note. Milk may be defined as the whole, fresh, clean, lacteal secretion obtained by the complete milking of one or more healthy milch animals, excluding that obtained within 15 days before or 5 days after calving or such periods as may be necessary to render the milk practically colostrum-free, and containing the minimum prescribed percentages of milk fat and milk-solids-not-fat. In India, the term 'milk', when unqualified, refers to cow or buffalo milk, or a combination of the two. (Also see 1.4.)

1.3 The Market Milk Industry in India and Abroad

(a) Although a beginning in organized milk handling was made in India with the establishment of Military Dairy Farms (oldest: Allahabad, 1889), the salient features of the market milk industry so far have been:

(i) Handling of milk in Co-operative Milk Unions (oldest: Allahabad, 1913) established all over the country on a small scale in the early stages.

(ii) Long distance refrigerated rail-transport of milk from Anand to Bombay since 1945.

(iii) Pasteurization and bottling of milk on a large scale for organized distribution was started at Aarey (1950), Worli (1961), Calcutta (Haringhata, 1959), Delhi (1959), Madras (1963), etc.

(iv) Establishment of Milk Plants under the Five-Year Plans for Dairy Development all over India. These were taken up with the dual object of increasing the national level of milk consumption and ensuring better returns to the primary milk producer. Their main aim was to produce more, better and cheaper milk. The actual expenditure is given in Table 1.1.

TABLE 1.1

Actual expenditure on the market milk industry in India's Five-Year Plans

Plan Period		Expenditure
I Five-Year Plan	(1951–6)	Rs 7.8 crores
II –do–	(1956–61)	Rs 12.0 crores
III –do–	(1961–6)	Rs 36.6 crores
Spill-over I to III	(1966–7)	Rs 25.7 crores

SOURCE: *Dairying in India* by Khurody (1974).

(b) The present status of the market milk industry in this country may be gauged from the following facts and figures:

(i) Total annual milk production in India has been estimated at 25 million tonnes (1976).

(ii) Although India possesses nearly one-fifth of the world's bovine population (cow, buffalo and goat), milk production in India accounts for only about one-sixteenth of the world's total of 428 million tonnes (1975).

(iii) Due to the large human population, daily per capita milk consumption today (1975) works out to about 114 g, while that recommended by the Medical Authorities is 280 g.

(iv) The main reasons for this acute shortage of milk are low milk-yielding capacity of the average Indian cow and acute shortage of feeds and fodder.

(v) Lack of organized milk production and collection, restricted transport facilities (especially refrigerated) and shortage of processing and marketing organizations have greatly hampered the growth of the market milk industry.

(vi) Poor-quality milk, widespread adulteration, and lack of quality consciousness among the great majority of consumers have further aggravated the situation.

(c) Table 1.2 gives India's position in relation to some of the important milk producing countries of the world:

TABLE 1.2

*India's position in relation to milk producing countries
of the world*

Country	Animals in milk (millions)	Milk yield/ milking cow/ annum (kg)	Total milk production* (1000 × tonnes)
U.S.S.R.	41.2	2200	82,900
U.S.A.	14.1	4154	52,800
France	8.7	3130	30,413
India	53.0	B—450 C—157	21,360
W. Germany	5.9	3779	22,545
Poland	6.2	2361	14,860
U.K.	5.3	3950	13,000

*Cows, buffaloes, goats and sheep.

SOURCE: *F.A.O. Production Year Book*, 1970.

(d) The production of milk in India for selected years is given
n Table 1.3.

TABLE 1.3

Milk production in India

Year	Production (Million tonnes)
1951–2	17.5
1956–7	19.7
1961–2	20.4
1968–9	21.2
1973–4	23.2
1978–9	28.6 (estimate)

SOURCE: *Dairying in India*, IDSA Publication, 1976.

(e) The proportion of cow, buffalo and goat milks to total milk
production in India is given in Table 1.4.

(f) The density of milk production (i.e., daily milk production)
for India is given in Table 1.5.

(g) A summary showing the utilization of 19.4 million tonnes
of milk in India (1966) is given in Table 1.6.

TABLE 1.4
Species contribution to total milk production in India

Type of Milk	Total production	
	Per cent	Amt (1000 × tonnes)
Cow	33.6	8,400
Buffalo	63.6	15,900
Goat	2.8	681

Source: *F.A.O. Production Year Book*, 1974.

TABLE 1.5
Density of milk production in India

Category	Per village	State	Per sq. km
Min.	11 kg	Assam	2.1 kg
Ave.	88 kg	Indian Union	15.6 kg
Max.	472 kg	Delhi	98.0 kg

Note. District Amritsar 113.3 kg/sq. km
Denmark 362.1 kg/sq. km
Source: *Report of the Marketing of Milk in the Indian Union* (1961).

TABLE 1.6
Summary of utilization of milk in India

Items	Percentage in relation to	
	Total milk production	Total quantity converted into milk products
Fluid milk	44.5	—
Manufactured milk	55.5	(100)
Ghee	32.7	58.9
Dahi	7.8	14.0
Butter	6.3	11.4
Khoa	4.9	8.8
Ice cream	0.7	1.3
Cream	1.9	3.4
Other products (Mainly chhana)	1.2	2.2

Source: *Indian Dairyman* (1976), **28** (11), 512.

(h) The daily per capita consumption of milk in some of the major developed dairying countries (1970) is given in Table 1.7, and that in developing countries in Table 1.8.

TABLE 1.7

Daily per capita milk consumption in some developed countries of the world (1970)

Country	Estimated daily per capita consumption in terms of liquid milk (g)	Country	Estimated daily per capita consumption in terms of liquid milk (g)
U.K.	1315	France	1335
Australia	1144	W. Germany	1301
New Zealand	2032	Netherlands	1121
Canada	1158	Norway	2046
U.S.A.	1003	Sweden	1812
Denmark	1188	Switzerland	1588
Finland	2165		

SOURCE: Miscellaneous.

TABLE 1.8

Daily per capita milk consumption in some developing countries of the world (1975)

Country	Estimated daily per capita consumption in terms of liquid milk (g)	Country	Estimated daily per capita consumption in terms of liquid milk (g)
Bangladesh	51	Israel	577
India	114	Japan*	122
Iran	172	Pakistan	225
Iraq	170	Philippines	2

*Now considered a developed country.
SOURCE: *Indian Dairyman*, **29** (3), 150 (1977).

Note. The market milk industry in the advanced dairying countries of the world has now reached a high level in sanitary production, transportation, processing and distribution. These improved conditions are a result of the passage of dairy and milk-control ordinances in nearly all major cities, and of control laws in states where dairying is important. Credit should also be given to many producers, distributors and manufacturers of dairy equipment for setting high standards.

1.4 Indian Standards

According to the Prevention of Food Adulteration (PFA) Rules, 1976, the standards for different classes and designations of milk in India should be as given in Table 1.9.

TABLE 1.9

Standards of different milks in India

Class of milk	Designation	Locality	Minimum	
			% MF*	% MSNF†
Buffalo milk	Raw, pasteurized, boiled, flavoured and sterilized	Assam; Bihar; Chandigarh; Delhi; Gujarat; Maharashtra; Haryana; Punjab; Uttar Pradesh; West Bengal	6.0	9.0
	–do–	Andaman and Nicobar; Andhra Pradesh; Dadra and Nagar-Haveli; Goa, Daman and Diu; Kerala, Himachal Pradesh; Lakshadweep; Tamilnadu; Madhya Pradesh; Manipur; Karnataka; Nagaland; NEFA; Orissa; Pondicherry; Rajasthan; Tripura	5.0	9.0
Cow milk	–do–	Chandigarh; Haryana; Punjab	4.0	8.5
	–do–	Andaman and Nicobar; Andhra Pradesh; Assam; Bihar; Dadra and Nagar-Haveli; Delhi; Gujarat; Goa, Daman and Diu; Himachal Pradesh; Kerala; Madhya Pradesh; Maharashtra; Tamilnadu; Karnataka; Manipur; Nagaland; NEFA; Pondicherry; Rajasthan; Tripura; Uttar Pradesh; West Bengal; Lakshadweep	3.5	8.5

*Milk fat.
†Milk-solids-not-fat.

Class of milk	Designation	Locality	Minimum	
			% MF*	% MSNF†
		Orissa	3.0	9.0
Goat or sheep milk	Raw, pasteurized, boiled, flavoured and sterilized	Chandigarh; Haryana; Kerala; Madhya Pradesh; Maharashtra; Punjab; Uttar Pradesh	3.5	9.0
	–do–	Andaman and Nicobar; Andhra Pradesh; Assam; Bihar; Dadra and Nagar-Haveli; Delhi; Goa, Daman and Diu; Gujarat; Himachal Pradesh; Lakshadweep; Tamilnadu; Karnataka; Manipur; Nagaland; NEFA; Pondicherry; Orissa; Rajasthan; Tripura; West Bengal	3.0	9.0
Standardized milk		All India	4.5	8.5
Recombined milk		All India	3.0	8.5
Toned milk		All India	3.0	8.5
Double toned milk		All India	1.5	9.0
Skim milk	–do–	All India	Not more than 0.5	8.7

Note. (i) When milk is offered for sale without any indication of the class, the standards prescribed for buffalo milk shall apply.

(ii) The heat-treatment for the various designated milks shall be as follows:

Designation	Heat-treatment
Raw	Nil
Pasteurized	Pasteurization
Boiled	Boiling
Flavoured	Pasteurization or sterilization
Sterilized	Sterilization

1.5 Composition

(a) *Milk constituents.* The constituents of milk may be listed diagrammatically as in Fig. 1.1.

The 'major' constituents of milk are: water, fat, protein, lactose, ash or mineral matter. The 'minor' constituents are: phospholipids, sterols, vitamins, enzymes, pigments, etc. The 'true' constituents are: milk fat, casein, lactose.

(b) *Composition of milk*

(i) The average chemical composition of milk of different species is given in Table 1.10.

TABLE 1.10

Chemical composition of milk of different species

Name of species	Percentage composition				
	Water	Fat	Protein	Lactose	Ash
Ass	90.0	1.3	1.7	6.5	0.5
Buffalo	84.2	6.6	3.9	5.2	0.8
Camel	86.5	3.1	4.0	5.6	0.8
Cat	84.6	3.8	9.1	4.9	0.6
Cow (foreign)	86.6	4.6	3.4	4.9	0.7
Dog	75.4	9.6	11.2	3.1	0.7
Elephant	67.8	19.6	3.1	8.8	0.7
Ewe	79.4	8.6	6.7	4.3	1.0
Goat	86.5	4.5	3.5	4.7	0.8
Guinea-pig	82.2	5.5	8.5	2.9	0.9
Human	87.7	3.6	1.8	6.8	0.1
Llama	86.5	3.2	3.9	5.6	0.8
Mare	89.1	1.6	2.7	6.1	0.5
Porpoise	41.1	45.8	11.2	1.3	0.6
Reindeer	68.2	17.1	10.4	2.3	1.5
Sow	89.6	4.8	1.3	3.4	0.9
Whale	70.1	19.6	9.5	—	1.0

SOURCE: *Chemistry of Milk* by Davies (1939).

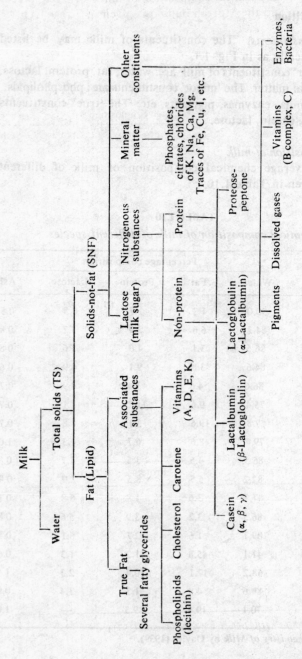

SOURCE: *A Text-book of Dairy Chemistry* by Ling (1948).

Fig. 1.1 Milk Constituents

(ii) The average chemical composition of milk of a few breeds of Indian cows and the Murrah buffalo is given in Table 1.11.

TABLE 1.11

Chemical composition of milk of Indian breeds

Breed of cow/buffalo	Percentage composition				
	Water	Fat	Protein	Lactose	Ash
Sindhi	86.07	4.90	3.42	4.91	0.70
Gir	86.44	4.73	3.32	4.85	0.66
Tharparkar	86.58	4.55	3.36	4.83	0.68
Sahiwal	86.42	4.55	3.33	5.04	0.66
Murrah	83.63	6.56	3.88	5.23	0.70

SOURCE: *IDRI Annual Report* (1948).

Note. See Appendix II for more information on the composition of buffalo milk.

(iii) The average chemical composition of milk of some foreign breeds of cows is given in Table 1.12.

TABLE 1.12

Chemical composition of milk of foreign breeds of cow

Breed	Percentage composition				
	Water	Fat	Protein	Lactose	Ash
Holstein	87.74	3.40	3.22	4.87	0.68
Shorthorn	87.19	3.94	3.32	4.99	0.70
Ayrshire	87.10	4.00	3.58	4.67	0.68
Brown Swiss	86.59	4.01	3.61	5.04	0.73
Guernsey	85.39	4.95	3.91	4.93	0.74
Jersey	85.09	5.37	3.92	4.93	0.71

SOURCE: *The Fluid-Milk Industry* by Henderson (1971).

(iv) The detailed composition of milk is given in Table 1.13.

TABLE 1.13
Detailed composition of milk

Constituents or group of constituents	Approx. concentration (Weight per litre of milk)
Water	860 to 880 g
Lipids in Emulsion Phase	
Milk fat (a mixture of mixed triglycerides)	30 to 50 g
Phospholipids (lecithins, cephalins, sphingomyelins, etc.	0.30 g
Sterols	0.10 g
Carotenoids	
Vitamins A, D, E and K	
Proteins in Colloidal Dispersion	
Casein (α, β, γ fractions)	25 g
β-lactoglobulin(s)	3 g
α-lactalbumin	0.7 g
Albumin, pseudoglobulin, etc.	
Enzymes (catalase, peroxidase, phosphatases, amylases, lipases, proteases, etc.)	
Dissolved materials	
Carbohydrates	
Lactose (α and β)	45 to 50 g
Glucose	50 mg
Inorganic and Organic Ions and Salts	
Calcium*	1.25 g
Phosphate (as PO_4)	2.10 g
Citrates* (as citric acid)	2.00 g
Chloride	1.00 g
Sodium, potassium, magnesium, etc.	
Water-soluble Vitamins	
Thiamine, riboflavin, niacin, pyridoxine, pantothenic acid, biotin, folic acid, vitamin B_{12}, etc.	
Ascorbic acid	
Nitrogenous Materials (not Proteins or Vitamins)	
Ammonia, amino-acids, urea, creatine or creatinine, uric acid, etc.	
Gases (milk exposed to air)	
Carbon dioxide, oxygen, nitrogen, etc.	
Trace Elements	
Those usually present are copper, iron, etc.	

*Partly in colloidal dispersion.

SOURCE: *Principles of Dairy Chemistry* by Jenness and Patton (1969).

1.6 Factors Affecting Composition of Milk

(a) Milk differs widely in composition. All milks contain the same kind of constituents, but in varying amounts. Milk from individual cows shows greater variation than mixed herd milk. The variation is always greater in small herds than in large ones. In general, milk fat shows the greatest daily variation, then comes protein, followed by ash and sugar.

(b) The factors affecting the composition of milk are:

(i) *Species.* Each species yields milk of a characteristic composition.

(ii) *Breed.* In general, breeds producing the largest amounts of milk yield milk of a lower fat percentage.

(iii) *Individuality.* Each cow tends to yield milk of a composition that is characteristic of the individual.

(iv) *Interval of milking.* In general, a longer interval is associated with more milk with a lower fat test.

(v) *Completeness of milking.* If the cow is completely milked, the test is normal; if not, it is usually lower.

(vi) *Frequency of milking.* Whether a cow is milked two, three or four times a day, it has no great effect on the fat test.

(vii) *Irregularity of milking.* Frequent changes in the time and interval of milking result in lower tests.

(viii) *Day-to-day milking.* May show variations for the individual cow.

(ix) *Disease and abnormal conditions.* These tend to alter the composition of milk, especially when they result in a fall in yield.

(x) *Portion of milking.* Foremilk is low in fat content (less than 1 per cent), while strippings are highest (close to 10 per cent). The other milk constituents are only slightly affected on a fat-free basis.

(xi) *Stage of lactation.* The first secretion after calving (colostrum) is very different from milk in its composition and general properties. The change from colostrum to milk takes place within a few days.

(xii) *Yield.* For a single cow, there is a tendency for increased yields to be accompanied by a lower fat percentage, and vice versa.

(xiii) *Feeding.* Has temporary effect only.

(xiv) *Season.* The percentages of both fat and solids-not-fat show slight but well-defined variations during the course of the year.

(xv) *Age.* The fat percentage in milk declines slightly as the cow grows older.

(xvi) *Condition of cow at calving.* If the cow is in good physical condition when calving, it will yield milk of a higher fat percentage than it would if its physical condition was poor.

(xvii) *Excitement.* Both yield and composition of milk are liable to transient fluctuations during periods of excitement, for whatever reason.

(xviii) *Administration of drugs and hormones.* Certain drugs may effect temporary change in the fat percentage; injection or feeding of hormones results in increase of both milk yield and fat percentage.

1.7.   Food and Nutritive Value of Milk

Milk is an almost ideal food.* It has high nutritive value. It supplies body-building proteins, bone-forming minerals and health-giving vitamins and furnishes energy-giving lactose and milk fat. Besides supplying certain essential fatty acids, it contains the above nutrients in an easily digestible and assimilable form. All these properties make milk an important food for pregnant mothers, growing children, adolescents, adults, invalids, convalescents and patients alike.

(a) *Proteins.* Milk proteins are complete proteins of high quality, i.e. they contain all the essential amino-acids in fairly large quantities.

(b) *Minerals.* Practically all the mineral elements found in milk are essential for nutrition. Milk is an excellent source of calcium and phosphorus, both of which, together with vitamin D, are essential for bone formation. Milk is rather low in iron, copper and iodine.

(c) *Vitamins.* These are accessory food factors which are essential for normal growth, health and the reproduction of living organisms. Milk is a good source of vitamin A (provided the cow is fed sufficient green feed and fodder), vitamin D (provided the cow is exposed to enough sunlight), thiamine,

---

*The drawbacks are: it is very bulky; and is deficient in iron, copper and vitamin C.

riboflavin, etc. However, milk is deficient in vitamin C.

(d) *Fat*. Milk fat (lipid) plays a significant role in the nutritive value, flavour and physical properties of milk and milk products. Besides serving as a rich source of energy, fat contains significant amounts of so-called essential fatty acids (linoleic and arachidonic). The most distinctive role which milk fat plays in dairy products concerns flavour. The rich pleasing flavour of milk lipids is not duplicated by any other type of fat. Milk fat imparts a soft body, smooth texture and rich taste to dairy products. Lastly, milk lipids undoubtedly enhance the consumer acceptability of foods; they also serve the best interests of human nutrition through the incentive of eating what tastes good.

(e) *Lactose*. The principal function of lactose (carbohydrate) is to supply energy. However, lactose also helps to establish a mildly acidic reaction in the intestine (which checks the growth of proteolytic bacteria) and facilitates assimilation.

(f) *Energy value*. The energy-giving milk constituents and their individual contributions are as follows:

Milk fat	9.3 C/g
Milk protein	4.1 C/g
Milk sugar	4.1 C/g

where 1 C (Food Calorie) = 1000 c (small calorie).

Note. The energy value of milk will vary with its composition. On average, cow milk furnishes 75 C/100 g and buffalo milk 100 C/100 g.

(g) *Effect of processing*. (i) Pasteurization carried out with reasonable care has no effect on vitamin A, carotene, riboflavin and a number of remaining vitamins B, and vitamin D. Of the remainder, a 10 per cent loss of thiamine and a 20 per cent loss of ascorbic acid may be expected. (ii) Sterilization increases the losses of thiamine and ascorbic acid to 30–50 per cent and 50 per cent respectively, though the remaining vitamins are but little affected.

(h) A balanced diet is essential for proper health and growth. The role of milk and milk products in providing the nutrients required for a balanced diet is indicated in Table 1.14.

TABLE 1.14

Role of milk and milk products in a balanced diet

Nutrients	Purpose	Sources
Proteins	Essential for muscle building and repair; give the body energy and heat	Meat, poultry, fish, *milk*, *cheese*, beans, peas, nuts
Carbohydrates	Body energy and heat	Bread, cereals, pastry, sugar, vegetables, fruit
Fats	–do–	*Butter*, *ghee*, oils
Minerals	Bone, teeth, body cells	*Dairy products*, fruit, vegetables
Vitamin A	Growth, health of the eyes, structure and function of the skin and mucous membrane	*Fat-rich dairy products*, eggs, spinach, carrots, tomatoes, fish liver oils
Vitamin B_1 (Thiamine)	Growth, aids appetite, prevents beri-beri, function of the nervous system	Whole grains, eggs, green vegetables, yeast, liver, kidney
Vitamin B_2 (Riboflavin)	Growth, health of skin and mouth, functioning of the eyes	*Milk*, cabbage, carrots, spinach, liver, eggs, yeast, lean meat, prunes
Niacin	Functioning of the stomach, intestines and nervous system	Meat, heart, kidney, liver, eggs, fish, *milk*, peanuts, yeast
Vitamin C	Aids bones and teeth, prevents scurvy	Citrus fruit, maize, tomatoes, lettuce, cabbage
Vitamin D	Aids in calcium-absorption which strengthens bones, prevents rickets	Eggs, *milk*, fish liver oils

1.8 Physico-Chemical Properties of Milk Constituents

A. *Major Milk Constituents*

(a) *Water*. Constitutes the medium in which the other milk constituents are either dissolved or suspended. Most of it is 'free', and only a very small portion is in the 'bound' form, being firmly bound by milk proteins, phospholipids, etc.

(b) *Milk fat (lipid)*. The bulk of the fat in milk exists in the form of small globules, which average approximately 2 to 5 microns in size (range 0.1 to 22 microns). This is an oil-in-water type emulsion. The surface of these fat globules is coated with an adsorbed layer of material commonly known as the fat globule membrane. This membrane contains phospholipids and proteins in the form of a complex, and stabilizes the fat emulsion. In other words, the membrane prevents the fat globules from coalescing but keeps separated from one another. The emulsion may, however, be broken by agitation (at low temperatures), heating, freezing, etc. When milk is held undisturbed, the fat globules tend to rise to the surface to form a cream layer. The thickest cream layer is secured from milks which have a higher fat content and relatively large fat globules (such as buffalo's milk when compared with cow's milk).

Chemically, milk fat is composed of a number of glyceride-esters of fatty acids; on hydrolysis, milk fat furnishes a mixture of fatty acids and glycerol. (That milk fat is a mixture of true fats is established from the fact that it has no sharp melting point.) The fatty acids are saturated or unsaturated. Saturated fatty acids are relatively stable. On the other hand, the unsaturated ones play an important role in the physico-chemical properties of milk fat.

(c) *Milk proteins*. Proteins are among the most complex of organic substances. They are vital for living organisms as they constitute an indispensable part of the individual body cell. Proteins are composed of a large number of amino-acids, some 'essential' and others 'non-essential'. The essential amino-acids are necessary in the diet for the formation of body proteins. On hydrolysis, proteins furnish a mixture of amino-acids. The proteins of milk consist mainly of casein, β-lactoglobulin, α-lactalbumin, etc. Casein exists only in milk and is found in the form of a calcium caseinate-phosphate complex. It is present in the colloidal state. It forms more than 8 per cent of the total protein in milk. It may be precipitated by acid, rennet, alcohol, heat and concentration. Casein itself is composed of α, β, γ fractions. The heterogeneous nature of α-casein can be observed through electrophoresis. α-casein is the component in casein micelle that is responsible for the stabilization of the micelle in milk. Later studies have also revealed that α-casein is composed of at least two sub-fractions, viz., α_s-casein precipitable by calcium-ion under certain conditions and also called 'calcium-sensitive casein'; and K-casein, also called 'calcium-insensitive casein', not precipitable by calcium-ion. K-casein is the richest repository of carbohydrates as against other casein fractions. It is also the site for rennin action.

β-lactoglobulins and α-lactalbumin are also known as whey or serum-proteins. They are also present in the colloidal state and are easily coagulable by heat.

(d) *Milk sugar or lactose.* This exists only in milk. It is in true solution in the milk serum. On crystallization from water, it forms hard gritty crystals. It is one-sixth as sweet as sucrose. Lactose is responsible, under certain conditions, for the defect known as 'sandiness' in ice cream and sweetened condensed milk. Chemically, lactose is composed of one molecule each of glucose and galactose. Lactose occurs in two forms, α and β, both of which occur either as the hydrate or the anhydride. It is fermented by bacteria to yield lactic acid and other organic acids and is important both in the production of cultured milk products and in the spoilage of milk and milk products by souring.

(e) *Mineral matter or ash.* The mineral matter or salts of milk, although present in small quantities, exert considerable influence on the physico-chemical properties and nutritive value of milk. The major salt constituents, i.e. those present in appreciable quantities, include potassium, sodium, magnesium, calcium, phosphate, citrate, chloride, sulphate and bicarbonate; the trace elements include all other minerals and salt compounds. The mineral salts of milk are usually determined after ashing. Although milk is acidic, ash is distinctly basic. Part of the mineral salts occur in true solution, while a part are in the colloidal state.

B. Minor Milk Constituents

(a) *Phospholipids.* In milk, there are three types of phospholipids, viz. lecithin, cephalin and sphingomylin. Lecithin, which forms an important constituent of the fat globule membrane, contributes to the 'richness' of flavour of milk and other dairy products. It is highly sensitive to oxidative changes, giving rise to oxidized/metallic flavours. Phospholipids are excellent emulsifying agents, and no doubt serve to stabilize the milk fat emulsion.

(b) *Cholesterol.* This appears to be present in true solution in the fat, as part of the fat globule membrane complex and in complex formation with protein in the non-fat portion of milk.

(c) *Pigments.* These are: (i) fat soluble, such as carotene and xanthophyll, and (ii) water soluble, such as riboflavin. Carotene is the colouring matter of all green leaves, where it is masked by chlorophyll. Carotene (the pure substance of which has a reddish-brown colour) is fat soluble and responsible for the yellow colour of milk, cream, butter, ghee and other fat-rich dairy products. Besides contributing to the colour of cow milk, carotene acts as an anti-oxidant and also as a precursor of vitamin A. One molecule of β-carotene yields two molecules of vitamin A, while α-carotene yields only one.

Dairy animals differ in their capacity to transfer carotene from feeds to milk fat; this varies with species, breed and individuality. Cows in general, and some breeds in particular (such as Guernsey and Jersey), can transfer more carotene from their feed to the milk fat than buffaloes, who do not seem to possess this capacity. Hence buffalo milk is white in colour. (The carotinoid content of buffalo milk varies from 0.25 to 0.48/ug/g, while that of cow milk may be as high as 30/ug/g.)

Riboflavin, besides being a vitamin, is a greenish-yellow pigment which gives the characteristic colour to whey. (Earlier, the terms 'lactochrome' and 'lactoflavin' were used instead of riboflavin.)

(d) *Enzymes.* These are 'biological catalysts' which can hasten or retard chemical changes without themselves participating in the reactions. The enzymes are protein-like, specific in their actions, and inactivated by heat; each enzyme has its own inactivation temperature. The important milk enzymes and their specific actions are as follows: (i) Analase (diastase)—starch splitting; (ii) Lipase—fat splitting, leading to rancid flavour; (iii) Phosphate—capable of splitting certain phosphoric acid esters (basis of phosphatase test for checking pasteurization efficiency); (iv) Protease—protein splitting; (v) Peroxidase and Catalase—decomposes hydrogen peroxide.

(e) *Vitamins.* Although present in foods in very minute quantities, these are vital for the health and growth of living organisms. As of today, over 25 vitamins have been reported. Those found in milk are: fat-soluble vitamins A, D, E and K; and water-soluble vitamins of the 'B Complex' group (such as thiamine or B_1, riboflavin or B_2, pantothenic acid, niacin, pyridoxine or B_6, biotin,

B_{12}, folic acid, etc.) and vitamin C (ascorbic acid). Absence of vitamins in the diet over prolonged periods causes 'deficiency diseases'.

1.9 Physico-Chemical Properties of Milk

A. *Physical State of Milk*

Water is the continuous phase in which other constituents are either dissolved or suspended. Lactose and a portion of the mineral salts are found in solution, proteins and the remainder of the minerals in colloidal suspension and fat as an emulsion.

B. *Acidity and pH of Milk*

(a) *Acidity.* Freshly-drawn milk is amphoteric to litmus, i.e. it turns red litmus blue and blue litmus red. However, it shows a certain acidity as determined by titration with an alkali (sodium hydroxide) in the presence of an indicator (phenolphthalein). This acidity, also called Titratable Acidity (T.A.) as it is determined by titration, is known as 'natural' or 'apparent' acidity and is caused by the presence of casein, acid-phosphates, citrates, etc., in milk. The natural acidity of individual milk varies considerably depending on species, breed, individuality, stage of lactation, physiological condition of the udder, etc., but the natural acidity of fresh, herd milk is much more uniform. The higher the solids-not-fat content in milk, the higher the natural acidity (N.A.) and vice versa. The titrable acidity of cow milk varies on an average from 0.13 to 0.14 per cent and buffalo milk from 0.14 to 0.15 per cent. 'Developed' or 'real' acidity is due to lactic acid, formed as a result of bacterial action on lactose in the milk. Hence the titrable acidity of stored milk is equal to the sum of natural acidity and developed acidity. The titrable acidity is usually expressed as a 'percentage of lactic acid'.

(b) *pH.* The pH of normal, fresh, sweet milk usually varies from 6.4 to 6.6 for cow milk and 6.7 to 6.8 for buffalo milk. Higher pH values for fresh milk indicate udder infection (mastitis) and lower values, bacterial action.

Note. The acidity and pH of fresh milk vary with: (i) species; (ii) breed;   (iii) individuality;   (iv) stage of lactation; (v) health of the animal, etc.

C. *Density and Specific Gravity*

Whereas density of a substance is its mass (weight) per unit volume, specific gravity is the ratio of density of the substance to density of a standard substance (water). Since the density of a substance varies with temperature, it is necessary to specify the temperature when reporting densities or specific gravities. The specific gravity of a substance (when referred to water at 4°C) is numerically equal to the density of that substance in the metric system. The specific gravity of milk is usually expressed at 60°F (15.6°C).

The density or specific gravity of milk may be determined by either determining the weight of a known volume or the volume of a known weight. The weight of a known volume may be determined either with a pycnometer or with a hydrostatic balance; while the volume of a known weight is determined by using lactometers, the scale of which is calibrated not in terms of volume but as a function of either density or specific gravity. The common types of lactometers are Zeal, Quevenne, etc.

Milk is heavier than water. The average specific gravity ranges (at 60°F) from 1.028 to 1.030 for cow milk, 1.030 to 1.032 for buffalo milk and 1.035 to 1.037 for skim milk. The specific gravity of milk is influenced by the proportion of its constituents (i.e. composition), each of which has a different specific gravity approximately as follows: water—1.000; fat—0.93; protein—1.346; lactose—1.666; and salts—4.12 (solids-not-fat—1.616).

As milk fat is the lightest constituent, the more there is of it the lower the specific gravity will be, and vice versa. However, although buffalo milk contains more fat than cow milk, its specific gravity is higher than the latter's; this is because buffalo milk contains more solids-not-fat as well, which ultimately results in a higher specific gravity.

The specific gravity of milk is lowered by addition of water and cream, and increased by addition of skim milk or removal of fat.

The percentage of total solids or solids-not-fat in milk is calculated by using the following formula, *vide IS: 1183*, 1965 (Revised).

$$\% \ TS = 0.25D + 1.22F + 0.72$$
$$\% \ SNF = 0.25D + 0.22F + 0.72$$

where, $D = 1000(d - 1)$

$d =$ density of sample of milk at 20°C (68°F)

$F =$ fat percentage of sample.

Note. The specific gravity of milk should not be determined for at least one hour after it is drawn from the animal; else a lower-than-normal value will be obtained (due to the Recknagel phenomenon).

D. *Freezing Point of Milk*

Milk freezes at temperatures slightly lower than water due to the presence of soluble constituents such as lactose, soluble salts, etc., which lower or depress the freezing point. The average freezing point depression of Indian cow milk may be taken as 0.547°C (31.02°F) and buffalo milk 0.549°C (31.01°F). Most bulk milk samples have a freezing point depression of 0.530°C (31.05°F); a freezing point depression lower than this value indicates added water. Mastitis milk shows a normal freezing point. The freezing point test of milk is a highly sensitive one and even up to 3 per cent of watering can be detected.

While the freezing point of normal fresh milk is remarkably constant and employed mainly for detection of adulteration of milk with water, souring results in a lowering of the freezing point due to increase in the amount of soluble molecules. Hence the freezing point should be determined on unsoured samples for greatest accuracy. Boiling and sterilization increase the value of freezing point depression, but pasteurization has no effect. The fat and protein contents of milk have no direct effect on the freezing point of milk. The drawbacks of the freezing point test are: (i) it does not detect the addition of skim milk or removal of fat from the milk sample; and (ii) watered milk, which has subsequently soured, may pass the test.

E. *Colour of Milk*

The colour is a blend of the individual effects produced by: (i) the colloidal casein particles and the dispersed fat globules, both of which scatter light, and (ii) the carotene (to some extent xanthophyll) which imparts a yellowish tint. Milk ranges in colour from yellowish creamy white (cow milk) to creamy white (buffalo milk). The intensity of the yellow colour of cow milk depends on various factors such as breed, feeds, size of fat globules, fat percentage of milk, etc. Certain breeds of cow impart a deeper yellow tint to their milk than others. The greater the intake of green feed, the deeper yellow the colour of cow milk. The larger the fat globules and the higher the fat percentage, the greater the intensity of the yellow colour. Skim milk has a bluish, and whey a greenish yellow colour (which in milk is masked by the other constituents present).

Note. (i) The colour of foods is an important aspect of their marketability. Colour has three aspects, viz. tint, intensity and uniformity. Variation in intensity is tolerated as it occurs in practice.

(ii) The colour of an opaque object is the colour it reflects; the colours of the visible spectrum are absorbed. Thus an object is yellow because more yellow light is reflected to the eye than any other colour. (A white object reflects all the colours of light that fall on it, while a black object absorbs them all.)

F. *Flavour*

This is composed of smell (odour) and taste. The flavour of milk is a blend of the sweet taste of lactose and salty taste of minerals, both of which are damped down by proteins. The phospholipids, fatty acids and fat of milk also contribute to the flavour.

Changes in the flavour of milk occur due to type of feed, season, stage of lactation, condition of udder, sanitation during milking and subsequent handling of milk during storage. The sulfydryl compounds significantly contribute to the cooked flavour of heated milks.

Note. A pronounced flavour of any kind is considered abnormal to milk. The sources of abnormal flavours may be: (i) bacterial growth; (ii) feed; (iii) absorbed; (iv) chemical composition; (v) processing and handling; (vi) chemical changes; (vii) addition of foreign material.

1.10 Microbiology of Milk

A. *Introduction*

Nearly all the changes which take place in the flavour and appearance of milk, after it is drawn from the cow, are the result of the activities of micro-organisms. Of these, the most important in dairying are bacteria, mould, yeast and virus—the first one predominating. Micro-organisms are visible only with the aid of a microscope. A few are desirable, while most cause undesirable changes; a relatively small proportion are disease-producing types, and are called 'pathogens'. In the dairy industry considerable effort is expended in controlling micro-organisms which cause spoilage. The greater the bacterial count in milk, i.e. the greater the number of bacteria per ml of milk, the lower is its bacteriological quality.

Bacteria are microscopic, unicellular fungi (plants without chlorophyll) which occur principally in the form of spherical, cylindrical or spiral cells and which reproduce by transverse fission. In milk and its products, the spherical and cylindrical forms are predominant. Most bacteria vary from 1 to 5 microns in size. Although individual bacterial cells are invisible to the naked eye, they form bacterial 'colonies' (consisting of a large number of individual cells) which are visible. Bacteria are found nearly everywhere in nature. They are found in large numbers in the soil, sewage, decaying plants or animals; and are also present in air, water, etc. Under favourable conditions, bacteria multiply very rapidly and may double their number in 15 minutes or less. Some bacteria also form 'spores', which are tough resistant bodies within the bacterial cell. Spores, when placed in an environment favourable to growth, form new vegetative cells. Spore-forming bacteria cause trouble in the dairy industry because of their resistance to pasteurization and sanitization procedures.

Moulds are multi-cellular, differing greatly in most respects from bacteria. Although the individual cells are not visible to the naked eye, at maturity they may be observed readily as 'Mycelium'. They are found in soil, feeds, manure and poorly-washed utensils. Most spores of moulds are destroyed by pasteurization. They are of considerable importance in cheese-making and are responsible for some defects in butter and other milk products.

Yeasts are unicellular but are somewhat larger in size than bacteria. Spores of yeasts are readily destroyed during pasteurization.

Viruses include all ultra-microscopic forms of life. In the dairy industry, only those viruses that are parasitic on lactic acid bacteria and known as Starter Bacteriophage (or simply Phage) are of special importance. The viruses range in size from 0.22 to 0.23 microns. The lactic phages are usually not destroyed by normal pasteurization of milk employed for cheese and cultured buttermilk, but they can be destroyed by higher heat-treatment.

B. *Growth of Micro-Organisms*

In microbiology, growth refers to increase in numbers. Milk drawn from a healthy cow already contains some bacteria. Their numbers multiply during production and handling, depending on the cleanliness of these operations. Subsequently, their numbers may grow still further (either substantially or only slightly) depending on storage conditions.

The changes which take place in the physico-chemical properties of milk are the result of the activities of the individual microbial cells during their period of growth (development and reproduction) or of substances produced during such activity.

(a) *Stages of growth.* The growth of micro-organisms normally takes place in the following stages: (i) initial stationary phase; (ii) lag phase (phase of adjustment); (iii) accelerated growth phase (log phase); (iv) maximum stationary phase; and (v) phase of accelerated death.

(b) *Factors influencing growth.* The growth of micro-organisms is influenced by the following factors: (i) *Food supply*. Milk and most dairy products furnish all the food requirements of micro-organisms. (ii) *Moisture*. Milk contains adequate moisture (dry products, due to their low moisture content, keep longer). (iii) *Air*. Supplies oxygen to aerobic types of bacteria and to moulds in general. (iv) *Acidity or pH*. Most common types prefer a pH from 5.6 to 7.5. (v) *Preservatives*. These check or destroy growth, depending on their concentration. (vi) *Light*. Is more or less harmful. (vii) *Concentration*. High sucrose or salt content in product checks growth, and (viii) *Temperature*. An important means for controlling growth. Each species of micro-organism has its optimum, maximum and minimum temperatures of growth.

According to their optimum growth temperatures, bacteria can be classified into:

Psychrotropic. Can grow at refrigeration temperatures (5–7°C).

Mesophilic. Can grow at temperatures ranging between 20°C and 40°C.

Thermophilic (heat loving). Can grow at temperatures above 50°C.

Note. In general, low temperatures (below 10°C) retard microbial growth. Hence milk and dairy products should be adequately refrigerated to prevent rapid spoilage. The optimum growth rate of the majority of micro-organisms will be found at temperatures between 15 and 38°C. Most micro-organisms are destroyed at high temperatures, viz. 60°C or above.

(c) *Products of microbial growth.* These are: (i) enzymes; (ii) decomposition products (of fats, proteins, sugars, etc.); (iii) pigments; (iv) toxins; and (v) miscellaneous changes.

(d) *Results of microbial growth in milk.* These are:

(i) *Souring.* Most common. Caused by transformation of lactose into lactic and other volatile acids and compounds, principally by lactic acid bacteria. (The development of a sour acid flavour is not due to lactic acid, which is odourless, but due to volatile acids and compounds.)

(ii) *Souring and gassiness.* Caused by Coli group, which are commonly found in soil, manure, feed, etc., and therefore indicate contamination of milk and dairy products.

(iii) *Aroma production.* Due to production of desirable flavour compounds such as diacetyl (in ripened-cream-butter).

(iv) *Proteolysis.* Protein decomposition leading to unpleasant odours. (Sometimes desirable flavours may develop, as in cheese curing.)

(v) *Ropiness.* Long threads of milk are formed while pouring.

(vi) *Sweet curdling.* Due to production of a rennin-like enzyme, which curdles milk without souring.

C. *Destruction of Micro-Organisms*

This may be done by means of:

(i) *Heat.* Most widely used. Different types of heat-treatment (temperature-time combination) are employed, such as pasteurization, sterilization, etc.

(ii) *Ionizing radiation.* Such as ultra-violet rays, etc.

(iii) *High frequency sound waves.* Such as supersonic and ultrasonic.

(iv) *Electricity.* Here, the micro-organisms are destroyed, actually, by the heat generated.

(v) *Pressure.* Should be about 600 times greater than atmospheric pressure, and

(vi) *Chemicals.* These include acids, alkalis, hydrogen peroxide, halogens, etc.

1.11 Milk and Public Health

It is well established that milk can be a potential carrier of disease-producing organisms. Milk-borne epidemics have occurred in the past throughout the world. Unless proper precautions are taken, such outbreaks of milk-borne diseases can occur anywhere, any time, especially if raw milk is consumed.

Diseases which are known to be transmissible through milk are listed below, together with the manner in which they may enter the milk:

(i) *Infection of milk directly from the cow.* These diseases are essentially bovine. The causative organisms enter the milk through the mammary glands or through faecal contamination, and may cause a diseased condition in persons who consume the milk. Examples: Bovine tuberculosis; Undulant fever or Malta fever; etc.

(ii) *Infection from man to cow and then to milk.* These diseases are essentially human, but can become established in the cow's udders. Examples: Septic sore throat; Scarlet fever, Diphtheria; etc.

(iii) *Direct contamination of milk by human beings.* These diseases may be transmitted to the milk by direct contamination through human contact, either by carriers or patients. Examples: Septic sore throat; Scarlet fever; Typhoid fever; Paratyphoid fever; Dysentery; Gastroenteritis; Diphtheria; etc.

(iv) *Indirect contamination of milk by human beings.* These are human diseases, the pathogenic organisms of which enter the milk through contaminated bottles or other utensils, water supply, insects and dust. Examples: Typhoid or Paratyphoid fever; Dysentery or Diarrhoea; etc.

1.12 Safeguarding the Milk Supply

Whereas 'cleanliness' implies freedom from extraneous matter (such as manure, dust, etc.), 'safety' means freedom from pathogenic micro-organisms. For human consumption, milk that is both clean and safe is highly desirable.

The sanitation of the milk supply can be safeguarded in two ways: (a) production and handling of raw milk in such a manner as to prevent its contamination by pathogenic organisms. This will require: (i) ensuring the health of dairy cattle by various control measures; (ii) safeguarding the health of employees by regular medical examination; (iii) protection of the water supply from contamination by pathogenic organisms; (iv) flies and their control, etc. Examples: 'Certified milk', 'Grade A raw milk', etc.

(b) Pasteurization of milk, so as to kill all pathogenic organisms and avoidance of any post-pasteurization contamination. (This will be discussed later.)

1.13 Clean Milk Production

(a) The following standards, *vide* Table 1.15, are suggested as a guide for grading raw milk in this country:

TABLE 1.15
Bacteriological standards of raw milk

SPC/ml (or g)	Grade
Not exceeding 200,000	Very good
Between 200,000 and 1,000,000	Good
Between 1,000,000 and 5,000,000	Fair
Over 5,000,000	Poor

SOURCE: *IS : 1479* (Part III), 1962.

Note. The pasteurized milk (at the plant, in its final container) should have a SPC/ml (or g) not exceeding 30,000.

(b) The sources of contamination of milk and their control have been given in Table 1.16.

TABLE 1.16
Sources of contamination of milk and their control

Sources of Contamination	Control Measures
Interior of the udder	(i) Check for mastitis (ii) Discard foremilk
Exterior of the cow, particularly udder and flanks	(i) Wash and wipe udder (ii) Clip the udder and flanks (iii) Dry milking (iv) Use small-top milk-pail
Barn air and dust	(i) Keep milk covered
Flies and other vermin	(i) Eliminate breeding places (ii) Fly control with fly sprays, fly traps, etc.
The milker	(i) Clean habits (ii) Dry milking
Utensils	(i) Clean, sanitize and dry before use

Source: *Market Milk* by Sommer (1952).

Note. Besides the above, two other control measures are used, viz. straining and cooling (which will be discussed later).

1.14 Buying and Collection of Milk

A. *Buying*

Various methods for buying milk are employed, singly or in combination, as given below:

(a) *Payment according to weight or volume* (also known as a flat rate). *Advantages*: (i) saves time; (ii) simple to calculate. *Disadvantage*: (i) encourages watering or skimming. Payment by weight is preferred to payment by volume as the former is not affected by either foam or specific gravity. (It is popular in the unorganized sector.)

(b) *Payment according to the fat content of milk* (includes, among others, the straight fat method of payment). *Advantages*: (i) practical; (ii) discourages adulteration with water. *Disadvantages*: (i) does not prevent removal of skim milk; (ii) does not take into account the solids-not-fat content of milk. (Practised by most dairies.)

(c) *Payment according to the use made of milk.* This practice is followed mainly for milk products.

(d) *Payment of premiums.* Usually confined to market milk. Based on quality of milk as measured by (i) sediment test; (ii) flavour score; (iii) bacterial count or Methylene Blue Reduction Time. (Encourages the production of high-grade milk.)

(e) *Payment according to the cost of production.* Complicated, although rational.

Note. The urgent need for a sound pricing policy for milk and milk products in this country is being increasingly realized by dairy planners today. The problem, no doubt, is complicated, as the price has to be acceptable to the producers, processors and manufacturers, distributors and finally consumers. Further, the approach must be of long-range significance to dairy development.

A rational milk pricing policy should ensure: a guaranteed price and market to the producers throughout the year, which will be an incentive to them to produce more milk; a regular supply of wholesome milk at reasonable rates to the consumers; and an attractive margin of profit to the milk processors and product manufacturers.

In fixing the producers' price for fluid milk, the following basic considerations have to be kept in view: the price should be related to the cost of milk production and ensure a fair margin of profit to the producers; it should take into account the seasonal variation in production (supply) and demand; and should be linked with the consumers' price index, taking into account general market trends.

From the point of view of the milk processor/milk-product manufacturer, the price of milk should take into account the following: the stage of operation of the plant; the costs of transportation, processing/manufacturing and distribution; plant capacity, so as to utilize all surplus milk in the milk-shed area; and the market objective of the plant, including its programme of product diversification.

The consumers' price has to be fixed after consideration of the size of the population that is to be covered by the milk scheme;

the distribution of people in different occupational and income groups (viz., lower, middle and higher) that are to be served; and the total cost of transportation, processing/manufacturing and distribution (which should be adequately covered, besides leaving a reasonable margin of profit to the milk plant).

It is, therefore, necessary to strike a balance between the producers' price which is to serve as a production incentive and the consumers' price which should be within the purchasing power of the average consumer throughout the year.

At present each milk plant or dairy product factory has evolved an arbitrary system of milk pricing, which seems to have no relation to the actual cost of milk production. Liquid milk plants have a differential pricing system for flush and lean months based on the fat and SNF contents of milk, with provision for the payment of a premium for a higher fat and SNF content than the specified standard. Dairy product factories purchase milk by and large on a per kilo fat basis at different prices for different seasons.

The minimum standards prescribed by the PFA (1976) rules for cow milk are 3.0 to 4.0 per cent fat and 8.5 to 9.0 per cent solids-not-fat, while those for buffalo milk are 5.0 to 6.0 per cent fat and 9.0 per cent solids-not-fat throughout the country. With a view to encouraging milk production through high yielding indigenous and cross-bred cows, it is necessary to adopt a pricing policy which would provide an adequate incentive for production of cow milk. In this context, the National Dairy Development Board has suggested the two-axis milk pricing policy. Such a policy ensures payment for milk on its compositional quality evaluated rationally on its fat and solids-not-fat components. This would discourage adulteration of buffalo milk and at the same time ensure a common pricing approach to cow and buffalo milks.

However, one difficulty that can be foreseen in this system is the accurate testing of milk at source for its solids-not-fat content. Since the estimation of solids-not-fat in milk is a time-consuming process, research would have to be undertaken to develop a rapid test which could be carried out under field conditions.

The overall pricing policy for milk products should encourage efficiency of production, minimization of costs, quality of the product, etc. Dairy factories should try to create the feeling that the price of producers' milk is not predetermined unilaterally at a fixed rate but varies, rather, with season and quality.*

B. *Collection*

In almost all developed dairying countries, production of milk is confined to rural areas, while demand is mostly urban in nature. Hence milk has to be collected and transported from production points in the milk-shed areas to processing and distribution points in cities.

(a) The common systems for collection (assembling) of milk are as follows:

(i) *By co-operative organizations.* Formed by individual or collective milking societies. Suits producers best as no profit-making middlemen are involved.

(ii) *By contractors.* Less return to producers.

(iii) *By individual producers.* Practical for those situated near processing dairies.

Note. A 'milk-shed' is the geographical area from which a city dairy receives its fluid milk supply. The allocation of definite milk-sheds to individual dairies for the purpose of developing the same is now being considered in India.

(b) *Milk collection-cum-chilling centres/depots.* Normally attached to city dairies.

Objects. These are: (i) to preserve the quality of raw milk supplies, and (ii) to provide easy transport to the processing dairy.

Location. This is guided by: (i) adequate milk production; (ii) adequate (potable) water supply; (iii) proximity to a good road or railway station; (iv) electric supply, and (v) sewage disposal facilities.

Major items of equipment. (i) Milk weigh tank/pan and weighing scale (ii) Drop (dump) tank with cover; (iii) Can washer; (iv) Milk pump (sanitary type); (v) Surface/plate cooler; (vi) Refrigeration unit (of suitable capacity); (vii) Cold room (of suitable capacity); (viii) Milk testing unit, etc.

Operational procedure. Essentially this is the same as in a small dairy. On arrival, the milk is graded for acceptance/rejection, weighed, sampled for testing, cooled and stored at a low temper-

---

*Adapted from: R. K. Patel, 'Sound basis of pricing milk', *Indian Dairyman* **27** (3), 91 (1975).

ature until despatch to the processing dairy. (Detailed discussion follows later in the book.)

1.15 Cooling and Transportation of Milk

A. *Cooling*   (On the farm or at the chilling centre)

(a) *Importance.* Milk contains some micro-organisms when drawn from the udder; their numbers increase during subsequent handling. The common milk micro-organisms grow best between 20 and 40°C. Bacterial growth is invariably accompanied by deterioration in market quality due to development of off-flavours, acidity, etc. One method of preserving milk is by prompt cooling to a low temperature.

(b) *Effect of temperature.* Table 1.17 shows the bacterial growth factor in milk at different storage temperatures:

TABLE 1.17

Effect of storage temperature on bacterial growth in milk

Milk held for 18 hours at temperature (°C)	Bacterial growth factor*
0	1.00
5	1.05
10	1.80
15	10.00
20	200.00
25	1,20,000.00

*Multiply initial count with this factor to get final count.

It will be seen from Table 1.17 that 10°C is a critical temperature for milk. Freshly drawn (raw) milk should, therefore, be promptly cooled to 5°C or below and also held at that temperature till processed.

(c) *Principle.* The principle of heat-exchange, i.e. heating and cooling, will be discussed later.

(d) *Methods.*

I. *In-can or can-immersion method.* From carrying-pails, the milk is poured directly into cans through a strainer. When the can is full, it is gently lowered into a tank/trough of cooling water. (*Note*: The water level in the tank should be lower than the level of milk-in-cans, to prevent water entering into the milk.)

Advantages: (i) Not only is the milk cooled, but it also stays cool. and (ii) a much smaller mechanical refrigeration unit is required.

Disadvantages: (i) It cools the milk very slowly, and (ii) there is danger of milk contamination in case tankwater enters milk-in-can.

II. *Surface cooler*. This may be plain-conical, spiral or horizontal-tubular in shape, although the last-named is now commonly used. The milk is distributed over the outer surfaces of the cooling tubes from the top by means of a distributor pipe or trough and flows down in a continuous thin stream. The cooling medium, mostly chilled water, is circulated in the opposite direction through the inside of the tubes. The cooled milk is received below in a receiving trough, from which it is discharged by gravity or a pump.

Advantages: (i) Transfers heat rapidly and efficiently; (ii) is relatively inexpensive; (iii) also aerates the milk, thus improving its flavour.

Disadvantages: (i) Requires constant attention for rate of flow (which must neither be too slow nor too fast); (ii) greater chances of air-borne contamination; (iii) cleaning and sanitization not very efficient, and (iv) slight evaporation losses.

III. *In-tank or bulk-tank cooler*. Used extensively in developed dairying countries like the U.S.A. Properly designed bulk milk tank coolers, which are normally run by a mechanical refrigeration system, will cool the milk rapidly to a low temperature (5°C or below) and automatically maintain this temperature during the storage period. Milk can be poured directly from the milking pail (under Indian conditions) into the tank. Subsequently milk can be drawn into cans or pumped into a tanker, for despatch to the city dairy.

Advantage: Permits collection of producers' milk on alternate days.

Disadvantage: Relatively expensive in initial equipment.

IV. *Milk chilling centres*. Now that electricity is available even in most Indian villages, these have great scope in this country, largely because of predominantly small and scattered milk production. The number of organized dairy farms in India is rather small. Consequently, the centres can provide the only alternative solution to the collection and chilling of village milk. They can profitably be run by the producers themselves through their co-operative organizations.

B. *Transportation*

(a) *Importance.* Under Indian conditions, milk has to be regularly collected and transported twice a day (morning and evening).

(b) *Modes of transport.* These depend upon the carrying load, the distance of collection and local conditions. Their particulars have been given in Table 1.18.

TABLE 1.18

Modes of milk transportation in India

Mode	Optimum load (kg)	Optimum distance (km)	Remarks
Head-load	15–25	3–8	Generally employed for small loads and distances. Important in hilly areas.
Shoulder-sling	up to 40	3–6	Meant for heavier loads but for shorter distances than head-load.
Pack-animal	up to 80	6–10	Ponies, horses and donkeys usually employed.
Bullock-cart	300–400	10–12	Rather slow.
Tonga	250–300	12 or more	Larger quantities transported; faster than head-load, shoulder-sling and pack-animal.
Bicycle	40 or more	15 or more	Quick and handy; easily accessible to milk producer's home.
Cycle-rickshaw	150–200	10 or more	More carrying capacity than bicycle.
Boat	40–200	2–8	Only means of transport when rivers, etc., have to be crossed.
Auto-rickshaw	250–500	15 or more	Greater carrying capacity and faster than cycle-rickshaw.
Motor truck	$\frac{1}{2}$ to 3 tonnes	15 or more	Increasingly in use with more road building and improvement programmes.
Railway wagon	11 tonnes or more	80 or more	Great scope in future.
Tankers (road or rail)	5 tonnes or more	80 or more	Great scope in future

(c) *Road vs Rail Transport.* The individual advantages of each have been stated in Table 1.19.

TABLE 1.19

Individual advantages of road and rail transport

Type of Transport	Advantages
Road	(i) Loading and unloading possible directly at godown of seller and buyer. (ii) Cheaper than rail over short distances. (iii) Less time-consuming.
Rail	(i) Cheaper than road over long distances. (ii) Larger quantity of milk can be handled at a time.

(d) *Can vs Tanker Transport.* The individual advantages of each have been given in Table 1.20.

TABLE 1.20

Individual advantages of can and tanker transport

Type of Transport	Advantages
Can	(i) Handling small quantities of milk possible.
Tanker	(i) Quicker mode of transport; (ii) Lower cost; (iii) Better temperature control; (iv) Less risk of contamination; (v) More time and labour saving; (vi) Lower investment in cans; (vii) Overall saving in detergents, etc.

(e) *Types of containers used.* These are made of:
  (i) baked earth
 (ii) wood or bamboo
(iii) metal (generally brass)
(iv) galvanized-iron (GI)
 (v) second-hand tins (mainly vegetable oil/ghee)

(vi) tinned-iron or aluminium-alloy (used by organized dairies).

(f) *Problems.* The problems in relation to collection and transportation of milk are:

  (i) milk is liquid, perishable and bulky;

 (ii) small and scattered production of milk;

(iii) tropical climate;

(iv) lack of transport facilities;

 (v) lack of countrywide organizations for milk collection and transport;

(vi) vested interests among local milk merchants.

1.16 Action of Milk on Metals

(a) *Introduction.* Milk acts on certain metals, so that a small amount of the metal is dissolved in it. The metallic salts thus formed may give rise to a 'metallic' taste in the milk. Some salts act as catalysts, thus hastening the oxidation of fat and producing an oxidized flavour. These metals are said to taint milk.

The factors which influence the degree of action by milk on the metal are: (i) temperature of milk; (ii) period of contact; (iii) cleanliness and polish of metal; (iv) amount of free air in milk; (v) acidity of milk, etc.

(b) *Selection of metals for dairy equipment.* The metals used for the milk-contact surfaces must, as far as possible, meet the following requirements: they should be (i) non-toxic; (ii) non-tainting; (iii) insoluble (in milk or its products); (iv) highly resistant to corrosion (by milk, cleaning and sanitizing agents, etc.); (v) easy to clean and keep bright; (vi) light yet strong; (vii) good agents of heat transfer; (viii) good in appearance throughout life; (ix) low in cost; (x) non-absorbent, and (xi) durable.

Note. No single metal or alloy meets all these requirements. However, 18 : 8 stainless steel and aluminium alloy are the most satisfactory at present.

The characteristics of the different metals and their alloys used for dairy equipment have been given in Table 1.21.

(c) *Corrosion control.* Corrosion cannot be entirely prevented in dairy equipment, but its rate can be controlled to a large extent. To prevent corrosion of stainless steel surface: (i) keep the surface clean; (ii) permit surface to air-dry, whenever possible; (iii) use cleaners and sanitizers in the lowest concentration and

TABLE 1.21

Characteristics of different metals and their alloys used for dairy equipment

Name of metals and alloys	Type of equipment generally fabricated	Action of milk on metal	Toxicity	Workability (Ease in fabrication of equipment)	Durability (Resistance to corrosion)	Other characteristics
1	2	3	4	5	6	7
Copper and its alloys	Milk pails, coolers, vats, strainers, pipe fittings, milk pumps, pasteurizer coils, etc. (used for tinning only)	Taint milk/dairy products unless coated with tin	Green corrosion product 'Verdigris' is toxic	Soft metal; easy to work with	With tin coating quite durable	(i) High conductivity: which promotes rapid heat transfer (ii) Reasonable in cost (iii) Repaired easily; retinning cheap
Aluminium and its alloys	Milk cans, milk pails, linings for tanks and tankers, etc.	Do not taint milk	Nil	Soft metal; easy to work with	'Impure' aluminium not durable; aluminium alloyed or anodized much more durable	(i) Light-weight: a great advantage (ii) Aluminium quite porous, hence difficult to clean (iii) Suffers corrosion from common alkaline dairy cleaners and sanitizers (iv) Difficult to solder (v) Suffers corrosion from high acid products
Iron and its alloys	(i) Low-carbon steel widely used for bodies of tanks, vats, bottle-washers, conveyors, etc. (ii) Stainless steel (18 : 8) widely used for all milk/dairy product contact surfaces	Pure iron taints milk/dairy product while stainless steel does not	'Rust' slightly toxic	Tough metal; presents problems in fabrication	Stainless steel highly durable	*Stainless steel:* (i) Highly resistant to corrosion by common acids and alkalis (ii) Takes high polish and therefore easy to clean (iii) Corroded by brine and chlorine solution (iv) Welding has to be done to repair cracks etc.

	Uses	Effect on milk flavour	Toxicity	Mechanical property	Durability	Remarks
Tin	Used mainly as a 'coating' for milk/dairy product contact surfaces of cans, vats, etc.	Does not taint milk although quite soluble in it	Nil	Too soft to be used for any kind of equipment	Tin coating not durable	(i) Wears off readily by corrosion, abrasion, etc. (ii) Retinning process not at all difficult
Nickel and its alloys	Nickel used as a coating for milk/dairy product contact surfaces of pasteurizing vats, coolers etc. Ni-alloy used in freezing chamber of ice-cream freezers, cylinders and plungers of homogenizers, etc.	Very slight effect on milk flavour although the most soluble in milk among dairy metals	Mildly toxic	Alloy with iron tough and quite difficult to handle during fabrication	Much more durable than tin coating, but more expensive	(i) Corroded by milk acids (lactic) (ii) Not corroded by alkaline washing powders (iii) Most expensive, when compared with chromium and tin
Chromium and its alloys	Coating on various types of equipment for milk/dairy product contact surfaces	Non-tainting	Nil	—do—	—do—	(i) Expensive (ii) Resistant to corrosive action by acid and alkaline cleaners

Note: (i) Glass-enamelled steel vats are also used considerably. Milk does not act upon such surfaces and hence they cause no flavour changes.

(ii) For milk cans, tinned steel is commonly used, mainly for economic considerations, durability, sturdiness, availability, etc. [See *IS–1373* (1967) and *IS–1825* (1971) for milk cans; and *IS–2336* (1963) and *IS–2337* (1963) for milk vats.]

for the shortest duration that will do the desired cleaning job.

Note. (i) When the stainless steel surface is dry and exposed to the atmosphere, an invisible film of chromium oxide forms on it. This film protects it from corrosion. When the film breaks or wears away, the active metal gets exposed and corrodes more easily. This oxide film is self-forming when the stainless steel surface is dry and exposed to air.

(ii) Chlorine and its compounds are very corrosive. Equipment should be sanitized with chlorine solutions, preferably just before it is to be used, so as to avoid prolonged contact, and thus corrosion (pitting).

1.17　Manufacture, Packaging and Storage of Pasteurized Milk

1.17.1　Flow Diagram

Receiving milk
[Grading, Sampling, Weighing, Testing]
|
Pre-heating (35–40°C)
|
Filtration/Clarification
|
Cooling and Storage (5°C or below)
|
Standardization
|
Pasteurization (63°C/30 mts or 72°C/15 sec)
|
Homogenization (2500 psi)
|
Bottling/Packaging
|
Storage (5°C or below)

1.17.2　Details

I. Receiving milk

A. *Introduction.* Milk may be delivered to the Milk Plant/ Dairy in cans or tankers (road or rail). The milk in these containers has to be graded, emptied, measured by weight or volume, sampled, and bulked to provide continuity of supply to the pasteurizing equipment.

In the absence of mechanical aids, the cans are off-loaded

manually to the tipping point, where the lids/covers are removed and the milk inspected. They are then tipped manually and both cans and lids passed on to a can-washer via a drip saver or drain rack. Where a higher throughput is required, the procedure is mechanized and the cans are unloaded directly from the truck onto the conveyor (power-driven or by gravity-roller) and the tipping, sampling, and weight-recording may be completely automatic.

If milk is measured by weight, as is usual, it is tipped into the weigh tank/pan; this is suspended from a weighing machine, the indicating dial of which is calibrated in weight and so placed that it can be easily seen by the checker. Two weigh tanks can be used for quick reception. The discharge valve has a large diameter so as to permit rapid emptying, and should be easily controlled by the tipper/checker. The milk is discharged into a dump tank placed immediately below the weigh pan; from this, milk may be pumped continuously to a raw-milk storage tank, normally situated at a higher level to give gravity flow to the pasteurizing plant.

The reception of milk from large rail or road tankers is primarily a matter of providing a covered area under which emptying and subsequent cleaning can take place. The tanker outlet must be connected to sanitary piping. The milk may be removed by a milk-pump, situated at a lower level than the tanker, or a compressed-air line may be connected to the top of the tanker and the milk forced out by air pressure. Washing and sanitization of the tanker should follow immediately after emptying is complete. The measurement of milk delivered by tankers can be done either by using a weigh-bridge or flow-meter.

If milk is being received from milk-chilling centres, it has already been graded, weighed, sampled and cooled. It may be weighed and sampled again, or the Centre's report may be used. The latter procedure applies especially to tanker deliveries.

Milk reception should be so planned and the equipment so chosen that intake operations are expedited. This is especially important where large volumes of milk are received. Delays permit deterioration of milk awaiting dumping, increase labour costs and may increase the operating cost of the can-washer. The deliveries of milk should follow a schedule. If the milk is received continuously during the scheduled period, operations in the plant will not be interrupted and employees in the various sections will be fully occupied. The aim should be to complete milk reception within

3–4 hours, especially in tropical countries.

Market milk requires milk of a higher quality (from the stand-point of good health, flavour, sanitary quality, keeping quality and aesthetic quality) than is required by any other branch of the dairy industry. The quality of the incoming (intake) milk greatly influences the quality of the processed milks (or manufactured products).

It is well known that the sanitary quality of milk on the receiving platform/dock depends on its background on the farm, viz., healthy cows, clean milk production, clean utensils. freedom from colostrum, prompt cooling, and refrigerated transport. How-ever, there is need for systematic and thorough inspection of all milk supplies every day by conscientious and experienced milk graders.

When milk is received at the Milk Plant/Dairy, it should be at 5°C or below. The milk should be clean, sweet, of pleasant flavour, free from off-flavours and reasonably free from extraneous mate-rial. Contamination with antibiotics, pesticides and other chemi-cals or metals is highly undesirable. No abnormal milk should be accepted. Acid development is objectionable, for not only does it indicate an excessive bacterial count, but it also reduces the heat-stability of milk.

B. *Milk reception operations.* The operation of receiving milk may be subdivided into: (a) unloading; (b) grading; (c) sampling; (d) weighing; and (e) testing.

(a) *Unloading.* The motor truck carrying the filled milk cans is backed up (or brought aside) to the unloading platform. The milk cans are then unloaded manually. If the level of the truck surface is in line with the platform, the unloading requires the least effort. (No lifting up or down, but only pulling on a level surface.) Then the milk cans are assembled for grading in a defi-nite order, according to each supplier, viz. the contractor or patron. If a milk tanker is being used, it is first properly positioned so that connections can be made conveniently.

(b) *Grading.* This refers to the classification of milk on the basis of quality, for price-fixing purposes. It is well known that the quality of the finished product depends on that of the raw material used. The milk grader is the key man for the proper selec-tion of milk. The principle of grading is based on organoleptic (sensory) tests, such as those for smell (odour), taste, appearance and touch; acidity; sediment, etc. These are included under platform tests.

Note· The term 'Platform Tests' includes all those tests which are performed to check the quality of the incoming milk on the receiving platform, so as to make a quick decision regarding its acceptance/rejection. They are performed on each can/tanker of milk with the object of detecting milk of inferior or doubtful quality, so as to prevent it being mixed with high-grade milk. Sometimes the term 'Rapid Platform Test' is used to refer mainly to the organoleptic or sensory tests which take very little lime to perform.

The technique of grading milk may be described as under:

(i) *Milk tanker* (Road/Rail). Actually the grading should have been done at the milk collection-cum–chilling centre. As the milk should be cold (5°C or below), it is not possible to detect off-odours. Only the appearance can be noted, as testing of raw milk is usually avoided. After thoroughly mixing it for 5–10 minutes, a sample is taken for laboratory testing.

(ii) *Milk can.* The main tests applied to each can of milk consist of smell, appearance and temperature (touch); other tests such as taste (seldom carried out with raw milk) and sediment might be used to substantiate the initial findings. Tests involving time, laboratory facilities and special techniques are best done by the quality control technician, for which a sufficiently large sample is properly taken as the milk is being received. (Even if the cans of milk have been despatched from a chilling centre, it is wise to inspect each can separately.)

The various platform tests are discussed below:

(i) *Smell* (Odour). This furnishes an excellent indication of the organoleptic quality of milk. It can be ascertained very quickly (in just a few seconds). In making the test, the cover of each can is removed, inverted and raised to the nose. The odour/smell will be representative of that in the can. The top of the milk in the can may simultaneously be noted for smell. By replacing the lid and shaking the can vigorously, the test may be repeated. An experienced milk grader with a 'trained nose' usually relies to a great extent in the acceptance/rejection of the intake milk on the odour test alone. The milk should be free from any off-flavours.

(ii) *Appearance.* By regularly observing the milk in each can after the odour test has been made, any floating extraneous matter, off-colour, or partially churned milk may be noted. The milk should be normal in colour, free from churned fat globules and reasonably free from any floating extraneous material.

(iii) *Temperature.* The temperature at which milk is delivered is often an indication of its quality. A daily check on the temperature of milk is helpful in grading the milk on the receiving platform. With practice, the grader can tell with a high degree of accuracy whether or not the milk is sufficiently cold by touching the side of the can. A temperature of 5°C or below is satisfactory.

(iv) *Sediment.* The sediment test shows the visible foreign matter contained in the milk. It need not be made daily, but should be made sufficiently often to ensure a clean milk supply. For this purpose a reliable sediment tester (such as an off-the-bottom sediment tester), by which the work may be expedited, should be selected. The intensity of discoloration and sediment on the pad will depend to some extent upon the manner in which the test is taken. Any method by which maximum sediment will be revealed should be considered satisfactory. A low sediment is desirable.

Note. The sediment test is used as a check on the milk production and handling methods on the farm. A low sediment need not necessarily mean a low bacterial count in milk, although the reverse is often true. (A clean sediment disc does not indicate clean methods; it may be a pointer, rather, to the milk having been filtered/strained on the farms.)

(v) *Acidity.* It has already been pointed out that 'natural' or 'apparent' acidity of milk does not make the milk taste sour, nor does it affect the normal properties of milk or jeopardize its quality or its behaviour towards processing heat. However, 'developed' or 'real' acidity does adversely affect the quality of milk.

Note. Determination of the Titrable Acidity of milk (which is equal to Natural Acidity plus Developed Acidity) for deciding acceptance/rejection of milk on the basis of an arbitrarily set limit cannot serve much useful purpose in India today, especially in view of the fact that the milk suppliers are freely adding neutralizers to milk to reduce its acidity. Nevertheless, the 'acidity test' does have its proper place on the milk reception dock; and with the daily incoming milk it is always well to have a certain acidity above which milk should not be accepted. A modified form is known as the 'rapid acidity test'.

(vi) *Lactometer Reading.* The addition of water to milk results in the lowering of its lactometer reading. Hence this test is applied for detection of adulteration of milk with water. As it does not take much time, it is often used as a platform test in the milk collection/chilling centres in this country. However, this test has its drawbacks.

(c) *Sampling.* The importance of securing an accurate and representative sample of milk for subsequent chemical and bacteriological analysis cannot be over-emphasized. While strict precautions regarding sterility of the stirrer, sampler, container, etc., are required for obtaining a bacteriological sample, dryness and cleanliness of the above equipment should suffice for a chemical sample.

The first prerequisite of sampling is thorough mixing of the milk. This can be done with a plunger or stirrer (agitator), operated manually or mechanically in the milk-in-cans or tankers, as the case may be. With the former, a representative sample may also be taken after quick dumping of the milk into the weigh tank, whereby it gets mixed so thoroughly that a representative sample may be taken without further mixing.

Samples may be: individual; composite (mixture of two or more individual lots of milk); drip (representing the entire day's supply); etc. Samplers may be: dipper; tube or proportionate (also known as milk thief); automatic vacuum; drip; etc. The characteristics of these are given in Table 1.22.

If the composite sample is to be successful, the milk must be kept sweet while the sample is being assembled. This is accomplished by use of a preservative. It is a good plan to place the preservative in the empty bottle before milk is added. A wide-mouthed glass bottle with a rubber stopper has been found to be the most reliable and practical container for keeping composite samples of milk or cream. The common preservatives used are: (i) *Mercuric chloride or corrosive sublimate.* This is very poison-

TABLE 1.22

Characteristics of milk samplers

Type	Principle	Advantage	Disadvantage	Remarks
Dipper	Secures 10–15 ml milk	(i) Fairly fast and easy to work with (ii) Quite accurate when milk is mixed adequately before sampling	Inaccurate when wide variations exist in milk lots, both in quality and quantity	Most commonly used. Most useful for cream
Proportionate	Secures aliquot portion of milk	Most accurate	(i) Cumbersome to use (ii) Larger sample bottle needed	Not so commonly used (not so useful for cream)
Automatic vaccum	Secures aliquot portion by vacuum automatically	(i) Very fast in operation (ii) Very accurate	Expensive	Increasingly used in large market milk plants and product factories
Drip	Milk collects in drops in the sampie bottle (which is kept under refrigeration)	Helpful in fat and SNF accounting of the total intake	Not useful for individual sampling	Useful in large product factories

ous. It may be added in the form of tablets, which are coloured (usually bright red) to prevent the milk being mistaken for food. (ii) *Formalin.* This is a 40 per cent solution of formaldehyde. Being in liquid form, it is very convenient to handle. However, it interferes with the fat test. (iii) *Potassium dichromate.* This is not as effective as the above two, but it is easy to handle in dairy plants because it is available in tablet form.

Note. The composite samples should be stored in a cool place away from direct sunlight. Each bottle should be properly labelled.

(d) *Weighing.* This is an essential step in accounting for milk receipts and disposal, making payments for milk, etc. The milk-in-cans is dumped into the weigh tank, either manually or mechanically. The tank is mounted on scales and the scale dial set at zero when the empty tank is on the scale, thus enabling the operator to make a direct reading of the weight of the milk. Automatic printing of the weight is also now becoming common. (Weighing is facilitated by the use of a dial reading or some other indicating scale, rather than a beam scale.)

The milk in tankers (road or rail) may be measured by volume by passing it through a flowmeter; and its measurement converted into weight by multiplying the volume with an agreed density. In case of road milk tankers, another common alternative is to use a weigh-bridge, the tanker being weighed once when it is full, and again after it has been emptied. However, any mud or snow on the tanker should be washed off before weighing, adjustments to fuel or water should not be made between weighings, and the driver and his accoutrements should be either on or off the vehicle on both occasions.

The characteristics of measuring by weight and by volume have been shown in Table 1.23.

TABLE 1.23

Measurement of milk by weight vs volume

Method	Characteristics
By weight	(i) Gives accurate reading, regardless of foam or temperature;
	(ii) Involves considerable initial expense for both apparatus and its installation;
	(iii) Involves problems with maintenance.
By volume	(i) Not so accurate, as affected by foam and temperature, both influencing density;
	(ii) Lower initial expense;
	(iii) Presents maintenance problems;
	(iv) Definitely a factor to be considered in the overall picture of sanitation.

(e) *Testing.* Apart from initially accepted/rejected lots of milk, there are always some of doubtful quality. All the accepted lots have already been properly sampled; these, together with samples of the remaining two categories, have to be tested in the quality control laboratory for the final verdict of acceptance/rejection. Further, a record of the chemical and bacteriological quality of all accepted milk has to be maintained for making payments, etc. (For 'Methods of Test', consult *Indian Standards* : *IS : 1479* (Part I), 1960; (Part II), 1961; (Part III), 1962.)

The common quality control tests have been given in Table 1.24.

TABLE 1.24

Quality control tests for milk and their significance

Name of Test	Purpose	Remark
Acidity	To determine final acceptance/ rejection of milk (on the basis of a pre-determined level)	Applied as such, or in a modified form, as a platform test
Ethanol (Alcohol)	To determine the heat-stability of milk	Applied as a platform test
Alcohol-Alizarin	To determine both heat-stability and pH of milk	–do–
COB (Clot-on-boiling)	To determine the heat-stability of milk	–do–
Dye-reduction test (MBR or Resazurin)	To determine the extent of bacterial contamination and growth in milk	2-mts. Resazurin applied as a platform test
DMC (Direct microscopic count)	To identify the types of micro-organisms present in milk	Applied as a laboratory test
SPC (Standard plate count)	To determine the extent of bacterial contamination and growth in milk	–do–
Lactometer	To detect adulteration of milk with water	Applied as a platform test
Freezing point	–do–	Applied as a laboratory test
Fat and/or SNF	To make payment for milk received	–do–

II. *Pre-heating*

This term refers to heating before the operation which follows immediately. The milk is pre-heated for efficient filtration/clarification. Pre-heating becomes essential if the incoming milk is cold, as otherwise the flow of milk is hampered. As the temperature of the milk increases, the viscosity decreases and more efficient filtration/clarification results. The usual temperature of pre-heating is 35–40°C, and the equipment used may be a plate or tubular heater.

III. *Filtration/Clarification*

(a) *Object.* To improve the aesthetic quality of milk by removing visible foreign matter which is unsightly and may therefore cause consumer complaints.

(b) *Principle.* While filtration removes suspended, foreign particles by the straining process, clarification removes the same by centrifugal sedimentation.

(c) *Types of filters and clarifiers.* There are two types of filters/clarifiers, viz., those that operate with cold milk and those operating with warm milk. While the latter is commonly used throughout the world, the former has the following advantages and disadvantage:

Advantages. (i) No need for pre-heating, and (ii) less likelihood of 'soluble' dirt going into the solution.

Disadvantage. The flow of milk is slow.

(d) *General construction and operation of filters and clarifiers.*

Filters. Their important features are: (i) a filter cloth or pad of the desired pore size which can retain the smallest particle; (ii) a frame or support to compress and hold the margins of the cloth or pad, so that milk can pass only through the pores; (iii) a perforated metal or other support for the cloth or pad which will not tear or break under the pressure of the milk; (iv) an enclosure to confine both the unfiltered and filtered milks in a closed system fitted suitably with inlet and outlet connections for sanitary piping; (v) a means of distributing the incoming stream of milk so that it does not damage or tear any part of the cloth or pad by vigorous washing, and (vi) a design so planned that filter cloths or pads can be changed quickly, and all parts are easily accessible for washing.

Where continuous operation is essential, or where large volumes of milk are processed, two or more filters are used so that operations need not be interrupted when it becomes necessary to change the filter cloth. The frequency with which the cloth is changed will depend upon the temperature of the milk, the amount of foreign matter in it, etc. It is best to use filter cloths only once; a washed cloth, besides being a source of contamination, results in inefficient filtration.

Clarifiers. In general appearance and construction, clarifiers are quite similar to centrifugal cream separators. However, the main differences are: (i) in clarifiers, there is only one outlet, while in separators there are two (one for cream and another for skim milk); (ii) the discs in the clarifier bowl are smaller in diameter (so as to provide a large space for the accumulation of slime) than separators, and (iii) the milk distribution holes are at the outer edge of the discs in clarifiers, but near the centre in separators.

(e) *Location of filter/clarifier in the processing line.* In some cases, it is the practice to locate the filter in the raw milk line before the milk enters the pasteurizing plant; in others, the filter is located at a convenient point in the regeneration section where the temperature of the milk may be 50–60°C.

The clarifier may be located in one of the following places in the processing line, as shown in Table 1.25:

TABLE 1.25

Location of clarifier in the processing line

Location	Type of clarification
Between: Reception and Storage Tanks	Cold
Storage Tank and Pasteurizer	Cold
Pre-heater and Pasteurizer	Warm
Regeneration and Heating Section of HTST	Warm
Heating Section and Holding Tube of HTST	Warm

(f) *Relative efficiency.* Clarification removes sediment much more efficiently than filtration; clarifiers remove still finer particles that escape filters.

(g) *Composition of clarifier slime.* While the material retained on the filter cloth includes suspended foreign particles, milk fat, protein and some leucocytes and bacteria, the slime that accumulates in the clarifier bowl consists of foreign matter, milk proteins, leucocytes, fragments of the secreting cells from the udder, fat, calcium phosphate and other ash, bacteria and occasionally red blood corpuscles.

The amount of clarifier slime is influenced by the amount of foreign matter, the condition of the udder, the stage of lactation, the bacterial count and acidity of milk, the clarifying temperature, the velocity of the bowl, and the amount of milk run through the bowl (or the length of time the bowl is run).

The composition of clarifier slime varies considerably due to the factors stated above. Separator slime is usually considered to be identical with clarifier slime. The typical composition of clarifier/separator slime under American conditions is given in Table 1.26.

TABLE 1.26

Composition of clarifier slime

Constituent	Moist Slime (%)
Water	67.3
T.S.	32.7
Fat	1.1
Protein	25.9
Ash	3.6
Lactose	2.1

SOURCE: *Market Milk and Related Products* by Sommer (1952).

Note. The removal of clarifier slime does not affect the composition of milk to a significant extent; the loss in solids resulting from clarification is usually 0.01 per cent or less.

(h) *General remarks*

(i) Both filtration and clarification tend to decrease the depth of the cream layer that will form on milk, and this effect becomes more pronounced as the processing temperature increases.

(ii) Neither filtration nor clarification improve the keeping quality of milk.

(iii) Milk should neither be filtered nor clarified after pasteurization, as this might contaminate it.

Note. Bactofugation is the process of removing 99 per cent of the bacteria in milk by centrifugal force. It is claimed that this method triples the shelf-life of market milk. Generally it removes the bacteria from milk with two centrifugal clarifiers in a series, the first operating at high velocity (20,000 rpm). The process is considered supplementary to pasteurization, for it is still necessary to destroy the bacteria not removed.

IV. *Cooling and storage of raw milk*

A. *Cooling* (In the Dairy)

(a) *Introduction.* The importance of cooling and the effect of temperature have already been discussed (see 1.15). As soon as milk is received in the Plant, it is chilled to 5°C or below and stored cool till used, to prevent deterioration in its bacteriological quality during the interim period.

(b) *Methods* (In the Dairy).

Surface Cooler. Either an Individual Unit or Cabinet type. The latter consists of two or more individual units, compactly assembled, and enclosed in a cabinet. It is usually larger than those used on the farm/chilling centre.

Plate Cooler. For continuous cooling. Commonly used in the dairy industry, especially for large-scale handling. It consists of a number of thin, flat, grooved, stainless steel plates, sealed at the edges with a gasket and clamped tightly within a press. The spaces between the plates are occupied alternately by the milk and the cooling medium (chill water/brine); thus one side of each plate is exposed to milk and the other side to the cooling medium. Plates may be added to provide increased capacity at nominal cost.

Advantages. (i) Cooling (heat-exchange) is quick and efficient; (ii) not exposed to air-borne contamination; (iii) no evaporation losses; (iv) cleaning and sanitization are easy.

Internal Tubular Cooler. For continuous cooling. It consists of a stainless steel tube about 2.5 to 5.0 cm. in diameter surrounded by a similar tube, forming a concentric cylinder. Several such tubes may then be connected in a series to obtain sufficient cooling. The cooling medium flows counter to the milk flow.

Advantages. (i) Cooling is quite efficient; (ii) not exposed to air-borne contamination; (iii) no evaporation losses.

Disadvantages. (i) Cooling efficiency is lower than plate cooler; (ii) larger floor space is needed.

Jacketed vat/tank. For batch cooling, especially of small quantities. It consists of a tank within a tank, with the space between the two being used for circulation of the cooling medium, by either pump or main pressure. An agitator is provided to move the milk (which is in the upper tank) for rapid cooling.

Disadvantages. (i) Cooling efficiency is rather low; (ii) too much agitation is required, which causes churning and impairs the creaming property of milk.

B. *Storage*

(a) *Introduction.* Modern milk plants hold both raw and pasteurized milks for a much longer period than before. Normally the milk storage capacity is equal to one day's intake. This allows a more nearly uniform work-day for processing and bottling operations with less dependence on the time for receiving raw milk.

Storage tanks are used in Milk Plants for the storage of raw, pasteurized, or processed* products, often in very large volumes. Because of the longer periods of holding, storage tanks are among the most important items of equipment. They must be designed for ease in sanitization, preferably by the circulation-cleaning method. In addition, the tanks should be insulated or refrigerated, so that they can maintain the required temperature throughout the holding period. Agitation should be adequate for homogeneous mixing, but gentle enough to prevent churning and incorporation of air.

(b) *Objects.*

(i) To maintain milk at a low temperature so as to prevent any deterioration in quality prior to processing/product manufacture;

(ii) to facilitate bulking of the raw milk supply, which will ensure uniform composition;

(iii) to allow for uninterrupted operation during processing and bottling;

(iv) to facilitate standardization of the milk.

(c) *Types.*

(i) *Insulated or Refrigerated.* In the former, there are 5 to 7.5 cm. of insulating material between the inner and outer linings; in the latter, the space between the two linings is used for circulation of the cooling medium. Another variation of the refrigerated type is the cold-wall tank.

(ii) *Horizontal or Vertical.* While the former requires more floor space and less head space, the latter requires less floor space and more head space. Modern circulation cleaning methods have made very large vertical storage tanks practical.

(iii) *Rectangular, Cylindrical or Oval.* Of these, the first suffers

---

*The term 'processed' is generally used in a wide sense in dairying, and includes pasteurization, homogenization, evaporation, drying, etc. It is desirable to use a specific term when only one process is meant.

from the disadvantage of having dead corners during agitation, while the other two do not.

(iv) *Built for gravity flow, air-pressure or vacuum operation.* The first is the most common. However, air pressure is sometimes used to evacuate the product. This requires special construction of the storage tank for greater strength than necessary for normal operations under gravity flow (i.e. atmospheric pressure).

(d) *Location.* In one system, the storage tanks are located on an upper floor. The milk is pumped from the receiving room to the floor above. It then flows by gravity to the pre-heater, filter or clarifier, pasteurizer, cooler and bottling machine. In another system, the milk is pumped from the storage tanks through a pre-heater and filter into the pasteurizer. Thence it may flow by gravity to the cooler, or it may be pumped to the cooler while hot.

(e) *Parts of a Storage Tank.*

(i) Sight glass; (ii) light glass and lamp; (iii) ladder; (iv) manhole; (v) agitator; (vi) outlet valve; (vii) inlet; (viii) air vent; (ix) safety valve; (x) legs; (xi) indicating thermometer; (xii) volume-meter.

V.   *Standardization*

(a) *Definition.* Standardization of milk refers to the adjustment, i.e. raising or lowering, of the fat and/or solids-not-fat percentages of milk to a desired value, so as to conform to the legal or other requirements prescribed.

(b) *Procedure.* Milk is standardized by the addition of milk or cream with a higher or lower fat percentage than that of the material to be standardized; sometimes the addition of skim milk will do To solve the problem, it is necessary to find the relative amounts of the original material and the standardizing material to be mixed together to give a product with the desired fat content. Once these relative amounts/proportions have been determined, it is easy to calculate the exact amount of each which must be mixed together to give a certain weight of the finished product or the exact amount of standardizing material needed to use up a given weight of milk or cream A simple scheme, the Pearson's Square, can be used to calculate the relative quantities of the materials involved in a standardization problem. It should be remembered that all measurements based on these calculations are by weight and not by volume.

The Pearson's Square method is as follows: draw a square and place in the centre of it the fat percentage desired. Place at the left-hand corners of the square the fat percentage of the materials to be mixed. Next, subtract the number in the centre from the larger number at the left-hand side of the square and place the remainder at the diagonally opposite right-hand corner. Subtract the smaller number on the left-hand side from the number in the centre and place the remainder at the diagonally opposite right-hand corner. The numbers on the right-hand side now represent the number of parts of each of the original materials that must be blended to make a product with a fat test given by the number in the middle of the square. The number at the upper right corner refers to the parts of material whose fat test was placed at the upper left corner, and the number at the lower right corner refers to the parts of material whose fat test was placed at the lower left corner. If the numbers on the right are added, the sum obtained will represent the parts of the finished product, with the fat test given by the number obtained in the middle of the square.

Problem I. How many parts by weight of 40% cream and 3% milk must be mixed to make milk testing 5% fat?
Solution.

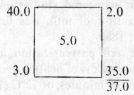

40.0   2.0

5.0

3.0   35.0

37.0

Hence, 2.0 parts of 40% cream when mixed with 35 parts of 3.0% milk will give 37 parts of 5% milk.   *Ans.*

Problem II. How many kg each of 28% cream and 3% milk will be required to make 500 kg of a mixture testing 4% fat?

Solution.

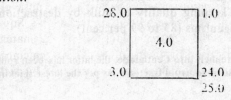

28.0   1.0

4.0

3.0   24.0

25.0

$1.0 : 25.0 = C : 500$, where C is cream required in kg

or $\dfrac{1}{25} = \dfrac{C}{500}$ or $C = \dfrac{500}{25} = 20$ kg *Ans.*

Milk (3%) $= 500 - 20 = 480$ kg *Ans.*

Proof.

500 kg of 4% milk contains $\dfrac{500 \times 4}{100} = 20$ kg fat

20 kg of 28% cream contains $\dfrac{20 \times 28}{100} = 5.6$ kg fat

480 kg of 3% milk contains $\dfrac{480 \times 3}{100} = 14.4$ kg fat

$14.4 + 5.6 = 20$ kg

VI. *Pasteurization*

A. *History.* The term pasteurization has been coined after the name of Louis Pasteur of France, who in 1860–4 demonstrated that heating wine at a temperature between 122 to 140°F (50 to 60°C) killed the spoilage organisms and helped in its preservation. The application of this process gave rise to the new term 'Pasteurization', which soon became current in technical language. Although Louis Pasteur pioneered studies on heat-treatment for preservation, pasteurization of milk was first attributed to Dr Soxhlet of Germany in 1886.

B. *Definition.* The term pasteurization, as applied to market milk today, refers to the process of heating every particle of milk to at least 63°C* (145°F) for 30 minutes, or 72°C (161°F) for 15 seconds (or to any temperature-time combination which is equally efficient), in approved and properly operated equipment. After pasteurization, the milk is immediately cooled to 5°C (41°F) or below.

C. *Object* (Purpose).

(a) To render milk safe for human consumption by destruction of cent per cent pathogenic micro-organisms;

(b) to improve the keeping quality of milk by destruction of almost all spoilage organisms (85 to 99 per cent).

---

*While converting Fahrenheit into Centigrade, the latter has been rounded off throughout this book so as to avoid fractions (as per the latest thinking in ISI).

D. *Need.* As it is difficult to exercise strict supervision over all milk supplies, it becomes necessary to pasteurize milk so as to make it safe for human consumption. Any impairment of nutritive value is of the slightest extent.

E. *Objections.*

(a) Pasteurization encourages slackening of efforts for sanitary milk production;

(b) it may be used to mask low-quality milk;

(c) it diminishes *significantly* the nutritive value of milk;

(d) it reduces the 'cream line' or 'cream volume';

(e) pasteurized milk will not clot with rennet;

(f) pasteurization may be carelessly done; it gives a false sense of security;

(g) it fails to destroy bacterial toxins in milk;

(h) in India pasteurization is not necessary, as milk is invariably boiled on receipt by the consumer.

F. *Formulation of standards.* The following considerations were involved in the formulation of the standards of pasteurization:

(a) *Bacterial destruction.* Cent per cent for pathogens. *Mycobacterium tuberculosis*, being considered the most heat-resistant among pathogens, was chosen as the index organism for pasteurization. Any heat treatment (i.e. temperature-time combination), which killed T.B. germs, also destroyed all other pathogens in milk.

(b) *Cream line reduction.* The creamline or cream volume is reduced progressively with increase in the temperature-time of heating. (The consumer judges the quality of milk on the basis of the creamline.)

(c) *Phosphatase inactivation.* The complete destruction of phosphatase by pasteurization. (The phosphatase test is used to detect inadequate pasteurization.)

Thus the standards of pasteurization were such as to ensure: (a) complete destruction of pathogens; (b) negative phosphatase test; and (c) least damage to the cream line. As T.B. germs are destroyed by a heat-treatment slightly lower than that for phosphatase inactivation, pasteurization is carried out at a heat-treatment temperature *above* that for phosphatase inactivation and yet *below* that for cream line reduction, as shown in Table 1.27.

Table 1.27

Pasteurization requirements

Particulars	30 minutes	15 seconds
To kill T.B. germs	138°F/58.9°C	158°F/70°C
To inactivate phosphatase	142°F/61.1°C	160°F/71.1°C
Pasteurization requirements	143°F/61.7°C*	161°F/71.7°C
Creamline reduced	144°F/62.2°C	162°F/72.2°C

G. *Salient remarks.*

(a) Although pasteurization is now considered a health measure, it is actually a commercial expedient;

(b) pasteurization is neither a cure-all, nor is it fool-proof;

(c) post-pasteurization should be avoided.

H. *Pasteurizing process and equipment.*

(aa) *Introduction.* The equipment for pasteurization and the needs or specifications for adequate heat-treatment of milk have been developed simultaneously. To ensure proper pasteurization with a minimum amount of equipment and controls and the least risk, holding methods or batch processes were developed. As operations grew, it became evident that higher temperatures would reduce the necessary holding time for pasteurization; this would result in a continuous operation, and with more compact equipment less plant space would be necessary.

(bb) *Principles of heat-exchange.* The general principles for efficient heat-exchange are:

(i) Rapid movement of film of fluids on both sides of the heat transfer surface;

(ii) thorough and certain mixing of this film with the body of the fluids;

(iii) use of the counterflow principle.

(iv) as great a temperature difference as possible, consistent with accurate temperature control and prevention of any deleterious effect on the product treated;

(v) the use of the least number of intermediate fluids as possible;

(vi) as thin a sheet of heat-transfer wall as possible, consistent with proper mechanical strength;

(vii) use of metals of good conductivity.

*145°F/62.8°C (since 1956).

(cc) *Considerations involved in the heating of milk.*

(i) The problem in heating milk is to obtain quick heat transfer without imparting a cooked flavour (and also impairing the creaming properties of milk).

(ii) The rate of heat transfer is mainly dependent on: the temperature gradient, renewal of surface films, thermal conductivity of the heat-transfer wall, heat-transfer area, etc.

(iii) The temperature gradient is initially quite high, but becomes smaller as milk approaches the desired pasteurization temperature. (A gradient which is too high at the end may injure the flavour and creaming properties of milk.)

(iv) Efficient renewal of surface films hastens heat transfer, so that a high temperature gradient is unnecessary. (Renewal of surface films involves flow or agitation of two liquids, viz. milk and water. Agitation of milk is limited, as at high temperatures it may cause partial 'homogenization' of fat globules; while that of water is limited only by considerations of design, cost of pumping, etc.)

(v) In case of two liquids, viz. milk and water, the principle of a counter-current flow is invariably used. (Only by a counter-current flow can milk fully attain the temperature of the heating/cooling medium; if the two are co-current, an intermediate temperature will result.)

(vi) Efficiency of renewal of surface films can eliminate use of metals of high thermal conductivity.

(vii) Provision of as large a heat-transfer area as possible contributes towards rapid heat transfer. For this purpose, the plates of the heat-exchanger are corrugated in various ways to increase their surface area. (The corrugations also give high efficiency turbulent flow.)

(viii) The heating medium is almost invariably hot water; sometimes steam under partial vacuum is also used. The hot water is circulated under pump pressure.

(dd) *Methods.*

(a) *In-the-bottle pasteurization.* Bottles filled with raw milk and tightly sealed with special caps are held at 63–66°C (145–150°F) for 30 minutes. Then the bottles pass through water sprays of decreasing temperatures which cool both the product and the bottle.

Advantage. Prevents possibility of post-pasteurization contamination.

Disadvantages. (i) Transfers heat very slowly; (ii) there is greater risk of bottle breakage; (iii) oversized bottles have to be used, to allow for milk expansion during heating; (iv) special types of water-tight caps have to be used. This method is at present outdated, although in-the-bottle sterilization of milk is widely prevalent.

(b) *Batch/holding pasteurization.* This is also called the Low-Temperature-Long-Time (LTLT) method. The milk is heated to 63°C/145°F for 30 minutes and promptly cooled to 5°C or below. In this system, heating is done indirectly; the heat moves through a metal wall into the product for heating, and out of the product for cooling. The pasteurizer may be of three types:

(i) *Water-jacketed vat.* This is double-walled around the sides and bottom in which hot water or steam under partial vacuum circulates for heating, and cold water for cooling. The outer wall (lining) is usually insulated to reduce heat loss. The heat-exchange takes place through the wall of the inner lining. The difference between the temperature of the heating water and the milk is kept to a minimum. The milk is agitated by slowly moving (revolving) paddles/propellors. When heating, the vat cover is left open for escape of off-flavours; and when holding, the cover is closed. During the holding period, an air space/foam heater (steam or electrically heated) prevents surface cooling of milk.

Advantage. Flexibility in use. (It is also known as a multi-purpose or multi-process vat.)

(ii) *Water-spray type.* A film of water is sprayed from a perforated pipe over the surface of the tank holding the product. The product is agitated as above. A rapidly moving continuous film of water provides rapid heat transfer.

Advantage. The same as above.

(iii) *Coil-vat type.* The heating/cooling medium is pumped through a coil placed in either a horizontal or vertical position, while the coil is turned through the product. The turning coil agitates the product (but additional agitation may be necessary).

Disadvantage. Coils are difficult to clean, which accounts for the decline in their use.

Note. (i) As vat heating/cooling is rather slow and involves too much agitation, causing churning and impairment of creaming properties, this operation can be efficiently carried out by Plate or Tubular Heat Exchangers.

(ii) With the vat holding system, a continuous flow of milk can be obtained with multiple vat installation; however, this may encourage the growth of thermophilic organisms over long periods.

(c) *High Temperature Short Time (HTST) pasteurization.*

1. *Introduction.* This was first developed by A. P. V. Co. in the United Kingdom in 1922. It is the modern method of pasteurizing milk and is invariably used where large volumes of milk are handled. The HTST pasteurizer gives a continuous flow of milk which is heated to 72°C (161°F) for 15 seconds and promptly cooled to 5°C or below.

2. *Advantages.* (i) Capacity to heat-treat milk quickly and adequately, while maintaining rigid quality control over both the raw and finished product; (ii) less floor space required; (iii) lower initial cost; (iv) milk packaging can start as soon as pasteurization begins, thus permitting more efficient use of labour for packaging and distribution; (v) easily cleaned and sanitized (system adapts itself well to CIP-cleaning); (vi) lower operating cost (due to fullest use of regeneration): (vii) pasteurizing capacity can be increased at nominal cost; (viii) reduced milk losses; (ix) development of thermophiles not a problem; (x) the process can be interrupted and quickly restarted; (xi) automatic precision controls ensure positive pasteurization.

3. *Disadvantages.* (i) The system is not well-adapted to handling small quantities of several liquid milk products; (ii) gaskets require constant attention for possible damage and lack of sanitation; (iii) complete drainage is not possible (without losses exceeding those from the holder system); (iv) margins of safety in product sanitary control are so narrow that automatic control precision instruments are required in its operation; (v) pasteurization efficiency of high-thermoduric count raw milk is not as great as it is when the holder system is used; (vi) greater accumulation of milk-stone in the heating section (due to higher temperature of heating)

4. *Milk flow.* The following steps or stages are involved as milk passes through the HTST pasteurization system: balance tank; pump; regenerative heating; holding; regenerative cooling; and cooling by chill water or brine. An arrangement for incoropr-

ation of the filter/clarifier, homogenizer, etc., in the circuit is also made when desired. There is some variation in the use or order of these steps in different milk processing plants.

5. *Functions of the important parts.*

(i) *Float-Controlled Balance Tank* (*FCBT*). Maintains a constant head of milk for feeding the raw milk pump; also receives any sub-temperature milk diverted by FDV.

(ii) *Pump*. Either a rotary positive pump between the regenerator and heater (USA), or a centrifugal pump with a flow control device to ensure constant output, after FCBT (UK and Europe) is used.

(iii) *Plates*. The Plate Heat Exchanger (also called Paraflow) is commonly used in the HTST system, especially for heating to temperatures which are below the boiling point of milk. The plate heat exchanger is a compact, simple, easily cleaned and inspected unit. Its plates may be used for heating, cooling, regeneration and holding. These plates are supported in a press between a terminal block in each heating and cooling section. The heat moves from a warm to a cold medium through stainless steel plates. A space of approximately 3 mm. is maintained between the plates by a non-absorbent rubber gasket or seal which can be vulcanized to them. The plates are numbered and must be properly assembled. They are tightened into place, and are so designed as to provide a uniform but not excessively turbulent flow of products with rapid heat transfer. Raised sections (corrugations) on the plates in the form of knobs, diamonds and channels, help provide the turbulent action required. Greater capacity is secured by adding more plates. Ports are provided in appropriate places, both at the top and bottom of the plates, to permit both the product and the heating/cooling medium to flow without mixing.

(iv) *Regeneration* (*Heating*). The (raw) cold incoming milk is partially and indirectly heated by the hot outgoing milk (milk-to-milk regeneration). This adds to the economy of the HTST process, as the incoming milk requires less heating by hot water to raise its temperature for holding.

(v) *Filter*. Variously shaped filter units to connect directly to the HTST system are placed after the pre-heater or regenerative (heating) section. These units, using 40–90 mesh cloth, are usually cylindrical in shape. Usually two filters are attached but they are used one at a time. This permits continuous operation, the flow being switched from one to the other while replacing a filter.

(vi) *Holding*. The holding tube or plate ensures that the milk is held for a specified time, not less than 15 seconds, at the pasteurization temperature of 72°C (161°F) or more.

(vii) *Flow diversion valve (FDV)*. This routes the milk after heat treatment. If the milk has been properly pasteurized, it flows forward through the unit; that which is unpasteurized (i.e., in which the temperature does not reach the legal limit) is automatically diverted back to the FCBT for reprocessing. It is usually operated by air pressure working against a strong spring. Should the temperature fall, air pressure is released and the valve snaps shut immediately. When the temperature is regained, air pressure builds up and the valve opens to forward flow. The system is so arranged that any failure of air or electricity moves the valve in the diverted position.

Note. The flow of unpasteurized milk can also be stopped with a 'pump stop', which automatically stops the milk-pump motion if the product temperature drops below the desired level. When the proper temperature is reached, the pump stop restarts the operation and allows the flow of milk to continue.

(viii) *Regeneration (cooling)*. The pasteurized hot outgoing milk is partially and indirectly cooled by the incoming cold milk (milk-to-milk regeneration). This again adds to the economy of the HTST process. In fact, when pre-cooled (raw) milk is received, the high degree of regeneration (72 to 85%) allows water cooling to be dispensed with entirely.

(ix) *Control panel*. Contains instruments, controls, FDV-mechanism and holding system, all centralized in one moisture proof panel. The lower half of the panel forms an air-insulated chamber which carries the holding tube.

(x) *Hot water set*. Circulates hot water through the heating section of the machine to maintain the correct milk temperature within very fine limits.

(xi) *Automatic control devices*. These include:

Steam pressure controller. Maintains a constant hot water temperature for heating milk accurately to the required pasteurization temperature. (Acts as a reducing valve in the steam supply line, so as to give a constant steam pressure.)

Water temperature controller. Regulates the amount of steam entering the hot water circulating system.

Milk temperature recorder. Records the temperature of milk leaving the holding tube/plate. This is an electric contact instrument that operates either a FDV or a milk pump, automatically preventing milk from leaving the holding section at sub legal temperatures. Both the frequency and dura .ion of the flow diversion and the temperature of milk leaving the holder are recorded on the thermograph (recording chart) by means of two separate pens. (The 'check thermometer' is placed near the milk temperature recorder.)

6. *Pressure in the system.* The normal pressures maintained in the HTST system are:

Pasteurized milk	15 psi
Raw milk	14 psi
Heating/cooling medium	12 to 13 psi

7. *Holding time test.* The holding time of a HTST pasteurizer is the flow time of the fastest particle of milk at a prescribed temperature through the holding section. The holding time is calculated between the points at which the heated milk leaves the heating section and reaches the FDV. The efficiency of pasteurization in the HTST system depends as much on the correct maintenance of temperature as on the holding time. Hence the latter should be checked periodically. Several methods are used for determination of the holding time, viz. the electrical conductivity method (of a salt solution); the dye injection method; the electronic timer method; etc.

(d) *Electric pasteurization.* (See *Fluid Milk Industry* by Henderson (1971)).

(e) *Vacuum pasteurization (Vacreation).* This refers to pasteurization of milk/cream under reduced pressure by direct steam. The process was first developed in New Zealand by M/s Murray Deodorizers Ltd. who called the equipment a 'Vacreator' and the process 'Vacreation'. It was designed to remove feed and other volatile flavours from cream, and to pasteurize it for buttermaking.

The vacreator consists of three stainless steel chambers connected to one another for steam heating and vacuum treatment with continuous product flow. The product, in the form of fine droplets, enters the first chamber of the vacreator where pasteurization occurs. The chamber is operated under a vacuum of 5 inches Hg which maintains a temperature of 90 to 95°C, while steam, fed from the top, falls by gravity to the bottom of the chamber. Then the product and some free steam are moved from the bottom of the first chamber to the top of the second one. The temperature of the second chamber is maintained at 71 to 82°C under a vacuum of 15 to 20 inches Hg. A portion of the steam previously added is removed, and the product moves down through the chamber. Some of the tainting substances and off-flavours are removed by heat and vacuum treatment. The product then moves on to the third chamber at 43°C by maintaining a vacuum of 26 to 28 inches Hg, and here more water and off-flavours are removed. A multi-stage centrifugal pump removes the product from the third chamber. Altogether, it takes the product about 10 seconds to move continuously through the unit. (Steam of uniform pressure, normally ensured by a uniform pressure reducing and regulating valve, should be provided. It must not contain any boiler compounds which may contaminate the product.)

(f) *Stassanization.* This method of pasteurization is carried out in a tubular heat exchanger consisting of three concentric tubes. It was invented in France by Henri Stassano and is used to a considerable extent in French, Danish, Italian and other milk plants. The principle of its operation is the heating of milk to the desired temperature by passing it between two water-heated pipes through the narrow space of 0.6 to 0.8 mm. The milk is heated to about 74°C (165°F) for 7 seconds and then promptly cooled as usual.

(g) *Ultra-high temperature pasteurization.* Ultra-high temperature (UHT) pasteurization was developed in the 1950s. This usually encompasses temperature-time combinations of 135 to 150°C (275 to 302°F) for no-hold (a fraction of a second). The success of UHT heat-treatment of milk depends on immediate aseptic packaging.

(h) *Flash pasteurization.* In earlier days, this term was used for what is today called HTST.

(j) *Uperization.* This is itself a shortened form of the word 'Ultra-pasteurization', which has been developed in Switzerland. In this process milk is heated with direct steam up to 150°C (302°F) for a fraction of a second. The process is continuous.

The method of manufacture of uperized milk is as follows:

high quality raw milk is immediately clarified on receipt, then chilled and stored in tanks. In the first part of the uperization process, the milk is forewarmed to 50°C and de-aerated to remove most of the dissolved oxygen and volatile off-flavours by vacuum treatment. In the second part, the milk is first pre-heated to about 80–90°C and then heated in the uperization chamber with high pressure steam to around 150°C for $\frac{1}{3}$ to $\frac{3}{4}$ second. After this heating, the product moves into an expansion chamber at near atmospheric pressure, thereby forcing some evaporation of moisture. The product is then moved to a cooler and then into storage.

The advantages claimed for uperized milk are: (i) long keeping quality; (ii) removal of feed and other volatile off-flavours; (iii) appreciable homogenization effect; (iv) reduction in acidity; (v) efficient destruction of micro-organisms; (vi) effect of uperization on nutritive value and flavour no greater than that of pasteurization.

J. *Alternatives to pasteurization.* Various types of treatment have been proposed from time to time as alternatives to pasteurization. These include: (a) the Hofius process; (b) electronic heating; (c) ultra-violet irradiation; (d) ultra-sonic vibration, etc.

VII. *Homogenization.* A considerable proportion of market milk pasteurized in developed dairying countries is now homogenized as well. The homogenizer may be located immediately after regenerative heating, or between final heating and holding, or after FDV and before regenerative cooling. (See 2.2 for more information.)

VIII. *Bottling/Packaging*

A. *Introduction.* The pasteurized and cooled milk is promptly bottled/packaged so as to serve the dual purpose of: (a) protecting the milk against contamination, loss, damage or degradation (due to: micro-organisms or insects; exposure to heat, light, moisture or oxygen; spillage, evaporation or pilferage), and (b) helping in the sale and distribution of the milk (by packaging it in an easy-to-carry-and-open, sufficiently strong and leak-proof, non-tainting container).

B. *Bottling and Capping*

(aa) *Bottles.* The glass bottle is still universally used. It is usually transparent, although in some countries brown bottles have been tried. (Brown bottles prevent light-induced off-flavours in milk; but on the other hand, the product is not visible for inspection.) The glass bottle is generally round, but may also be square in shape (as in the USA); the latter is considered to be more economical of storage space. Light-weight yet sturdy, the glass bottle is best since it decreases the pay-load of retail vehicles.

Bottles should be examined for their colour, capacity and strength, before use. The tests (prescribed in *IS:1392*, 1959) include the following: (i) colour and appearance; (ii) shape; (iii) dimensions (height and neck diameter); (iv) weight; (v) serrations; (vi) minimum wall thickness; (vii) nominal capacity; (viii) strength or durability (these consist of thermal shock test, internal pressure test, impact test, polariscope examination, etc.).

In plants of small capacity, milk may be bottled with hand fillers operated manually with a lever and capable of filling 4 to 12 bottles at a time. The caps are then usually applied with a hand capper. In larger plants, automatic, continuous, mechanical bottle fillers and cappers are used. These are broadly of two types, viz., gravity fillers and vacuum fillers. In the former, the milk flows by gravity into the bottles as they are pressed against the filling valves; in the latter, the bottles are filled by creating a vacuum within them. The milk from the cooler usually goes directly into the bowl of the bottle-filling machine, the connecting pipe being equipped with a valve that regulates the flow. Bottle washing operations are so timed in relation to the processing of milk that washed and sanitized bottles arrive at the filler as needed for immediate bottling.

There are two principles in filling, viz. level filling and quantity filling. Level filling is quicker and more common; most bottle fillers are designed to fill milk bottles to a pre-determined level; however, a constant low temperature of milk at the time of filling, should be maintained. Quantity filling, although more accurate since it is not affected by either temperature or foam, is slower and hence seldom used.

(bb) *Bottling (Bottle filling)*

(a) *Gravity fillers.* These consist mainly of six different parts, viz., the drive, bowl, filler valves, carrier, capper and star wheels. The circular bowl receives the milk to be bottled. The level of milk is kept constant by a float valve on the inlet pipe. Filling valves are attached radially to the bottom of the bowl. Bottles are fed by hand or directly from the bottle washer by a conveyor. They are mechanically centred into lifters which are located directly under the filling valves and which revolve with them. These lifters rise automatically as the filler revolves and the mouth of the bottle is forced against a tightly fitting rubber valve. The rising bottle pushes up the valve and the milk flows down into the bottle. As the filling valve almost completes a revolution, the lifter on which the bottle is carried is lowered automatically and the valve closes and remains closed until the next bottle opens it. The filled bottle is then transferred to a capper where it is automatically sealed and the lifter, now in the lowered position, is ready to receive another empty bottle for filling. While the bottle is being filled, the air which is displaced by the incoming milk escapes through a vent tube, which extends from the bottom of the valve sleeve to a point above the milk level in the bowl. The height of the bowl-tank is adjusted by the operator to suit the size of each bottle that is to be filled. Bottles are automatically discharged from the capper onto a conveyor that delivers them to an accumulating table, from where they may be loaded into crates manually or mechanically.

Advantages: (i) relatively simple to operate; (ii) maintenance not too complicated; (iii) easily and swiftly cleaned.

Disadvantages: (i) slow filling and hence limited capacity; (ii) leakage losses high (due to badly sealed bottle, bottle with chipped mouth, faulty valve, etc.).

(b) *Vacuum fillers*. These may be either vacuum-assisted (single-bowl) or straightforward vacuum (double-bowl) types. In the former, the typical gravity bowl, which has open vent tubes and conventional gravity valves, is closed with an air-tight cover. In the latter, there is a rotary bowl and a float bowl. The float bowl is slightly below the level of the tops of the filling head. When the bottle is raised against the rubber ring on the filling head, a seal is formed and air inside the bottle is immediately drawn out through vertical vacuum pipes, and the milk is drawn from the float bowl through the milk pipes to the filling head and is released into the bottle. Foam is drawn off through the vacuum pipes into the vacuum tanks. Excess milk collecting in the vacuum tank automatically goes into the float bowl. Towards the end of the revolution of the filler, the lifters, on which the bottles are carried, are lowered, and the seal is broken. Any milk remaining in the milk pipe syphons back into the float bowl and that remaining in the vacuum line is drawn back into the vacuum tank.

Advantages: (i) rapid filling; (ii) will not fill a bottle with a chipped mouth or bad seal, thus saving milk; (iii) no milk drip through faulty valves.

Disadvantages: (i) maintenance complicated; (ii) relatively complicated to operate; (iii) cleaning more time-consuming.

(cc) *Caps and capping.* The capping machine is often incorporated into the filler, and in any case, its work must synchronize with it. The milk bottle cap or closure has three main functions: (i) to retain the milk within the bottle; (ii) to protect the pouring lip from contamination; and (iii) to seal the bottle against tampering. (In this case, tampering refers to the removal or replacement of milk from a bottle without this being evident from the appearance of either the bottle or the milk within it.)

The caps may be: (i) cardboard discs, impregnated with a moisture-proof layer (paraffin wax or polythene); (ii) aluminium foil caps; (iii) crown corks. The cardboard discs with separate hoods were the first to be introduced, but are not much used now. The aluminium foil cap is most commonly used. It is either pre-formed or formed-in-place, both types having their advantages and disadvantages. The foil may be 0.05 to 0.15 mm. thick and of 50 mm. width (see *IS:1705*, 1960). Crown corks are generally used for sterilized milk; they are made of lacquered tin plate, the inner surface of which is lined with water-proof paper/polythene, and are more expensive. (All types of caps or closures can be printed or embossed with names or trade marks and can be coloured for coding purposes.)

(dd) *Inspection of filled bottles.* Before being (manually) placed in crates, filled milk bottles should be inspected for dirt, etc. by rotating them as they are removed from the machine.

(ee *Decrating and recrating of bottles.* Removing dirty bottles from crates (decrating) and refilling them with bottles of pasteurized milk (recrating) are among the most back-breaking and labour-consuming operations in the dairy. Both decrating and recrating machines look the same. The decrator lifts the empty bottles by vacuum-operated rubber-grippers and rejects any that are damaged. The recrator lifts the filled bottles by compressed-air operated rubber-grippers. In decrating, the crates of empty bottles are at first correctly positioned before lifting, while in recrating, a special marshalling mechanism allows bottles from the filler to assemble in correctly positioned groups, ready to be picked up for transfer to the crates.

(ff) *Crate stacker.* This stacks crates containing filled bottles, thereby relieving labour of another back-breaking job.

C. *Packaging* (Also see Appendix I)

Although the glass milk bottle is still the traditional packaging medium for retail milk distribution, single-service paper/plastic containers are increasingly being adopted for the same purpose. A survey has shown that in some European countries they have captured two-thirds of the market. A beginning in this field has also lately been made in India. As far as milk packaging is concerned, paper is a carrier for a water-proof layer of either polyethylene or wax. The provision for 5 to 10 per cent of synthetic fibres is said not to influence the printing or folding capacity of paper, but rather to provide better wet strength. Dominated, in milk packaging, by polyolefines (such as polypropylene and polyethylenes), used singly or blended to offer a wide range of materials, plastics have superseded paper in recent times. The polyolefines of interest are coating grades for cartons, film grades for sachets and extrusion/blowing grades for bottles.

Cartons are commonly used for both bulk and retail sale. They are made of combinations of food grade paper and wax or plastics. The distribution advantages of cartons are: maximum space utilization in vehicles and storage, ability to carry attractive printing, and convenience for the purpose of stacking milk on super-market shelves. The carton systems in common use are: Perga (U.K.); Pure Pak (U.S.A.); Zupack, Blockpack (W. Germany); and Tetra Pak (Sweden). When filling the cartons, either preformed or pre-cut blanks may be used. Pre-formed cartons are supplied in a fully erect form ready for filling; in the pre-cut system the blanks are supplied in a knocked down shape and the final carton is set up, formed, filled and sealed on one machine.

Sachets are flexible water-proof bags. Since it is difficult to pour from sachets, they are usually equipped with a jug. The sachet systems in common use are: Polypack, Bertopack (Switzerland); Finnpack (Finland); Milk-Pack, Rotapack (W. Germany); and Prepac (France). Sachet filling of milk usually follows a form/fill/seal system. The sachets are formed from a reeled film over a shoulder and tube-forming sealer. Their size is changed simply by pushing a button without stopping the machine. They are filled by a time-regulated valve accurate within ± 3 ml./litre. Ultra-violet light is used to sterilize the inside of the film.

D. *Glass Bottle vs Paper/Film Package*

The relative advantages and disadvantages of paper/film packaging of milk over bottling are given below:

Advantages: (i) light in weight, easy to handle and no danger of breakage; (ii) distribution costs lower (occupies less space, lower pay-load due to light weight, no collection of empties); (iii) bottle-washing costs eliminated (saving in equipment, detergents, steam, etc.); (iv) tamper-proof; (v) effective sales message can be printed; (vi) less noisy (during filling, sealing and transportation); (vii) no exposure to sunlight; (viii) filling machinery compact and occupies much less space; (ix) no container deposit needed.

Disadvantages. (i) Costs higher per unit milk distributed; (ii) product not visible; (iii) difficult to remove cream; (iv) inspection of milk (for sediment) not possible; (v) regular supply of special paper/film essential; (vi) not so easy to open; and (vii) some cases of leakage may occur.

IX. *Storage.* In any milk plant, it is necessary to provide refrigerated rooms where milk can be stored until delivery. The temperature of milk storage rooms should be 5°C or below so as to check bacterial growth.

1.18 Distribution*

(a) *Introduction.* Distribution of milk is the last or final stage of the market milk industry. Others are preparatory to placing the product into the hands of the consumer. The quality of the

---

*All developed countries today invariably adopt the bottled/packaged milk distribution system. Nevertheless, unpacked (i.e., loose) milk distribution is quite prevalent in developing countries, as in India. While the disorganized sector of the Indian dairy industry follows the loose milk :tion system, the organized sector pursues the pattern of developed ..es. A notable exception is the Mother Dairy, Delhi, which has adopted the NDDB-devised bulk-milk-vending system since 1974.

This dairy has set up milk-vending booths in various parts of the city. In each booth there is installed an NDDB-designed coin(token)-operated milk vending machine, popularly known as the 'push-button mini-dairy'. The milk holding capacity of these machines varies from 1000 to 1300 litres each. The consumer is expected to bring his/her own container large enough to hold the milk. He/she is expected to go to the concessionaire and exchange

product alone will not assure its wide distribution, which should be planned and executed intelligently.

Distribution facilities consist of: (i) the physical equipment and personnel required for transporting the products from the milk storage rooms to the consumer/retailer; (ii) sales promotion personnel; and (iii) advertising.

A successful distribution programme requires: (i) a product of high quality; (ii) an attractive package; (iii) neat and courteous route salesmen; (iv) delivery equipment of pleasing appearance; (v) efficient use of men and equipment; (vi) effective advertising.

(b) *Route organization.* This varies with the size and the type of business. In a small plant, the same drivers and trucks may deliver both wholesale and retail goods. In larger organizations, wholesale and retail distribution are usually handled by separate personnel and equipment. Wholesale routes handle larger volumes and have fewer stops than do retail routes. For economical operation, the truck should be utilized for a maximum number of hours per day for milk distribution.

(c) *Payment of route salesmen.* Three different methods are in use: (i) *Flat salary.* Gives no incentive to sell more products, secure new customers, etc.; (ii) *Salary plus commission.* Most satisfactory; (iii) *Straight commission.* Used when the driver owns the route and equipment.

(d) *Checking out the routes.* Different systems may be used for loading the trucks in checking out the routes. The trucks must be loaded rapidly so that the drivers are not delayed at loading stations. The principal systems are: (i) loading directly from the storage rooms through one or more doors; (ii) using a long loading platform with conveyors from the milk-storage rooms; (iii) loading platform-trolleys in the storage room with orders for the different routes. The platform trolleys are then wheeled onto the loading platform and finally loaded into the

money for metal tokens. The container is to be placed under the tap. On inserting the token into the slot the button lights up. On pressing the button, the first half litre of milk flows out. The process is repeated to get the second instalment of milk by inserting another token, and so on. The dairy claims that this method enables it to pay more to the milk producers (on account of the savings effected in the cost of packaged milk distribution), and yet operate the dairy on a 'no-profit-and-no-loss' basis. The results of this unique experiment are awaited with great interest.

delivery trucks. (The first two systems are suitable for medium size and large plants, the third for small ones.)

(e) *Checking in the routes.* This consists of verifying the driver's count of empty bottles and unsold goods and conveying the bottles to the washers or to storage. The driver usually places the bottles on the platform, conveyor or platform-trolley.

(f) *Sales outlets.* These include (for both wholesale and retail sales) the following: (i) home delivery: (ii) milk booths or distribution depots/bars; (iii) stores; (iv) soda fountains; (v) coin vending machines; (vi) automatic dispensers; (vii) factories, hospitals, jails, restaurants, schools, etc.; (viii) lunch counters.

(g) *Anticipating daily demand.* This is usually based on past experience, taking into consideration holidays, fairs and festivals, special events, etc.

(h) *Frequency of distribution.* Due to highly changeable temperatures during most seasons and the lack of refrigeration facilities at the average customer's home in India the milk has to be distributed twice daily, viz., morning and evening. In cold countries, one-time delivery is usual.

(j) *Utilization of returned milk.* Unsold milk presents a problem of economic disposal. Under tropical conditions, as in India, the returned milk should not be sent again for sale as liquid milk since exposure to high temperatures during its inward and outward journeys subject it to quality deterioration and hence may cause consumer complaints. The unsold milk can be given for separation or utilized for preparation of dahi, etc.

(k) *Systems of collection for the payment of milk.* These are credit, cash or advance payment (coupon/monthly card). Their relative merits and demerits are given in Table 1.28.

TABLE 1.28

Comparison of different collection-systems for the payment of milk

System	Merits	Demerits
Credit	(i) Attractive to customers (as no immediate payment and locking up of money) (ii) Rapid deliveries (iii) Accounting is easy	(i) Losses through bad accounts (ii) Needs special check on amount delivered

System	Merits	Demerits
Cash	(i) No losses through bad accounts as money collected on the spot	(i) Slows down deliveries as some customers may not bring correct change (ii) Less attractive to customers (iii) Counterfeit coins are a problem (iv) Carrying of large amounts of cash may be risky (for dairy staff)
Coupons	(i) No losses through bad accounts (ii) Curbs corruption (especially on the part of dairy staff)	(i) Slows down deliveries (ii) Increases the sale price of milk (iii) Less attractive to customers (as money locked up) (iv) Final accounting is cumbersome (v) Special check needed for misuse of coupons (lost or stolen from rightful owner) (vi) Chances of fraudulent printing of coupons

1.19   Cleaning and Sanitization of Dairy Equipment

A. *Definitions*

Cleaning or washing of dairy equipment implies the removal of 'soil' from the surface of each machine.

Sanitization (also referred to as sterilization) implies the destruction of all pathogenic and almost all non-pathogenic microorganisms from equipment surface.

Note.   'Soil' consists primarily of milk or milk product residues which may be more or less modified by processing treatment, or by interaction with water or cleaning materials previously used, or by dust, dirt or other foreign matter. (Soil may be one or more of the following: liquid milk films, air-dried films, heat-precipitated films, heat-hardened films, milk-stone and miscellaneous foreign matter.)

Detergents or cleaning/washing compounds are substances capable of assisting cleaning.

Sanitizers are substances capable of destroying all pathogenic and almost all non-pathogenic micro-organisms.

Milk-stone is an accumulation of dried milk solids and salts from hard water and washing solutions. It consists largely of calcium phosphate, milk protein, precipitated, coagulated and baked-on by heat, and insoluble calcium-salts from water and washing solutions. It has the following approximate composition:

Moisture	2.7 to 8.7%
Fat	3.6 to 17.7%
Protein	4.4 to 43.8%
Ash	42.0 to 67.3%

B. *Importance*

All dairy equipment should be properly cleaned and sanitized as milk provides an excellent medium for the growth of micro-organisms. At the same time, detergents and sanitizers used for cleaning and sanitization should be so selected as not to affect the material of the equipment.

Cleaning and sanitization are complementary processes; either of them alone will not achieve the desired result, which is to leave the surfaces as free as possible from milk residues and viable organisms.

C. *Detergents*

(a) Detergents should have the following desirable properties: (i) wetting and penetrating power; (ii) emulsifying power; (iii) saponifying power; (iv) deflocculating power; (v) sequestering and chelating power; (vi) quick and complete solubility; (vii) should be non-corrosive to metal surfaces; (viii) free rinsing; (ix) economical; (x) stability during storage; (xi) should be mild on hands; (xii) should possess germicidal action.

Note. No single detergent possesses all the above properties. Hence two or more detergents are compounded for different operations so as to combine cleaning efficiency with safety.

(b) Dairy detergents may be broadly classified into 4 groups:

(i) *Alkalis.* Sodium hydroxide (caustic soda), sodium carbonate (washing soda), sodium phosphates, sodium bicarbonate/sesquicarbonate, sodium silicate/sulphite (as inhibitors), etc.

Strong alkalis are used to saponify fat and weak alkalis to dissolve protein.

(ii) *Acids*. (Mild) Phosphoric, tartaric, citric, gluconic and hydroacetylic; (Strong) Nitric. Mild acids are used for milk-stone removal; nitric acid may be used in not more than 1 per cent concentration for stainless steel surfaces.

(iii) *Polyphosphates and chelating chemicals*. These are used together with acids or alkalis. Examples: Tetraphosphate, hexametaphosphate, tripolyphosphate, pyrophosphate, etc.

(iv) *Surface-active/wetting agents*. These are either used alone or in conjunction with acids or alkalis. Examples: Teepol, Acinol-N, Idet-10, common soaps, etc.

Note. By careful choice from the above materials it is possible to prepare mixtures possessing the desired degree of cleaning efficiency.

D. *Sanitizers*.

These should have the following desirable properties: (i) non-toxic (ii) quick acting; (iii) relatively non-corrosive to hands and equipment; (iv) easily and quickly applied; (v) relatively inexpensive. The commonly used dairy sanitizers are: steam, hot water, and chemicals (chlorine compounds, iodophor and quaternary ammonium compounds). The method of chemical sanitization broadly consists of: flushing, spraying, brushing, fogging and submersion.

E. *Cleaning and Sanitizing Procedure*

I. *Principles*. In the selection of any particular detergent, consideration should be given to: type of soil, quality of water supply, material of surface and the equipment to be cleaned, and method of cleaning, viz., soaking, brushing, spraying and/or recirculation. Detergents are invariably used as an aqueous solution. In the selection of dairy sanitizers, the following considerations are kept in mind: (a) *High temperature sanitizing*. Main advantages are penetrating ability and quick drying of the equipment. Heat is the most reliable sanitizer, especially when both temperature and time are controlled. Thus effective sanitization can be done by steam (15 psi for 5 minutes or 0 psi for 15 minutes) or scalding water (90-95°C for 10 minutes). (b) *Low temperature sanitizing*. Main advantages are: (i) permits sanitizing immediately before equipment is used (when hot equipment will be injurious to the quality of milk or milk products); (ii) avoids excessive strain on equipment (such as ice-cream freezers); and (iii) permits flushing out of equipment immediately before use, thereby removing any possible dust that may have entered. Generally, chlorine solution at 15–20°C containing 150 to 200 ppm available chlorine, is used for a contact time of 1 to 2 minutes.

The usual procedure for cleaning and sanitization of major items of dairy equipment should consist of:

(i) *Draining*, to remove any residual loose milk and any other matter.

(ii) *Pre-rinsing*, with cold or tepid water, to remove as much milk residue and other matter as possible.

(iii) *Warm to hot detergent washing* with detergent solution of 0.15 to 0.60 per cent alkalinity, to remove the remaining milk-solids.

(iv) *Hot water rinsing*, to remove traces of detergents.

(v) *Sanitizing*, to destroy all pathogens and almost all non-pathogens. (Usually also done just before using the equipment.)

(vi) *Draining and drying*, to help prevent bacterial growth and corrosion. (Drying readily accomplished by heat and ventilation; never use a cloth or towel of any kind. Drying not necessary if equipment is to be immediately refilled with a dairy product.)

The selection and precautions in the use of detergents and sanitizers for different surface-materials of dairy equipment are given in Table 1.29.

TABLE 1.29

Selection of detergents and sanitizers

Material	Cleaning	Sanitization
Stainless steel	All alkalis may be used. Care should be taken with acids.	All sanitizers may be used.
Mild steel	All alkalis may be used. Acids should be used together with inhibitors.	–do–

Material	Cleaning	Sanitization
Tinned steel/copper	Weak alkalis, together with sodium sulphite as inhibitor, should be used.	All sanitizers may be used.
Bronze	–do–	–do–
Galvanized	–do–	–do–
Aluminium alloy	Weak alkalis, together with sodium silicate as inhibitor, should be used.	–do– –do–
Glass	All alkalis and acids may be used.	–do–
Vitreous enamel	Weak alkalis, together with sodium silicate as inhibitor, should be used.	–do–
Plastics	Cleaning temperatures should not be above the softening point of plastic.	Only chemical sanitizers should be used.
Rubber	Strong alkalis should be used to remove any fatty material stuck to the surface.	–do–

Note. (i) Chlorine sanitizers, if left in contact with metal surfaces, cause corrosion. Hence they should preferably be used just before processing.

(ii) Inhibitors are substances which minimize the corrosive action of acids or alkalis on metal surfaces. *Examples*: Sodium sulphite for a tinned surface and sodium silicate for an aluminium/aluminium-alloy surface.

The choice of general purpose detergents in organized dairies is given in Table 1.30.

TABLE 1.30

Choice of detergents in organized dairies

S. No.	Ingredients	Quantity	Remarks
1.	Tri-sodium phosphate Wetting agent	850 g. 150 g.	For general use
2.	Tri-sodium phosphate Sodium meta-silicate Wetting agent	650 g. 200 g. 150 g.	For aluminium utensils
3.	Tri-sodium phosphate Sodium sulphite Wetting agent	750 g. 100 g. 150 g.	For tinned utensils

Note. (i) Under Indian conditions, tri-sodium silicate is usually replaced by sodium carbonate, mainly due to the lower cost and easy availability of the latter. However, sodium carbonate has a lower cleaning efficiency than tri-sodium silicate.

(ii) In organized dairies, the sanitizers chosen may be steam, scalding water (90 to 95°C) or chlorine solution (150 to 200 ppm. available chlorine).

II. *Methods.* These include hand washing, mechanical washing and cleaning-in-place (or in-place-cleaning).

(aa) *Hand washing.* (a) The normal cleaning and sanitization of hand-washed dairy equipment in organized dairies should be done as follows:

(i) Prepare 0.8 to 1.0 per cent of the detergent mixture (any set in Table 1.29) in tap water, so as to give a minimum alkalinity of 0.5 per cent (pH over 11.0) in a wash-up tank and maintain the temperature at about 50°C.

(ii) Thoroughly rinse the utensils with clean cold water (or tepid water in winter).

(iii) Introduce the detergent solution into the equipment (quantity of solution to be determined by requirement and experience). Thoroughly brush the equipment surface, inside and outside, with a clean can-brush.

(iv) Wash the utensil with enough fresh cold water (tepid water in winter), using a clean brush again if needed, to remove all traces of detergent.

(v) Allow the equipment to drain thoroughly and let it dry (for at least one to two hours).

(vi) Sanitize the equipment surface by steam or hot water after cleaning, and/or by rinsing with chlorine solution (200 ppm. available chlorine) just before using.

Note. (i) Use rubber gloves to avoid skin injury from detergent action.

(ii) Two compartment wash-up tank, one for warm detergent solution and the other for hot water (with a drain outlet in each tank) together with a steam jet/chest is helpful.

(iii) Use fresh detergent and sanitizing solutions.

(b) Bottles may be hand-washed as follows: The operator uses either a hand-brush or a motor-driven brush, and a mild alkaline solution which will not be injurious to the hand. A three-compartment tank (with a drainage outlet for each) is helpful; table space at both ends should also be provided. Two-thirds of the first compartment is filled with water at 50–55°C containing alkali detergent (any set in Table 1.29). The second compartment is filled similarly with water only at 50-55°C. The third compartment contains enough clean cold water, with 150 to 200 ppm. available chlorine. The (drained) bottles are put into the first compartment, and allowed to soak there for a few minutes, then brushed with a clean bottle-brush both inside and outside. After brushing, the bottles are placed in the second compartment where they remain until all bottles in the batch are washed. Then a new batch of bottles is placed in the first compartment to be soaked; and the bottles in the second compartment, after careful emptying, are placed in the third compartment; the bottles remain here while the second batch of bottles is brushed and transferred from the first to the second compartment. The crates are also carefully cleaned, inside and outside, and the bottles from the third compartment left upside down to be drained and dried. (As before, use rubber gloves to avoid skin injury from detergent action and as a protection against broken bottles, and use fresh detergent and sanitizing solutions when needed.)

(bb) *Mechanical washing.* This consists mainly of can- and bottle-washing:

(a) *Can-washing.* Cans may be cleaned and sanitized either manually or mechanically. The mechanical can-washer may be of either the Rotary or Straight-through/Tunnel type. The rotary can-washer is used in small plants; in this loading and unloading are done at the same point, and the cans move in a circle. The capacity usually ranges from 2 to 6 cans and lids per minute. *Advantages*: (i) occupies little space; (ii) machine can be operated by a single worker. The straight-through type is used in bigger plants; in this loading is done at one end and unloading at the other, and the cans move in a straight line. The capacity usually ranges from 4 to 12 cans and lids per minute. *Advantage*: (i) Greater capacity.

The cleaning and sanitization procedure for mechanical can-washing (can and lid) consists of the following stages:

   (i) drainage stage for liquid milk residues;
  (ii) pump-fed pre-rinsing with cold or luke-warm water;
 (iii) drainage stage;
  (iv) pump-fed jetting with detergent at not less than 70°C;
   (v) drainage stage;
  (vi) rinsing stage, pump-fed or by steam and water ejector at not less than 88°C;
 (vii) final fresh water rinsing with steam and water ejector at 88 to 93°C;
(viii) live-steam injection;
  (ix) hot-air drying at 95 to 115°C.

Note. (i) Detergent mixture used should be suitable for the can metal; not more than 0.5 per cent alkalinity is desirable.
         (ii) Sanitization with chlorine is not recommended for tinned milk cans since it attacks tin-surfaces, especially if left in contact with the tin for any length of time.

   (b) *Bottle-washing.* The mechanical bottle-washer may either be a Soaker (soaking), or Hydro (jetting) or Soaker-Hydro (part soaking and part jetting). Further, it may be of the Come-back or Straight-through type; in the former, loading and unloading take place at the same end, while in the latter they are done at opposite ends. Generally, soaker-hydro-come-back types are popular for small capacities, and straight-through-hydro types are used for larger capacities. In all machines, bottles are loaded manually or semi-automatically with manual assistance, and are discharged automatically onto one or more conveyors.

   The stages of treatment in a mechanical bottle-washer are given below:

   (i) *Pre-rinse*, using water at 32 to 38°C.

   (ii) *Detergent wash*, usually 1–3 per cent caustic soda, together with chelating and wetting agents, given preferably in two stages at different temperatures within 60 to 75°C. *Sanitizes the bottles as well.*

   (iii) *Warm water rinse*, to remove all traces of detergent. Reduces bottle temperature for next stage. Water temperature varies from 25 to 45°C and is usually re-circulated.

   (iv) *Cold water rinse*, normally re-circulated chlorinated water (containing 35 to 50 ppm. available chlorine) is used to prevent re-contamination of bottles.

(v) *Draining*, after the bottles come out of the machine.

Note. Visual inspection of washed bottles is important. Under Indian conditions, this is done by workers examining each bottle through a large magnification lens. In developed dairying countries, an electronic device (Rototector) is used for detection of foreign matter in glass bottles, although it is not entirely satisfactory.

(cc) *Cleaning-in-place* (CIP)

(a) *Definition.* Also called In-place-cleaning (IPC). This refers to that system of cleaning and sanitization which does not require the daily dismantling of dairy equipment.

(b) *Merits.* The merits of the CIP system are:

(i) Ensures that all equipment receives uniform treatment day after day, by eliminating the human factor;

(ii) less damage to equipment (due to daily dismantling and assembling);

(iii) saving of (25 per cent or more) total clean-up costs and in man-hours;

(iv) reduces possibility of contamination through human error;

(v) improved plant utilization and appearance.

(c) *Success factors.* The success of the CIP system depends upon:

(i) Proper selection of pipes and fittings, installation and development of circuits;

(ii) proper temperature of cleaning solution;

(iii) adequate velocity of cleaning solution;

(iv) use of detergents designed specifically for re-circulation cleaning;

(v) proper concentration of detergent solution;

(vi) sufficient cleaning time.

(d) *Types.* The types of CIP systems are:

1. *Manual control.* In this case, the completion and setting up of the product and CIP-circuits is done manually, the valves are hand-operated and the entire process is controlled by the operator. (The use of key-pieces is recommended for safety.)

2. *Automation.* Broadly speaking, the levels may be:

(i) *Low level.* Setting up of CIP and product-circuits is done automatically.

(ii) *Medium level.* Setting-up of CIP and product-circuits as well as the different types of treatment are all controlled automatically.

(iii) *High level.* Use of computer for complete control of the entire product manufacture and CIP system in large plants.

(e) *Procedure.*

1. *HTST Pasteurizer.* The CIP method of cleaning and sanitization of the HTST pasteurizer is as follows:

(i) Pre-rinse, with cold or tepid water till discharge water runs clear.

(ii) Acid-rinse, with acid (phosphoric) solution of 0.15 to 0.60 per cent acidity, re-circulated at 65 to 71°C for 20 to 30 minutes. (Wetting agent may be added to increase cleaning ability.)

(iii) Drain out acid solution.

(iv) Hot water rinse, with water at 65 to 71°C for 5 to 7 minutes. Rinse water drained out.

(v) Alkali rinse, with alkali detergent solution of 0.15 to 0.60 per cent alkalinity, re-circulated at 65 to 71°C for 20 to 30 minutes. (Wetting agent may be added to increase cleaning ability.)

(vi) Drain out alkali solution.

(vii) Final hot water rinse, with water at 71 to 82°C, till the whole system has been heated. Rinse water drained out. Then slightly loosen plates for drainage and drying.

Note. (i) Nitric acid may be used with stainless steel plates.

(ii) At regular intervals, the equipment may be dismantled for thorough cleaning and inspection of all milk contact surfaces.

2. *Milk Storage Tank/Milk Tankers.* The programme of cleaning and sanitization of milk storage tanks or milk tankers by the CIP method is given below. Especially designed spray arms and nozzles (turbine or ball spray) are normally used to ensure uniform spraying of detergent and sanitizing solutions over the surface:

(i) Pre-rinse with tap water;

(ii) drain for 3 to 5 minutes;

(iii) hot detergent wash with sodium hydroxide solution (sodium hydroxide 90 parts, sodium thiosulfate 9 parts and wetting agent 1 part) of 0.35 to 0.50 per cent strength at 71°C for 15 to 20 minutes. Once or twice a week, an acid-alkali programme may be used. The acid may be phosphoric or nitric; this should be followed by alkali as above.

(iv) Drain for 3 to 5 minutes.

 (v) Post-rinse with hot water at 65 to 70°C.

(vi) Drain for 3 to 5 minutes.

(vii) Sanitize, usually with hot water at 90°C for 2 to 3 minutes, otherwise with chlorine solution at 15 to 20°C containing 150 to 200 ppm available chlorine for a contact time of 1 to 2 minutes.

(viii) Drain for 3 to 5 minutes.

(ix) Hot air blow for 1 to 2 minutes.

 (f) *Systems.* These are:

 (i) *Total loss system.* In this, the detergent solutions are drained out after use. *Advantages*: (i) less steam required for heating water; (ii) compact CIP unit; and (iii) fewer pipelines.

(ii) *Saving solutions system.* The detergent solutions are returned to their respective tanks. The strength of the solutions, however, is maintained automatically. *Advantage*: (i) Saving in detergent solutions.

Note. The system to be used will depend largely on the hardness of water and the type of soil.

1.20 Judging and Grading of Milk

A. *Introduction.* Judging of milk refers to the act of evaluating its 'Eating Quality' on the basis of various attributes. Grading refers to its classification into different grades. The 'Eating Quality' of a dairy product is determined by organoleptic/sensory tests, which include all the five senses of sight, smell, taste, touch and sound. Of these, taste and smell are the most important in judging and grading.

B. *Importance.* The consumer acceptability of a dairy product is determined primarily by its eating quality, i.e. by the sensations of smell, taste, feel, etc., which the consumer experiences when the product is tasted or consumed. It is well known that dairy products cannot be of a higher quality than the raw material from which they are made. Hence, milk producers should have definite knowledge as to what constitutes desirable and undesirable flavours in milk, as well as the factors causing them; only then will they be in a position to produce milk that would make high-scoring finished products. A processor of milk (and manufacturer of dairy products) should have the ability to discriminate against certain objectionable flavours and manufacturing defects; and to recognize desirable flavours and make-up characteristics, since these will enable him to make a product of good consumer acceptability. The consumer should have adequate knowledge of desirable and undesirable flavours in milk and milk products, as these will enable him to purchase the same wisely and get his money's worth.

C. *Score Card.* This is given in Table 1.31.

TABLE 1.31

Score card for milk and cream (ADSA)

Items	Perfect score
Flavour (smell and taste)	45
Bacteria	35
Sediment	10
Temperature	5
Container and closure	5
Total	100

D. *Procedure for Examination (and scoring)*

(a) *Sampling.* Secure a representative sample aseptically by the standard procedure for bacterial count determination.

(b) *Sequence of observations.*

(i) *Sediment.* The sediment discs should be compared with standard charts for scoring. (However, sediment scoring of packaged milk is no longer done in standard contests.)

(ii) *Closure (cap).* After having scored for sediment, the closure should be carefully observed and scored.

(iii) *Container.* The glass container is examined next for fullness, cleanliness and freedom from cracks and chips, particularly about the pouring lip. The paper container is examined for cleanliness, freedom from leakage, smoothness and the adherence of a coating to its surface. Correct fillage can be determined only by actual measurement of the volume of milk in a graduated cylinder.

(iv) *Flavour* (smell and taste). This is scored only after the above items have been considered. The temperature of the milk should be around 16–21°C (60–70°F). The milk should be well-mixed before it is sampled in a small clean drinking-glass/beaker/paper-cup. As soon as the milk sample has been taken, sip (but do not swallow) a sufficient amount of it (5 to 10 ml.) to yield a normal taste reaction and yet one sufficiently small to permit its easy manipulation in the mouth. Roll it about the mouth, note the flavour and sensation, and then expectorate it. Note the after-taste as well. By placing the nose directly over the milk when it has been shaken, any off-smell may be detected.

E. *Requirements of High-Grade Market Milk*

(i) The container should be neat and clean and contain the full volume of milk represented. The milk in the bottle should be protected from contamination by a well-made, well-seated, waterproof cap, which protects the pouring lip fully. The bottle itself should be bright, shining, free from dirt, dust, etc.; it should not be cracked or chipped, particularly on the pouring lip. Paper/plastic containers should be clean and fresh with no leakage, pronounced bulging, etc.

(ii) The milk should be delivered at 10°C or below.

(iii) It should have the least amount of sediment.

(iv) It should have a low bacterial count. (High quality milk is low in bacteria, but low-bacteria milk may not always have the best flavour.)

(v) The flavour of the milk should be pleasantly sweet, and should have neither a foretaste nor an aftertaste, other than what is imparted by its natural richness.

F. *Grades of manufacturing milk.* Although there should be a single minimum standard of quality for all milk, whether it is to be used directly as fluid milk or for the manufacture of various products, this is not so in practice. The following classification may be used:

(a) *Grade I.* Milk with a clear pleasant flavour, MBR time over $5\frac{1}{2}$ hours and practically no sediment on sediment disc. (Tolerance for: slightly feed, flat or salty off-flavours.)

(b) *Grade II.* Milk having off-flavours such as: definitely feed, flat or salty; slightly barny, bitter, foreign, malty, metallic, musty, oxidized or rancid; or very slightly weedy; MBR time between $2\frac{1}{2}$ and $5\frac{1}{2}$ hours; or milk which shows a medium amount of sediment.

(c) *Grade III.* Milk having off-flavours such as: definitely barny, bitter, foreign, malty, metallic, musty, oxidized or rancid; or slightly high-acid; MBR time between 20 minutes and $2\frac{1}{2}$ hours; or definitely high in sediment.

(d) *Reject or no grade.* Milk with markedly high-acid, rancid, weedy, or foreign flavours; MBR time of less than 20 minutes and containing an extremely high amount of sediment or any noxious foreign matter.

Note. The use to which each grade of milk is put will depend upon public health regulations concerning conditions of production and upon the specific character of the product. In general, the following categorization may be made:

Grade   I = Market milk, Sterilized milk, Evaporated milk, Sweetened condensed milk, Milk powder (whole or skim); Infant food, Cheese, etc.

Grade II = Butter, Ice cream, Flavoured milks, Fermented milks, Khoa, Chhana/Paneer, Butteroil, Ghee, etc.

Grade III = Ghee, Casein, etc.

1.21 Flavour Defects in Milk, their Causes and Prevention

Milk has a flavour defect (i.e. off-flavour) if it has an undesirable smell, foretaste or aftertaste, and if the mouth does not feel clean and pleasant after it has been tasted. These flavour defects may arise due to faulty methods of production, processing and storage. The common flavour defects in milk, their causes and prevention are given in Table 1.32.

TABLE 1.32

Flavour defects in milk, their causes and prevention

Flavour defects	Causes	Prevention
Barny	(i) Improper ventilation of milking byre/barn;	(i) Proper ventilation of milking byre/barn;
	(ii) Milk not properly covered during production.	(ii) Keep milk properly covered during production.
Bitter	(i) Intake of bitter weeds by milch animals;	(i) Eradicate offending weeds;
	(ii) Using late lactation milk.	(ii) Use normal lactation milk.

Flavour defects	Causes	Prevention
Cooked	Overheating of milk.	Avoid overheating of milk.
Feed	Feeding of milk-tainting feeds (such as silage) within 3 hours before milking.	Feed milk-tainting feeds (such as silage) soon after milking.
Foreign	Addition or absorption of foreign smelling substances in milk.	Avoid contact of milk with foreign smelling substances.
High-acid/Sour	Excessive lactic acid development (due to considerable growth of lactic acid producing micro-organisms).	Store milk at 5°C (40°F) or below (to check bacterial growth and acid development).
Malty	Growth of *Str. lactis* var. *mattigenes* micro-organisms in milk.	Store milk at 5°C (40°F) or below to check bacterial growth.
Rancid	Fat hydrolysis due to lipase action.	Inactivate lipase by proper pasteurization of milk.
Oxidized, Oily, Metallic, Tallowy	Fat oxidation due to: direct contact of milk with copper or iron, exposure of milk to light, etc.	(i) Tin milk-holding vessels properly; or use aluminium alloy/ stainless steel as milk-contact surfaces; (ii) De-aerate/vacuumize pasteurized milk.
Salty	Milk of animals suffering from mastitis, or far advanced in lactation.	Avoid mastitis or late lactation milk.
Weedy	Intake of milk-tainting weeds (within 3 hours of milking).	(i) Eradicate milk-tainting weeds; (ii) Vacuum pasteurization of milk.

Note. In the souring of milk, lactic acid is the main fermentation product, but the sour smell is not caused by lactic acid (which is non-volatile). Volatile substances, such as acetic acid, formic acid, propionic acid, acetaldehyde, acetone, diacetyl and methyl-acetyl carbinol, are responsible for the characteristic smell of sour milk.

1.22 Uses of Milk

(i) In the daily diet, as a nutritive food for pregnant mothers, growing children, adolescents, adults, the aged, invalids, convalescents and patients alike;

(ii) as raw material for the production of various processed milks and manufactured products;

(iii) in bakeries and confectionaries;

(iv) as an additive to improve the quality of various recipes.

2 SPECIAL MILKS

Under this category are included those processed or fermented milk products which physically resemble and behave like liquid milk.

2.1 Sterilized Milk

2.1.1 Definition
Sterilized milk may be defined as (homogenized) milk which has been heated to a temperature of 100°C or above for such lengths of time that it remains fit for human consumption for at least 7 days at room temperatures. (Commercially sterilized milk is rarely sterile in the strict bacteriological sense. This is because the requirements for complete sterility conflict with the consumer's preference for normal colour and flavour in the sterilized product. The spore-forming bacteria in raw milk, which are highly heat-resistant, survive the sterilization temperature-time employed in the dairy and ultimately lead to the deterioration of sterilized milk.)

2.1.2 Requirements
Sterilized milk must: (i) keep without deterioration, i.e., remain stable and be of good commercial value for a sufficient period to satisfy commercial requirements; (ii) be free of micro-organisms harmful to consumer health, i.e., pathogenic, toxinogenic germs and toxins; (iii) be free of any micro-organisms liable to proliferate, i.e. it should not show signs of bacterial growth (which leads, *inter alia*, to an absence of deterioration).

2.1.3 Advantages and disadvantages
(a) *Advantages*: (i) remarkable keeping quality; does not need refrigerated storage; (ii) no cream layer/plug; (iii) forms a soft digestible curd, and hence useful for feeding of infants and inva-

lids; (iv) distinctive 'rich' flavour (due to homogenization); (v) economical to use; (vi) less liable to develop oxidized taints.

(b) *Disadvantages*: (i) increased cost of production; (ii) more loss in nutritive value than pasteurization (50 per cent of the vitamin C and 33 per cent of vitamin B originally present, are destroyed, and there is a slight reduction in the biological value of the milk proteins); (iii) Gerber test by normal procedure not so accurate.

2.4.1 Method of manufacture

A. In-bottle sterilization.

(a) *Flow diagram of manfacture.*

Receiving milk
|
Cooling to 5°C and bulk storage
|
Pre-heating (35–40°C)
|
Filtration/Clarification
|
Cooling to 5°C
|
Standardizing and storage (5°C)
|
Pre-heating (60°C)
|
Homogenization (2500 psi) (60°C)
|
Clarification (60°C)
|
Filling and capping
(in cleaned and sanitized bottles)
|
Sterilizing (108–111°C/25–30 min.)
|
Cooling (room temperature)
|
Storage (room temperature)

(b) *Details of manufacture.* The raw milk, on receipt, should be strictly examined by the prescribed physico-chemical and bacteriological tests and only high-quality milk should be used for production of sterilized milk. Care should be taken to accept milk supplies which have no developed acidity and which contain the least number of spore-forming bacteria. The intake milk should be promptly cooled to 5°C for bulk storage in order to check any bacterial growth. Next, it should be pre-heated to 35–40°C for efficient filtration/clarification, so as to remove visible dirt, etc., and to increase its aesthetic quality. The milk should again be cooled to 5°C so as to preserve its quality. It should then be standardized to the prescribed percentages of fat and solids-not-fat content in order to conform to legal standards (which vary from State to State for both cow and buffalo milk). It must be stored at 5°C until processing. The milk should be promptly pre-heated to 60°C for efficient homogenization to prevent any subsequent formation of a cream layer; usually single-stage homogenization is carried out at 2500 psi pressure. (Refer to 2.2 for more information on homogenization.) The homogenized milk must be clarified so as to remove the sediment formed during the homogenization process. The hot milk from the homogenizer should be filled into the (hot) cleaned and sanitized bottles coming from the bottle-washing machine and then sealed with special caps (of the crown seal type). The filled and capped bottles should then be placed in metal crates for sterilization by the Batch Process, or fed into conveyors for the Continuous Process. Usually the milk is sterilized at 108–111°C (225–230°F) for 25–30 minutes. The sterilized milk bottles should be gradually cooled to room temperature. Any sudden cooling may lead to bottle breakage. Finally the milk-in-bottles should be stored in a cool place.

(c) *Sterilizers.* These may be: 1. Batch; 2. Continuous.

1. *Batch.* These may either be rotary or non-rotary in type. The batch (tank) sterilizers are rectangular, horizontal, boiler-shaped retorts with a steam inlet and condensate outlet, fitted with clamp-down covers, into which steam is adjusted for the required temperature and time for sterilization.

Advantages. (i) simplicity and flexibility of operation; (ii) less initial capital and recurring expenditure.

Disadvantages. (i) Usually produces a brownish appearance and cooked taste in the finished product; (ii) sterilization may be faulty; (iii) cooling has to be slow to avoid breakage; (iv) economic advantages of large-scale processing are not obtained.

In the batch-rotary type, the filled bottles are put into holders which are rotated at 6–7 rpm. The sterilized milk is of a slightly better quality in rotary-type sterilizers than in non-rotary ones.

2. *Continuous.* In this type, the filled and sealed milk bottles are automatically placed by means of a slat conveyor into the pockets of carrier cages. They then pass into water at or near boiling temperature; from there, they enter the sterilizing zone, which

consists of a steam chamber at 108–111°C (225–230°F). Here the bottles remain for a pre-determined time, viz., 25–30 minutes, for milk sterilization.

(d) *Cooling.* After heat-treatment in the batch/tank sterilizers, the milk bottles may be cooled in air or water. If cooling is too rapid, the bottles may crack; if too slow, there is a danger of browning due to caramelization. In the continuous system, after leaving the sterilizing zone, the bottles enter a column of hot water where the cooling process begins. This is followed by their passage through another tank of water (at a lower temperature than the previous one) for further cooling, and lastly through a shallow tank of cold water for final cooling. The bottles are then automatically discharged and conveyed to a point where they are placed in crates in which they are transferred to the storage room.

B. *Ultra high temperature (UHT) methods of sterilization.* In these processes, the milk is heated to 135–150°C for a few seconds, generally in a plate or tubular heat-exchanger. The milk, which is then almost sterile, has to be filled into containers for distribution; the filling has to be done aseptically. In many cases pre-sterilization, as above, is followed by in-bottle sterilization.

2.1.5 Distribution
Once a week. This is why sterilized milk has great scope in warm countries as long as household refrigerators are not in common use.

2.1.6 Tests
(i) Turbidity test. (This is the official test.)
(ii) Bacterial count.

Note. Phosphatase test is not applicable to sterilized milk.

2.1.7 Faults
The most common is browning. Because of this fault, 'Plain' sterilized milk is not so popular. Flavoured (and simultaneously coloured) sterilized milk is more popular.

2.2 Homogenized milk

2.2.1 Definition
According to the United States Public Health Service, homogenized milk is milk which has been treated in such a manner as to

insure breakup of the fat globules to such an extent that after 48 hours' quiescent storage no visible cream separation occurs on the milk; and the fat percentage of the milk in the top 100 ml. of milk in a quart bottle. or of proportionate volumes in containers of other sizes, does not differ by more than 10 per cent of itself from the fat percentage of the remaining milk as determined after thorough mixing. (In efficiently homogenized milk, the fat globules are subdivided to 2 microns or less in diameter.)

Note. Homogenization refers to the process of forcing the milk through a homogenizer with the object of sub-dividing the fat globules. (See 2.2.6 for Homogenizer.)

2.2.2 *Merits and demerits*

(a) *Merits.* (i) No formation of cream layer/plug; (ii) fat in milk does not churn due to rough handling or excessive agitation; (iii) better adapted for bulk dispensing; mixing not necessary; (iv) more palatable due perhaps to brighter appearance, heavier body and richer flavour; (v) produces soft curd and is better digested; hence recommended for infant feeding; (vi) less susceptible to oxidized flavour development.

(b) *Demerits.* (i) Increased cost of production; (ii) returned homogenized milk difficult to salvage; fat recovery is a problem; (iii) sediment appears to a greater degree; (iv) curdling in cookery; (v) more susceptible to production of activated or sunshine flavour defect; (vi) greater tendency for milk 'seepage' through bottle cap.

2.2.3 *Factors influencing homogenization*

(a) *Temperature of homogenization.* The milk should, at the time of homogenization, be at a temperature above the melting point of fat, viz., above 33°C (91°F). This is because fat should be in the liquid state for proper sub-division. The enzyme lipase should be inactivated, preferably prior to homogenization or immediately afterwards. This can be achieved by heating the milk to a temperature of 55°C (131°F) or above. In routine practice, the milk is heated to 65-70°C (149-158°F) for homogenization. (The danger zone for lipase activity, viz., temperatures 38-49°C (100-120°F), should be avoided during or after homogenization.)

(b) *Pressure of homogenization.* In a single stage, upto 6 per cent fat milk, usually 2000–2500 psi pressure is sufficient. Higher pressures may increase the tendency for the milk to curdle when cooked, due to the increased destabilizing effect on milk-proteins. For liquid products with more than 6 per cent fat, two-stage homogenization is needed to prevent fat clumping: 2000 psi at the first stage and 500 psi at the second.

2.2.4 Sequence of various processes involved in production of homogenized milk

The possible sequences are:

  (i) Clarification, pre-heating, homogenization, pasteurization, cooling.

  (ii) Clarification, pre-heating, pasteurization, homogenization, cooling.

  (iii) Pre-heating, homogenization, clarification, pasteurization, cooling (*Recommended under Indian conditions*).

  (iv) Pre-heating, clarification, homogenization, pasteurization, cooling.

  (v) Pre-heating, clarification, pasteurization, homogenization, cooling.

Note. The main considerations are: (i) All homogenized milk must be pasteurized either prior to homogenization or immediately after; (ii) the homogenized milk should preferably be clarified after homogenization; (iii) under Indian conditions, the sequence underlined above is desirable, so as to avoid any post-pasteurization contamination.

2.2.5 Method of manufacture

Flow diagram of manufacture:

Receiving milk
|
Cooling to 5°C and bulk storage
|
Pre-heating (35–40°C)
|
Filtration/Clarification
|
Cooling to 5°C
|
Standardizing and storage (5°C)
|
Pre-heating (60 C)
|

[*Contd. next page*

Flow Diagram (Contd.)

Homogenization (2500 psi) (60°C)
|
Pasteurization (Holder or HTST)
|
Cooling (5°C)
|
Bottling
|
Storage (5°C)

(b) *Details of manufacture*

'Receiving Milk' to 'Pre-heating' (60°C). Refer to 2.1.

Homogenization. The pre-heated (60°C) milk is homogenized at 2500–3000 psi pressure in a single-stage homogenizer. This causes sub-division of the original fat globules to less than 2 micron size (diameter), which is considered satisfactory.

'Pasteurization' to 'Storage'. Refer to 1.17.

2.2.6 Homogenizer

This is a machine which causes the sub-division of fat globules. It consists of a high pressure piston pump which forces the milk at high pressures (and velocity) through a narrow opening between the homogenizing valve and its seat; the fat globules in the milk are thereby sub-divided into smaller particles of more uniform size. The homogenizing valve is held down by a heavy pressure spring against the seat of the valve. The valve and its seat are made of extremely hard material (e.g. stelite) and the contact faces are carefully ground so that the valve sits accurately on its seat. Homogenizers are either single stage or double stage.

Note. (i) A viscolizer is a machine similar to a homogenizer, but usually operates at a lower pressure and has smaller openings.

(ii) A clarifixator is a machine, developed in Sweden, which not only clarifies but also homogenizes the milk.

2.3 Soft-curd Milk

2.3.1 Definition

Soft-curd milk is milk that forms a soft curd when coagulated with rennet or pepsin under standardized procedure. Soft-curd milk has a curd tension (CT) of less than 25 g.

Note. The standardized procedure, such as the Hill Curd-Tension test consists in coagulating milk by means of a pepsin-calcium chloride solution and then measuring the resistance (in g.) which a special multi-bladed curd knife encounters in its passage through the coagulated milk.

2.3.2 Characteristics

Soft-curd milk is characterized by: (i) low casein content; (ii) low calcium content.

The average casein and calcium contents of Indian cow and buffalo milks, as compared to human milk, have been given in Table 2.1.

TABLE 2.1
Casein and calcium content of different milks

Type of milk	Casein (%)	Calcium (%)
Indian cow	2.5	0.13
Indian buffalo	3.0	0.19
Human	0.4	0.03

Mother's milk is best for feeding (human) infants, since it forms a soft curd when coagulated in the stomach and is apparently more quickly digested by infants than cow or buffalo milks.

2.3.3 Methods of preparation of soft-curd milk

These are:

(i) *Natural soft-curd milk.* It is possible to assemble a herd of cows that will produce milk with a curd tension of 30 g. or less.

(ii) *Dilution with water.* This has the effect of lowering the casein and calcium contents.

(iii) *Heat treatment:*

Boiling   Fairly effective and is the standard practice in India.

Sterilization ⎫
Super-heating ⎭ Markedly effective.

(iv) *Homogenization.* A pressure of 2500–3000 psi markedly reduces the curd tension.

(v) *Acidification.* A fine coagulation of casein is brought about by acidification with lactic acid, facilitating digestive action.

(vi) *Enzyme treatment.* When milk is acted upon under controlled conditions by certain proteolytic enzymes such as trypsin, the curd tension is reduced.

(vii) *Addition of salts.* The curd tension of milk may be lowered by the addition of the following salts: Sodium citrate, Sodium pyrophosphate, Sodium hexametaphosphate, etc.

(viii) *Base-exchange treatment.* This process consists in passing milk acidified with citric acid through a zeolite filter-bed in which about 20 per cent of ionic calcium is exchanged for sodium.

2.3.4 Various milks arranged in descending order of digestibility and for infant use

These are given in Table 2.2.

TABLE 2.2
Milks suitable for infant use

Type of milk	CT in g. (Average)	Remarks
Human	0	Breast milk best possible food for human infant and used as a standard for comparison
Boiled (cow milk)	3	Suitable for infant feeding
Trypsin-treated (cow milk)	10	–do–
Homogenized (cow milk)	14.5	–do–
Pasteurized (cow milk)	44.5	Unsuitable for infant feeding
Raw (cow milk)	55	–do–

2.4 Flavoured Milks

2.4.1 Definition

Flavoured milks are milks to which some flavours have been added. When the 'milk' is used, the product should contain a milk fat percentage at least equal to the minimum legal requirement for market milk. But when the fat level is lower (1–2 per cent), the term 'drink' is used.

2.4.2 Purpose

(i) to make milk more palatable to those who do not relish it as such; (ii) to stimulate the sale of milk; (iii) to put skim milk to profitable use.

2.4.3 Types

The main types are: (i) chocolate milks/drinks; (ii) fruit flavoured milks/drinks; (iii) sterilized flavoured milks/drinks.

2.4.4 Method of manufacture of chocolate/fruit flavoured milks/ drinks

(a) *Flow diagram of manufacture*:

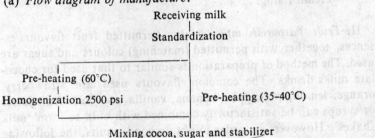

```
                        Receiving milk
                             |
                        Standardization
        |_____|
        |                                    |
Pre-heating (60°C)                           |
        |                                     |
Homogenization 2500 psi          Pre-heating (35–40°C)
        |_____|
                             |
            Mixing cocoa, sugar and stabilizer
                            OR
            Mixing flavour/essence, colour and sugar
                             |
                Pasteurization (71°C/30 min)
                             |
                        Cooling (5°C)
                             |
                Bottling and storage (5°C)
```

(b) *Details of manufacture*

I. *Chocolate milks/drinks*. The following formula may be used:

  (i) Cocoa powder   1 to 1.5%
 (ii) Sugar   5 to 7.0%
(iii) Stabilizer   0.2%
      (Sodium Alginate)
 (iv) Fat level in milk/drink—Minimum legal standard 2%.

The milk on receipt is standardized, pre-heated to 35–40°C and filtered; alternatively, after standardization it is pre-heated to

60°C, homogenized at 2500 psi and then clarified. To the warm milk, the desired amounts of cocoa-mix, sugar and stabilizer are slowly added and stirred so as to dissolve them properly. (The cocoa powder may also be added in the form of syrup, and the stabilizer in the form of solution.) The mixture is then pasteurized at 71°C/30 minutes, cooled rapidly to 5°C, bottled and kept under refrigeration (5°C) until used. The bottles are invariably inverted up and down a few times before consumption.

Note. Standardized milk is homogenized to prevent or delay the rising of cream. It may be homogenized after addition of cocoa and sugar, but this has the effect of increasing sedimentation. Stabilizer is usually added to delay or prevent settling of cocoa particles; it also aids in the prevention of cream rising.

II. *Fruit flavoured milks/drinks.* Permitted fruit flavours/essences, together with permitted (matching) colours and sugar are used. The method of preparation is similar to that used for chocolate milks/drinks. The common flavours used are strawberry, orange, lemon, pineapple, banana, vanilla, etc. Pure fruit juices or syrups can be satisfactorily combined with milk to form 'milk shakes'. However, in order to obtain good results, the following precautions should be taken:

(i) No acid (citric or tartaric) should be added to the fruit syrup, as this may cause curdling. The pH of the milk-syrup mixture should be about 5, which is safe from curdling.

(ii) Excessively sweet syrups should be avoided. The best sugar content of the syrup is 45–55 per cent.

(iii) Add 1 part of fruit syrup to 5 parts of milk. (The fruits which give particularly good results are strawberry, orange, lemon, pineapple, blackberry, raspberry and black currant.)

(iv) Care should be taken to see that there is a pleasant blend of sweet, fruity and milky flavours (together with an appealing colour).

2.4.5 Method of manufacture of sterilized-flavoured milks/drinks

These combine the advantages of both sterilized and flavoured milks/drinks. The method of preparation is given below.

(a) *Flow diagram of manufacture*:

Receiving milk
to
Clarification } Same as for Sterilized milk (2.1)

|

Mixing flavour/essence, colour and sugar

|

Filling and capping
to
Storage (Room temperature) } Same as for Sterilized milk (2.1)

(b) *Details of manufacture.* The method of preparation consists of all the steps indicated under 2.1. In addition, in between clarification and filling, flavour or essence, permitted (matching) colour and sugar (syrup) are added and mixed into the milk.

2.5 Vitaminized/Irradiated Milk

(a) Vitaminized milk is milk to which one or more vitamins are added. Irradiated milk is milk in which the vitamin D content has been increased by exposure to ultra-violet rays. (Mineralized milk is milk to which minerals have been added.)

(b) It is well known that lack of vitamins in the diet causes specific deficiency diseases which, in turn, can be cured by the intake of those particular vitamins. Addition of vitamins (and minerals) to milk is called fortification, and such milk is called fortified milk. The vitamins (and minerals) may be added singly or, more commonly, as multi-vitamin preparations.

(c) Some common vitamin deficiency diseases have been listed in Table 2.3.

TABLE 2.3
Some vitamin deficiency diseases

Name of vitamin	Results of deficiency
Vitamin A	Poor growth in young; lowered resistance to infections; night blindness
Vitamin D	Rickets in children and Osteomalacia in adults
Vitamin B$_1$ (Thiamin)	Beri-beri
Vitamin B$_2$ (Riboflavin)	Sore mouth and tongue in children
Vitamin C	Scurvy (swollen gums)

(d) Commercial vitamin D milks can be prepared by any of the following methods:

(i) *Metabolized.* By feeding irradiated yeast to milch ani-/mals, whereby the vitamin D content of milk can be increased.

(ii) *Irradiated.* By exposing a thin, rapidly flowing film of milk to an intensive source of ultra-violet radiation, such as a carbon arc lamp or a quartz mercury vapour lamp, the milk develops an increased vitamin D potency (as a result of conversion of milk cholesterol to vitamin D by rays of wavelength 2700–2900 A).

(iii) *Fortified.* By adding a definite amount of standardized vitamin D concentrate.

2.6 Frozen Concentrated Milk

This refers to milk which has been partially concentrated and then solidified by freezing.

(a) *Advantages.* (i) long keeping quality; (ii) easy transportation.

(b) *Disadvantage.* (i) destabilization of fat and casein, resulting in oiling-off and sediment formation.

Note. Unconcentrated frozen cow milk has been regularly supplied from Rajasthan to the Delhi Milk Scheme for the past several years. The raw milk is filled in metallic cylinders which are covered and then lowered in refrigerated brine. After 10 to 12 hours, they are frozen. These cylinders containing frozen milk are transported overnight in insulated railway wagons.

2.7 Fermented Milk

2.7.1 Introduction

Fermented milks refer to those milks which have been made by employing selected micro-organisms to develop the characteristic flavour and/or body and texture.

Fermentation has been defined as the metabolic process in which chemical changes are brought about on an organic substratum, whether protein, carbohydrate, or fat, through the action of enzymes liberated by specific living micro-oganisms. (In dairying, the most important fermentation is the lactic acid fermentation or souring of milk.)

2.7.2 Merits

(i) Much more palatable than milk; (ii) nutritive value usually increased; (iii) more easily assimilated by the human system than milk; (iv) may contain beneficial antibiotics; (v) may possess therapeutic properties; (vi) regular consumption of some types claimed to increase longevity of human beings.

2.7.3 Types

The fermented milks, which will be discussed here, are: Natural buttermilk, Cultured buttermilk, Acidophilus milk, Bulgarian buttermilk, Kumiss, Kefir, Yoghurt and Dahi.

2.7.4 Starter propagation, quality and defects

(a) *Introduction.* The term 'starter' refers to an active bacterial culture that has been propagated for use in the manufacture of fermented milks (or milk products). Lactic starter is usually considered to indicate a culture containing lactic streptococci. A number of different kinds of starters or cultures are commercially available for use in the dairy industry. Micro-organisms commonly found in fermented milks belong to the germs Streptococcus. They may or may not contain associative organisms of the genus Leuconostoc. Starter species most commonly used in the industry are: *Str. lactis, Str. cremoris, Str. diacetilactis, Leuc. citrovorum* and *Leuc. dextranicum.* A starter may contain a single lactic strain or a mixture of lactic streptococci with or without Leuconostoc species.

An active starter performs three important functions in the manufacture of a fermented product: (i) acid production; (ii) desired, characteristic flavour production; (iii) prevention of growth of undesirable micro-organisms that may have survived pasteurization or contaminated the product. (Inhibition is caused principally by the production of lactic acid which establishes a pH unfavourable to growth.)

Each fermented milk requires a select starter culture in its manufacture. Commercial starter cultures are prepared by commercial laboratories, usually from carefully selected species of bacteria, and are available in liquid, tablet or powder forms; they may be freeze-dried as well.

'Mother starter/culture' refers to stock lactic cultures prepared routinely in the laboratory or dairy plant from day to day for bulk propagation. 'Bulk starter/culture' is made in large amounts to be actually added to the milk, etc., whenever required for the manufacture of fermented milks or milk products.

(b) *Mother starter.* The preparation of starters/cultures involves the following basic considerations:

(i) *Selection of milk.* The milk (preferably skim milk) should be of high quality: low count milk from healthy animals is desirable; presence of antibiotics and inhibitory substances in milk should be avoided. (Spray dried skim milk re-constituted with distilled water to give 10–11 per cent milk solids may be used for mother starter.)

(ii) *Heat treatment.* It should preferably be not less than 82°C (180°F) for not less than 1 hour. After heating, the milk should be slowly cooled to 21–22°C (70–72°F) for inoculation. Severe milk heating (distinct browning) should be avoided as it may adversely affect starter activity.

(iii) *Containers.* Wide mouth, screw cap, heat-resistant glass bottles preferred for mother starter. Both bottles and cans should be thoroughly cleaned and sanitized before use.

(iv) *Inoculation.* Usually 1 per cent inoculation is performed with a sterile pipette from mother stock under aseptic conditions. Mixing of inoculation is done by rotating the bottle after capping.

(v) *Incubation.* The inoculated milk is placed in a controlled incubator at 22°C (72°F), and incubated without further agitation for 14 to 16 hours until a titratable acidity of 0.75 to 0.85 per cent is developed.

(vi) *Cooling.* It is then removed and quickly cooled to 5°C (40°F) and stored in the refrigerator. It is extremely important that 'mother' and 'bulk' starters should be cooled rapidly as soon as the desired acidity is reached, as otherwise rapid losses in culture activity result. Stirring or shaking for cooling should be avoided.

(c) *Bulk starter.* The preparation of starter cultures in bulk or larger volumes presents many difficulties. It is considerably less difficult to maintain sterility in bottles (flasks) than in cans (vats). Bulk starter milk is usually heated between 85 to 93°C (185 to 200°F) for 45 to 60 minutes and cooled rapidly to an inoculation temperature of 22°C (72°F). The bulk milk is inoculated immediately with a 1 per cent inoculation from a fresh mother starter/culture which has demonstrated the proper degree of activity in laboratory tests. The inoculated starter milk is stirred briefly (under aseptic conditions) to allow proper mixing of the inoculum, and then allowed to ripen at 22°C (72°F) for 14 to 16 hours. As soon as a titratable acidity of 0.75 to 0.85 per cent is reached, the starter is rapidly cooled to 5°C (40°F) and held at that temperature for use.

(d) *Flow diagram of starter propagation*:

	New Commercial Culture		Capsule			
1st	propagation	(18–24 hrs)		MS_1		
2nd	–do–	(15–16 hrs)	MS_2	MS_2	MS_2	
3rd	–do–	(–do–)	MS_3	MS_3	MS_3	
4th	–do–	(–do–)	MS_4	MS_4	MS_4	BS_1
5th	–do–	(–do–)	MS_5	MS_5	MS_5	BS_2

etc.

Legend: MS—Mother starter
            BS—Bulk starter

(e) *Starter qualities.*

(i) *Flavour.*   Mild, pleasant, 'nutty' smell; clean, acid taste.

(ii) *Body.*   Soft and firm; curd should give a clean and smooth break; should have no gas holes or whey pockets.

(iii) *Texture.*   Smooth, free from lumps.

(iv) *T.A.*   0.75 to 0.85 per cent.

Note.   The colour will be yellowish for (whole) cow and whitish for (whole) buffalo milk.

(f) *Starter defects.*   Insufficient flavour development; insufficient acidity development; hard and lumpy curd; excessive development of acidity; gas holes; whey pockets; ropiness; bitterness; presence of bacteriophage; etc.

2.7.5   Natural Buttermilk
This is a by-product of churning cream for butter making. Ripened cream which has undergone a clean, lactic fermentation, is usually preferred. Also included, under Indian conditions, is country buttermilk obtained as a by-product of churning whole milk curd for production of country butter.

2.7.6   Cultured buttermilk
This is obtained by inoculation and incubation of pasteurized skim milk with lactic starter.

(a) *Flow diagram of manufacture*:

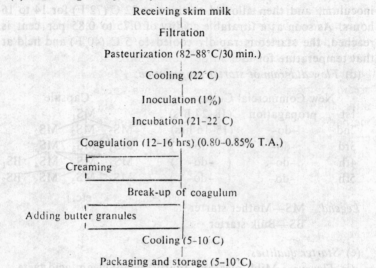

Receiving skim milk
|
Filtration
|
Pasteurization (82–88°C/30 min.)
|
Cooling (22°C)
|
Inoculation (1%)
|
Incubation (21–22°C)
|
Coagulation (12–16 hrs) (0.80–0.85% T.A.)
|
Creaming
|
Break-up of coagulum
|
Adding butter granules
|
Cooling (5–10°C)
|
Packaging and storage (5–10°C)

(b) *Details of manufacture*

(i) *Preparation*. Fresh skim milk is preferable. The solids content should range from 9 to 10 per cent. The skim milk should be free from antibiotics and inhibitory substances. If milk containing an appreciable amount of fat is used, it should be homogenized. If cream or butterfat is desired in the product, it may be added to the cold buttermilk when the curd is broken up. Manufacturing milk is heated in a holder pasteurizer vat to 82–88 C (180–190 F) for 30 minutes with frequent stirring, and then cooled to 22 C (72°F). One per cent bulk lactic starter is added and mixed thoroughly in the milk, and then allowed to incubate at 21–22°C (70–72°F) without further agitation until coagulation occurs and an acidity between 0.80 and 0.85 per cent is reached. The curd is broken up by slow agitation to give a smooth consistency and cooled to 5–10°C. It is then packaged and stored at 5–10°C until distribution. Care is taken not to incorporate air in the product during agitation and filling. Acidity at packaging should be between 0.85 to 0.90 per cent.

(ii) *Creaming*. Cream imparts a rich flavour to the buttermilk and has the effect of decreasing the viscosity. (Viscosity can also be decreased by adding 20 to 25 per cent of pasteurized sweet whole milk during break-up of the curd.)

(iii) *Salting.* Salt at 0.1 per cent may be added to the finished product to increase its flavour.

(iv) *Adding butter granules.* Butter granules or flakes are sometimes added to cultured buttermilk made from skim milk to simulate an old-fashioned churned buttermilk appearance. Butter granules can be made in several ways, e.g. by churning cultured cream, by passing hot butteroil through a screen into cold buttermilk and/or spraying hot butteroil into cold buttermilk. One method is to prepare butter granules from 20 per cent cultured cream and add them to cultured skim milk when breaking up the curd. Churned buttermilk may be prepared by culturing milk containing 1–2 per cent butterfat, cooling the coagulated milk to 13°C (56°F), and then churning the milk until butter granules the size of rice grains appear. Butter colour may be added to increase the colour of the granule, if desired. The product is cooled and packaged.

2.7.7 Acidophilus milk

This type of fermented milk is produced by development in milk of a culture of *Lactobacillus acidophilus*. It is claimed that acidophilus milk has therapeutic and health-promoting properties. It is also claimed that the growth of *Lact. acidophilus* under the conditions existing in the intestinal tract will replace undesirable putrefactive fermentations with a beneficial lactic fermentation.

(a) *Flow diagram of manufacture*:

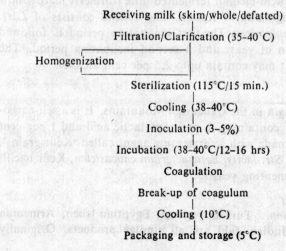

```
        Receiving milk (skim/whole/defatted)
                        |
              Filtration/Clarification (35–40°C)
          _____|_____
         |                                 |
   Homogenization                          |
         |_____|
                        |
              Sterilization (115°C/15 min.)
                        |
                 Cooling (38–40°C)
                        |
                 Inoculation (3–5%)
                        |
           Incubation (38–40°C/12–16 hrs)
                        |
                   Coagulation
                        |
             Break-up of coagulum
                        |
                  Cooling (10°C)
                        |
          Packaging and storage (5°C)
```

(b) *Details of manufacture.* Skim, whole, or partly defatted milk may be used. Milk containing more than 1 per cent fat should be homogenized. Acidophilus milk can simply be made with added sugar or honey, or with tomato or carrot juice. Fresh milk is heated to 115°C (240°F) for 15 minutes (or heated intermittently) to obtain sterile milk. The addition of 1 per cent of glucose or honey, or 5 per cent tomato juice helps to hasten the fermentation, but is not essential. The milk is cooled to 38–40°C (100–104°F) and inoculated with 3–5 per cent inoculum (mother starter). The inoculated milk is mixed thoroughly and incubated at 38–40°C (100–104°F) until the milk coagulates. The coagulum is slowly broken up and cooled to 10°C (50°F). Five to ten per cent lactose or dextrin may be added if desired. The milk is stirred until smooth, packaged, and stored at 5°C (40°F) until used.

Note. Strains of *Lact. acidophilus* are difficult to maintain and propagate because of the ease with which contaminating bacteria outnumber them.

2.7.8 Bulgarian Buttermilk
A pure single strain starter of *Lact. bulgaricus* is propagated for product manufacture. The incubation temperature ranges from 38 to 43°C (100–110°F). The finished product is characterized by a higher acidity (1.2–1.5 per cent).

2.7.9 Kumiss
This is a lactic acid-alcohol fermented milk (formerly mare's, now cow's milk), originated in Russia. The culture consists of *Lact. acidophilus* or *bulgaricus*. The first incubation period is followed by the addition of yeast and a second incubation period. The finished product may contain upto 2.5 per cent alcohol.

2.7.10 Kefir
This has its origin in the Caucasian Mountains. It is a self-carbonated beverage containing 1 per cent lactic acid and 1 per cent alcohol. It is made with a fermenting agent called 'Kefir grains', which contains *Str. lactis*, *Betabacterium caucasicum*, Kefir bacilli and lactose fermenting yeasts.

2.7.11 Yoghurt
(a) *Introduction.* Turkish yoghurt, Egyptian leben, Armenian matzoon and Indian dahi are all similar products. Originally

yoghurt was made from boiled concentrated whole milk, but most modern methods of manufacture use whole or partly defatted milk containing small amounts of skim milk powder or concentrate. The fat content in yoghurt may vary from 0 to 5 per cent and the solids content from 9 to 20 per cent.

Two micro-organisms, *Lact. bulgaricus* and *Str. thermophilus* growing together symbiotically, are responsible for the lactic fermentation of yoghurt. In some countries, it contains lactose fermenting yeast. Leuconostoc strains, *Str. diacetilactis* and *Lact. acidophilus* are also added to improve the flavour of the yoghurt.

The method of culture control is very important in yoghurt manufacture, and for this reason stock (mother) cultures are best maintained individually, rather than mixed. The optimum pH and temperature for growth of *Str. Thermophilus* is 6.8 and 38°C (100°F); *Str. thermophilus* cultures normally attain acidities of 0.85 to 0.95 per cent, whereas *Lact. bulgaricus* reaches acidities of 1.20 to 1.5 per cent. The extreme sensitivity of both these micro-organisms to Penicillin makes it essential to select antibiotic-free milk for yoghurt manufacture and all starter propagation.

Mother starter is prepared as follows: Fresh or reconstituted skim milk is autoclaved at 15 psi for 10–15 minutes, cooled to 41°C (105°F) and inoculated with 0.2 to 1 per cent inoculum. Cultures of *Str. thermophilus* are incubated at 38°C (100°F) and *Lact. bulgaricus* at 43°C (110°F). Normal coagulation occurs in 12–18 hours, at which time the cultures are cooled to 5°C (40°F). Transfers should preferably be made daily. A commercial yoghurt culture, which contains both micro-organisms should be incubated between 41 to 43°C (105 to 110°F), or according to the supplier's instructions.

Bulk starters are carried in stainless steel vessels or vats with sufficient capacity to contain 2 parts of starter for every 100 parts of yoghurt made. The necessary quantity of skim milk is heated to 85–88°C (185–190°F) for 30–45 minutes, cooled to 43°C (110°F) and inoculated preferably with 1 per cent each of *Str. thermophilus* and *Lact. bulgaricus*, which in a starter or product have a marked effect on its flavour and odour. Starters are mixed in the milk and the latter incubated at 41–43°C (105–110°F) until coagulation occurs. The bulk starter is cooled to 10°C (50°F) and stored at 5°C (40°F) if not required for immediate use.

(b) *Method of preparation of Yoghurt (Firmbodied)*

(i) *Flow diagram of manufacture*:

Receiving whole/defatted milk
|
Addition of skim milk powder concentrate
|
Filtration/clarification (35–40°C)
|
Pre-heating the mix (60°C)
|
Homogenization (2500 psi)
|
Pasteurization (85°C/30 min)
|
Cooling (43–44°C)
|
Inoculation (2%)
|
Packaging
|
Incubation (41–42°C/3 hrs) (0.75% T.A.)
|
Cooling and storage (5–7°C)

(ii) *Details of manufacture.* Skim milk powder/concentrate is added to whole or partly defatted milk to increase the solids-not-fat content by 2–3 per cent to a total of approximately 12 per cent. The mix is pre-heated to 60°C (140°F) and homogenized single-stage at 2000–2500 psi. Stabilizers are frequently added to the mix but are not essential and excessive amounts are to be avoided. The mix is heated in a vat to 85°C (185°F) for 30 minutes and then cooled to 43–44°C (110–112°F), inoculated with 2 per cent bulk starter and stirred briefly to ensure proper mixing. The mix is then packaged, care being taken that the temperature does not fall below 41°C (106°F) during the filling operation. The time interval between inoculation and filling should not exceed 45 minutes. Yoghurt is incubated in the package without further agitation at 41–42°C (106–108°F) for about 3 hours, till a titratable acidity of 0.75 per cent is reached. It is then placed under refrigeration to cool to 5–7°C (40–45°F); approximately 8 hours are required, at which time the product is ready for distribution. A final acidity of 0.9 per cent is desired in the product.

(c) *Method of preparation of flavoured yoghurt.* Flavoured yoghurt has become popular in recent years. Flavours are of three types, viz., synthetic or artificial, natural with synthetics added, and natural fruits. These flavours may be added to yoghurt in one of the following ways:

(i) *By mix blending*. The flavouring material, sugar and colour are added to the mix prior to fermentation.

(ii) *Fruit on bottom*. Preserves or fruits are added to the package prior to filling or setting.

(iii) *Bulk mixing*. Yoghurt is prepared, bulk chilled and mixed with a fruit dressing and packaged. Fresh fruit, preserves, flavours, sugar and colour are blended in after fermentation.

Note. Flavoured yoghurt has a definite advantage over plain yoghurt in that harsh acidity in the product is less pronounced, the incidence of objectionable off-flavours is reduced and much of the need for concentrating the milk is eliminated.

2.7.12 Dahi (See 11.10)

2·8 Standardized Milk

2.8.1 Definition
This is milk whose fat and/or solids-not-fat content have been adjusted to a certain pre-determined level. The standardization can be done by partially skimming the fat in the milk with a cream separator, or by admixture with fresh or reconstituted skim milk in proper proportions.

Under the PFA Rules (1976), the Standardized Milk for liquid consumption should contain a minimum of 4.5 per cent fat and 8.5 per cent solids-not-fat throughout the country.

Note. Standardized milk may be marketed as such or used for making certain products; in the latter case, the fat and solids-not-fat contents may be varied according to the product requirement.

2.8.2 Merits
(i) Ensures a milk of practically uniform and constant composition and nutritive value to the consumer; (ii) the surplus fat can be converted into butter and ghee; (iii) possible to supply cheaper milk; (iv) more easily digestible (because of reduced fat content).

Note.   The initial reaction of the consumer may be that standardized milk is 'thinner' than whole milk.

2.8.3   Method of preparation.   (Already discussed in 1.17)

2.9   Reconstituted/Rehydrated Milk

2.9.1   Definition
This refers to milk prepared by dispersing whole milk powder
(also called dried whole milk) in water approximately in the proportion of 1 part powder to 7–8 parts water. (Usually spray-dried
powder is used, since it is more soluble and produces less sediment.)

2.9.2   Merits
(i) Helps in making up the shortage of fresh milk supplies in
developing countries; (ii) used by the Armed Forces in other
countries.

2.9.3   Method of manufacture
   (i) *Flow diagram of manufacture*:

Receiving water in pasteurizing vat
|
Pre-heating to 38–43°C
|
Addition of whole milk powder and mixing
|
Filtration
|
Pasteurization (63°C/30 min)
|
Cooling (5°C)
|
Packaging and storage (5°C)

   (ii) *Details of manufacture.*   The calculated amount of potable
water is received in the pasteurizing vat/tank equipped with an
agitator. The water is heated, while the agitator is kept in motion,
to 38–43°C. Then the calculated amount of spray dried whole
milk is slowly added at the point of agitation, and the mixture
thoroughly agitated till it dissolves completely. Special Powder
Mixer equipment may be used for this purpose. The mixture is
then pumped through a filter, pasteurized at 63°C for 30 minutes,
and promptly cooled to 5°C or below until distribution.

2.10 Recombined Milk

2.10.1 Definition

This refers to the product obtained when butteroil (also called dry/anhydrous milk fat), skim milk powder and water are combined in the correct proportions to yield fluid milk. The milk fat may also be obtained from other sources, such as unsalted butter or plastic cream.

Under the PFA Rules (1976), Recombined Milk should contain a minimum of 3.0 per cent fat and 8.5 per cent solids-not-fat throughout the country.

2.10.2 Merits

(i) Helps in making up the shortage of fresh milk supplies in developing countries; (ii) helps prevent price rise of liquid milk in cities.

2.10.3 Method of manufacture

(i) *Flow diagram of manufacture:*

Receiving water in pasteurizing vat
|
Pre-heating (38–49°C)
|
Addition of skim milk powder and mixing (38–43°C)
Addition of butteroil and mixing (42–49°C)
|
Filtration
|
Pasteurization (63°C/30 min)
|
Homogenization (2500 psi/63°C)
|
Cooling (5°C)
|
Packaging and storage (5°C)

(ii) *Details of manufacture.* A calculated amount of potable water is received in the pasteurizing vat/tank equipped with an agitator. The water is heated, while the agitator is kept in motion, to a temperature of 38–43°C. A proportionate amount of spray dried skim milk is slowly added at the point of agitation. When the water reaches a temperature of 43–49°C, another proportionate amount of butteroil is added. These constituents are thoroughly agitated till a homogeneous mixture is obtained. The mixture is then pumped through a filter and later pasteurized at 63°C for 30

minutes. It is then homogenized at the pasteurization temperature at 2500 psi single stage to ensure proper emulsification of
the milk fat. The product is quickly cooled to 5°C, packaged and
stored at 5°C or below until distribution.

Note. Recombined milk was extensively produced under the
'Operation Flood' scheme in the four major cities of India,
viz. Bombay, Calcutta, Delhi and Madras, during 1970–5,
from the butteroil and skim milk powder donated under
the World Food Programme Project by the Food and Agri-
culture Organisation of the United Nations.

2.11   Toned Milk

2.11.1   Definition

Toned Milk (also called Single Toned Milk) refers to milk obtained
by the addition of water and skim milk powder to whole milk.
In practice, whole buffalo milk is admixed with reconstituted
spray dried skim milk for its production.

Under the PFA Rules (1976), toned milk should contain a minimum of 3.0 per cent fat and 8.5 per cent solids-not-fat throughout
the country.

2.11.2   History

Toned Milk is the brainchild of D. N. Khurody (India), who is
also credited with coining its name. Under his auspices, it was
first produced in 1946 in the Central Dairy of the Aarey Milk
Colony and marketed in Bombay City. Soon other cities, notably
Calcutta, Madras and Delhi started producing and marketing
Toned Milk, which has become a permanent feature ever since of
the market milk industry in India. In the words of Mr Khurody:
'By merely adding water to whole buffalo milk, both the fat and
solids-not-fat content are reduced. But by adding skim milk
powder to the mixture, solids-not-fat is 'toned up' or increased to
the original level. As the product was neither whole milk nor
standardized, a new name Toned Milk was given to it.' (All skim
milk powder was earlier imported.)

2.11.3   Merits

(i) Increases the supply of milk. The buffalo milk initially used is increased by 100–150 per cent; (ii) reduces the price of milk, so as to reach lower-income groups of the population.

2.11.4   Method of manufacture
(i) *Flow diagram of manufacture*:

Receiving water in pasteurizing vat
|
Pre-heating (38–43°C)
|
Addition of skim milk powder and mixing, and
addition of whole buffalo milk and mixing
|
Filtration
|
Pasteurization (63°C/30 min.)
|
Cooling (5°C)
|
Packaging and storage (5°C)

(ii) *Calculation*
Problem: Given: 1,000 kg of whole buffalo milk testing 7.5% fat and 9.8% SNF; SMP testing 0.5% fat and 96.5% SNF; Toned Milk to contain 3.0% fat and 8.5% SNF.

Solution.   Let the amount of water required be W kg and SMP be S kg.

Amount of Toned Milk = $(1000 + W + S)$ kg.

The following equations can be formed:

$$\left(1000 \times \frac{7.5}{100}\right) + \left(S \times \frac{0.5}{100}\right)$$

$$= (1000 + W + S) \times \frac{3}{100} \quad \dots \text{(I) (Fat equation)}$$

$$\left(1000 \times \frac{9.8}{100}\right) + \left(S \times \frac{96.5}{100}\right)$$

$$= (1000 + W + S) \times \frac{8.5}{100} \dots \text{(II) (SNF equation)}$$

Solving the above equations,

$$\left.\begin{array}{l} W = 1382.1 \text{ kg} \\ S = 141.5 \text{ kg} \end{array}\right\} \textit{Ans.}$$

(iii) *Details of manufacture.*   The calculated amount of potable water is received in the pasteurizing vat/tank equipped with an agitator. The water is heated while the agitator is kept in motion to 38–43°C. Then a proportionate amount of spray dried skim milk is slowly added at the point of agitation and the mixture thoroughly agitated till it dissolves completely. A calculated amount of whole buffalo milk is now added and the mixture again agitated thoroughly till a homogeneous mixture is obtained. The mixture is then pumped through a filter, pasteurized at 63° for 30 minutes, rapidly cooled to 5°C, packaged and kept at 5°C or below until distribution.

2.12 Double Toned Milk

2.12.1 Definition
Same as Toned Milk, except that under the PFA Rules (1976), Double Toned Milk should contain a minimum of 1.5 per cent fat and 9.0 per cent solids-not-fat throughout India.

2.12.2 History
2.12.3 Merits
2.12.4 Method of manufacture

Same as for 'Toned Milk', but to conform to 'Double Toned Milk' standards.

2.13 Humanized Milk
When whole cow or buffalo milk is so modified in its chemical composition that it resembles human milk, it is called Humanized Milk.

2.14 Miscellaneous Milks

2.14.1 Filled Milk
Same as Recombined Milk, except that the fat is derived from a vegetable source.

2.14.2 Imitation Milk
A product resembling milk but of non-dairy origin.

2.14.3 Vegetable Toned Milk
The milk protein of skim milk powder is substituted by vegetable protein isolated from groundnut. (Example: MILTONE of the Central Food Technological Research Institute, Mysore.)

2.14.4 Soya Milk
Made from soya bean by special patented processes.

3 CREAM

3.1 Introduction

Cream has been known from time immemorial as the fatty layer that rises to the top of the milk when it stands undisturbed for some time. The production of cream in India in 1966 was estimated to be about 1.9 per cent of the total milk production and 3.4 per cent of the milk used for manufacture of dairy products. (See Table 1.6.)

3.2 Definition

Cream may be defined as:

(i) 'that portion of milk which is rich in milk fat', or

(ii) 'that portion of milk into which has been gathered and which contains a large portion of milk fat', or

(iii) 'when milk fat is concentrated into a fraction of the original milk, that portion is known as cream'.

According to the PFA Rules (1976), cream, excluding sterilized cream, is the product of cow or buffalo milk or a combination thereof which contains not less than 25 per cent milk fat.

3.3 Classification

Cream is not a definite specific substance. It contains all the milk constituents but in varying proportions. The milk fat in cream may vary from 18 to 85 per cent; the solids-not-fat constituents occur in lower proportions than in milk.

Cream may be classified broadly as: (a) market cream, which is used for direct consumption, and (b) manufacturing cream, which is used for the manufacture of dairy products.

The various types of cream are:

(i) Table cream ⎫
(ii) Light cream ⎬ containing 20–25 per cent milk fat.
(iii) Coffee cream ⎭

(iv) Whipping cream
(v) Heavy cream } containing 30–40 per cent milk fat.
(vi) Plastic cream   containing 65–85 per cent milk fat.

3.4 Composition

The chemical composition of two specific creams has been given in Table 3.1.

TABLE 3.1

Chemical composition of cream

Constituents	Fercentage	
	I	
Water	68.20	45.45
Fat	25.00	50.00
Protein	2.54	1.69
Lactose	3.71	2.47
Ash	0.56	0.37
Total solids	31.80	54.55
Solids-not-fat	6.80	4.55

SOURCE: *A Dictionary of Dairying* by Davis (1965).

Note. It will be observed from the above that the higher the fat percentage in cream, the lower the solids-not-fat content. The formula for determining the percentage of solids-not-fat in cream is:

$$\% \text{ SNF in cream} = \frac{100 - \% \text{ fat in cream}}{100 - \% \text{ fat in milk}} \times \% \text{ SNF in milk.}$$

3.5 Food and Nutritive Value

Cream is rich in energy-giving fat and fat-soluble vitamins A, D, E and K, the contents of which depend on the fat level in cream.

3.6 Physico-chemical Properties

(a) *Viscosity.* This may be defined as the resistance offered by a liquid to flow. It is an important property of cream from the commercial point of view, since the consumer judges the 'richness' of cream from its viscosity.

Viscosity of cream may be affected by the following factors:

(i) *Fat percentage*. The higher the fat percentage, the greater the viscosity, and vice versa.

(ii) *Temperature*. The higher the temperature, the lower the viscosity, and vice versa.

(iii) *Separation conditions*. The higher the temperature of separation, the lower the viscosity, and vice versa. (A lower temperature of separation, however, leads to higher fat losses.)

(iv) *Homogenization*. Single-stage homogenization increases viscosity in direct relation to pressure used; double-stage homogenization reduces viscosity.

(v) *Cooling*. Slow cooling of cream increases viscosity.

(vi) *Ageing*. Increases viscosity.

(vii) *Clumping*. The greater the degree of clumping, the greater the viscosity.

Note. Clumping refers to the tendency of fat globules to loosely adhere to one another to form clumps or clusters. The degree of clumping largely depends on: (i) *Fat globule size*. Large globules clump more readily than smaller ones; (ii) *Temperature*. The maximum clumping takes place around 7°C (45°F); clumping decreases with rise in temperature; (iii) *Agitation*. At a favourable temperature, i.e. around 7°C (45°F), clumping increases by agitation; at an unfavourable temperature, i.e. around 60°C (140°F), clumping decreases and previously formed clumps are broken up; (iv) *Method of separation*. Gravity-separated cream clumps to a greater degree than centrifugally separated cream of the same fat content; (v) *Adhesives* (such as gelatin). Help in clumping.

(b) *Whipping quality*. Whipping refers to the beating of cream to produce froth or foam (emulsion of gas/air in a liquid). Whipped cream is a special foam possessing remarkable stability and is used in cakes, ice creams, etc., for decorative purposes.

The main factors affecting whipping quality are:

(i) *Fat percentage*. The most satisfactory is 30–35 per cent.

(ii) *Whipping temperature.* Lowers progressively above 4°C (40°F).

(iii) *Separation temperature.* 32°C (90°F) more satisfactory than 38°C (100°F).

(iv) *Ageing.* For 24 hours at 4°C (40°F) is optimum.

(v) *Homogenization.* Above 300 psi is detrimental.

(vi) *Acidity.* Reduces progressively.

(vii) *Addition of stabilizers.* Reduces.

(c) *Specific gravity.* This depends on its fat percentage, as is evident from Table 3.2.

TABLE 3.2

Effect of fat percentage of cream on its specific gravity

Fat percentage	S.G.	Fat percentage	S.G.	Fat percentage	S.G.
0.025	1.037	14	1.019	28	1.006
1	1.036	15	1.018	29	1.005
2	1.035	16	1.017	30	1.004
3	1.034	17	1.016	31	1.003
4	1.032	18	1.015	32	1.002
5	1.031	19	1.014	33	1.001
6	1.030	20	1.013	34	1.000
7	1.029	21	1.012	35	0.999
8	1.027	22	1.011	36	0.999
9	1.026	23	1.010	37	0.998
10	1.025	24	1.009	38	0.997
11	1.024	25	1.008	39	0.996
12	1.022	26	1.008	40	0.995
13	1.020	27	1.007		

SOURCE: *Engineering for Dairy and Food Products* by Farrall (1963).

(d) *Acidity.* The per cent titratable acidity of all fresh cream should be consistent with the fat percentage of the cream. There exists an inverse relationship between the per cent fat and per cent titratable acidity. The per cent titratable acidity of freshly separated cream is always lower than that of the milk from which it was separated, and can be calculated by the formula:

$$\% \text{ Titratable Acidity of cream} = \frac{\% \text{ Serum in cream}}{\% \text{ Serum in milk}}$$
$$\times \% \text{ Titratable Acidity of milk}$$

$$= \frac{100 - \% \text{ fat in cream}}{100 - \% \text{ fat in milk}}$$

$$\times \% \text{ Titratable Acidity of milk}$$

3.7 Production

A. *Principle.* The basic principle of cream separation, whether by gravity or centrifugal methods, is based on the fact that milk fat is lighter than the skim milk portion. At 16°C (60°F), the average density of milk fat is 0.93 and skim milk 1.036. Hence when milk, which may be considered to be a mixture of fat (as cream) and skim milk, is subjected to either gravity or a centrifugal force, the two components, viz. cream and skim milk, by virtue of their differing densities, stratify or separate from one another.

B. *Methods.* Cream is obtained from milk by either gravity or centrifugal methods:

I. *Gravity methods.* When milk is allowed to stand for some time, there is a tendency for the fat to rise. The velocity, or rate at which the fat globules rise, is given by the following equation, which is known as Stocke's Law:

$$V = \frac{2G}{9} \frac{(ds - df)r^2}{n},$$

where.

$V =$ velocity or rate at which a single fat globule rises
$G =$ acceleration due to gravity
$ds =$ density of skim milk
$df =$ density of fat
$r =$ radius of fat globule
$n =$ viscosity of skim milk

From Stoke's Law it will be observed that, theoretically, velocity is increased by:

(i) increase in radius of fat globule;

(ii) increase in difference in densities of skim milk and fat;

(iii) decrease in viscosity of skim milk.

However in practice the important factors affecting the rate of rise of cream in gravity methods are:

(i) *Size of fat globules.* As the size of fat globules increases, the rate at which cream rises also increases. (Thus in buffalo milk,

gravity creaming occurs faster due to the larger size of fat globules than those in cow milk.)

(ii) *Temperature.* As temperature increases, viscosity decreases and hence velocity increases.

(iii) *Clumping.* A clump or cluster acts like a single globule in
so far as movement through skim milk is concerned. Thereby, the
effective 'r' is increased, which in turn increases velocity, as
shown in Table 3.3.

TABLE 3.3

Effect of size of fat globules on its rate of rise

Diam. of fat globule or cluster (micron)	Rate of rise (mm/hr)
3.20	1.26
41	242

SOURCE: *The Buttermakers' Manual* by McDowall (1953).

(iv) *Addition of adhesives.* Ultimately helps in increasing the
rate at which fat globules rise.

Note. Gravity methods, being very slow, are no longer used
commercially for cream separation.

II. *Centrifugal methods* (used commercially). When milk enters
the rapidly revolving bowl of the cream separator, it is immediately subjected to a tremendous centrifugal force, which is 3000
to 6000 times greater than gravitational force. While both the fat
and skim milk are subjected to the centrifugal force*, the difference in density affects the heavier portion (i.e. skim milk)
more intensely than the lighter portion (i.e. cream). Thereby the
skim milk is forced to the periphery while the fat portion moves
towards the centre. The skim milk and cream both form vertical
walls within the bowl and are separated by being led through separate

---

* $F = K \times W \times R \times N^2$,
where
　F = centrifugal force
　W = mass (weight) of the revolving body
　R = radius of the circle in which body revolves
　N = r.p.m. of revolving body
　K = constant.

outlets. (The cream outlet is at a higher level than the skim milk outlet, both being near the axis of rotation.)

(a) The important parts of the centrifugal cream separator (open-bowl type) are as follows: Supply can; Faucet; Regulating chamber (Float); Cream or skim milk screw; Bowl shell; Milk distributor; Cream spout; Skim milk spout; Top disc; Discs; Bowl nut; Rubber ring; Spindle; Set of gears; Crank handle, etc.

(b) The various types of cream separators are as follows:

 (i) Warm milk separator
 (ii) Cold milk separator
(iii) Power driven separator (Factory)
(iv) Hand driven separator (Farm)
 (v) Open bowl or Gravity fed separator
(vi) Semi enclosed separator
(vii) Hermetically-sealed, or Air tight, or Pressure fed, or Foam-less separator.

(c) The merits and demerits of the different types of cream separators are given in Table 3.4.

TABLE 3.4

Merits and demerits of different types of separators

Type of Separator	Merits	Demerits
Warm milk	(i) Close skimming	(i) Lower viscosity of cream
	(ii) Higher capacity of opera-tion	(ii) More foam formation
Cold milk	(i) Less foam formation	(i) Lower capacity of opera-tion
	(ii) Higher viscosity of cream	(ii) Partial churning
	(iii) Higher quality of cream and skim milk	
Factory	(i) Higher capacity	(i) Expensive
Farm	(i) Cheap	(i) Lower capacity
Open bowl	(i) Useful in small diaries	(i) Lower capacity
		(ii) Foam is produced
Semi enclosed	(i) Has some of the advantages of air tight separators	(i) Has some of the disadvantages of open bowl separators

Types of Separator	Merits	Demerits
Air tight or foamless	(i) No foam produced	(i) Expensive
	(ii) Higher capacity	(ii) Maintenance complicated
	(iii) Fat percentage in cream can be regulated by external control without stopping separator	
	(iv) Cream and skim milk can be delivered to respective storage tanks without additional pumps	
	(v) Keeps products away from contact with air	
	(vi) Cream viscosity greatly increased.	

Note. The drawback of frequent stoppage of the usual type of centrifugal cream separators for cleaning, especially with high-sediment milk (such as obtained in this country), has been overcome today by what is known as the self-cleaning separator. Of slightly different design, its characteristic feature is that the bowl can be opened for discharging the accumulated slime while the machine is running. This in turn means that the machine can be operated continuously for any length of time while still maintaining the high efficiency of a clean bowl. It can be cleaned by circulation of detergent (CIP), thereby making time and labour-consuming dismantling and manual cleaning unnecessary. The bowl is opened after a certain period of time just before it is estimated that slime will begin to interfere with the separating efficiency. Opening is effected by hydraulic pressure and the impulse of opening can be supplied manually or, preferably, by an automatic timer. The functioning of these machines is in other respects similar to that of a conventional separator. The fat percentage in cream can be controlled from outside and foam-free cream and skim milk are discharged at about 70 psi.

(d) Stoke's Law applied to centrifugal separation is as follows:

where
$$V = r^2 \frac{(ds - df)}{n} N^2 \cdot R \cdot K$$

V = velocity of movement of a single fat globule

r = radius of fat globule

ds = density of skim milk

df = density of fat

N = speed of bowl (r.p.m.)

R = distance of fat globule from the axis of rotation

K = constant

n = viscosity of skim milk.

(e) It will be seen from the above that the speed (rate) of cream separation is increased by:

   (i) greater radius of fat globule

   (ii) greater difference in density between skim milk and fat

   (iii) greater speed of bowl (r.p.m.)

   (iv) greater size of bowl

   (v) lower viscosity of skim milk.

(f) Gravity and centrifugal cream separation have been characterized in Table 3.5.

TABLE 3.5

Characteristics of gravity and centrifugal creaming methods

Particulars	Gravity method	Centrifugal method
Nature of force causing separation	Gravitational	Centrifugal
Speed of separation	Extremely slow	Practically instantaneous
Direction of movement of fat and skim milk particles	Vertical	Horizontal
Bacteriological quality of cream and skim milk	Low	High
Fat percentage of:		
Cream	10-25	18-85 (can be controlled)
Skim milk	0.2 or above	0.1 or below
Scale of operation	Small	Large
Fat percentage recovered in cream	Not more than 90	99-99.5

C. *Factors influencing fat percentage of cream.* The important factors influencing the fat percentage of cream by centrifugal separation are:

(a) position of the cream screw (or skim milk screw);

(b) fat percentage in milk;

(c) speed of the bowl;

(d) rate of inflow of milk;

(e) temperature of milk;

(f) amount of water or skim milk added to flush the bowl.

(a) *Position of the cream screw (or skim milk screw).* (Cream screw IN or Skim milk screw OUT, higher fat percentage in cream and vice versa.) The cream screw/outlet consists of a small, threaded, hollow screw pierced by a circular orifice through which the cream emerges. This screw can be driven IN or OUT, thus bringing it nearer to, or away from, the centre of rotation. Similarly, the skim milk screw/outlet is for the removal of skim milk. Once the cream screw or skim milk screw has been adjusted, the cream separator delivers, under normal conditions, a definite ratio of skim milk and cream, which is usually 90 : 10 (or 85 : 15) by volume. Basically, any change in the separation procedures which alters the relative quantities of skim milk and cream will influence the fat test of the cream. By altering the position of the cream screw (or skim milk screw), the ratio of skim milk to cream changes. Thus, when the cream screw is moved IN towards the axis of rotation, a higher fat percentage in cream is obtained, and vice versa; this is because the force tending to discharge cream through the orifice is decreased ('R' in the formula $F = KWRN^2$ is decreased), while that tending to discharge skim milk remains unaltered. A smaller proportion of cream is therefore discharged, which, containing the same quantity of fat, shows a higher fat percentage. Screwing OUT the cream screw produces thinner cream. Similarly, the skim milk screw OUT results in richer cream, and vice versa.

(b) *Fat percentage in milk.* (The higher the fat percentage in milk, the higher the per cent fat in cream, and vice versa.) Since practically all the fat in milk is contained in the cream, the cream from the separation of high-fat milk has a higher fat content than that from low-fat milk; a greater fat content in cream, the amount of which remains unaltered in the two cases, will obviously show a higher fat percentage in it, and vice versa.

(c) *Speed of bowl*. (The higher the speed of the bowl, the higher the fat percentage in cream, and vice versa.) The higher the speed of the bowl, the greater will be the centrifugal force, and the more rapidly will the skim milk leave the bowl. An increase in bowl speed, therefore, increases the capacity of skim milk discharge. This means less cream is discharged and, consequently, with the same fat content, a higher fat percentage in cream will obtain.

(d) *Rate of milk inflow*. (The higher the rate of milk inflow, the lower the fat percentage in cream, and vice versa.) When the rate of inflow increases, the discharge from the cream outlet increases, as the skim milk discharge remains constant (with constant centrifugal force); more cream containing the same amount of fat results in a lower test, and vice versa.

(e) *Temperature of milk*. (The lower the temperature of milk during separation, the higher the fat percentage of the cream, and vice versa.) Lowering of temperature increases viscosity of both cream and skim milk, but that of cream increases (proportionately) more than skim milk. Hence the quantity of cream discharged is reduced (due to clogging of the bowl), thereby resulting in a higher fat test.

(f) *Amount of water or skim milk added to flush the bowl*. (The greater the quantity of water or skim milk added to flush the bowl, the lower the fat percentage in cream, and vice versa.) The addition of more water or skim milk will cause an increase in the amount of cream produced, which, with the same fat content, will show a lower fat test.

D. *Factors affecting fat loss in skim milk during separation*

(a) The 'skimming efficiency' (SE) of a cream separator refers to the 'percentage total fat from milk recovered in the cream. The higher the fat percentage in milk and/or the greater the fat loss in skim milk, the lower is the skimming efficiency, and vice versa. (The best index for SE is the fat test of skim milk, which should be checked regularly.)

Examples:

1. *Given*: 100 kg milk testing 7.5% fat; cream produced 14.1 kg testing 52.5% fat.

$$SE = \frac{14.1 \times (52.5/100)}{100 \times (7.5/100)} = 98.7$$

2. *Given*: 100 kg milk testing 4.8% fat; cream produced 10.3 kg testing 45.5% fat.

$$SE = \frac{10.3 \times (45.5/100)}{100 \times (4.8/100)} = 97.6$$

Note. In the above examples, high-test milk shows a higher SE than low-test milk.

(b) The factors affecting fat loss in skim milk are:
   (i) temperature of milk;
   (ii) speed of bowl;
   (iii) rate of milk inflow;
   (iv) position of cream screw;
   (v) mechanical condition of the machine:
      1. vibration of the separator
      2. condition of the discs
      3. amount of separator slime in the bowl;
   (vi) size of fat globules;
   (vii) degree and temperature of agitation given to milk before separation;
   (viii) presence of air in milk;
   (ix) acidity of milk.

(i) *Temperature of milk*. (The lower the temperature, the higher the fat loss in skim milk, and vice versa.) For efficient separation, the temperature of milk should be above the melting point of fat, so that the milk fat in the fat globules is entirely in liquid form. A satisfactory temperature for separation is around 40°C (104°F). The higher the temperature, the more efficient the separation. There is no marked increase in efficiency after 43–49°C (110–120°F). On the other hand, separation at low temperatures (in warm-milk separators) may lead to partial clogging of the bowl due to the high viscosity of cream at these temperatures, resulting in a greater fat loss in skim milk.

Note. The milk is invariably heated before separation (in warm-milk separators) to 35–40°C, in plate or tubular heaters, for efficient separation. This is known as 'pre-heating/forewarming' of milk.

(ii) *Speed of bowl*. (The lower the speed, the higher the fat loss in skim milk, and vice-versa.) At below-rated speed there will be more fat loss in skim milk because insufficient centrifugal force is generated for efficient cream separation. However, at above-rated speeds, the skimming efficiency will not increase greatly.

(iii) *Rate of milk inflow.* (The higher the rate of inflow, the ~~her~~ the fat loss in skim milk, and vice versa.) If the rate of in-~~.ow~~ is increased above the designed capacity of the separator, the milk passes through the bowl too rapidly to allow for complete separation, thereby resulting in a higher fat loss in skim milk. On the other hand, underfeeding the separator does not greatly increase the efficiency of the separation.

(iv) *Position of the cream-screw.* If up to 50 per cent cream is present, there is little effect on the fat test of skim milk; where there is 50 to 60 per cent cream, there is greater fat loss in skim milk; if above 60 per cent of cream is obtained, still higher fat losses in skim milk at low-temperature separation result. A good separator is designed to give efficient skimming within a fairly wide range of positions of the cream screw, so that the fat test of the cream can be varied without influencing the efficiency of skimming. With most separators. the position of the cream screw has little effect on the fat test of skim milk until the cream test is above 45 to 50 per cent. From this point up to a 60 per cent fat test in cream, the fat content of the skim milk increases. Separation of very thick cream at low temperatures may lead to higher losses through clogging of the bowl with viscous cream.

(v) *Mechanical condition of the machine.* Unsatisfactory mechanical condition of the cream separator causes greater fat loss in skim milk. These include:

1. *Vibration of the separator.* This reduces the efficiency of separation by disturbing the counter-currents of cream and skim milk. (Vibration is caused by installation on an insufficiently firm foundation, the bowl being out of balance, bearings being worn out, the axis of rotation not exactly vertical, etc.)

2. *Condition of discs.* Discs in an unsatisfactory condition suffer a loss of skimming efficiency due to the uneven flow of the counter-current streams of cream and skim milk between them. (An unsatisfactory disc is one which is out of shape, dirty, scratched or rough.)

3. *Amount of separator slime in bowl.* If too much slime accumulates, the fat loss in skim milk increases; this is caused not only by a disturbance in the even flow of the counter-currents of cream and skim milk, but by reduction in the centrifugal force (because of

decrease in the 'effective' diameter of the bowl).

Note: Separator slime (which is usually considered identical with clarifier slime) consists of the slimy mass which accumulates inside the bowl shell of the cream separator. It is made up of foreign matter, milk proteins, leucocytes, fragments of the secreting cells from the udder, fat, calcium-phosphate and other minerals, bacteria and, occasionally, red blood corpuscles.

The average composition of separator slime is given in Table 3.6.

TABLE 3.6

Composition of separator slime

Constituent	Moist Slime %	Dry Slime %
Water	68.2	—
Fat	1.4	4.4
Protein	25.3	79.6
Lactose	1.8	5.6
Minerals	3.3	10.4

SOURCE: *The Butter Industry* by Hunziker (1940).

(vi) *Size of fat globules.* (The greater the number of fat globules of less than 2 micron size, the higher the fat loss in skim milk and vice versa.) Fat globules of less than 2 micron size usually enter the skim milk, as they are not subject to sufficient centrifugal force to be recovered in the cream. Hence, the greater the number of less-than-2 micron size globules, the greater is the fat loss in skim milk.

(vii) *Degree and temperature at which milk is agitated before separation.* (The higher the degree and temperature of agitation, the greater the loss in skim milk and vice versa.) Agitation of hot milk causes the disintegration of the normal fat globules into smaller ones which escape the effect of centrifugal force, thereby leading to more fat loss in skim milk.

(viii) *Presence of air in milk.* (The greater the amount of air, the higher the fat loss in skim milk). If the milk delivered to the separator contains entrapped air bubbles, separation of air as a consequence of centrifugal force disturbs the counter-current streams of cream and skim milk between the discs, and lowers the efficiency of separation. The effect of air in the milk is greater with hermetic than with non-hermetic separators.

(ix) *Acidity of milk.* (The higher the acidity, the lower the efficiency of separation.) The higher the acidity, the lower the stability of casein particles, which in turn get precipitated and clog the bowl, thereby lowering the efficiency of separation.

E. *Yield of cream.* This can be calculated by the formula:

$$C = M \times \frac{fm - fs}{fc - fs},$$

where

C = weight of cream (kg);
M = weight of milk (kg);
fm = fat percentage of milk;
fs = fat percentage of skim milk;
fc = fat percentage of cream.

F. *Yield of skim milk.* This can be calculated by the following formula:

$$S = M \times \frac{fc - fm}{fc - fs},$$

where

S = weight of skim milk (kg);
M =⎫
fc =⎪
fm =⎬ as above.
fs =⎭

G. *Fat recovery in cream.* This can be calculated by the formula:

$$\text{Per cent fat recovered in cream} = \frac{\text{Kg fat in cream}}{\text{Kg fat in milk}} \times 100.$$

H. *Fat lost in skim milk.* This can be calculated by the formula:

$$\text{Per cent fat lost in skim milk} = \frac{\text{Kg fat in skim milk}}{\text{Kg fat in milk}} \times 100 \ldots \text{I}$$

$$= \frac{fc - fm}{fc - fs} \times \frac{fs}{fm} \times 100 \qquad \ldots \text{II}$$

where fc, fm and fs are as above.

Note: In formula II, weights are not required.

J. *Quality of cream.* 'Cream is no better than the milk from which it is made.' It is not possible to obtain good (bacteriological) cream from low-grade milk. In order to produce high quality cream,

the following steps are needed:
   (i) clean milk production;
   (ii) cooling of milk soon after production (preferably within 3 hours);
   (iii) separating milk under hygienic conditions (cream separator should be thoroughly cleaned and sanitized before use);
   (iv) prompt cooling of cream and its storage at a low temperature;
   (v) transport of cream to the dairy under low temperature.

3.8   Collection of Cream (for butter-making)

Factory butter is made either from cream separated on the farms or from cream separated from milk delivered to the factory. The cream used for commercial butter-making is collected mainly by motor truck/lorry. Each vehicle is allocated one (or more) chosen routes, which is identified (preferably) by a letter, while the suppliers on each route are numbered. The collection is done either by the creamery-factory itself or by private agencies who may themselves operate small cream buying stations/depots; in the depots, cream is received in producers' cans, weighed, sampled, tested and bulked in creamery-owned cans for shipment to the factory.

3.9   Neutralization of Cream (for butter-making)

A. *Definition*. Neutralization of sour cream for butter-making refers to a partial reduction in its acidity.

B. *Objects*. These are:
(a) To avoid excessive fat loss in buttermilk that results from churning highly acid pasteurized cream. (When pasteurizing sour cream, the casein curdles, thereby entrapping fat globules; as the bulk of the curd goes in buttermilk, this causes high fat loss.)

(b) To guard against the production of an undesirable off-flavour in cream (which may result when high-acid cream is pasteurized).

(c) To improve the keeping quality of butter made from high-acid cream. Salted-acid-butter develops a fishy flavour during commercial storage at −23 to −29°C (−10 to −20°F).

Note: If cream is neutralized, the correct method should be followed. Improper methods and over-neutralization are both harmful to the flavour and keeping quality of butter.

C. *Procedure.* The procedure for correct neutralization is:
(a) adoption of a definite standard of churning acidity;
(b) testing correctly for acidity;
(c) correct amount of neutralizer to be added;
(d) adding neutralizer to cream by the correct method;
(e) checking results by re-testing acidity.

(a) *Adoption of a definite standard for churning acidity*
(i) *Butter for long storage.* Cream acidity should be reduced to 0.06–0.08 per cent before churning for optimum results.
(ii) *Butter for early consumption.* Cream acidity should be reduced to 0.25–0.30 per cent before churning.

Note: (i) As acidity in cream is contained chiefly in the serum portion, cream-serum acidity is more reliable than cream acidity.
(ii) The richer the cream, the higher the cream-serum acidity. The relation between cream acidity (CA) and cream-serum acidity (CSA) is calculated by the following formula:

$$\frac{\%\ CA}{\%\ CSA} = \frac{100 - \%\ \text{fat in cream}}{100}.$$

(b) *Testing correctly for acidity.* The procedure is:
(i) Take a sample of cream after thorough mixing.
(ii) Heat cream to boiling point for 1 minute before testing for acidity. (This method is satisfactory for sweet cream only.)
(iii) First partially neutralize acid cream with a known amount of standard alkali, then treat as above. (Recommended method for acid cream.)
(iv) Determine lactic acidity of cream by titration of a fixed weight (10 g.) with a standard alkali (N/9 sodium hydroxide solution), using phenolphthalein as an indicator.

Note: The dissolved carbon dioxide in cream acts as carbonic acid and increases the titratable acidity value because it reacts with sodium hydroxide; but it does not utilize any of the bicarbonate neutralizer added, thereby over-neutralizing the cream.

(c) *Correct amount of neutralizer to be added.* The considerations are:
(i) The quantity of neutralizer to be added to a vat of cream varies with the acidity of cream, the final acidity desired in

pasteurized cream and with the neutralizer compound used.

(ii) It is necessary, first, to calculate the quantity of lactic acid to be neutralized per 100 kg cream. Then the amount of neutralizer required must be calculated.

(iii) There are two groups of neutralizers available for use, viz. lime (calcium hydroxide and magnesium hydroxide) and soda (caustic soda, sodium carbonate, sodium bicarbonate and sodium sesquicarbonate). The following equations represent the neutralizing actions:

$$NaHCO_3 + CH_3 \cdot CHOH \cdot COOH = CH_3 \cdot CHOH \cdot COONa + H_2O + CO_2$$
$$\underset{(84)}{} \qquad \underset{(90)}{}$$

$$Ca(OH)_2 + 2CH_3 \cdot CHOH \cdot COOH = (CH_3 \cdot CHOH \cdot COO)_2Ca + 2H_2O$$
$$\underset{(74)}{} \qquad \underset{(2 \times 90)}{}$$

$$Na_2CO_3 + 2CH_3 \cdot CHOH \cdot COOH = 2CH_3 \cdot CHOH \cdot COONa + 2H_2O + CO_2$$
$$\underset{(106)}{} \qquad \underset{(2 \times 90)}{}$$

$$NaOH + CH_3 \cdot CHOH \cdot COOH = CH_3 \cdot CHOH \cdot COONa + H_2O$$
$$\underset{(40)}{} \qquad \underset{(90)}{}$$

$$Mg(OH)_2 + 2CH_3 \cdot CHOH \cdot COOH = (CH_3 \cdot CHOH \cdot COO)_2Mg + 2H_2O$$
$$\underset{(58)}{} \qquad \underset{(2 \times 90)}{}$$

(iv) The requirements, both theoretical and practical, of two selected neutralizers are given in Table 3.7.

TABLE 3.7

Amount of neutralizer required

Name of neutralizer	Requirement of neutralizer per kg (lactic acid)		
	Theoretical (kg)	Practical (kg)	
Sodium bicarbonate	0.93	0.83*	upto 0.30 per cent cream acidity
		0.91†	beyond 0.30 per cent cream acidity
Calcium hydroxide (low-magnesium lime)	0.41	0.49‡	

SOURCE: *The Buttermakers' Manual* by McDowall (1953).

*The practical (i.e. actual) amount is lower than it is in theory owing to the presence in variable amounts of carbon-dioxide, which raises the titer value.

† The increase in neutralizer requirement is due to the decreasing proportional effect of carbon dioxide with rise in cream acidity.

‡ The actual neutralizing capacity of lime is only 80 per cent of the amount used, since nearly 20 per cent of it reacts with casein and phosphates, and so is not available for acid-neutralization.

(v) The comparative merits and demerits of lime and soda neutralizers are shown in Table 3.8.

TABLE 3.8
Characteristics of neutralizers

Particulars	Lime	Soda
Purity	Low	High
Solubility	Low	High
Neutralizing speed	Low	High
Foam production	None	Variable
Cost	Low	High
Over-neutralization effect	Limy flavour	Soapy flavour

(d) *Correct procedure for adding neutralizer to cream*

(i) The neutralizer should never be dry when added, but should be dissolved/suspended in clean, potable water and properly diluted (mixed with 10–15 times its weight in water). It should be distributed quickly and uniformly in the cream and mixed thoroughly by stirring vigorously.

(ii) The temperature of cream when adding the neutralizer should preferably be 29–32°C (85–90°F). The stirring should be continued for 5–10 minutes after adding the neutralizer; then the cream should be pasteurized.

(e) *Checking results by re-testing acidity*. The cream acidity should now be determined to check whether it has been correctly neutralized.

D. *Role of carbon dioxide in neutralization of cream with sodium bicarbonate*. Fresh cream always contains some dissolved carbon dioxide; acid cream contains more of it. The carbon dioxide (as carbonic acid) reacts with sodium hydroxide during titration and shows a higher acidity test. But the carbon dioxide does not react with sodium bicarbonate neutralizer and consequently over-neutralization results.

E. *Double neutralization with lime and soda*. The following sequence is recommended:

(i) first use lime neutralizer to bring the cream acidity down to 0.3–0.4 per cent.

(ii) next use soda neutralizer to bring the cream acidity down to the desired level.

Note: The objects of double neutralization are: (i) to avoid the intense effect on flavour of a large amount of any one neutralizer with high-acid cream; (ii) to avoid production of excessive carbon dioxide by the use of sodium bicarbonate with high-acid cream.

3.10 Standardization of Cream

(a) *Definition*. This refers to the adjustment of the fat level in cream to the desired percentage, conforming to standard requirements.

(b) *Procedure*. The fat percentage in cream is usually adjusted to the prescribed level by the addition of a calculated amount of skim milk, as explained earlier.

Problem. Given 1,000 kg cream testing 50% fat. How much skim milk testing 0.1% fat must be added to obtain 40% fat in the standardized cream?

Solution.

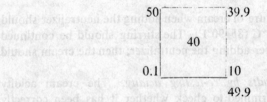

From the Pearson's Square above, it will be seen that 39.9 parts by weight of 50% cream, when mixed with 10 parts by weight of 0.1% skim milk, will give 49.9 parts by weight of standardized 40% cream.

As the amount of cream is 1,000 kg, the amount of skim milk (S) is to be calculated by the formula:

$$39.9 : 10 = 1,000 : S$$

3.11 Pasteurization of Cream

(a) *Definition*. Pasteurization of cream refers to the process of heating every particle of cream to not less than 71°C (160°F) and holding it at such a temperature for at least 20 minutes, or to any suitable temperature-time combination, using approved and properly-operated equipment.

(b) *Objects*

(i) To destroy the pathogenic micro-organisms in cream so as to make it, and also the resultant butter, safe for human consumption;

(ii) to destroy undesirable micro-organisms and inactivate the enzymes present, so as to prolong the keeping qualities of the cream and butter;

(iii) to complete the neutralization process;

(iv) to eliminate some of the gaseous tainting substances;

(v) to make possible the removal of some volatile off-flavours (such as feed and weed flavours) during vacreation.

(c) *Methods* (also see 1.17)

(i) *Holder pasteurization.* This is a batch process used for small-scale handling. The cream is heated in a batch/holder pasteurizer to 71°C (160°F) for 20 minutes and then promptly cooled. (A multiprocessing vat may be used for crea n pasteurization and cooling.)

(ii) *HTST (Plate) pasteurization.* This is a continuous process used for large-scale handling. It allows for much greater regeneration than would be possible with any other process. The plate pasteurizer is better suited to freshly-separated sweet cream than neutralized cream, as the latter more easily forms burnt-on films on the plates. The maximum heating temperature may be 95–100°C (203–212°F) for 15–16 seconds.

(iii) *Vacuum pasteurization (vacreation).* This is also a continuous process. A noteworthy characteristic of vacuum pasteurization is that a dilution of the initial cream takes place and the fat test may be lowered by 6 to 8 per cent; this fact has to be kept in view when standardizing cream.

3.12 Manufacture of Different Types of Cream

(a) *Sterilized or canned cream.* The various steps are:

(i) Fresh, sweet cream is first standardized to 20 per cent fat;

(ii) pre-heated to 80°C (176°F), without holding;

(iii) double-homogenized at 80°C (176°F), using 2,500–3,000 psi in the first stage and 500 psi in the second stage;

(iv) immediately cooled to 16°C (60°F), preferably over a surface cooler using brine;

(v) filled into tin-cans (or bottles) and immediately sealed;

(vi) sterilized in retorts (as for Evaporated Milk) employing 15 minutes for coming-up, 12–15 minutes for holding at 118°C (244°F), and 15 minutes for cooling to room temperature.

(b) *Plastic cream.* This is obtained by:

(i) re-separating normal cream (30–40 per cent) in a normal cream separator, or

(ii) separating milk in an especially designed plastic cream separator.

Note: In both the above cases, the initial product is pasteurized at about 71–77°C (160–170°F) for 15 minutes and cooled to 60–66°C (140–150°F) before separation.

(c) *Frozen cream*

1. *Objects.* (i) To improve the keeping quality of cream during transportation over long distances;

(ii) to store surplus cream for use during shortage. Mainly used by ice cream manufacturers who add sucrose (10–15 per cent 'by weight) to cream before freezing to prevent 'oiling-off' after thawing.

2. *Method of manufacture*

(i) Separate and standardize cream to 40–50 per cent fat;

(ii) pasteurize at 77°C (170°F) for 15 minutes;

(iii) cool to below 4°C (40°F) and fill into paper/plastic containers or tin-cans and seal well;

(iv) freeze quickly and store at −12°C (10°F) or below.

3. *Effects of freezing on cream.* The membranes enclosing the fat globules are partially ruptured by ice crystals. Frozen cream tends to 'oil-off' on thawing, especially at higher temperatures. This 'oiling-off' impairs the whipping property of the product.

(d) *Clotted cream.* This it prepared by heating cream to 77–88°C (170–190°F) in shallow pans and then allowing it to cool slowly. The surface layer consists of clotted cream, which is skimmed off and strained.

(e) *Sour cream.* This is a heavy-bodied ripened cream of high acidity (0.6 per cent lactic acid), clean flavour and smooth texture made by inoculating sweet, pasteurized and homogenized cream with a culture of lactic acid and allowing fermentation to proceed until these desired qualities are obtained.

(f) *Synthetic cream.* This is a mixture of flour, egg-yolk, sugar, water and a vegetable fat, usually groundnut oil.

3.13 Packaging, Storage and Distribution of Table Cream

(a) *Packaging*. Table cream is packaged for retail sale in units similar to those for milk, such as a glass bottle, paper* carton, LDPE† sachet, plastic bottle, etc.

(b) *Storage and Distribution*. Same as for milk. In other words, cream is stored, preferably at 5–10°C (41–50°F), and distributed as early as possible, but preferably within 3 hours of removing it from cold storage.

3.14 Judging and Grading of Cream

I. *Table cream*

    A. *Score card*. Same as for Market Milk (See 1.20).

    B. *Procedure of examination*

(a) *Sampling*. Will be discussed later (Step 2/(v) below).

(b) *Sequence of observations*. Carefully transfer bottle/container from refrigerator/cold room (5–10°C/40–50°F) to the laboratory in a vertical position, avoiding undue agitation. Then examine in the following order:

  (i) take note of serum separation;

  (ii) take note of sediment at the bottom of the bottle;

  (iii) observe container and closure for fullness, cleanliness and general appearance;

  (iv) take note of cream plug, if any;

  (v) secure representative sample for bacterial count (aseptically by standard procedures), to be used later for other tests;

  (vi) temper cream to 10°C (50°F) and determine viscosity;

  (vii) take about 20 ml cream in a 100 ml beaker. Warm it to 15–21°C (60–70°F) and note the smell. Then put some cream in the mouth and note the taste;

  (viii) determine percentage of titratable acidity and fat;

  (ix) Test for defects such as oiling-off, feathering in coffee, etc.

    C. *Requirements of high-grade table cream*. High quality table cream should have a clean, sweet, pleasant, nutty flavour. The body should be smooth, uniform and reasonably viscous for the percentage of fat present. The physical appearance should be good.

---

* Coated with a water-proof layer of either polyethylene (polythene) or wax.
† Low density polyethylene.

II. *Manufacturing cream*

(a) *Requirements for high grade product.* Sweet cream, which is to be processed or manufactured into other dairy products, should be of a high quality. The cream should have a low acidity and clean flavour, should be fresh and delivered to the dairy factory in a clean, sanitary container adequately protected from contamination and against heat in transit.

3.15 Defects in Cream, Their Causes and Prevention

Defects in cream may arise from low grade milk and faulty methods of production, processing and storage. The common defects in both table and manufacturing creams, their causes and prevention, are given in Table 3.9.

TABLE 3.9

Defects in cream, their causes and prevention

Name of defect	Causes	Prevention
A. *Table cream*		
(a) *Flavour*		
Cooked	Excessive heating of cream during pasteurization.	Proper heating of cream during pasteurization.
Note: Cooked flavour is becoming less objectionable, since it is an indication of good keeping quality.		
Feed and weed	Feeding of milk-tainting feeds and weeds within 3 hours before milking.	(i) Feeding of milk-tainting feeds and weeds soon after milking (ii) Eradication of milk-tainting weeds (iii) Vacuum pasteurization of cream.
Highly acid/ sour	(i) Using sour milk for separation (ii) Acid development in cream.	(i) Using fresh, sweet milk for preparation (ii) Neutralization of cream.
Oxidized/oily/ Metallic/ Tallowy	Fat oxidation due to direct contact of milk with copper or iron, exposure of milk or cream to sunlight, etc.	(i) Proper tinning of milk- or cream-holding vessels, or using aluminium alloy or stainless steel as contact surface

Name of defect	Causes	Prevention
		(ii) Vacuum pasteurization of cream.
Rancid	Fat hydrolysis due to lipase action in milk or cream.	Inactivating lipase by proper pasteurization of milk and cream.

(b) Miscellaneous

| Feathering in hot coffee | (i) Excessive homogenization pressure
 (ii) Using sour cream
 (iii) Addition of salts. | (i) Proper homogenization pressure
 (ii) Using sweet cream
 (iii) Avoiding addition of salts. |

B. Manufacturing cream

(a) Flavour

Barny	(i) Poor ventilation of milking byre/barn (ii) Not keeping milk properly covered during production.	(i) Proper ventilation of milking byre/barn (ii) Keeping milk properly covered during production.
Bitter	(i) Intake of bitter-weeds by milch animals (ii) Lipase activity during (raw) cream separation (iii) Growth of proteolytic bacteria in cream	(i) Eradication of off-ending weeds (ii) Checking lipase activity by avoiding the 'danger zone' (38–49°C) during raw cream separation (iii) Storage of cream at 5°C (40°F) or below to check bacterial growth.
Cheesy	Growth of proteolytic bacteria leading to casein breakdown.	Storage of cream at 5°C (40°F) or below to check bacterial growth.
Coarse-acid/Sour	Uncontrolled acid development in cream.	Storage of cream at 5°C (40°F) or below to check acid development.
Cooked Feed and weed Rancid Oxidized etc.	— Same as Table Cream —	
Fruity	Development of by-products of growth of certain undesirable micro-organisms.	Storage of cream at 5°C (40°F) or below to check microbial growth.

Name of defect	Causes	Prevention
Utensil	Using dirty utensils.	Using well-cleaned utensils.
Yeasty	Growth of lactose ferment-ing yeast.	Storage of cream at 5°C (40°F) or below to check yeast growth.

3.16 Uses of Cream

(i) For direct consumption as table/coffee/whipping creams;

(ii) in the preparation of special dishes;

(iii) in the production of plastic, frozen and cultured (sour) creams;

(iv) in the manufacture of butter, cream, cheese, ice cream, butteroil and ghee (India);

(v) for creaming cottage cheese.

4 BUTTER

4.1 Introduction

Butter leads amongst the milk products manufactured in developed dairying countries of the world today. The world's recorded annual butter production in 1969 (vide *F.A.O. Production Year Book*, 1970) has been estimated to have been 5,584 thousand tonnes; and India's contribution in the same was 448 thousand tonnes, i.e. 8 per cent of the world's total. The production of creamery butter in India in 1966 was estimated to have been about 6.3 per cent of the total milk production and 11.3 per cent of the milk used for the manufacture of dairy products. (See Table 1.6.)

Butter serves as the balance wheel of the dairy industry; surplus milk is converted into butter, while during times of scarcity the milk intended for butter-making is used for more essential products.

4.2 History

The art of butter-making has a long history. The manufacture of creamery butter has been confined to the 'colder' regions of the world, where gravity creaming has been successful. References to butter are found in the Old Testament. In the past, butter was an article of commerce and a sign of wealth. Upto the middle of the nineteenth century, factory butter-making was unknown; most butter was made on the farm from cream obtained by gravity creaming. However, with the development of the centrifugal cream separator (1879), Fat test (Babcock, 1890; Gerber, 1892), butter churns, artificial refrigeration, etc., factory butter-making developed rapidly.

4.3 Definition

Butter may be defined as a fat concentrate which is obtained by churning cream, gathering the fat into a compact mass and then working it.

According to the PFA Rules (1976), table (creamery) butter is the product obtained from cow or buffalo milk or a combination thereof, or from cream or curd obtained from cow or buffalo milk or a combination thereof, with or without the addition of common salt and annatto or carotene as colouring matter. It should be free from other animal fats, wax and mineral oils, vegetable oils and fats. No preservative except common salt and no colouring matter except annatto or carotene may be added. It must contain not less than 80 per cent by weight of milk fat, not more than 1.5 per cent by weight of curd and not more than 3 per cent by weight of common salt. Diacetyl may be added as a flavouring agent but, if so used, the total diacetyl content must not exceed 4 ppm. Calcium hydroxide, sodium bicarbonate, sodium carbonate, sodium polyphosphates may be added, but must not exceed the weight of butter as a whole by more than 0.2 per cent.

4.4 Classification

Many kinds of butter are to be found in the market. These differ with the type of cream from which they are made and with variations in the manufacturing process. Unless specifically mentioned, the different kinds of butter may or may not have been salted. A brief description of several kinds of butter follows:

(a) *Pasteurized cream butter.* Made usually from pasteurized sweet cream. Such butter usually has a milder flavour than that made from similar cream not pasteurized.

(b) *Ripened cream butter.* Made from cream in which a pleasant delicate aroma has been developed before churning by ripening (i.e. inoculating the cream with a butter culture and holding it at a desired temperature). Properly made, ripened cream butter has a delicate flavour which is sometimes referred to as 'real butter flavour'.

(c) *Unripened cream butter.* Made from unripened cream. The flavour of such butter is usually mild.

(d) *Salted butter.* Butter to which salt has been added.

(e) *Unsalted butter.* Contains no added salt.

(f) *Sweet cream butter.* In this case, the acidity of the churned cream does not exceed 0.20 per cent.

(g) *Sour cream butter.* Made from cream which has more than 0.20 per cent acidity.

(h) *Fresh butter.* Such butter has not undergone cold storage. (Usually, fresh butter is not kept for more than 3 weeks.)

(j) *Cold storage butter.* Here, it has been stored at a temperature of about −18°C (0°F) for some time. (Generally cold storage butter is from one to six months old when offered for retail trade.)

(k) *Dairy butter (USA).* Made on a farm. It is usually made from unpasteurized sour cream which has not been standardized for acidity. This butter generally has a sour flavour due to the high acid content of the cream.

(l) *Creamery butter.* Made in a creamery or dairy factory. It is more uniform in quality than 'dairy butter'.

4.5 Composition

According to the PFA Rules (1976), table/creamery butter should contain not less than 80 per cent fat, not more than 1.5 per cent curd and not more than 3.0 per cent common salt. The typical composition of Indian butter has been given in Table 4.1.

TABLE 4.1
Composition of (Indian butter)

Constituent	Percentage
Butter fat	80.2
Moisture	16.3
Salt	2.5
Curd	1.0

Note: The standards for composition of butter are prescribed either as 80 per cent fat or 16 per cent moisture.

4.6 Food and Nutritive Value

Butter is very high in fat and fat-soluble vitamins A, D, E and K.

4.7 Method of Manufacture, Packaging and Storage

A. *Flow diagram of manufacture*:

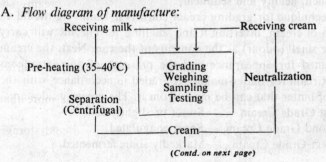

(*Contd. on next page*)

Flow Diagram (Contd.)

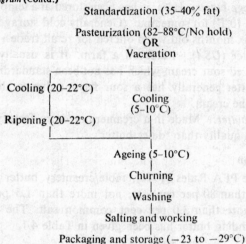

Standardization (35–40% fat)
|
Pasteurization (82–88°C/No hold)
OR
Vacreation

Cooling (20–22°C)
|
Ripening (20–22°C)

Cooling
(5–10°C)

Ageing (5–10°C)
|
Churning
|
Washing
|
Salting and working
|
Packaging and storage (−23 to −29°C)

B. *Details of manufacture*

(aa) *Receiving milk/cream.* This consists of: (a) unloading; (b) grading; (c) sampling; (d) weighing; (e) testing. The reception of milk has already been discussed in 1.17. We will now discuss the reception of cream.

(a) *Unloading.* The cans of cream brought to the creamery/ butter-making factory are unloaded on the receiving platform which is at truck-deck height, and arranged according to the route and the patrons.

(b) *Grading.* The purpose of grading is to pay for the product on the basis of its quality. Grading and quality payment are the efforts made by dairies/creameries to establish a reputation for high quality products. Cream is graded on the same principles as is milk, i.e. on examinations for smell, taste (seldom carried out), appearance, touch, acidity and sediment.

The technique for grading cream consists in removing the lid of each can of cream, inverting it and smelling it. The lid will carry the same smell (odour) as the contents of the can. Next, the cream is examined for appearance and the presence of any extraneous matter. Cream for butter-making is graded in accordance with the grades of butter that can be made from it. The cream grades are:

First Grade Cream   — Sweet or slightly sour
Second Grade Cream — Sour, coagulated
Reject Grade Cream — Markedly sour, fermented.

(c) *Sampling*.   Before sampling, the cream in the can is thoroughly mixed by a combined rotary and vertical movement of the plunger/stirrer. If required, the lidded cans of cream may be sprayed with hot water to reduce cream viscosity, and facilitate mixing. Then a representative sample may be drawn for testing purposes.

(d) *Weighing*.   The cans of cream, which have been accepted, are then weighed and the weight recorded for accounting and other purposes. First-grade creams are tipped directly into the main neutralizing vats, while second-grade creams are segregated in some factories in a separate vat for separate churning. (The cream adhering to the inner walls of the cans is recovered by inverting the cans over steaming jets for short periods.)

(e) *Testing*.   The cream samples drawn are then tested for fat, solids-not-fat, acidity, etc., by standard methods.

(bb) *Pre-heating of milk*.   To increase efficiency of cream separation.

(cc) *Separation of milk*.   By centrifugal methods.

(dd) *Neutralization of cream*.   See 3.9.

(ee) *Standardization of cream*.

(a) *Definition*.   See 3.10.

(b) *Object*.   To obtain the lowest fat loss in buttermilk during churning.

(c) *Procedure*.   See 3.10.

(ff) *Pasteurization/Vacreation of cream*.   See 3.11.

(gg) *Cooling and ageing of cream*.   Cream is cooled by lowering its temperature, and aged by holding it at this (low) temperature for a few hours. After pasteurization, the cream has to be cooled and then aged to make churning possible. Cream will not churn until the butterfat in the fat globules has at least partially solidified (crystallized); if insufficiently solid, due to improper cooling and ageing of the cream, the fat loss in the buttermilk will be excessive and the butter obtained will have an unsatisfactory, weak body. Under Indian conditions, the optimum temperature for the cooling and ageing of cream should preferably be 5–10°C (41–50°F). Cooling cream to abnormally low temperatures, and ageing at near about the same ones, renders the fat globules so firm (solid) that they coalesce with each other during churning only with difficulty, thereby greatly prolonging the churning process. High cooling and ageing temperatures of cream shorten the churning period, yield large fat losses in buttermilk and produce butter which has a relatively soft body. Low cooling and ageing temperatures prolong the churning period, decrease fat losses and produce a firm body that has a satisfactory standing-up capacity. The ageing period should be at least 2 to 4 hours, preferably 15–16 hours (overnight). During ageing, crystallization of fat in the fat globules should be satisfactorily completed. The optimum temperature for cooling and ageing cream depends on: composition of fat, size of fat globules, fat percentage of cream, period of ageing, temperature of churning, and acidity of cream. Adopting the optimum temperature of cooling and ageing (together with the optimum temperature of churning) provides a degree of solidification of fat in cream that may yield a normal churning period, reasonably exhaustive churning, satisfactory washing and a satisfactory firmness in the body of butter.

Note: 'Shock' cooling of warm cream with ice is not conducive to proper fat crystallization, since there is a subsequent temperature rise due to latent heat. Consequently, inexhaustive churning and an unsatisfactory, weak-bodied butter results.

(hh) *Ripening of cream*
(a) *Definition*.   This refers to the fermentation of cream with the help of desirable starter cultures.

Note: Fermentation means, strictly, the decomposition of carbohydrate (sugars) by micro-organisms only. In the dairy industry, the most important fermentation is lactic acid production or souring of milk; while less important are those for the production of flavour, etc.

(b) *Objects*.   (i) To produce butter with a pleasing, pronounced characteristic flavour and aroma, uniformly from day to day; (ii) to obtain exhaustive churning, i.e. a low fat loss in buttermilk.

(c) *Procedure*.   The butter starter culture (see 2.7) containing lactic acid producers such as *Str. lactis* and/or *Str. cremoris*, together with aroma (diacetyl) producers such as *Str. diacetilactis*, *Leuc. citrovorum* and *Leuc. dextranicum*, in correct proportions, is added to the standardized, pasteurized and cooled (20–22°C/68–72°F) cream at 0.5–2.0 per cent. After being thoroughly mixed, the cream is incubated at 21°C (70°F) for 15–16 hours.

(d) *Role of diacetyl*.   The typical flavour of butter from ripened cream is mainly the effect of diacetyl (biacetyl), and, to a smaller extent, of acetic and propionic acids. There is no diacetyl in sweet cream. The flavour intensity in butter depends on its diacetyl content, as shown in Table 4.2.

TABLE 4.2

Correlation of flavour intensity of butter with its diacetyl content

Diacetyl content in butter	Flavour intensity
None	Flavourless
0.2 to 0.6 p.p.m.	Mild flavour
0.7 to 1.5 p.p.m.	Full flavour

SOURCE: *The Butter Industry* by O. F. Hunziker (1940)

Note: (i) The normal diacetyl content of ripened-cream butter is on average 2.5 p.p.m. and rarely over 4 p.p.m.

(ii) Diacetyl is produced from its mother substance acetyl-methyl-carbinol.

(c) *Synthetic flavours.* Cream ripening is expensive, time-consuming and exacting. Further, most of the flavouring substances enter into the buttermilk and washwater, and are lost to the butter. Hence the use of starter, starter-distillate or synthetic flavour compounds, which are mixed with sweet-cream butter during the working process to impart the characteristic flavour of ripened-cream butter to the finished product. However, the addition of the above ingredients is not entirely satisfactory, for the following reasons: (i) such butter has a somewhat harsh unnatural aroma; (ii) it lacks the pleasing, mellow, uniformly blended aroma of ripened-cream butter; (iii) the aroma lacks permanence; etc.

Note: One way to improve the flavour of butter is to increase the citric acid content of cream or milk before fermenting begins.

(jj) *Churning*

(a) *Definition.* Churning of cream consists of agitation at a suitable temperature until the fat globules adhere, forming larger and larger masses, and until a relatively complete separation of fat and serum occurs.

(b) *Factors contributing towards stability of fat-in-skim-milk emul-*

sion. The object of churning cream is to produce butter. In milk/cream, the fat exists in the form of an emulsion, i.e. a continuous phase. This emulsion is fairly stable. As long as it remains intact, there is no formation of butter. The factors contributing towards the stability of this fat-in-skim-milk emulsion are: (i) force of surface tension; (ii) phenomenon of adsorption; (iii) electric charge on the fat globules; and (iv) viscosity of cream.

(i) *Force of surface tension.* This causes the fat globules in milk/cream to retain their individuality and prevent butter formation.

(ii) *Phenomenon of adsorption.* The surface layer of the fat globules contains an adsorbed phospholipid-protein complex, which resists de-emulsification.

(iii) *Electric charge.* The fat globules carry a negative charge and repel each other. This prevents their coalescence. (The charge decreases as cream acidity increases.)

(iv) *Viscosity.* Increased viscosity retards churning.

(c) *Churning cream vs. whole milk.* A greater concentration of fat globules in cream promotes a more profuse and rapid coalescence and aggregation than in milk.

(d) *Agitation in relation to temperature of cream.* Above the melting point of fat (31–36°C/88–97°F), agitation of cream results in subdivision of fat globules. At lower temperatures (maximum effect at 7–8°C/45–46°F), agitation causes coalescence of fat globules.

(e) *Churning of cream.* Good churnability refers to:

(i) *ease of churning,* i.e. a clear breaking stage and churning until the grains of butter are of the correct size;

(ii) *completeness of churning,* i.e. exhaustiveness of churning (which refers to fat losses in buttermilk);

(iii) *satisfactory washing,* which is possible if the grains of butter are sufficiently firm;

(iv) *optimum churning period.* This in turn affects the firmness of body and exhaustiveness of churning.

(f) *Factors influencing churnability of cream and body of butter:*

(i) chemical composition of fat;
(ii) size of fat globules;
(iii) viscosity of cream;
(iv) temperature of cream at churning;
(v) fat percentage of cream;
(vi) acidity of cream;

(vii) load of churn;

(viii) nature of agitation;

(ix) speed of churn;

(x) pre-churning holding period.

(i) *Chemical composition of fat.* Milk fat is a mixture of numerous fats (glycerides) of widely varying melting and solidifying points. Thus, fats with low melting points are known as soft fats (such as tri-butyrin, olein, etc.); while those with high melting points are called 'hard' fats (such as stearin, palmitin, etc.). An increase in the proportion of soft fats shortens the churning period, diminishes the firmness of butter and increases the fat losses in buttermilk and vice versa. Fresh green succulent feeds increase the proportion of soft fats, while dry hard feeds increase the proportion of hard fats.

(ii) *Size of fat globules.* Small fat globules churn with difficulty, while large ones churn readily. Therefore, the higher the proportion of small-sized fat globules, the longer the churning time and the greater the fat loss in buttermilk, and vice versa.

(iii) *Viscosity of cream.* The greater the viscosity of cream, the greater the churning period, and vice versa.

(iv) *Temperature of cream at churning.* This is important for controlling the rapidity and exhaustiveness of churning and the body of butter. Under Indian conditions, the optimum churning temperature ranges from 9 to 11°C (48 to 52°F). A higher churning temperature causes a shorter churning time, higher fat loss and a weak body in butter (which is difficult to wash, and from which it is difficult to remove curd particles properly). A lower churning temperature prolongs the churning period. The optimum churning temperature will give an optimum churning period (30 to 60 minutes), a butter of satisfactory firmness and exhaustive churning.

(v) *Fat percentage of cream.* The higher the fat percentage of cream, the lower the churning period, and vice versa. The optimum fat level of cream for churning, according to Hunziker, lies within 30 to 35 per cent (average 33 per cent), while McDowall suggests 40 per cent. On the other hand, Indian research* seems to indicate 40 per cent for cows and 35 per cent for buffaloes.

(vi) *Acidity of cream.* According to Hunziker, cream churns more rapidly and exhaustively than sweet cream. However,

---

* Sukumar De and B. N. Mathur, 'Some Investigations on the Churning Efficiency of Indian Creams', *Indian Dairyman*, 20(12), 351 (1968).

McDowall believes that the reverse is the case.

(vii) *Load of churn.* The optimum load of cream which the churn can take seems to be between one-half and one-third its total capacity. Overloading prolongs churning time, while underloading reduces the normal capacity of the churn.

(viii) *Nature of agitation.* This is influenced by the size, type (design) and r.p.m. of the churn, and affects the churning period.

(ix) *Speed of churn.* Should be as prescribed by the manufacturer, since this maximizes agitation and shortens the churning period.

(x) *Pre-churning holding period.* Refers to cooling and ageing of cream (see 4.5).

(g) *Churning operation*

(i) *Preparing the churn.* A new churn (especially a wooden one) requires careful pre-treatment before use. An old churn (wooden and metal) requires proper sanitization and cooling, to render it clean.

(ii) *Filling cream into the churn.* The cream should be strained so as to remove lumps and chance objects. The amount then filled should preferably be slightly below the rated capacity.

(iii) *Addition of butter colour.* This is done to maintain the uniformity of yellow colour in butter throughout the year for consumer satisfaction. The amount of standard colour added (under Indian conditions) varies from 0 to 250 ml or more per 100 kg of butterfat. The butter colour should preferably be added to the cream in the churn.

Note: Butter colour should have the following properties: it should be harmless (i.e., non-toxic), free from off-flavours, concentrated, permanent, and oil-soluble. Butter colours are of the following types:

1. *Of vegetable origin.* Annatto and carotene. Annatto is obtained from the seeds of the annatto plant (*bixa orellana*). The yellowish-red colouring substance is extracted from the seeds by dissolving it in a neutral oil (such as castor, ground-nut, sesame or til). The Annatto plant is of tropical origin and is grown in the West Indies, India, Brazil, etc. Carotene is extracted from carrots and other carotene-rich vegetable matter. This colour is slightly on the greenish side. Its use is growing for it increases vitamin A potency.

2. *Of mineral origin.* Harmless, oil-soluble coal-tar dyes are mixed with neutral oil as above. Examples are: Yellow AB (Benzene Azo-β-naphthyl-amine), Yellow OB (Ortho Tolune Azo-β-naphthyl-amine). These have the advantages of being more concentrated and permanent. Butter colour should be stored in opaque, air-tight containers at room temperature (18–21°C/60–70°F), and not unduly agitated, so as to ensure long keeping quality and usefulness.

(iv) *Operating the churn.* After initially rotating the churn for 5 to 10 minutes, the liberated gas is removed once or twice by opening the churn vent. *Then the cream sample is drawn for the fat test.* During the churning process there is invariably a rise in temperature from 1 to 3°C. Churning is accompanied by foaming. Then comes the 'breaking' stage, when the cream breaks away from the spy glass which becomes clear. At this stage the fat in the skim-milk emulsion breaks and very small butter granules of the size of pinheads make their appearance. It is sometimes necessary, especially in the tropics, to add 'break water' at this stage, to reduce the temperature of the churn contents, and thereby control the body of the butter. The amount and temperature of break-water depends on the temperature reduction required. After the breaking stage, the churning is continued until the butter grains are of the desired size (viz., 'pea-size' in large churns).

Note: In the tropics, addition of break water can be avoided by providing an air-conditioned butter-making room and/or chill-water spray over the butter churn.

(h) *Churning difficulties.* The usual causes are:
(i) excessive hardness of fat;
(ii) small-sized fat globules;
(iii) excessively thin cream;
(iv) over-loading of the churn;
(v) excessively low churning temperature of cream;
(vi) abnormal cream (causing excessive foaming).

(j) *Factors affecting fat loss in buttermilk:*
(i) *Fat percentage of cream at churning.* The lower the fat percentage of cream, the lower the fat percentage of buttermilk, but the greater is the per cent total fat loss in buttermilk, and vice versa.

(ii) *Size of fat globules.* The greater the proportion of small-sized fat globules (2 micron or less), the greater the fat loss, and vice versa. The small globules escape churning action and pass on to the buttermilk.

(iii) *Acidity of cream at churning.* According to Hunziker, sour cream causes a lower fat loss than sweet cream; but according to McDowall, the reverse is true.

(iv) *Physical properties of fat.* The softer the fat, the more the fat loss, and vice versa.

(v) *Conditions of cooling and ageing.* Insufficient cooling and ageing (i.e. improper fat crystallization) causes more fat loss, and vice versa.

(vi) *Conditions of churning.* Over-loading, gross under-loading and under-churning all cause a greater fat loss.

(kk) *Washing*

(a) *Draining the buttermilk.* When the cream has been churned, the churn is stopped in the proper position, a drain-plug fixed, and the buttermilk removed through a sieve.

(b) *Purpose of washing.* (i) to remove all loose buttermilk adhering to butter grains so as to reduce the curd content* of butter, thereby improving its keeping quality; (ii) to correct defects in the firmness of butter by proper adjustment of wash water temperatures, and (iii) to decrease the intensity of certain off-flavours (in case of poor quality cream); etc.

(c) *Procedure of washing.* After it has been drained, chilled water is added to the butter grains in the churn. The temperature of the water is usually 1–2°C lower than the churning temperature of cream, and an amount equal to the quantity of buttermilk removed. After a few revolutions, the wash water is drained out. Normally one wash is enough for good quality butter.

(d) *Quality of wash water.* Should be physically clean and bacteriologically and chemically safe. It is best to use freshly pasteurized and cooled water.

(ll) *Salting and working*

I. *Salting.* This refers to the addition of salt to butter.

(a) *Object/Purpose*:

(i) to improve keeping quality;

(ii) to enhance taste;

(iii) to increase overrun.

(b) *Amount and quality.* Usually common salt is added at the rate

---

* Unwashed butter grains contain about 1.1–1.5 per cent curd, while normal washed butter has a curd content of 0.6–1.0 per cent

of 2 to 2.5 per cent of butterfat. The quality of salt should be good and it should be free from any extraneous matter and germs. Excessive salt damages the flavour of butter. The amount of salt added to butter in a churn is calculated as follows:

Problem. Fat in churn = 850 kg. Butter is to contain 2.0% salt. How much salt should be added to the churn (without loss of salt during working)?

Solution. Butter is to contain 2.0% salt. Assuming 80% fat in butter, the requirement of salt per 100 kg. fat

$$= \frac{2.0 \times 100}{80} = 2.5 \text{ kg.}$$

Hence the amount of salt to be added to the churn

$$= \frac{850 \times 2.5}{100} = 21.25 \text{ kg. } Ans.$$

(c) *Method of salting*

(i) *Dry salting.* Most common. Consists in adding the desired amount of dry salt (in instalments, if required) by sprinkling it over the surface of the butter during working.

(ii) *Wet salting.* The calculated amount of salt is wetted in the least amount of potable water and then sprinkled over the butter during working. Satisfactorily incorporates salt in the butter.

(iii) *Brine salting.* The salt is added in the form of a saturated solution of brine. Practicable when only light salting is required.

(d) *Specifications of butter salt.* See *IS: 1845*, 1961.

(i) *Screen test* (for particle size). It should be coarse grained and free from lumps. It should pass completely through an IS Sieve-85 (aperture 842 microns). The salt should not be used in powder/dust form, as this tends to lump on wetting and does not mix properly.

(ii) *Chemical purity.* 99.5 to 99.8 per cent sodium chloride in dry salt.

(iii) *Bacteriological purity.* Bacterial count less than 10/g.

(iv) *Solubility.* Complete.

(v) *Rate of solution.* High.

(vi) *Sediment.* Negligible.

Note: 1. Salt should be white in colour and free from any visible impurities.

2. Presence of traces of calcium and magnesium chlorides in salt causes it to moisten and cake. It should be stored in air-tight containers and in a dry atmosphere, away from

foreign odours such as kerosene, petrol etc., which it readily absorbs.

II. *Working.* This refers to the kneading of butter.

(a) *Object/purpose:*

(i) to completely dissolve, uniformly distribute and properly incorporate the salt;

(ii) to expel buttermilk an to control the moisture content of butter;

(iii) to fully incorporate the added make-up water in butter;

(iv) to bring the butter grains together into a compact mass for convenient handling and packaging.

Note: During working, the moisture in butter is reduced to droplets of microscopic size, which are mostly sterile.

(b) *Procedure.* The working should be continued until the butter has a compact body, a closely-knit grain, a tough waxy texture and an even distribution of salt and moisture. There should be no free moisture on the trier plug drawn from the butter. (Indicator paper develops coloured spots if free moisture is present.) Throughout the working process, the temperature should be controlled. Both over-working and under-working are harmful and should be avoided; the former damages the body and texture of butter, while the latter produces leaky butter. Working increases the air-content of butter. Normally-worked butter has an air-content of 0.5 to 10 ml. (average 4.0 ml.) per 100 g. of butter. The air-content of butter is important because it affects (i) the density of butter; (ii) its microbial spoilage; and (iii) its oxidative spoilage.

Note: 'Vacuum churns' have been developed for working butter under partial vacuum (0 to 68.5 cm. of mercury). The resultant butter is denser, more glossy in appearance and of closer texture. Working tends to reduce the intensity of the colour and flavour of butter.

III. *Moisture control.* The legal limit for the moisture content in butter in most countries is 16 per cent, although in others (including India today) it is 80 per cent fat. After the addition of salt, working is continued until the butter is 'dry'. A representative sample of butter is then taken and the 1st Moisture Test done. After calculation of the amount of 'make-up' water, it is added. Working is recontinued until make-up water is thoroughly incorporated and butter has the correct body. The moisture content in the finished butter is then checked. The rough formula for calculation of make-up water is:

$$W = \frac{F \times 1.5 \times (M - m)}{100}$$

where W = make-up water (kg.), F = fat in churn (kg.), M = final Moisture Test desired (%), and m = 1st Moisture Test (%).

(mm) *Packaging and storage*

I. *Packaging*

(a) *Removing butter from the churn.* This is done either manually, or by gravity, or by mechanical means, viz. by means of compressed air (3 to 5 psi). In the last case, the butter has to be soft.

(b) *Types of packs.* (i) *Bulk or wholesale*: in boxes, tubs, casks (NZ—56 lb.; US—63 lb.; Europe—50 kg.). (ii) *Retail*: 1, 2, 4, 8, 16 oz. or 25, 50, 100, 250, 500 g. pats; also in collapsible (metal) tubes.

(c) *Objects of packaging.* (i) To offer protection against contamination and damage (mutilation); (ii) to protect the butter against loss in weight and degradation (deterioration of flavour); (iii) to provide ease and safety of transport; (iv) to provide a convenient form of disposal; (v) to identify the contents and increase sales appeal, appearance, etc.

(d) *Packaging materials.* These include:

(i) *Wood or timber.* White Ash or Spruce, White Pine, Firkin Teakwood, etc.

(ii) *Parchment paper/substitutes.* Vegetable parchment paper/butterpaper; cellophane; pliofilm; polythene; etc.

(iii) *Aluminium foil/laminates.* Moisture and greaseproof; non-tainting and non-toxic; opaque; air-tight; etc.

(iv) *Tin-plate cans.* Advantageous in tropical countries not only in preventing melted butter from escaping in hot weather but also in preventing absorption of foreign flavours.

(e) *Technique of packaging*

(i) *Hand moulding and wrapping.* Slow and cumbersome.

(ii) *Mechanical moulding, patting and wrapping.* Reduces labour costs and losses; suitable for large-scale operations; etc.

Note: (i) The standard butter packaging machines are either semi-automatic or fully automatic. The well-known brands are: Benhill and Kustner (both German), and SIG (Swiss). The weight of the packaged butter pats should be checked regularly as they come out of the machine.

(ii) Vacuum packaging of butter in tin cans does not significantly improve its keeping quality, because the oxygen enclosed in the butter or dissolved in the fat is only partially removed.

(iii) 'Canned butter' is not sterile.

II. *Storage.* The temperature of commercial cold storage of butter ranges from $-23°C$ to $-29°C$ ($-10°F$ to $-20°F$). There is invariably some flavour deterioration of butter while it is in commercial cold storage. Thus, a fishy flavour develops in salted-acid-butter. Bacterial deterioration plays a negligible part, while chemical degradation plays a leading one.

III. *Shrinkage of stored patted butter.* Shrinkage refers to loss in weight and is caused mainly by evaporation of moisture from the butter pat. Butter packs must contain the correct weight of butter when sold to the consumer. In the patting of butter, allowance must be made for possible shrinkage of the wrapped butter pat. The extent of shrinkage depends on:

(i) *Type of wrapper.* Moistureproof/greaseproof wrappers cause less shrinkage than other types.

(ii) *Condition of moisture in butter.* The greater the quantity of 'free' moisture in butter, the greater the shrinkage, and vice versa.

(iii) *Size of pat.* The smaller the pat, the greater the shrinkage, and vice versa.

(iv) *Temperature of storage.* The higher the temperature, the greater the shrinkage, and vice versa.

(v) *Relative humidity of storage air.* The higher the humidity, the lower the shrinkage, and vice versa. (However, high humidity favours mould growth and is therefore avoided.)

(vi) *Period of storage.* The longer the period, the greater the shrinkage, and vice versa.

IV. *Keeping quality of stored butter.* The factors affecting this are:

(i) *Temperature of storage.* The higher the temperature, the lower the keeping quality, and vice versa.

(ii) *Copper and iron content of butter*

(iii) *Salt content of butter*

(iv) *Acidity content of butter*

(v) *Curd content of butter* (with poor quality cream)

(vi) *Air (oxygen) content of butter*

} The higher the content, the lower the keeping quality, and vice versa.

(vii) *Raw or pasteurized cream.* Pasteurization of cream increases the keeping quality of butter.

(viii) *Method of packaging.* Sanitized high quality packing materials and sanitary methods of packaging increase keeping quality, and vice versa.

(ix) *Exposure to light.* Lowers keeping quality.

Note. Sweet cream/unsalted butter has the maximum, and acid cream/salted butter the minimum keeping quality under commercial cold storage. Individually, both acid and salt improve keeping quality.

4.8 Distribution

This is usually done from the butter factory to the wholesaler in the original bulk package and to the retailer in wrapped pats in cartons/boxes or tin cans. The temperature during the entire period of distribution should preferably be at $-18°C$ to $-29°C$ (0 to 20°F). It may also be sold in retail trade from a deep freeze/refrigerated butter box.

4.9 Overrun

(a) *Introduction.* The weight of butter obtained from a given lot of cream exceeds the amount of fat in the cream. That amount of butter which exceeds the fat present in cream is called overrun.

(b) *Definition.* Overrun may be defined as the increase in the amount of butter made from a given amount of fat. It is usually expressed as a percentage.

(c) *Cause.* Overrun is caused by the presence (in addition to that of fat) of moisture, curd, salt, etc. in butter.

(d) *Importance.* It is a source of profit to the butter-maker (economical aspect); and also helps to check the efficiency of factory operations (technical aspect).

(e) *Types*

(i) *Theoretical(Pencil).* Maximum obtainable, viz. 25* per cent.

*Since the minimum legal fat content of butter is 80 per cent, the maximum amount of butter that can be made from 100 kg. of fat is: $(100/80) \times 100 = 125$ kg. This gives an overrun of 25 per cent, which, however, is not obtainable in actual practice

(ii) *Composition.* Based on composition of finished butter.

(iii) *Actual.* On the basis of fat actually bought and butter made therefrom.

(iv) *Factory.* On the basis of total butter recorded as packed for sale and fat recorded as received.

(v) *Churn.* For any particular churning.

(f) *Factors influencing overrun.* These are: inaccuracy in weight or fat test of milk, cream or butter; fat losses in skim milk or buttermilk; mechanical fat losses; unavoidable fluctuations in the fat content of butter; weight allowance in butter packs or cream or butter; handling losses, etc.

(g) *Formula*

$$\% \text{ OR} = \frac{B - F}{F} \times 100,$$

where

OR = overrun in butter (usually expressed as a percentage)
B = butter made (kg.)
F = fat in churn (kg.).

(h) *Overrun in a whole milk creamery*

(j) *Problem.* 10,000 kg. of 7% milk is received; 40% cream is separated; skim milk tests 0.1%; (unwatered) buttermilk tests 0.5%; amount of buttermilk = kg. cream − 1.20 × fat in cream; miscellaneous fat losses are 0.5% of total fat received in whole milk; butter contains 80.5% fat; weight allowance is 10 g. for 1 kg. pack. How much butter is packed for sale? What is the percentage overrun?

Solution. Butterfat bought $= 10,000 \times \frac{7}{100} = 700$ kg.

Skim milk separated $= 10,000 \times \frac{40 - 7}{40 - 0.1} = 8270.7$ kg.

Cream separated $= 10,000 - 8270.7 = 1729.3$ kg.

Fat lost in skim milk $= 8270.7 \times \frac{0.1}{100} = 8.3$ kg.

Fat in cream $= 700 - 8.3 = 691.7$ kg.

Buttermilk recovered $= 1729.3 - (691.7 \times 1.20)$
$= 899.3$ kg.

Fat lost in buttermilk $= 899.3 \times \frac{0.5}{100} = 4.5$ kg.

Miscellaneous losses $= 700 \times \frac{0.5}{100} = 3.5$ kg.

Fat in finished butter $= 691.7 - (4.5 + 3.5)$
$= 683.7$ kg.

$$\text{Butter manufactured} = 683.7 \times \frac{100}{80.5} = 849.3 \text{ kg.}$$

$$\text{Butter packed for sale} = 849.3 \times \frac{1000}{1010}$$

$$= 840.9 \text{ kg. } Ans.$$

$$\text{Percentage overrun} = \frac{840.9 - 700}{700} \times 100$$

$$= 20.1. \ Ans.$$

4.10 Yield

This is calculated by the formula:

$$Y = \frac{F \times (100 + \% \text{ OR})}{100},$$

where

Y = yield of butter (kg.)

F = fat content of cream (kg.)

% OR = percentage overrun in butter (Ave. 20–22).

Note: Under Indian conditions, assuming the percentage overrun to be 20, $Y = F \times 1.20$.

4.11 Theories of churning

There are three main theories on the churning of cream into butter, viz., Fisher and Hooker's Phase-Reversal Theory, Rahn's Foam Theory, and King's Modern Theory.

(a) *Fisher and Hooker's Phase-Reversal Theory (1917)*. According to this theory, churning is a process of phase reversal, i.e. changing an oil-in-water type emulsion (such as cream) to a water-in-oil type emulsion (such as butter). Agitation of cream in the churning process causes coalescence and clumping of fat globules until eventually the ratio of the surface area to the volume of fat units becomes so small that it can no longer contain all the buttermilk in stable form. The fat-in-water emulsion then suddenly breaks, yielding butter grains (consisting of an emulsion of water-in-butterfat) and free buttermilk.

Drawback. Butter is not a true water-in-fat emulsion. Microscopic studies reveal that a proportion of fat globules in butter are still intact in the worked butter.

(b) *Rahn's Foam Theory*. According to this theory, the presence of foam/froth is essential for churning. It also postulates that there is a 'foam-producing' substance present in cream (and milk) which gradually solidifies as the cream or milk is agitated. Foam is created during the churning period. The fat globules, due to surface tension effects, tend to concentrate and clump on the foam bubbles. The foam-producing substance assumes a solid character and the foam collapses. The fat globules then coalesce and butter is formed.

Drawback. Foam formation (i.e. the presence of air) is not required in some continuous butter-making processes.

(c) *King's Modern Theory*. According to this theory, the true explanation of what takes place during churning appears to lie midway between the first two theories. The modern conception of the mechanism of the churning process may be summarized as follows:

(i) In cooled cream at churning temperature, the fat is present as clusters (clumps) of fat globules; and within each globule it is present partly in solid and partly in liquid form.

(ii) Churning breaks up the clusters and causes foam/froth formation. The globules become concentrated to some extent in the film around the air bubbles in the foam and are thus brought into close contact with each other.

(iii) The movement of the globules over one another in the foam film and the direct concussion between them causes a gradual wearing away of the emulsion-protecting surface layer of the phospholipid-protein complex. The globules then adhere together to form larger and larger particles. Eventually these particles become visible as butter grains (granules). As the granules form, they enclose some of the air from the foam. The fat in the granules is still mainly in globular form.

(iv) The working of butter grains causes the globules to move over one another. Under the effect of friction and pressure, some of them yield up a portion of the liquid fat. Others are broken up during working. Finally there is enough free liquid fat present to enclose all the water droplets, air bubbles and intact fat globules.

4.12 History and Development of the Butter Churn

(a) *Early history*. The modern butter churn is the culmination of a long period of development in churn construction. The main purpose of the churn is to agitate the cream. This has been achieved over the years through the following basic designs:

(i) *Swinging churns.* The cream moves backwards and forwards in a horizontal plane. There are internal diaphragms in the churn to obstruct the flow of cream to some extent and thus to increase the intensity of agitation.

(ii) *Rotating churns.* These are either barrel or alfa churns. Barrel churns are of many types. Modern factory churns (wooden or metal) have been developed from rotating barrel churns.

(iii) *Dash churns.* In these, the cream-holding vessel is stationary, while the agitator or dasher (plunger, disc or rotating blade) is mobile.

Note: The Indian indigenous churn is a dash churn.

(b) *Later developments*

(i) *Combined-churn-and-butter-worker.* Early factory churns only churned the cream into butter; the working was done separately on circular/rectangular worker tables. The combined-churn-and-butter-worker was developed so that butter could be worked within the churn itself; the workers were installed on a trolley, which was pushed into the churn from either one of its ends or sides.

(ii) *Roller-less (roll-less) churns.* In these wooden churns, the working was effected without the aid of rollers, which were found to be unsanitary. Vanes were fixed to vane churns, to help in the churning and the working of butter.

(iii) *Modern metal churns.* These have been developed mainly in Denmark and the USA. The usual shapes are cylindrical, cubical or conical. The metal used for the product-contact surface is either stainless steel or aluminium alloy. The internal shape is so designed that working is effected by the rolling action of the butter.

(c) *Merits and demerits of metal churns*

(i) *Merits.* (i) Cleaned easily with alkali detergents; (ii) steam sterilization possible without damage to the churn body; (iii) moisture and salt control are more accurate; (iv) intermittent use without deterioration possible; (v) much more sanitary.

(ii) *Demerit.* Low heat-insulating capacity makes temperature control of churning rather difficult. (Obviated by use of air-conditioned butter-making room and/or provision of chilled water spray during churning and working).

4.13 Fat losses in butter-making

These are given in Table 4.3.

TABLE 4.3

Fat losses during various stages of creamery butter-making

Category of fat loss	Factors which cause fat loss	Percentage of total fat lost
Separation of milk	Conditions and operation of cream separator; condition of milk.	0.10
Spillage of cream	Residue of cream in cans; leaky valves, joints, pipelines; accidental spillage of cream.	0.20 to 0.50
Churning process	Richness of cream, size of fat globules; acidity of cream, neutralization; physical properties of butterfat; ageing of cream; churning time; addition of breakwater; type of churn; granule size, temperature of churning; etc.	1.20 (40% cream) to 2.37 (20% cream)
Mechanical losses in butter	Remnants of butter in churn; packing and printing equipment; soiled butter; shrinkage of butter.	0.20 to 0.50
	Total	1.70 to 3.47

SOURCE: *The Butter Maker's Manual* by McDowall (1953).

4.14 Continuous Buttermaking

(a) *Introduction.* From about 1890, the possibility of producing butter by a continuous process so as to avoid the disadvantages of the batch process, was studied by many research workers, and several prototype machines were built. While useful theories were tried out, none of the above machines could be applied commercially due to problems caused by operation at the separating temperatures, excessively high butter moisture, unsatisfactory drainage of buttermilk and clogging due to the use of acid cream. It was found difficult to ensure that the severe agitation treated alike every particle of cream. Interest subsided before World War I (1914–18) and little progress was made until 1932, when high-fat cream by the re-separation of normal cream was developed. Attempts towards continuous buttermaking were renewed during 1930–40 in Australia, 1937 in Sweden, and during World War II (1935–45) in Germany and the United States. A number of different systems have now been developed for regular commercial use. Whether these continuous processes will ultimately completely replace the conventional batch system of churning for large-scale production of butter is still an open question. Whatever the final outcome, it is apparent that the transition will be slow, because of: (i) the time required to re-equip the butter factories; and (ii) the cost involved in discarding equipment that may have only partly worn out.

(b) *Advantages.* (i) More economical—due to: lower capital cost, lower running cost (reduced power, labour, refrigeration, steam, detergent, etc.), reduced floor space, no expensive foundations to prepare, no time loss for fat crystallization, less butter wastage, etc.; (ii) more hygienic due to its being a closed system, free from air-borne contamination (so that finished butter has a greater shelf-life).

(c) *Disadvantages.* (i) Lack of uniformity in the quality of butter during the day (unless cream is bulked before conversion into butter); (ii) difficulty in selection of sample package for grading and analysis (due to fluctuation in the quality of butter as indicated above).

(d) *Basic principle.* The continuous methods of butter production developed since 1935 may be divided into three main groups:

(i) *Group I: The churning process.* (Such as Fritz; similar ones are Westfalia, Paasch and Silkeborg, and Contimab.) This involves the use of high-speed beaters to destabilize the fat emulsion in the chilled cream, and thus cause the formation of grains of butter in a matter of seconds. The buttermilk is drained away and the resulting grains worked in a kneading section prior to extrusion.

(ii) *Group II: The concentration and phase reversal process.* (Such as Alfa-Laval and Meleshin). This involves a system whereby cream of 30–40 per cent fat is concentrated in a special cream separator to 80–82 per cent fat. After standardization, the concentrated cream or 'butter mix' is subjected to combined cooling and mechanical action which causes phase reversal and the formation of butter, followed by its expulsion from the machine.

(iii) *Group III: The emulsification process.* (Such as Creamery Package and Cherry Burrell). This again involves the concentration of 30–40 per cent cream. During concentration, the emulsion is broken and the fat, water and salt content are standardized. This is followed by re-emulsification, cooling, working and finally extrusion.

Note: In making a study of methods of continuous manufacture, the following points require consideration: treatment of the cream, control of butterfat losses, control of moisture and salt and curd content, capital involved in relation to throughput, labour charges, the effect of the process on the finished product, overall economics of the process, etc. Most European countries and Australia have concentrated their research and development on the churning process; the USSR has followed the process of high fat separation; and the USA has utilized the principle of re-emulsification of a standardized fat mixture.

(e) *Methods*. One process in each group has been described below:

(i) *Group I: Fritz process*. The milk is pumped from the receiving vats to a separator from which cream of 45–50 per cent is obtained. The cream is pasteurized to 95°C (203°F)/No hold, cooled to 6–10°C (43–50°F) and held for some hours (or overnight) in a storage vat/tank. Next, it is pumped into a small control container which maintains the flow of cream at a constant pressure and adjustable rate. The cream is then passed into a small water-jacketed cylinder (about 25 cm. long and 25 cm. in diameter) which is kept cool by circulating cold water in the jacket. High-speed vanes in this cylinder churn the cream into butter in 1–2 seconds. The buttermilk and butter granules drop into an inclined section fitted with 2 spiral screws about 45 cm. long and 15 cm. in diameter, which rotate in opposite directions. Here the buttermilk runs off and butter is forced through a perforated plate from the farther side of which it is removed by rotating blades. It emerges as a ribbon 7.5 cm. × 3.7 cm. in cross-section, which can be bulk-packed directly, or cut and wrapped into retail sized pats. (A machine of modified design* called Westfalia Buttermatic was later developed and enables accurate moisture control below 16 per cent. It also permits the working and salting of butter. Working is effected by a series of

---

* Others of similar type are Contimab (French) and Paasch and Silkeborg Buttermaker (Danish).

screws, a perforated plate and spinners. It is salted with micro-fined salt by the injection of a 50/50 salt/water slurry in the butter early in the working stage.)

(ii) *Group II: Alfa-Laval*† *Process.* The milk is pre-heated to 45–50°C (113–122°F) and passed on to a hermetic Alfa-Laval separator to produce cream with a 25–35 per cent fat content. This cream is then pasteurized in a vacreator/plate pasteurizer at a temperature of up to 95°C (203°F) in a special cream separator to the fat content desired in the butter. In a small standardizing vat/tank, the calculated amount of salt, colour, water or skim milk can be added to allow for the adjustment of the composition of butter. The 'plastic' cream is then pumped through the transmutator where it changes from cream to butter. The transmutator consists of three jacketed stainless steel cylinders (each about 180 cm. long and 30 cm. in diameter) inside each of which rotates a stainless steel drum fitted with raised spiral strips. Brine circulates in the jackets at variable temperatures. Phase inversion starts in the first cylinder and is actually completed in the second one. The butter leaves the third cylinder in a semi-fluid form and is packaged immediately. Solidification takes place at once and is completed in the cold store.

(iii) *Group III: Cherry Burrell's process.* The cream is pumped from the receiving vats, through an agitating heater to destabilize the emulsion, and then directly to the centrifugal separator which concentrates the cream at up to 86–90 per cent fat, and breaks the emulsion. An automatic desludging type separator is used. Next, the butter fat containing dispersed serum is pasteurized in a vacreator, cooled to 43–46°C (110–115°F) and passed into standardizing vats. The standardization of acidity, moisture and salt content is an intermittent process. After standardization, the 'butter' mix is pumped through a chiller resembling an ice cream freezer and cooled to 5°C (40°F). It then passes through a texturator which crystallizes the fat more completely and later works the butter slightly by making it flow through a perforated plate. The butter emerges through a mouth-piece into a packing machine or bulk container. The whole process takes about half an hour.

(f) *Concluding remarks.* It has been widely reported that continuous-process butter has a better appearance, finer texture, lower

---

† The Alfa process was developed simultaneously in both Germany and Sweden. Subsequently the German process retained the name of Alfa while the Swedish one was changed to Alfa-Laval.

bacterial count and better keeping quality than conventional churned butter; the former is also said to be coliform free. It is, therefore, believed that continuous butter-making machines have come to stay. The change from batch to continuous butter making has been making slow but steady progress throughout the world.

4.15 Judging and grading of table butter

A. *Score card*. This is given in Table 4.4.

TABLE 4.4
Score card of table butter (ADSA)

Items	Perfect Score
Flavour	45
Body and Texture	30
Colour	10
Salt	10
Package	5
Total	100

Note: The scores of commercial grades of creamery (table) butter are:

Butter scoring 93 points	AA grade
–do–	92	–do–	A grade
–do–	90	–do–	B grade
–do–	89	–do–	C grade

B. *Procedure of examination*

(a) *Some requirements for judging*

(i) *Condition of judging room*. The butter judging room should be clean and well-ventilated. The temperature should be at about 16°C (60°F). There should be no foreign odours either within the room or nearby. There should be plenty of light for inspection of colour.

(ii) *Tempering of butter*. Cold butter should be kept in the judging room sufficiently in advance of the judging so as to bring it to the correct temperature (16°C). This is called 'tempering' the butter.

(b) *Sampling*. The sample plug is taken by a butter trier which is inserted in the block of butter diagonally near the centre, turned one-half of the way and then withdrawn.

(c) *Sequence of observations*. Immediately after withdrawing the plug, pass the trier slowly under the nose, inhale through the nose very slowly and notice the odour or aroma present. Then examine the colour for uniformity throughout. Next, examine the body and texture by pressing the ball of the thumb against the sides of the plug until it shows a break. Observe the presence or absence of free moisture or 'beads' of water and their clarity, and also the nature of the break. Then break off about 2–3 cm. at the end of the plug and put it into the mouth. Chew it until melted, then roll the melted butter about in the mouth until it reaches body temperature. Meanwhile examine for undissolved salt and the manner in which butter melts. Notice also the various sensations of taste and smell. Expectorate the sample and observe the after-taste.

Note. Rinse the mouth frequently with one per cent lukewarm saline water, preferably after judging each sample.

C. *Requirements of high grade butter*

The package should be neat, clean and tidy in appearance, and should have a good finish. The salt should have dissolved properly. The colour should be uniform throughout. The body should be firm and waxy, and its texture close-knit. The desired flavour is mildly sweet, clean and pleasant.

D. *Flavour defects that cause butter to be classified as 'No grade'*.
These are:

(a) *Chemical*. Chlorine smell (due to chlorine left inadvertently in butter churn, etc.).

(b) *Foreign*. Petrol, kerosene, fly spray, etc. (Cream or butter in an open vessel absorbs such flavours readily.)

(c) *Paint or varnish*. Absorption of paint or varnish smells (due to exposure or contact of the same with butter).

(d) *Surface taint or limburger*. A very serious flavour defect, resembling limburger cheese. (Caused by activity of proteolytic bacteria in the presence of low-acid-and-salt in butter.)

4.16 Defects in Butter, Their Causes and Prevention

Defects in butter may arise due to low quality milk or cream, and faulty methods of manufacture and storage of butter. The common defects in butter, their causes and prevention are given in Table 4.5.

TABLE 4.5

Defects in butter, their causes and prevention

Name of defect	Causes	Prevention
(a) Flavour		
Acid/High-acid/Sour	(i) Using acid (sour) cream (ii) Under-neutralization of cream.	(i) Using sweet cream (ii) Optimum neutralization of cream.
Alkaline/Neutralizer	Over-neutralization of cream.	Optimum neutralization of cream.
Bitter	(i) Intake of bitter-weeds by milch animals (ii) Lipase activity during (raw) cream separation (iii) Growth of proteolytic bacteria in cream.	(i) Eradication of offending weeds (ii) Checking lipase activity by avoiding the 'danger zone' (100–120°F) during raw cream separation (iii) Storage of cream at 5°C (40°F) or below to check bacterial growth.
Cheesy	Growth of proteolytic bacteria leading to casein break down.	Storage of cream at 5°C (40°F) or below to check bacterial growth.
Cooked	Over-heating of cream during pasteurization.	Optimum heating of cream during pasteurization.
	Note: Cooked flavour is less objectionable nowadays.	
Feed and weed	Feeding of milk-tainting feeds and weeds within three hours before milking.	(i) Feeding of milk-tainting feeds and weeds soon after milking (ii) Eradication of milk-tainting weeds (iii) Vacuum pasteurization of cream.
Fishy	High-acid salted butter in the presence of appreciable amounts of copper and/or iron content (under commercial cold storage conditions).	Unsalted sweet-cream butter (under commercial cold storage conditions).

Name of defect	Causes	Prevention
Flat	(i) Low diacetyl content in butter	(i) Adequate ripening of cream before churning
	(ii) Low salt content in butter	(ii) Correct salt content in butter
	(iii) Excessive washing of butter.	(iii) Optimum washing of butter.
Rancid	Fat hydrolysis due to lipase action in milk or cream.	Inactivating lipase by proper pasteurization of milk or cream.
Oxidized/oily/ metallic/ tallowy	Fat oxidization due to direct contact of milk/cream/butter with copper or iron, exposure of these products to sunlight, etc.	(i) Storage of milk/cream/butter in properly tinned or aluminium alloy or stainless steel vessels
		(ii) Vacuum pasteurization of cream.
Stale	(i) Cream of poor quality held too long before churning	(i) Avoiding long storage of cream during churning
	(ii) Butter stored at insufficiently low temperatures for long periods.	(ii) Correct temperature for storage of butter.
Yeasty	Using old, yeasty cream for churning.	Using fresh, sweet cream for churning.
(b) *Body and Texture*		
Crumbly	(i) Underworking of butter	(i) Adequate working of butter
	(ii) Seasonal changes in fat composition	(ii) Controlled cooling, ageing, churning and washing temperatures
	(ii) Sudden chilling of butter soon after production.	(iii) Avoiding shock-cooling of butter soon after production.
Greasy	(i) Overworking of butter	(i) Adequate working of butter
	(ii) Excessively high temperature of wash water.	(ii) Correct wash water temperature.
Gummy	High proportion of high melting point fats.	Avoiding feeds containing high melting point fats.
Leaky	(i) Underworking of butter	(i) Adequate working of butter

Name of defect	Causes	Prevention
	(ii) Excessively high churning temperature of cream	(ii) Correct churning temperature of cream
	(iii) Overchurning of butter	(iii) Optimum churning of butter
	(iv) Incorrect cooling and ageing of cream	(iv) Correct cooling and ageing of butter
	(v) Excessively high temperature of wash water.	(v) Correct temperature of wash water.
Mealy/Grainy	(i) Incorrect neutralization of high-acid cream with lime	(i) Correct neutralization of high-acid cream with lime
	(ii) 'Oiling off' of fat during butter making.	(ii) Avoiding 'oiling off' of fat during butter making.
Spongy/Weak	(i) Inadequate cooling and ageing of cream	(i) Adequate cooling and ageing of cream
	(ii) Churning cream at too high a temperature	(ii) Churning cream at optimum temperature
	(iii) High proportion of low melting point fats.	(iii) Adjusting churning conditions (to take care of high proportion of low melting point fats).
Sticky	Overworking of (crumbly) butter.	Adequate working of butter.
Gritty	(i) Undissolved coarse salt in butter	(i) Proper grinding of salt
	(ii) Incorrect salting of butter.	(ii) Correct salting of butter.
(c) *Colour*		
Mottled	(i) Inadequate washing of butter grains	(i) Adequate washing of butter grains
	(ii) Improper incorporation of salt in butter	(ii) Proper incorporation of salt in butter
	(iii) Inadequate working of butter.	(iii) Adequate working of butter.
Streaky/Wavy	(i) Uneven working of butter	(i) Even working of butter
	(ii) Incomplete working of two or more lots of butter.	(ii) Complete working of two or more lots of butter.
Dull/Pale	Overworking of butter.	Adequate working of butter.

4.17 Uses of Butter

(i) Direct consumption with bread;
(ii) in the preparation of sauces;
(iii) as a cooking medium;
(iv) in the baking and confectionary industries;
(v) in the manufacture of ice cream, butteroil and ghee (India).

5 BUTTEROIL

5.1 Introduction

Conversion of butter or cream into butteroil is a convenient method for the preservation of fat in the absence of refrigerated storage.

5.2 Definition

Butteroil refers to the fat-concentrate obtained mainly from butter or cream by the removal of practically all the water and solids-not-fat content. The terms milk fat, anhydrous milk fat, dry butter fat and dehydrated butter fat are used synonymously with butteroil, but the raw material for their preparation is usually cream.

5.3 Composition

This may be as given in Table 5.1.

TABLE 5.1
Chemical composition of butteroil

Constituent	Percentage
Butter fat	99.5 to 99.8
Moisture	0.1 to 0.3
Acidity (oleic)	0.2 to 0.5
Peroxide value	0.0 to 0.1

SOURCE: *The Butter Maker's Manual* by Mc-Dowall (1953).

Note: The United States Army Quartermaster Corps' specifications for butteroil are as given below:

Fat	Not less than	99.8 per cent
Moisture ...	Not more than	0.1 –do–
Free fatty acids (oleic)	Not more than	0.5 –do–

Copper content ... Not more than 0.25 per cent

Peroxide value ... 0

5.4 Food and Nutritive Value

Butteroil is the richest source of milk fat amongst western dairy products and is also expected to be high in fat-soluble vitamins A and D.

5.5 Methods of Manufacture

These are:
(a) *Direct evaporation*:
 (i) at atmospheric pressure
 (ii) under vacuum
(b) *Decantation*
(c) *Centrifugation followed by vacuum drying*
(d) *Direct from cream by de-emulsification and centrifugation.*

Note: The first three methods use butter as raw material.

(a) *Direct evaporation.* This is a batch process and may be carried out either at atmospheric pressure or under vacuum. The former resembles the Indian method of ghee production. Butter is placed in a large open vat/pan which can be heated through a steam jacket or coil. At first the heat is applied slowly till the butter melts. The temperature is then gradually raised, and the butter stirred, usually to 108–110°C (226–230°F). When all the moisture has evaporated, the residual butter fat is drained from the curd and filtered. The product obtained (butteroil) has a somewhat darker colour when compared with other methods; it has also got a cooked flavour. Direct evaporation under vacuum does not yield much advantage, either in the efficiency of production or in the quality of the finished product.

(b) *Decantation.* This is also a batch process. The butter is melted and allowed to stand undisturbed for sufficient time, until it stratifies into three layers, viz., top-scum, middle-fat and bottom-serum. The fat layer is drawn off from the top and cooled. A clean separation cannot be obtained by this process and fat recovery is low. As such this method is uneconomic, especially when employed on a large scale.

(c) *Centrifugal separation followed by vacuum drying.* This is a more or less continuous method and yields a high quality product. Different variants of this process have been used in many countries for large-scale production of butteroil from butter. A typical method has been described below.

(i) *Flow diagram of manufacture*

Receiving (unsalted) butter
|
Melting
|
Tipping in tank
|
Oil separator
|
Float-controlled balance tank
|
Vacuum pan
|
Butteroil receiving kettle
|
Packaging
|
Storage (Room Temp.)

(ii) *Details of manufacture.* Butter (unsalted) is dumped in the butter melter, which is a vertical jacketed stainless steel cylindrical tank fitted with an agitator (provided with reduction gear to work on variable speeds). If the butter is very cold and hard, it should be cut into small pieces before heating. Then a steam inlet to the jacket is opened and the agitator run at low speed.

The tipping tank, which is jacketed at the bottom, is filled with clean water and heated to 77–79°C (170–174°F) by opening the steam inlet of the jacket. The centrifugal oil separator is then started and when it has attained full speed, the hot water from the tipping tank is run into it. When the water has completely run out, the discharge valve of the butter melter is gradually opened to allow the melt to enter into the oil separator. The rate of flow of the melt is so regulated as to avoid overflow. The melt is now separated into oil and serum.

The oil flows into the float-controlled balance tank and thence into the vacuum pan due to suction. Here it is dehydrated at 56–62°C (133–145°F) under a vacuum of 57–62 cm. of mercury. At the end of the operation, the vacuum is broken and butteroil allowed to flow by gravity into the receiving kettle for subsequent cooling, packaging and storage at room temperature.

(d) *Directly from cream by de-emulsification and centrifugal separation.* This process utilizes the principle of de-emulsification of cream used in various continuous butter-making processes. De-emulsified fat may then be melted and clarified by centrifuging and vacuum heating. However, the direct production of anhydrous milk fat from cream has yet to achieve significant commercial application.

5.6 Cooling

This is an important aspect. Butteroil should be cooled and crystallized under careful control, so as to form a large number of fine crystals. The desired result may be obtained by rapidly super-cooling (to 13–18°C) and stirring the mass during forced crystallization (by adding 5–15 per cent of finely crystalline fat from a previous batch); this yields a smooth homogeneous mass which does not separate into solid and liquid layers on standing.

5.7 Packaging, storage and distribution

(a) *Packaging.* When packaging butteroil, care should be taken to exclude oxygen. Thus, it is important to avoid re-aeration of the product as it comes out of the vacuum dehydrator in a partially or a completely de-aerated form. Care should also be taken to leave a minimum of air in the head-space of the container, or to replace the air in the head-space with an inert gas. In tropical countries, allowance must be made for expansion of the product in deciding upon the size of the container to use. While filling, the fat should run into the bottom of the container in such a way as to avoid contact with the air. Tin cans are satisfactory for both bulk and retail packaging. Wooden casks and tubs with suitable liners (butter-paper or plastic film) may be used. Cardboard containers, waxed or plastic-coated, can also serve the purpose.

Note: The cans should preferably be lacquered on the inside surface with 'food enamel' in order to prevent corrosion.

(b) *Storage.* Under atmospheric conditions, dehydrated butter fat develops a perceptible oxidized flavour in the course of a month. Use of anti-oxidant ethyl gallate in a concentration of 0.05 per cent increases its shelf life to 3 months. Alternatively, packing the product in a 1-kg. container under 50 cm. vacuum prior to sealing, ensures satisfactory storage quality.

(c) *Distribution*. This is done in the original packing under atmospheric conditions.

5.8 Market quality

(a) *Physical quality*. The colour of butteroil prepared from cow milk is deep yellow, while that produced from buffalo milk is white when solid, and colourless when liquid. The product from both cow and buffalo milk has a raw (bland) or slightly cooked (caramelized) flavour, depending on the quality of the raw material and the method of production. The texture of the product, when no special conditions for cooling are adopted, is pasty.

(b) *Chemical quality*. See 5.3.

5.9 Keeping quality

(a) *Introduction*. Butter fat free from suspended moisture is immune to microbial attack; but when more than 0.3 per cent of water is present, mould growth can develop and cause a musty. rancid flavour in the fat. If the butter fat is water-free, the only deterioration to which it is readily subject is oxidation, development of a tallowy flavour and, frequently, bleaching of the colour. Butteroil is more susceptible to oxidative deterioration than butter, because portions of the anti-oxidants present in the butter, e.g. the phospholipid-protein complex, are lost in the butter serum. High grade dry butter fat will retain its quality for at least 6–12 months if properly packed and stored.

(b) *Influencing factors*. The resistance of fat to oxidation, i.e. its keeping quality, will depend on:

(i) *The copper and iron content*. These hasten the absorption of oxygen by fat, leading to the development of an oxidized flavour. A good sample of dry butter fat should have a copper content of not more than 0.02–0.03 p.p.m. and iron content of not more than 0.10 p.p.m. (All butteroil-making equipment should preferably be of stainless steel; alternatively, copper and iron vessels should be well-tinned.)

(ii) *Amount of air present*. Fat dissolves oxygen from air and the dissolved oxygen is only slowly removed from the fat. Vacuumizing and gas-packing help increase the keeping quality of the product. Fat, with oxygen content of less than 0.5 p.p.m. and stored in nitrogen, has been found to have good keeping quality.

(iii) *The holding temperature.* Within the normal range of variation of atmospheric shade temperatures, this does not greatly influence the keeping quality of anhydrous milk fat which has been properly de-aerated and sealed from contact with air and light; but there is some increase in the speed of oxidation with rise in temperature, and the product is best kept in cold storage (5–10°C).

(iv) *Absence of light.* Fat readily bleaches and goes tallowy if exposed to light, especially bright sunlight. Light accelerates the effect of copper and iron contamination in causing tallowiness.

(v) *Heat-treatment during extraction.* Dry butter fat obtained by a direct evaporation process has a keeping quality under open storage superior to that obtained by decantation or by centrifugal extraction. This is due to the retention in the butter fat of a portion of the anti-oxidant phospholipid. Some heat-treatment of the butter fat during its production is necessary for the destruction of lipase.

(vi) *Initial quality of butter fat.* The best butter fat for long storage is made from sweet cream butter.

5.10 Anti-oxidants as Preservatives

Anti-oxidants are substances which prevent or delay the development of an oxidized flavour in fat, when added. It appears that they themselves undergo oxidation and are, therefore, able to break the chain reaction which occurs during fat oxidation. The natural anti-oxidants of butter fat (such as lecithin) are retained by the direct evaporation process. The resistance of butteroil to oxidation can be improved by the addition of synthetic anti-oxidants, some of which are mentioned below:

(i) Nordihydroguiaretic acid (NDGA)—0.01 to 0.05 per cent

(ii) Ethyl gallate—0.005 to 0.01 per cent

(iii) Hydroquinone—0.01 to 0.10 per cent.

Note: The use of anti-oxidants is not permitted under the Food and Health Regulations of many countries. In India, the permitted anti-oxidant is Butylated Hydroxy Anisole (BHA). It can be added @ 0.02 per cent to ghee and butter and @ 0.01 per cent to whole milk powder and partly skim milk powder (by weight of the finished product).

5.11 Judging and Grading of Butteroil

(a) *Score card.* A tentative score card has been suggested in Table 5.1.

TABLE 5.1

Score card for butteroil

Items	Perfect score
Flavour	45
Texture	25
Acidity (oleic)	15
Colour	10
Package	5
Total	100

(b) *Procedure for examination and scoring.* Examine the container for cleanliness, and in the case of tin-containers also determine whether they are rust-free on the outside and inside when emptied. Open the container and examine aroma and colour. Then pour a small sample and observe the texture. Put a few drops in the mouth and note the taste. Determine percentage acidity (oleic), moisture and peroxide value.

(c) *Requirements of high grade butteroil.* The package should be clean and bright on the outside and rust-free inside. The product should have a deep yellow colour for cow fat and a white colour with a greenish tinge for buffalo fat, a fine crystalline (pasty) texture, a characteristic bland smell and a butter-like pleasant taste.

5.12 Defects in Butteroil, Their Causes and Prevention

Defects in butteroil may arise due to low quality milk or cream or butter, and faulty methods of production, processing and storage of butteroil. The common defects in butteroil, their causes and prevention are given in Table 5.2.

TABLE 5.2

Defects in butteroil, their causes and prevention

Name of defect	Causes	Prevention
Brownish colour	Presence of over-heated fine curd particles due to improper filtration in direct evaporation methods.	Adopting clarification-cum-vacuum method of production.
Coarse texture	Slow rate of cooling after production.	Fast rate of cooling after production.
Rancid flavour	Fat hydrolysis due to lipase action in milk/cream/butter.	Inactivating lipase by correct pasteurization of milk or cream.
Oxidised/oily/ metallic/ tallowy flavour	Fat oxidation due to: direct contact of milk/cream/ butter/butteroil with copper or iron, exposure of these products to sunlight, etc.	(i) Storage of milk/cream/ butter/butteroil in properly tinned or aluminium alloy/stainless steel vessels; (ii) vacuumizing/gas packing of butteroil; (iii) Addition of anti-oxidants to butteroil before packing; (iv) Storage of butteroil in opaque containers.

5.13 Uses

  (i) In the production of recombined milk;
  (ii) for reconstitution into butter;
  (iii) in ice cream manufacture;
  (iv) as cooking fat;
  (v) in the confectionary industry;
  (vi) in the manufacture of various types of fat spreads.

6 ICE CREAM

6.1 Introduction

Ice cream as an industry in India is of comparatively recent origin and may be said to have started in the nineteen-sixties. Today ice cream may be considered a luxury food item, although its popularity is increasing rapidly. The production of ice cream in India in 1966 was estimated to be about 0.7 per cent of the total milk production and 1.3 per cent of the milk used for manufacture of dairy products (see Table 1.6).

6.2 Definition

Ice cream may be defined as a frozen dairy product made by suitable blending and processing of cream and other milk products, together with sugar and flavour, with or without stabilizer or colour, and with the incorporation of air during the freezing process.

According to the PFA Rules (1976), ice cream is the frozen product obtained from cow or buffalo milk or a combination thereof or from cream, and or other milk products, with or without the addition of cane sugar, eggs, fruits, fruit juices, preserved fruits, nuts, chocolate, edible flavours and permitted food colours. It may contain permitted stabilizers and emulsifiers not exceeding 0.5 per cent by weight. The mixture must be suitably heated before freezing. The product should contain not less than 10 per cent milk fat, 3.5 per cent protein and 36.0 per cent total solids. However, when any of the aforesaid preparations contain fruits or nuts or both, the content of milk fat may be proportionately reduced but may not be less than 8 per cent by weight. Starch may be added to a maximum extent of 5 per cent, with a declaration to that effect on the label.

6.3 History and Development

The early history of ice cream manufacture is very scanty; however, the product is definitely known to have originated in Europe. Water ices were made in southern Europe as early as the fifteenth century. The first printed record of 'Cream ice' appeared in *The Experienced English House Keeper* in 1769, more than two hundred years ago. Since that time ice cream manufacture has continued to grow in popularity in England, though not nearly as rapidly as in the United States, where surveys indicate that ice cream forms a part of the daily diet and is the favourite American dessert.

Some of the factors contributing to the development of the ice cream industry in developed dairying countries are: (i) the perfection of mechanical refrigeration and its application to the food industry; (ii) improved manufacturing methods and equipment such as homogenizers, overrun testers, continuous freezers, packaging machines, etc.; (iii) more and better ingredients and growth in knowledge concerning ice cream manufacture, resulting in a better product; (iv) lower manufacturing costs through mass production; (v) extensive advertising of the product; (vi) a realization of the high food value of ice cream; (vii) changing economic conditions, better wages, more purchasing power and a high standard of living among consumers; (viii) improved storage facilities for ice cream at home.

6.4 Classification

No standard classification of ice cream has yet been adopted by the industry, even in developed countries. However, some of the important frozen desserts can be classified as follows:

(i) *Plain.* An ice cream in which the colour and flavouring ingredients together amount to less than 5 per cent of the volume of the unfrozen ice cream. Examples: Vanilla and Coffee ice creams.

(ii) *Chocolate.* Ice cream flavoured with cocoa or chocolate.

(iii) *Fruit.* Ice cream containing fruits, with or without additional fruit flavouring or colour. Fruits such as strawberry, apricot, pineapple, mango, banana, etc., may be fresh, frozen-packed, canned or preserved.

(iv) *Nut.* Ice cream containing nuts, such as almonds, pistachio, walnuts, cashewnut, etc., with or without additional flavouring or colour.

(v) *Milk ices or milk lollies.* According to the PFA rules (1976), these refer to the frozen product obtained from milk, skim milk or milk products with or without the addition of cane sugar, eggs, fruits, fruit juices, nuts, chocolates, edible flavours, and permitted food colours. It may contain permitted stabilizers not exceeding 0.5 per cent of the product. The mixture should be suitably heat-treated before freezing. The product should contain not more than 2.0 per cent milk fat, not less than 3.5 per cent proteins and not less than 20.0 per cent total solids.

(vi) *Ices*. Made of fruit juice, sugar and stabilizer, with or without additional fruit acid, colour, flavouring or water, and frozen to the consistency of ice cream. Usually contain 28 to 30 per cent sugar, 20 to 25 per cent overrun and no dairy products.

(vii) *Sherbet*. Made of fruit juices, sugar, stabilizer, and milk products. It is similar to an ice except that milk, either whole, skim, condensed or powdered, or ice cream mix, are used in place of all or part of the water in an ice.

(viii) *Fancy moulded*. Moulded in fancy shapes and composed either of one colour and flavour of ice cream or a combination of colours and flavours, or especially decorated. Examples are: brick ice cream, cakes, cake roll, moulds representing fruits, etc.

(ix) *Novelties*. A Novelty ice cream or frozen confection is an especially shaped and usually a low-priced package containing an individual serving whose main appeal consists in its shape, size, colour or convenience for eating.

(x) *Soft ice cream (Softy)*. Sold as drawn from the freezer without hardening.

6.5 Composition

The composition of ice cream is usually expressed as a percentage of its constituents, i.e. a percentage of milk fat, milk-solids-not-fat (serum solids), sugar, stabilizer, total solids, etc. Its composition varies in different localities and in different markets. The best ice cream composition for a manufacturer to produce is often difficult to establish. After consideration of legal requirements, quality of product desired, raw materials available, plant procedures, trade demands, competition and cost, there is a choice of a product of minimum, average or high fat/solids composition. Some factories may choose to manufacture only one of these products, others two and still others all three, i.e. an economy-brand product, a good average composition product as a trade brand, or a deluxe high-quality product.

It may be inadvisable for a small manufacturer to produce more than one brand of ice cream. If only one composition is manufactured, it is extremely important that every effort be made to produce the best product possible.

In ice cream, the percentage of milk fat varies more than any other constituent. As the fat content is increased, the milk-solids-not-fat must be decreased so as to avoid 'sandiness' (i.e. the crystallization of milk sugar or lactose in the finished ice cream). Table 6.1 gives the composition of economy and good average ice creams.

TABLE 6.1

Approximate composition of commercial ice cream (as a percentage)

Milk fat	Milk solids-not-fat/ Serum solids	Sugar	Stabilizer and Emulsifier	Total solids
Economy Ice Cream				
10	10 to 11	13 to 15	0.30 to 0.50	35 to 37
Good Average Ice Cream				
12	11	15	0.30	37.5 to 39

SOURCE: *Ice Cream* by Arbuckle (1968).

The ISI specifications for ice cream (*IS: 2802*, 1964) are given in Table 6.2.

TABLE 6.2

ISI specifications of ice cream

Characteristics	Requirements
Weight (g./litre) (min.)	525
Total solids (% wt.) (min.)	36.0
Milk fat (% wt.) (min.)	10.0 (Tentative)
Acidity (% lactic acid) (max.)	0.25
Sucrose (% wt.) (max.)	15.0
Stabilizer/Emulsifier (% wt.) (max.)	0.5
Standard plate count (per g.)	Not more than 2,50,000
Coliform count (per g.)	Not more than 90
Phosphatase test	Negative

Note: A satisfactory composition produces an ice cream which has the desired combinations of cost, food value, flavour, body and texture, cooling effect, colour scheme, viscosity, whipping ability (i.e. overrun) and freezing point. What is needed is a balanced mix, in which the proportions of the constituents and ingredients is such as will produce a fine and satisfactory ice cream.

6.6   Food and Nutritive Value

This depends not only on the composition of the ice cream but also upon the food and nutritive value of the products from which it is made. For instance, ice cream contains two to three times as much fat and slightly more protein than does milk. In addition, it may contain other food products such as fruits, nuts, eggs and sugar which enhance its food value. However, like milk, it lacks iron, vitamin C and some of the trace minerals.

Among milk products, ice cream is also a rich source of calcium, phosphorus and other minerals of vital importance in building good bones and teeth. Being rich in lactose, ice cream favours greater assimilation of the calcium content in the diet. The protein content of ice cream also rates high, both in quantity and quality. The proteins are largely derived from milk, a small amount from stabilizer (gelatin) and from eggs when they are used in the mix The milk and egg proteins are complete; that is, they contain all th amino-acids essential to animal life and are especially importan sources of tryptophane and lysine which are lacking in many pla᙮ proteins. Ice cream provides these valuable proteins in a very palả table form. In fact, ice cream (without eggs and gelatin) is the most palatable source of milk proteins to vegetarians.

Ice cream is an excellent source of food energy. Having twice to three times the fat content of milk, and more than half its total solids being sugar (sucrose and lactose), the energy value of ice cream is very high. It is, therefore, a very desirable food item for growing children and persons who need to put on weight.

Like milk, ice cream is a rich source of many essential vitamins, without which normal health and growth cannot be maintained. Thus it is an excellent source of vitamin A, a good source of vitamins B (Thiamine) and G (Riboflavin), and a fairly good source of Niacin, vitamin E, and in fruit ice cream, of vitamin C. The digestibility and palatability of ice cream is also very high.

6.7 Role of the Constituents in Ice Cream

(a) *Milk fat*. This is high in food value, but expensive. It enriches and mellows the ice cream, giving it a full, rich, creamy flavour. If the milk fat is even slightly off-flavoured, the defect will be noticeable. The fat also contributes to the body and melting resistance of ice cream while producing a smoothness of texture. Fat gives stability to the ice cream but impairs whipping ability.

(b) *Milk-solids-not-fat* (*MSNF*). Also known as serum solids, they consist of milk proteins, milk sugar and mineral matter. They are high in food value and also inexpensive. They add very little to the smell, but improve its body and texture. However, milk sugar adds to the sweet taste. The milk proteins help to make ice cream more compact and smooth. Milk-solids-not-fat should be added in as large a quantity as possible without risking the danger of sandiness.

(c) *Sugar*. The main function of sugar is to increase the acceptability of ice cream. The desired sweetening effect is only produced by sucrose. Sugars are usually the cheapest source of total solids in the mix.

(d) *Stabilizers*. These are used to prevent the formation of objectionably large ice crystals in ice cream, especially during storage. Since they are added in very small quantities, they have a negligible influence on food value and flavour.

(e) *Emulsifiers*. These are used mainly to improve upon and provide a uniform whipping quality to the mixture, and to produce a drier ice cream with smoother body and texture.

(f) *Flavour and colour*. Flavour increases the acceptability of ice cream, and colour its aesthetic appeal.

(g) *Advantages and limitations of ice cream constituents*. The advantages and limitations of the various ice cream constituents have been summarized by Sommer as follows:

I. *Milk fat*

Advantages. (i) Enriches the flavour; (ii) produces a characteristic smooth texture; (iii) helps give body to the ice cream.

Limitations. (i) Cost; (ii) fat slightly hinders, rather than improves, whipping; (iii) high fat content may limit the amount of ice cream consumed; (iv) high calorific value.

II. *Milk-solids-not-fat*

Advantages. (i) Improve the texture; (ii) help to give body; (iii) a higher overrun without snowy or flaky texture; (iv) a comparatively cheap source of solids.

Limitations. (i) A high percentage causes 'sandiness'; (ii) the 'condensed milk' flavour may be objectionable; (iii) may cause salty or cooked flavour.

III. *Sugar*

Advantages. (i) Is usually the cheapest source of solids; (ii) improves the texture; (iii) enhances the flavour.

Limitations. (i) Excessively sweet; (ii) lowers whipping ability; (iii) requires a lower temperature for proper hardening.

IV. *Stabilizer*

Advantages. (i) Very effective in smoothening the texture; (ii) very effective in giving body to the product.

Limitation. (i) Excess body and melting resistance.

V. *Emulsifier*

Advantages. (i) Improves whipping quality of mixture; (ii) gives smoother body and texture; (iii) reduces whipping time.

Limitations. (i) Homogenization of milk is essential; (ii) tends to favour 'shrinkage' defect; (iii) excess body and melting resistance.

VI. *Total solids*

Advantages. (i) Smoother texture; (ii) better body; (iii) more nutritious; (iv) ice cream not as cold.

Limitations. (i) Heavy, soggy or pasty body; (ii) cooling effect insufficiently high.

VII. *Flavour*

Advantage. (i) Increases acceptability.

Limitations. (i) Harsh flavour less desirable; (ii) intense flavours provide immediate satisfaction.

VIII. *Colour*

Advantages. (i) Improves appearance; (ii) aids in identifying flavours.

Limitation. (i) Intense and 'unnatural' colours reduce consumer acceptability.

6.8 Properties of Mix

The properties of practical importance in the mix are: viscosity, acidity (lactic) and pH, mix stability, specific gravity, surface tension, freezing point, and whipping rate.

A. *Viscosity.* This is defined simply as the resistance offered by liquids to flow. Viscosity is considered an important property of the ice cream mix, and a certain amount of it seems essential for proper whipping and the retention of air. Two types of viscosity exist in ice cream mixes: Apparent Viscosity, which is a thickened condition that disappears with agitation; and Basic Viscosity, which remains after the Apparent Viscosity disappears.

The viscosity of an ice cream mix is influenced by: (i) composition; (ii) kind and quality of ingredients; (iii) processing and handling of the mix; (iv) total solids concentration; and (v) temperature.

(i) *Composition.* Among the various mix ingredients, viscosity is more influenced by milk fat and stabilizer than the other ingredients. Gelatin affects viscosity to a great extent largely due to gel formation, while fat increases it slightly. Sugar, on the other hand, decreases the viscosity of the ice cream mix.

(ii) *Kind and quality of ingredients.* The kind of ingredient refers to whether it is a source of fat, serum-solids, sweetening, stabilizer, etc.; the quality indicates the emulsion stability of fat, colloidal stability of protein, etc. Those carrying the fat are especially important. Also, heat and salts (such as calcium, sodium, citrates, etc.) greatly affect the viscosity due to their effect on casein and other proteins. Among stabilizers, gelatin causes a decided increase in viscosity after ageing.

(iii) *Processing and handling of the mix.* These include: pasteurization, homogenization and ageing.

1. *Pasteurization.* At batch-holding temperatures followed by cooling, pasteurization causes a decrease in viscosity, while at higher temperatures it produces an increase in viscosity.

2. *Homogenization.* If the globules are small and individually dispersed, the basic viscosity of the mix remains at a minimum. However, the tendency of the sub-divided fat globules to clump or aggregate greatly increases.

3. *Ageing.* The ageing of mixes containing gelatin considerably increases their apparent viscosity. The increase is chiefly due to gel formation, but to some extent to the hydration of proteins and the clumping of fat globules. Aside from the increase in apparent viscosity, ageing causes an increase in basic viscosity as a result of a solidification of the butter fat and hydration of the milk proteins.

(iv) *Total solids concentration.* As the liquid phase is replaced by a solid phase in a mixture such as ice cream mix, the viscosity usually increases. Consequently, as the solids content of the ice cream mix is raised, the viscosity increases although the effect of the different solids in this respect varies with the type and source of the solid. For example, slight increases in fat content may effect the mix viscosity to only a limited extent, whereas a slight increase in gelatin will affect the mix viscosity greatly. The extent to which the mix solids increase mix viscosity depends largely upon the physical state of these solids. When the proteins are partially coagulated and when the fat globules form clumps, the mix viscosity increases on both counts.

(v) *Temperature.* With a lowering of temperature, the mix viscosity increases, and vice versa.

Note: It has not yet been determined how much viscosity is desirable in ice cream mix. A high viscosity was believed essential at one time, but for fast freezing (rapid whipping) in modern equipment, a lower viscosity seems desirable. In general, as viscosity increases, the resistance to melting and the smoothness of body increases, but the rate of whipping decreases. Viscosity is now considered a phenomenon that frequently accompanies rather than causes good whipping, body and texture. Therefore the mix should be properly balanced (in regard to composition, concentration and quality of ingredients) and then properly processed to produce the desired whipping ability, body and texture. Under these conditions, a desirable viscosity is assured. The basic viscosity of mix ranges from 50 to 300 centipoise.

B. *Acidity (lactic) & pH.* The normal acidity of ice cream mixes is dependent upon the serum solids content, and is calculated by the formula:

$$\% \text{ acidity of mix} = \% \text{ acidity of milk} \times \frac{\% \text{ serum solids in mix}}{\% \text{ serum solids in milk}}$$

A rule of thumb method to determine mix acidity, is to multiply the serum solids by 2 and divide by 100. The normal pH of mix is about 6.3. Acidity and pH are related to the composition of the mix and an increase in milk-solids-not-fat raises the percentage acidity and lowers the pH. If fresh dairy products of excellent quality are used in preparing the mix, it may be expected to have a normal acidity. When acidity is above normal, it indicates that lactic acid is present in the dairy products used in the mix. A high acidity is undesirable as it contributes to excessive mix viscosity, a decreased whipping rate, an inferior flavour and a less stable mix resulting in 'cook on' or possible coagulation during the pasteurizing and processing stages.

If the mix acidity is higher than normal, it can be neutralized to the level of normal acidity. Over-neutralization (below 0.15 per cent titratable acidity) should be avoided as the ice cream will tend to have a flat (or neutralized) flavour and a dull or even greyish colour. When neutralizing, add the sugar at 32°C (90°F) and place all the ingredients in the mixing vat before the acidity test is run. The neutralizer best suited to ice cream is sodium bicarbonate. Mix the neutralizer (1 kg. neutralizer to 1 kg. acid) with 10 times its weight of water. Heat the mix to 32°C (90°F), or slightly higher if butter is used. Keeping the agitator moving, add the neutralizer solution slowly so as to distribute it uniformly throughout the mix. The temperature should be maintained at 32°C (90°F) for at least 10 minutes before pasteurizing.

Note: It should be remembered that good ice cream cannot be made from a highly acidic mix.

C. *Mix stability.* This refers to stability or resistance to separation by the milk proteins in an ice cream mix. Instability results in separation of milk proteins as coagulated or precipitated material in the mix, and the resulting ice cream has a curdled appearance on melting. This defect is caused by various factors which affect the colloidal stability of the milk proteins, such as high mix acidity, low citrate and phosphate content, a high calcium and magnesium content, high homogenizing pressure, high (pasteurizing) heat-treatment, low ageing time (resulting in poor hydration), destabilizing effect of freezing, etc. Particle size, charge, and hydration are important factors influencing the stability of an ice cream mix; the most stable mix particle is the hydrophillic suspension because it is charged and hydrated; and the least stable suspension is that wherein the particle is neither hydrated nor carries a charge. It is the latter which results in instable mixes.

D. *Specific gravity.* The specific gravity or density of an ice cream mix varies with its composition and may range from 1.05 to 1.12. It can be determined by using the following formula:

Sp. Gr. at 16°C (60°F)

$$= \frac{100}{\dfrac{\% \text{ fat}}{0.93} + \dfrac{\% \text{ Sugar} + \% \text{ MSNF} + \% \text{ Stabilizer}}{1.58} + \dfrac{\% \text{ water}}{1}}$$

E. *Surface tension.* This pertains to the attraction between the molecules of a liquid at its surface. The greater the attraction between the molecules, the higher the surface tension, and vice versa. The unit of measurement of surface tension is dyne.

Investigations on the surface tension of ice cream are limited. Studies indicate that increasing the surface tension above that of a freshly-made mix (made from fresh ingredients) is difficult, although it may be readily decreased by the addition of products such as emulsifiers and the like. Mixes with lower surface tension values (caused by the addition of excessive amounts of emulsifier to the mix) have shown excessive rates of whipping, fluffy short body characteristics, and susceptibility to the shrinkage defect. The normal surface tension values of ice cream mix may range from 48 to 53 dynes sq. cm. (At 20°C/68°F the surface tension of water is 72.75, and of milk, 40 to 60.)

F. *Freezing point.* The freezing point of ice cream is dependent on the soluble constituents and varies with its composition. The mix constituents which affect the freezing point directly are sugar, milk sugar, milk salts, and any other substances that may have been added and are in true solution. Other mix constituents which affect the freezing point indirectly by replacing water are fat, protein and any other constituent not in true solution. Glucose depresses the freezing point almost twice as much as the same weight of sucrose, since the molecular weight of glucose is about one-half that of sucrose. On the other hand, corn syrup depresses the freezing point less than sucrose. In fruit ice cream, the freezing point will depend on the type of sugar used in fruit preparations (glucose or sucrose) and the extent to which the added sugar has undergone hydrolysis.

An average mix (containing 12 per cent fat, 11 per cent serum solids, 15 per cent sugar, 0.3 per cent stabilizer and 61.7 per cent water) has a freezing point of about 27.5°F. Mixes with high sugar and milk-solids-not-fat contents may range to 26.5°F; while high fat, low milk-solids-not-fat or low sugar content mixes may range to 29.5°F.

G. *Whipping rate.* A high whipping rate means the ability to whip rapidly to a high overrun. It is now definitely known that the differences in whipping ability cannot be explained on the basis of viscosity. The present hypothesis is that whipping ability is based on tensile strength and the strength of the lamella (i.e., walls around the air cells). Whipping ability is improved by a high processing temperature, proper homogenization and ageing the mix for 2–4 hours.

Smaller fat globules and less clumping increase whipping ability. Mixes made with butter, butteroil, or frozen cream have a less satisfactory dispersion of fat and poor whipping ability. Egg yolk solids, regardless of their source, and fresh cream buttermilk solids, improve whipping ability. The usual variations in concentration of milk-solids-not-fat have no pronounced effect on whipping ability, but qualitative variations in the milk-solids-not-fat are important. Sugar decreases the whipping ability except when added after homogenization, in which case it increases it. Finally, the construction and operation of the freezer itself determine whether the maximum whipping ability of a given mix can be obtained.

The rate of whipping is measured by calculating the overrun at one-minute intervals while the mix is being frozen in a batch freezer. Normally, within 3 to 5 minutes after the freezing process starts, the mix is frozen and within 7 minutes an overrun of 90 per cent is obtained. In mixes which have a rapid whipping rate, 90 per cent overrun may be reached in 5 minutes or less. Mixes requiring 8 minutes or more to reach 90 per cent overrun are considered to have a slow whipping rate.

6.9 Method of Manufacture, Packaging, Hardening and Storage

A. *Flow diagram of manufacture*

Selection of ingredients
|
Figuring the mix
|
Making the mix
|

(Contd. on next page)

(Contd. from prev. page)
Pasteurizing the mix (68°C/155°F for 30 min.)
|
Homogenizing the mix (I stage 2,500 psi)
(II stage 500 psi)
|
Cooling and ageing the mix (0–4°C/32–40°F)
|
Freezing the mix (−4 to −5°C/23 to 25°F)
|
Packaging of ice cream
|
Hardening and storage of ice cream
(−23 to −29°C/−10 to −20°F)

B. *Details of manufacture*

(aa) *Selection of ingredients.* The selection of ice cream ingredients depends on: (i) availability of milk products; (ii) perishability of the products; (iii) convenience in handling; (iv) effect on flavour, body and texture of ice cream; (v) cost, and (vi) equipment available. The selection of good ingredients is without doubt the most important factor in successful ice cream manufacture. A clean, fresh, creamy flavour in ice cream can be secured only by the use of products which have been carefully produced and handled.

Ice cream ingredients may be grouped into dairy and non-dairy products. Some dairy products supply the major source of fat, others the major source of milk-solids-not-fat and still others supply both fat and milk-solids-not-fat. The non-dairy products include sweetening agents, stabilizers and emulsifiers, flavours and colours, fruits and nuts, etc. The common ingredients used in each category have been listed below:

I. *Dairy products*

Source of fat: (i) Sweet cream—this is the most desirable concentrated source of fat for use in a mix; (ii) frozen cream; (iii) plastic cream; (iv) unsalted butter; (v) butteroil.

Sources of milk-solids-not fat: (i) skim milk; (ii) skim milk powder—this is most frequently used in the spray dried or flaked form; (iii) condensed skim milk (plain/sweetened); (iv) sweet cream buttermilk.

Sources of both fat and milk-solids-not-fat: (i) whole milk; (ii) whole milk powder; (iii) condensed whole milk (plains/weetened); (iv) evaporated milk.

II. *Non-dairy products*

Sweetening agents: (i) cane or beet sugar (sucrose)—most common; (ii) corn sugar (dextrose); (iii) corn syrup solids (dextrose + maltose); (iv) corn syrup; (v) invert sugar (glucose + fructose); (vi) saccharin.

Stabilizers: (i) gelatin—of animal source; orthodox vegetarians object to its use in ice cream; (ii) sodium alginate/Dariloid (modified form)—this is of vegetable origin and widely used; (iii) guar gum—this is of Indian origin; (iv) others.

Emulsifiers: (i) mono- or di-glycerides of fat-forming fatty acids.

Flavours: (i) vanilla—this is the most popular flavour all over the world; (ii) chocolate; (iii) strawberry; (iv) pineapple; (v) lemon; (vi) banana; (vii) mango; (viii) orange, etc.

Colours: (i) yellow; (ii) green; (iii) pink, etc.

Egg solids: yolk solids—improve whipping ability.

Fruits and nuts: (i) apple; (ii) banana; (iii) mango; (iv) pineapple; (v) grape; (vi) almond; (vii) pistachio; (viii) cashewnut; (ix) walnut, (x) groundnut.

(a) *Dairy products*. These constitute the basic materials for ice cream preparation and have either been discussed in the preceding chapters, or shall be so discussed in the succeeding ones.

(b) *Sweetening agents*. Many kinds of sweeteners are used in ice cream. These include: cane and beet sugar, corn sweeteners, brown sugar, honey, invert sugar and sugar substitutes. Cane or beet sugars are most commonly used. One-fourth to one-third of cane or beet sugar may be replaced by corn sugar with good results. The use of a combination or blend of sugars in either dry or liquid forms is a popular practice; sugar blends usually consist of 70 per cent sucrose and 30 per cent corn sweeteners. The different kinds of sugars do not produce an equal sweetening effect. Apart from sweetening, sugars affect the properties of the mix and the finished product. Sugars depress the freezing point of the mix, produce a thinner mix with a slower whipping rate, and an ice cream with a smoother body and texture with faster melting qualities. The different sweeteners commonly used are as follows:

(i) *Sucrose*. Commonly known as granulated cane or beet sugar, this is the most widely accepted source of sugar throughout the world. It depresses the freezing point of ice cream.

(ii) *Corn sweeteners*. These may be: refined corn sugar (dextrose) —a dry crystalline product; dried corn syrup or corn syrup solids; and corn syrup—a liquid.

Refined corn sugar—dextrose is 80 per cent as sweet as sucrose.

It has a lower freezing point than sucrose and can therefore be used to about 25 per cent of the total desired sugar.

Dried corn syrup solids—contain dextrose and maltose together with dextrin. Usually added to the extent of not more than one-third of the total sweetener.

Corn syrup—contains variable amounts of dextrose and maltose.

(iii) *Invert sugar.* Mixture of different parts of glucose and fructose (resulting from hydrolysis of sucrose) and generally obtained in the form of syrup. Sweeter than sucrose. Depresses the freezing point and hence should be used to supply not more than one-fourth to one-third of the total sugar in the mix.

(iv) *Saccharin.* Artificial sweetener. Sweetening effect up to 550 times that of sucrose. Used in 'diabetic ice cream'. Causes problems of low total solids and low overrun. (Continued consumption of 0.3 g. per day is liable to impair digestion, because of its antiseptic properties and preservative action. Lately, it has been suggested that it might be a cause of cancer.)

Note. Use of lactose as sweetener has the following problems: lactose is one-sixth as sweet as sucrose and is less soluble; moreover the crystals are hard and have sharp edges. When the water portion of the mix contains as much as 9 per cent lactose, the lactose may form crystals large enough to be discernible, and leave an undesirable 'sandy' taste in the mouth. This property definitely limits the concentration of lactose in ice cream mix. Since the source of lactose is milk-solids-not-fat of dairy products and about 54 per cent of milk-solids-not-fat is lactose, the maximum concentration of lactose that can be safely used is directly related to the maximum concentration of milk-solids-not-fat.

(c) *Stabilizers.* These may be defined as substances which help to preserve emulsions. Although added in small amounts, they perform a very important role. Stabilizers are added in ice cream to produce smoothness in body and texture, retard or reduce ice crystal growth during storage, and provide uniformity in the product and resistance to melting. Stabilizers function through their ability to form gel structures in water or combine with water as water of hydration.

Among the stabilizers which are permitted and used in making ice cream are: gelatin, sodium alginate, carageenan, agar agar, carboxy methyl cellulose, pectin; guar gum, and other gums. These are discussed below:

(i) *Gelatin.* Of animal origin, it was one of the first of the commercial stabilizers, and is still used. Its advantage lies in its ability to form a gel in the mix during the ageing period as well as during the freezing process, and even after the frozen product is placed in the hardening room. Its peculiar gel structure and its great affinity for water prevent the formation of large ice crystals in ice cream, and contribute to the smoothness in texture and firmness in body of the frozen product.

The amount of gelatin to be used depends on several factors such as the source of gelatin, whether from calf, pork skins or bone material; its gel strength as measured by the Bloom Test; its viscosity value; the composition of the mix, etc. In general, the amount to be used is approximately the amount required to produce a meltdown (in evenly melted ice cream) of about the same consistency as aged 40 per cent sweet cream. This amount is usually between 0.25 and 0.5 per cent for a 250 Bloom gelatin. The ice cream mix stabilized with gelatin usually requires about 4 hours of ageing to develop complete stabilizing properties, while other stabilizing materials do not require an ageing period.

Note: Several tests have been developed to determine gel strength and to serve as the guidelines to the amount to be used in the mix. Among these are the Bloom Test (by a Bloom Gelometer) for gel strength. Other factors being equal, the gelatin that carries the greatest gel strength per unit of cost is the one to select. Good quality gelatin should have a low bacterial count and should be practically odourless and colourless.

(ii) *Sodium alginate.* Of vegetable origin; it is also sold under the trade name of 'Dariloid'. The basic stabilizing principle, algin, is extracted from a giant ocean kelp (seaweed) growing on the shores of California and Japan. This product improves whipping ability and leaves a slightly cleaner flavour in the mouth. It dissolves properly only when added to the mix at about 68 to 71°C (155 to 160°F). A slightly smaller amount is needed to produce the same stabilizing effect as gelatin.

(iii) *Carageenan.* This is extracted from Carageen (Irish Moss), a seaweed growing on the coast of Ireland, etc. It is used together with gum stabilizers.

(iv) *Agar agar*. This is a product extracted from red algae (sea-weed) growing on the Pacific Coast. More useful for sherbets and ices.

(v) *CMC (Carboxy methyl cellulose)*. This has a high water-holding capacity and can be easily dissolved in the mix. Also acts as an emulsifier. Slightly less of it is to be used than gelatin. It does not form as firm a gel as gelatin and some of the vegetable stabilizers, but seems to be good for use in ice cream.

(vi) *Pectin*. This is a carbohydrate obtained mainly from citrus fruits. Not satisfactory as a stabilizer for ice cream, although suitable for sherbets and ices.

(vii) *Guar gum*. This is a carbohydrate obtained from Indian legume. Often used in combination with carageenan. It is readily soluble in cold solutions and used as stabilizer for mixes to be pasteurized by HTST or continuous pasteurization methods.

(viii) *Other gums* (such as Tragacanth, Arabic, Karaya, or India gums). These are exudates from incisions made in the bark of certain trees and plants growing usually in tropical countries. More useful for sherbets and ices.

Note: (i) The selection of a suitable stabilizer for use in the mix is dependent on several factors, such as: adaptability to the particular need of the plant; personal preference; availability; cost; freedom from toxicity; effect of stabilizer on the properties of the mix; whether or not an ageing period is necessary; kind of product being manufactured and method of processing adopted in the plant; effect on flavour and body and texture characteristics; and effect on melting and storage properties of the ice cream.

(ii) The amount of stabilizer used depends on the kind of stabilizer and the quality necessary to produce the desired stabilizing effect in the product being manufactured. There are four common ways of determining the amount of stabilizer to be used in the ice cream mix: the fat content of the mix; the total solids content of the mix; the kind of freezer used; and the use of a constant amount which may range from 0.15 to 0.50 per cent.

(iii) The method of incorporating stabilizers (and emulsifiers) in the ice cream mix is as follows: Mix with 4 to 5 parts of sugar and add before or during the heating process, disperse by gently adding to the mix without special handling, suspend in cold water and add them to the mix when mix temperature is 71°C (160°F) in the case of sodium alginate, or use a hopper and pump or some other special arrangement. When the batch method of pasteurization is employed, the stabilizer may be added to the cold or hot mix. This method gives greater latitude for the selection of a stabilizer. In the HTST pasteurization process, the stabilizer must be added to the cold mix ingredients and should disperse readily at a low temperature; the algin, guar and CMC type of products are commonly used in this processing method.

(d) *Emulsifiers.* These may be defined as substances which help to form emulsions. The value of emulsifying agents in the manufacture of ice cream lies mainly in the improved whipping quality of the mix, the production of a drier ice cream with a smoother body and texture, in their superior drawing qualities at the freezer, and the possibility of maintaining more precise control over the various manufacturing processes.

There are two kinds of emulsifiers used in the manufacture of ice cream, viz., mono- and di-glycerides derived by the chemical reaction of naturally occurring glycerides and polyoxyethylene derivatives of hexahydric alcohols, glycol and glycol esters. The mono-glycerides improve fat dispersion and whipping ability and have a moderate effect on stiffness and the melting rate. The poly-derivatives are effective in producing dryness, stiffness and increasing the melting time.

Emulsifiers are available in liquid, semi-solid and powder forms and may include glycerides, lecithin and fatty acid esters. In general, emulsifiers have little effect on the acidity, pH or viscosity of the ice cream mix. A significant reduction in whipping time is encountered when any emulsifier is used. The use of emulsifiers decreases the melting rate in the finished ice cream. Emulsifiers seem to produce somewhat smaller ice crystals which are more evenly distributed, and smaller air cells that result in a smoother ice cream. Several factors may affect the action of an emulsifier. Among these are: ingredients of the mix; procedure of processing, freezing and hardening; and the amount of emulsifier used. Some disadvantages in the use of emulsifiers are: homogenization of the mix is essential in order to obtain good results and they seem to favour the development of a 'shrinkage' defect. Excessive use of emulsifiers may cause a short body and poor texture, slow melting, and a curdy meltdown in the finished ice cream.

Note: Excellent ice cream, and considerable amounts of it, are made without adding stabilizer or emulsifier. Since milk and milk products contain natural stabilizing and emulsifying materials, viz., milk protein, fat, lecithin, phosphates and citrates, mixes of a certain composition and processing treatment may be stabilized by the effect of these natural materials. Further, egg yolk products are high in lecithin and have long been used in ice cream. These products produce results similar to, but not as pronounced as, those caused by commercial stabilizers and emulsifiers.

(c) *Flavours*. The two most popular flavours, viz., vanilla and chocolate, have been discussed in detail below.

(i) *Vanilla*

Introduction. Vanilla is undoubtedly the most popular flavour for ice cream throughout the world. In the United States of America, records show that about 75 per cent of all ice cream produced contains vanilla flavouring. It may be kept in mind that vanilla is often used in combination with other flavours or as a background flavour in many ice creams.

Vanilla flavouring is obtained from the perennial climbing plant, *Vanilla Planifolia Andrews*, a member of the orchid family. It is a native of Mexico and was introduced to the civilized world by the great Spanish explorer, Hernando Cortez, in 1528. The above plant and its related types have been introduced to other tropical regions such as the Madagascar Islands (now providing 80% of the world's supply), Indonesia (Java), certain islands in the West Indies, Mauritius, parts of Central and South America, etc.

Vanillin is the principal flavouring material in vanilla. However, there is no free vanillin in the beans when they are harvested, and the typical vanilla flavour is developed by fermenting the bean. Artificial or synthetic vanilla is a product of a slightly different flavour than the natural one.

Curing or fermentation. The vanilla plant can be grown only in tropical regions where climate, moisture and soil conditions are just right. The plant flowers during the second year, when the finest ones are promptly fertilized by hand. The development of the fruit or bean-pod follows. The mature fruit has little flavour and is yellow in colour; when ripe, they are harvested and sold to the curer.

Although the curing or fermentation process differs in different countries, it usually consists of a process called 'sweating' in which the beans are alternately dried in the sun and wrapped up in blankets at night so that they heat and ferment. This sweating process continues for approximately 4 weeks to 4 months. In the course of this process, an enzymatic reaction takes place and the complex fats, resins, tannins, essential and fixed oils, vanillin and other aromatic compounds are formed. (At least 28 distinct components have been isolated from the vanilla aroma, most of them still unidentified.) At the end of the curing period, the pods are carefully sorted out into various grades based on their quality. The colour now ranges from chocolate to almost black. They are then packed and shipped to their final destination where extraction will take place.

Extraction. Extraction of the vanilla flavour from cured beans is a delicate process, and much depends on the skill of the person carrying out the operation. Unless correctly treated at this stage, the true flavour of the vanilla from the beans will be ruined. The beans are first chopped by extra-fine knives. A solvent such as dilute ethyl alcohol must be used for extraction. The alcohol content of the extract varies between 35 to 50 per cent. The extract is obtained through a process of percolation, which consists in continuous circulation of the alcohol-water mixture (with or without sugar and glycerine) over the chopped beans, under precisely controlled conditions, until the extraction is completed.

Classification. Vanilla flavourings may be grouped under the following general classes: true vanilla flavourings; compound vanilla flavourings and imitation vanilla flavourings.

1. *True vanilla flavourings.* These may be sub-graded as:

True vanilla extract. This is prepared by the extraction of finely cut vanilla beans by a solution containing not less than 35 per cent ethanol. A standard single-strength pure vanilla extract contains soluble matter to the extent of 13.35 ounces of the vanilla beans (with or without added sugar glycerine or colouring matter) per gallon of extract. These true vanilla extracts are generally of such a strength that only 5 or 6 oz. of the extract are required to flavour 5 gallons of ice cream mix.

Concentrated vanilla extract. This is obtained by distilling off a large part of the solvent until the strength reaches the desired concentrations, which is then specified as 'two-fold (or double strength)', 'three-fold', etc. A two-fold extract would be twice as strong as the single-strength extract, and would therefore contain the extractives from 26.70 oz. of vanilla beans per gallon.

True vanilla powders. These are made either by mixing finely ground vanilla beans with sugar, or by incorporating the vanilla extractives with a dry carrier, evaporating and drying the solvent. The amount used would correspond by weight to the number of ounces used of a standard strength extract.

Vanilla paste. This is made by mixing the concentrated extractives with a dry carrier to form a paste. The amount used would be the same as for powders.

True vanilla flavour. This conforms to the same standards as for vanilla extract, except that it contains less than 35 per cent alcohol, propylene glycol or some other solvent being used as the carrier.

2. *Compound vanilla flavourings*

Reinforced vanilla. Not less than one-half of the flavour may be derived from the vanilla bean content. Not more than one ounce of vanillin should be used in conjunction with 13.35 oz. of vanilla beans. This type is also available in various degrees of concentration.

3. *Imitation vanilla flavourings*

Blends. These are composed of true vanilla extract, flavour or powder with added synthetics where less than half of the flavour is derived from the vanilla beans.

Synthetics. These are preparations that contain no vanilla bean extractives and are made up entirely of one of several combinations of substances, such as synthetics and natural extractives derived from sources other than vanilla beans. These preparations may contain added water, alcohol, propylene glycol, vanillin, caramel, colour, etc.

Usage. The amount of vanilla used in flavouring ice cream depends on the concentration of the vanilla flavouring material and the composition of ice cream. Vanilla flavouring is available in liquid or powder forms such as pure vanilla, reinforced vanilla with vanillin, and imitation vanilla. Concentration ranges from single strength (extractive from 13.35 oz. of vanilla beans per gallon extract) to a ten-fold or higher concentrate. Vanilla may be used at rates ranging from $\frac{1}{8}$ oz. to 5–6 oz. per 10 gallons of ice cream, depending upon the extract concentration. The amount of vanilla required decreases with decrease in the fat content of the mix and a low sugar level requires a higher vanilla level. An adequate amount of the best quality flavouring material should always be used. The vanilla flavour in the mix should not be too pronounced.

(ii) *Chocolate*

Introduction. Chocolate and cocoa rank second only to vanilla as flavouring for ice cream. They are obtained from cacao beans, the fruit of the perennial tree *Theobroma cocoa*, growing in such tropical regions as Mexico, Ghana, Brazil, Venezuela, Nigeria, Ecuador, the West Indies, the African Gold Coast, the East Indies, etc. The origin of the cacao tree is in dispute. Like vanilla, it was introduced to the civilized world by Cortez in 1528. The cacao tree is a strictly tropical plant thriving only in hot, humid climates. As with vanilla beans, cacao beans must be subjected to a fermentation process before the characteristic flavour develops. Besides fermentation, a rather extensive processing of the bean is necessary before the flavour can be used in food products.

Fermentation. The cacao trees of most strains will bear a full crop in the fifth year. The tree trunk and older branches bear pods, and there will be 25 to 40 beans per pod. The ripened pods. which are a rich golden red in colour, are cut from the tree, gathered in piles and left to ripen further for about 48 hours. The pods are then slashed open, the beans removed and placed in bags for about 10 days to undergo fermentation, after which the characteristic flavour and rich brown colour develop. The beans are then washed, cleaned, dried (either artificially or under the sun) sufficiently to prevent mould growth, sorted and graded prior to shipment to manufacturers of chocolate and cocoa.

Processing. At the factory the beans are first mechanically cleaned. Then they are roasted at a temperature of 121°C (250°F) or above for 30 minutes to 2 hours to eliminate the moisture and bring out the special chocolate flavour and aroma. The roasted beans are then quickly cooled by forced air, and run through a winnowing machine which crushes them into small pieces and separates the shells from the nibs (i.e., the seed part which is made into chocolate or cocoa).

Types. There are several types of chocolate flavouring used in ice cream:

1. *Chocolate liquor.* This is a high-fat product. It is the trade name for the liquid chocolate which is produced by crushing the nibs between heavy stone grinders or mills which reduce them to a liquid

(by heat generated by the friction of milling). It contains about 50 per cent fat and little flavouring material.

2. *Cocoa powder* (*Natural process*). This is a low-fat product. It is made from chocolate liquor by subjecting the liquid to high pressure in hydraulic presses. This process removes a large amount of the cocoa-fat, usually about 38–40 per cent of the total, and leaves a hard dry cake which normally contains 10 to 24 per cent fat (average 22). It also contains nearly all the flavouring material from the cacao bean. This cocoa cake is then cooled, pulverized and sifted into cocoa powder.

3. *Chocolate blends.* These are combinations of liquor and powder. The fat content ranges from 36 to 40 per cent.

4. *Dutch process cocoa powder.* This is made as per the Natural process, except that the cacao beans are treated with certain alkalis at the time of roasting to break up the cell structure. This alkali treatment makes the cocoa more soluble and gives it the desired dark colour, which distinguishes the Dutch process from Natural cocoa. It also helps to bring out the fully fine chocolate flavour when the cocoa is used in the finished product. Because the alkali counteracts the puckery acid taste which is found in Natural cocoa, Dutch process cocoa leaves no bitter taste when used as flavouring in ice cream.

Usage. Chocolate products used in flavouring ice cream are:

1. cocoa powder (20–25 per cent cocoa fat);
2. chocolate liquor (50–53 per cent cocoa fat);
3. chocolate blends (36–40 per cent cocoa fat);
4. chocolate syrups.

The amount of cocoa or chocolate liquor/blends to be used in ice cream depends upon several factors, such as consumer preference, colour desired in ice cream, strength of flavour, etc. The usual recommendation varies from as much as 4 kg. of cocoa (or 6 kg. of chocolate liquor) to 100 kg. of mix. Extra sugar should be added to compensate for the bitterness of the cocoa or chocolate, the usual recommendation being to use the same weight of sugar as of cocoa or chocolate.

Preparing chocolate syrup. The small manufacturer usually prefers to flavour chocolate ice cream by adding syrup at the freezer. Favourable results may be expected by using a formula of 20 kg. cocoa, 20 kg. sugar and enough water to make 38 kg. of finished syrup; 5 to 7 kg. of this syrup may be used to 19 kg. of mix. The syrup should be made in a chocolate kettle or double boiler. Mix the sugar and cocoa/chocolate together and add enough water to make a heavy paste. Heat gradually and add water slowly as necessary. (The final syrup should contain enough water for it to pour when cooled.) The syrup should be heated to boiling point and cooled before use so as not to prolong the freezing operation.

Adding the cocoa/chocolate. Whenever possible, an entire chocolate mix should be made by adding the cocoa (or chocolate) and extra sugar to the mix, along with the other dry ingredients, before pasteurization. The temperature of pasteurization is sufficient to incorporate the flavour properly. A chocolate mix made in this way whips more rapidly than plain mix plus syrup at the freezer and gives a better-flavoured, more uniform product, free of dark specks.

The best chocolate ice cream is made when the chocolate mix is compounded and processed. A typical formula is as follows: fat—10 per cent, milk-solids-not-fat—10 per cent, sugar—18 per cent, cocoa —2.5 per cent, chocolate liquor—1.5 per cent, stabilizer—0.2 per cent and total solids —42.2 per cent.

Freezing characteristics. Chocolate ice cream is one of the most difficult to freeze because it whips very slowly. This is due to the fact that chocolate ice cream is very viscous. The viscosity may be reduced and whipping time improved by adding one kg. of citrate or phosphate to 1,000 kg. of mix.

(f) *Colours.* Only harmless, edible, permitted food colours should be used. Generally, colours are matched with the flavours added.

(g) *Egg solids.* Frozen and powdered egg yolks are used by many ice cream manufacturers. Usually not more than 0.5 per cent of egg yolk solids are added to the mix. Egg yolk solids improve the whipping quality of the mix. They are especially desirable in mixes in which butter or butteroil constitute the main source of fat.

(h) *Fruits and nuts.* The fruits in ice cream may be fresh, frozen or canned. Fresh fruits must be considered the best source of flavour when available at low prices; they should be thoroughly washed and peeled or hulled before use. Fruits may be used whole, sliced or crushed. It is better to mix fruits with sugar in the ratio of 2–7 kg. fruit to 1 kg. sugar and hold them at about 5°C (40°F) for 12–24 hours before using @ 15–20 per cent of the mix. In India, pieces of chopped mango, banana, etc. are added towards the end of the freezing process @ 7–8 per cent of the mix. Care should be taken to exclude inedible and fibrous parts.

Nuts should be sound, clean, and free from rancid flavours. Considerable care should be taken to prepare them for the ice cream mix so that there are no foreign materials. To make them safe, nuts are dry-heated to pasteurizing temperatures or above; they may also be fried in oil or dipped in a boiling, slightly salted, sugar solution for a few seconds. All nuts should be chopped into very small pieces before they are added to the mix at 1–3 per cent.

(bb) *Figuring the mix.* A knowledge of calculation of ice cream mix is helpful in properly balancing a mix, in establishing and maintaining uniform quality and in producing ice cream that conforms to legal standards. Ice cream mix may be divided into two groups, namely simple and complex. Simple mixes require the least calculation and are made of ingredients each of which supplies one constituent. Complex mixes are more difficult to calculate. They include mixes where at least one constituent is obtained from two or more products. (Complex mixes require the use of the Pearson's Square, the Serum Point or Algebra method.) Before a mix can be calculated, it is necessary to:

(i) decide upon the composition of the mix to be made;

(ii) decide on the amount of mix to be made in the batch at one time. (Whatever the amount, it may be calculated on the basis of 100 kg., if so desired.)

(iii) choose from the available ingredients those that will give the desired quality characteristics and composition at the lowest cost;

(iv) be familiar with the composition (i.e. the analysis) of ingredients to be used.

Since ice cream contains a higher percentage of fat than fluid milk, one of the mix ingredients must be high in fat. Cream, plastic cream, or butter is usually used for this purpose. Ice cream also contains more solids-not-fat than milk; and a source high in these solids, such as condensed skim milk, condensed whole milk or (preferably skim) milk powder is needed. Fluid milk is usually used as the basic ingredient in ice cream mix. Calculation of the mix involves finding the required weights of these ingredients along with the necessary sugar and stabilizer.

The calculations are simplified by first finding the weights of the ingredients needed to make 100 kg. of the desired mix. With the algebraic method, symbols such as X, Y, Z are used to represent the weights of dairy ingredients required for a 100 kg. batch of mix. These symbols are then used in writing the three equations that express the weights of fat, serum solids (solids-not-fat) and the total weight of dairy ingredients needed for 100 kg. of mix. The method is applicable to all types of mix problems. A typical problem and its solution follows:

Problem: Prepare an ice cream mix containing fat—10 per cent, serum solids—11 per cent, sugar—14.5 per cent and stabilizer—0.3 per cent. Given: whole milk testing 6.8 per cent fat and 9.6 per cent serum solids, cream testing 40 per cent fat and 5.4 per cent serum solids, skim milk powder testing 0.5 per cent fat and 97 per cent serum solids, sugar and stabilizer (cent per cent dry matter).

Solution: Let

$$\text{whole milk required} = X \text{ kg.}$$
$$\text{cream required} = Y \text{ kg.}$$
$$\text{and, skim milk powder required} = Z \text{ kg.}$$

Hence,

$$X\left(\frac{6.8}{100}\right) + Y\left(\frac{40}{100}\right) + Z\left(\frac{0.5}{100}\right) = 10 \ldots \text{ I (Fat equation)}$$

$$X\left(\frac{9.6}{100}\right) + Y\left(\frac{5\,4}{100}\right) + Z\left(\frac{97.0}{100}\right) = 11 \ldots \text{ II (S.S. equation)}$$

$$X + Y + Z + 14.5 + 0.3 = 100 \ldots \text{ III (Weight equation)}$$

Solving the above,

$$\left.\begin{array}{l} X = 67.9 \\ Y = 13.4 \\ Z = 3.9 \end{array}\right\} \; Ans.$$

Note. For other problems using different kinds of ingredients, see standard text books

(cc) *Making the mix.* In order to make good ice cream, the milk products and other ingredients must first be selected and combined so as to produce the desired body and a delicately blended flavour. Obviously the selection of good, wholesome ingredients and calculation of a satisfactory composition precede the mixing of the ingredients in a vat, where they can be heated to facilitate dissolving, blending and pasteurizing. The mixing process may range in scope from the small batch operation, where each ingredient is weighed or measured into the pasteurizing vat, to the large automatic continuous operation where many of the ingredients are metered into the batch. Continuous mix-making procedures may be quite variable and some such operations may actually be modifications of the batch operation. (Modern electronic computers can be used to control the cost and quality of ice cream mixes by the mathematical technique known as linear programming.)

The order in which ingredients are added is as follows: all liquid ingredients are placed in the jacketed vat provided with a power stirrer, and the agitation and heating started at once. The dry ingredients, including skim milk powder, sugar and stabilizer (with a few exceptions), are added while the liquid material is agitated and before the temperature reaches 49°C/120°F. Proper suspension to avoid lumpiness of the dry ingredients may be obtained by either mixing the dry material thoroughly with part of the sugar before slowly adding it to the liquid, or by sifting/slowly adding these substances to the liquid.

If gelatin is the stabilizer used, it is best added after it is thoroughly mixed with an equal volume of sugar, and before the liquid material reaches 49°C (120°F); alternatively, it can be sprinkled on the surface of the cold liquid and allowed to soak before the mixture is heated, or soaked in water and then the mixture heated to completely dissolve the gelatin, which is usually added to a warm (38–49°C/100–120°F) mix.

If sodium alginate (Dariloid) is used, it should not be added until the temperature of the liquid material has reached at least 66°C (150°F). The dry Dariloid is not allowed to soak but is stirred up with cold water and immediately dumped into the hot mix.

When butter, plastic cream, frozen cream or other frozen products are used, they should be cut into fairly small pieces and added after time has been given to allow for complete melting before the pasteurizing temperature is reached. With a few exceptions, colouring and flavouring materials are added when the mix is frozen.

Pasteurizing the mix.   Proper pasteurization of all ice cream mixes should be compulsory because this process destroys all pathogenic or disease-producing bacteria, thereby safeguarding the health of the consumer. Pasteurization has come to be considered as highly desirable and requires only slight additional expense, since the homogenization process can be best accomplished at the pasteurization temperature level. The advantages of pasteurization are:

   (i) it renders the mix completely free of pathogenic bacteria;
  (ii) it dissolves and helps to blend the ingredients of the mix;
 (iii) it improves flavour;
 (iv) it improves keeping quality, and

(v) it produces a more uniform product.

Proper pasteurization consists in rapidly heating the mix to a definite temperature, holding it at that temperature for a definite minimum period of time and then rapidly cooling it to below 5°C (40°F). The ISI specifications (*IS: 2802*, 1964) for pasteurization temperature-time combination for ice cream mix are as follows:

Batch method—68.5°C (155°F) for not less than 30 min.

HTST method—80.0°C (175°F) for not less than 25 sec.

There is a trend towards the higher temperature process. In the batch system, the mix is usually heated and held before going to the homogenizer and from there passes over a cooler. The heating and holding may be accomplished in the vat used for mixing the ingredients.

(ee) *Homogenizing the mix.* Homogenization of the ice cream mix is essential. The main purpose of homogenization is to make a permanent and uniform suspension of the fat by reducing the size of the fat globules to a very small diameter, preferably not more than 2 microns. The advantages of homogenization are:

(i) it prevents fat separation during ageing;

(ii) produces more uniform ice cream with a smoother texture;

(iii) improves whipping ability;

(iv) shortens ageing period;

(v) decreases the risk of churning occurring in the freezer, and

(vi) leads to the use of slightly less stabilizer.

Note: Butter, butteroil, plastic cream and frozen cream can be used in the mix only when the latter is homogenized.

The mix is usually homogenized at temperatures from 63 to 77°C (145° to 170°F). At low temperatures, homogenization increases the formation of clumps of fat globules, as also the viscosity and the freezing time in batch freezers. The pressure required for homogenization depends upon several factors: desired viscosity; composition of the mix; stability of the mix; temperature used; and construction of the homogenizing machine. A pressure of 2,500 to 3,000 psi with one valve, or 2,500 to 3,000 psi at the first stage and 500 psi at the second will usually give good results for an average mix (with 3 to 12 per cent fat).

(ff) *Cooling and ageing the mix.* Cooling the mix immediately after homogenization to 0–5°C (32–40°F) is essential, after which it should be held in ageing tanks until used. Coolers of the surface or cabinet types are generally used for this purpose. Ageing the mix before freezing has been practised since the inception of the ice cream industry. Ageing refers to holding the mix at a low temperature for a definite time before freezing. The ageing temperature should not exceed 5°C (40°F). The ageing time under average commercial conditions may be 3 to 4 hours, except for sodium alginate which requires no ageing. Ageing produces the following results:

  (i) it improves the body and texture of ice cream;

  (ii) improves whipping capacity of mix;

  (iii) increases maximum overrun;

  (iv) increases melting resistance.

  (gg) *Freezing the mix.* When the mix has been properly aged, it is ready for the freezing process, which follows immediately. Freezing is one of the most important operations in the making of ice cream for upon it depends the quality, palatability and yield of the finished product.

The freezing process may, for convenience, be divided into two parts: 1. The mix, with the proper amount of colour and flavouring materials generally added at the freezer, is quickly frozen while being agitated to incorporate air in such a way as to produce and control the formation of small ice crystals—so necessary to give smoothness in body and texture, palatability and satisfactory overrun in the finished ice cream. 2. When the ice cream is partially frozen to a certain consistency, it is drawn from the freezer into packages and quickly transferred to cold storage rooms, where the freezing and hardening process is completed without agitation.

Note: Although the general procedure of the freezing process is easily learnt, the correct handling of the details to produce a uniform product requires expert judgement and almost split-second timing—a technique acquired only through experience guided by continual and careful study.

  (a) *Classification of freezers.* Freezers may be classified as follows:

  (i) *Batch freezer.* Horizontal, Direct Expansion (Freon or Ammonia).

  (ii) *Continuous freezer.* Horizontal, Direct Expansion (Freon or Ammonia).

  (iii) *Soft serve freezer.* Batch and Automatic Continuous Freezers of the Direct Expansion type.

  (b) *Importance of rapid freezing.* Rapid freezing is essential for a smooth product because ice crystals that are formed quickly are smaller than those formed slowly. Therefore, it is desirable to freeze and draw the mix from the freezer in as short a time as possible. A continuous freezer accomplishes this in a few seconds, while batch freezers take 6 to 10 minutes, depending on several factors. Also, since freezing continues after the ice cream is placed in the hardening rooms, the ice crystals formed during the hardening period are larger because they are formed more slowly than in the freezer. For this reason, it is desirable to freeze the ice cream as stiffly as possible and yet have it liquid enough to be able to draw it out of the freezer.

(c) *Factors influencing freezing time*

I. *Mechanical*

  (i) Type and make of freezer;
 (ii) condition of freezer wall and blades;
(iii) speed of dasher;
 (iv) temperature of refrigerant;
  (v) velocity of refrigerant passing around freezing chamber;
 (vi) overrun desired;
(vii) temperature at which ice cream is drawn;
(viii) rate at which freezer is unloaded.

II. *Character of mix*

  (i) Composition of the mix;
 (ii) freezing point of the mix;
(iii) acidity content of ingredients;
 (iv) kind of ingredients, particularly those carrying fat;
  (v) methods by which the mix is processed;
 (vi) kind and amount of flavouring materials added.

Note: The influence of type of freezer on the freezing time and temperature is shown in Table 6.3.

TABLE 6.3

Freezing time and drawing temperature for different freezers

Type of freezer	Approximate freezing time (to 90 per cent overrun)	Approximate drawing temperature	
		°C	°F
Batch	7 min.	−4 to −3	24 to 26
Continuous	24 sec.	−6 to −5	21 to 22

(d) *Changes which take place during the freezing process*

The function of the freezing process is to freeze a portion of the water of the mix and to incorporate air into the mix. This involves: lowering the temperature of the mix from ageing temperature to the freezing point, freezing a portion of the water in the mix, incorporating air into the mix, and cooling the ice cream from the temperature at which it is drawn from the freezer to hardening-room temperature.

The temperature of the mix which is put into the freezer drops very rapidly while the sensible heat is being removed and before any ice crystals are formed. This process takes less than a minute or two. Meanwhile, the rapid agitation reduces the viscosity by partially destroying the gel structure and by breaking up the fat-globule clusters. The gel structure may restore itself partially during the hardening process in the hardening room. Also, the rapid agitation hastens incorporation of air into the mix.

When the freezing point is reached, the liquid water changes to ice crystals which appear in the mix. These ice crystals are practically pure water in a solid form, and thus the sugar as well as the other solutes become more concentrated in the remaining liquid water. Increasing the concentration of these solutes slightly depresses the freezing point of the liquid portion, so that the temperature must be lowered before any more ice crystals will form. Thus, in freezing ice cream, the freezing point is continually being lowered by the formation of ice crystals; and while the temperature drops, more ice crystals are formed, increasing the concentration of sugar and other solutes in the remaining liquid water until the concentration is so great that further freezing will not occur. Thus all the water does not freeze even after long periods in the hardening room.

Table 6.4 shows the approximate percentage of water frozen in the mix at various drawing temperatures.

TABLE 6.4

Percentage water frozen in ice cream mix at different drawing temperatures

Temperature (°C/°F)	Percentage water frozen	Temperature (°C/°F)	Percentage water frozen
−4/25	33	−7/20	59
−4.5/24	41	−7.5/19	62
−5/23	47	−8/18	64
−5 5/22	52	−8.5/17	67
−6/21	56	−26/−15	90

The first phase of the freezing process accounts for the freezing of 33 to 67 per cent of the water, depending on the drawing temperature. The second phase, i.e. the hardening process, may then account for freezing another 23 to 57 per cent, depending on the drawing temperature.

(e) *Batch freezing.* The Batch Freezer consists mainly of a freezing chamber and a dasher. The dasher consists of two parts, viz., scraper blades and the beater. The dasher performs the following functions: aids in transmission of refrigeration by keeping the mix in continuous contact with the freezer walls, scrapes freezer walls free of ice crystals; beats in air and continually pushes mix forward, which is essential for unloading the freezer. (It is important that the dasher be in proper alignment, and the blades sharp.)

Note: The temperature of the refrigerant is rather important and may vary from -23 to $-29°C$ (-10 to $-20°F$) to ensure rapid formation of ice crystals, which results in a smoother ice cream. However, the freezing should be slow and ought to permit incorporation of the desired amount of air, since this affects the body and texture of ice cream as well.

The freezing procedure in the batch freezer consists of: (i) *Preparation of the freezer.* The freezer parts should be inspected to ensure that they are clean and dry. Then they should be assembled in accordance with the instructions from the manufacturer. The operator's hands should be clean. After the freezer is assembled, it should be sanitized either by running hot water at $82°C/180°F$ followed by a cold water rinse; or by a cold solution of a chemical sanitizing agent (such as chlorine solution containing 100 to 200 ppm available chlorine). After the addition of hot water, cold water or chlorine solution, the dasher should be revolved a few times and the particular liquid drained out. (ii) *Adding the mix.* It is always desirable that the temperature of the mix be below $5°C$ ($40°F$) when it goes into the freezer. Colour and flavour should be accurately measured, and poured into the mix. The total volume of the mix, flavour and colour should be about half the total capacity of the freezing chamber. The flavour and colour must be so added as to be uniformly distributed. Acid, fruits, nuts, etc., should be added only after some ice crystals have formed. The freezer should be operated uniformly as to speed, refrigerant, temperature, etc. (iii) *Freezing and incorporation of air.* The mix should now run into the freezer, the dasher should be started and then the refrigerant turned into the freezing chamber. This sequence must be preserved to avoid damage to the machine. To prevent the scraper blades from becoming blunt and wearing out rapidly, the dasher must never be operated when there is no mix in the freezer; neither should the refrigerant be turned on unless the dasher is in motion. This order of operation and these precautions apply to all freezers, regardless of size, type, or installation. (iv) *Drawing of ice cream.* When ice cream is drawn from the freezer, it should be sufficiently stiff to 'ribbon' or almost hold its shape, and yet soft enough to 'settle' or lose its shape within a minute or two. The container or package into which the ice cream is drawn should be cooled sufficiently to prevent the ice cream melting. This melting may cause a coarse and icy texture around the edge of the package and also loss of overrun. Formation of air-pockets within the container should also be avoided. The freezer should be emptied rapidly to prevent wide fluctuations in overrun in the packages. Therefore, avoid filling small packages directly from the batch freezer.

Note: When the freezer is not going to be used for 2 hours or more, it should be taken apart, cleaned and sanitized. (Refer to *IS : 5839*, 1970.)

(f) *Continuous freezing.* Continuous freezers are of two types in the market today: 1. One of these has two pumps just behind the freezer barrel. One pump pulls the mix from the supply tank and pumps it to the second one. This second pump operates at a speed approximately twice as great as that of the first pump. This has the effect of creating a partial vacuum between the two pumps. The valve device in the piping between the pumps allows for air to be sucked in. The amount of air incorporated can be regulated very accurately, and once it is in the system, it cannot get out provided the machine is operating normally. The mix and air are pumped into the freezing barrel by the second pump. As the mix freezes, semi-frozen ice cream is forced out from the front of the machine. 2. The second type operates in a very similar fashion as the first. However, here the two pumps are at the front. One pump pushes the mix into the rear end of the freezer and the other helps to pull out the semi-frozen ice cream from the freezer. There is a separate air pump that forces air directly into the freezer barrel. This second kind of continuous freezer is just as versatile as the first one.

Some important advantages of the continuous freezing method are:

(i) less stabilizer is needed;

(ii) a shorter ageing time is possible;

(iii) less flavouring material is needed;

(iv) smoother ice cream is obtained;

(v) tendency towards development of sandiness decreases;

(vi) a more uniform yield is obtained with less variation between packages.

Some disadvantages are:

(i) great care must be taken in handling the parts of the machine which fit with very small clearance;

(ii) operators and mechanics must have special experience and training in order to avoid operational difficulties and possible damage to the equipment;

(iii) it is difficult to prevent excessive overrun;

(iv) there is a greater tendency for ice cream to shrink in volume after hardening;

(v) initial cost of the equipment is high.

Note: The processing procedures in the manufacture of ice cream have become fully mechanized in developed countries and various degrees of automation of these processes are now common.

(hh) *Overrun in ice cream.* Overrun is usually defined as the volume of ice cream obtained in excess of the volume of the mix. It is usually expressed as a percentage. This increased volume is composed mainly of the air incorporated during the freezing process. The amount of air which is incorporated depends upon the composition of the mix and the way it is processed; and is regulated so as to give that percentage of overrun or yield which will give the proper body, texture and palatability necessary to a good quality product. Too much air will produce a snowy, fluffy, unpalatable ice cream while too little, a soggy, heavy product. In order to secure uniform overrun and yield, the following points should receive attention:

(i) uniformity in refrigerant temperature and rate of flow of refrigerant;

(ii) the use of overrun testers;

(iii) uniform make, etc., of freezer for the operator;

(iv) not too many freezers per operator;

(v) hopper system for filling containers if batch freezers are used.

The control of overrun is very important and should be as nearly constant as possible from batch to batch and from day to day. The correct overrun percentage depends upon the kind and composition of product and freezing equipment. The desirable percentage overrun in different ice creams is given in Table 6.5.

TABLE 6.5
Percentage overrun in ice creams

Products	Percentage overrun
Ice cream, packaged	70 to 80
Ice cream, bulk	90 to 100
Soft ice cream (softy)	30 to 50

There are two basic or fundamental methods for calculating percentage overrun, viz., by volume and by weight:

(i) $\% \text{ overrun} = \dfrac{(\text{volume of ice cream}) - (\text{volume of mix})}{\text{volume of mix}} \times 100$

(ii) $\% \text{ overrun} = \dfrac{\left(\dfrac{\text{weight of unit}}{\text{volume of mix}}\right) - \left(\dfrac{\text{weight of unit}}{\text{volume of ice cream}}\right)}{\text{weight of unit volume of ice cream}} \times 100$

(jj) *Packaging of ice cream.* When ice cream is drawn from the freezer, it is usually collected in containers which give it the desired shape or size for convenient handling during the hardening and marketing processes. The chief requirements for packages of ice cream are: protection against contamination; an attractive appearance; ease of opening and reclosure; and ease of disposal. Protection against moisture loss and temperature fluctuations is also desirable. Broadly speaking, ice cream packages are of two types, viz., multi-service and single-service:

(i) *Multi-service.* This type of container is seldom used in modern operations; a tinned-steel can is an example. They are cleaned, sanitized and used repeatedly.

(ii) *Single service.* This type of package has met with increasing favour, especially during recent years. The quantity filled may be for bulk or retail sale. Most bulk ice cream is packaged in fibre board cartons coated with wax or polythene-wax blends for protection against moisture and oxygen. The most recent trend for such factory-filled carry-home packages is the all-plastic cylindrical container with a recloseable lid. Retail ice cream may be packaged in cups, stick or bars. Cups may be of paper or cardboard, treated as above to make them impervious to moisture. The recent trend is towards multi-packs (such as six packs) in polythene bags, multi-bars in foil cartons, etc.

(kk) *Hardening and storage of ice cream.* When ice cream is drawn from the freezer and put into the container to be placed in the hardening room, it has a semi-fluid consistency not stiff enough to hold its shape. The freezing process is, therefore, continued without agitation during hardening until the temperature of the ice cream reaches $-18°C$ ($0°F$) or below. Here, as in the freezer, quick hardening is desirable, since slow hardening favours large ice crystals and coarseness. Most operators allow a hardening time of 12 hours. The factors affecting hardening time are: (i) size and shape of the ice cream package; (ii) speed of (cool) air circulation; (iii) temperature of cooling air; (iv) section of the hardening room; (v) temperature of ice cream drawn from the freezer; (vi) composition of mix, and (vii) percentage overrun in the ice cream being hardened.

The different hardening systems are given in Table 6.6.

TABLE 6.6
Ice cream hardening systems

Hardening systems	Temperature maintained	
	°C	°F
Hardening rooms	-12 to -45	10 to -50
Hardening tunnels	-34 to -45	-30 to -50
Hardening cabinets	-23 to -26	-10 to -15

After the ice cream is hardened, it may be immediately marketed, or it may be stored for a week or two at the most. The operation of storage rooms is the same as for the hardening room with two exceptions: the temperature should be maintained uniformly at a point between $-23°C$ to $-18°C$ ($-10°F$ to $0°F$) and the packages should be piled very close, to delay changes in ice cream temperature.

Some precautions to be observed in the operation of hardening/ storage rooms are:

(i) provide facilities for calling for aid, should the operator accidentally be trapped inside;

(ii) keep both an axe and a sledge hammer in a definite place just inside the door;

(iii) avoid fluctuations in temperature.

6.10 Distribution

When ice cream is marketed, the manufacturer usually transports it to the retailer under refrigeration at the same temperature as is maintained in the retailer's cabinet. The various means of refrigerating the distribution vehicle are:

(a) *'Dry Ice' refrigeration*. Dry ice is solid carbon dioxide with a freezing point of $-78°C$ ($-109°F$); it is used extensively for package deliveries. It is cut into pieces of an appropriate size, which are wrapped in paper to delay rapid evaporation, and then placed around the package of the ice cream inside an insulated packer or in a single service type packer. The latter is usually a cardboard box insulated with corrugated cardboard and is used especially for the carry-out package. This system is popular for retailing ice cream in push carts in large Indian cities.

Advantages. (i) It is neither moist nor messy; (ii) the package is neat in appearance; (iii) it does not waterlog the insulation, and (iv) it is very light.

Disadvantages. (i) At present, it is expensive and availability is limited; (ii) loss during handling and storage (up to 10 to 15%); (iii) danger of burns to 'handler' and (iv) greater opportunity for heat-shock, which may injure the texture of the ice cream.

(b) *Refrigerated truck*. This is the most commonly used means of transportation for ice cream in developed countries. The truck is refrigerated overnight, and loaded with hardened ice cream the following morning.

(c) *Frozen brine*. Jacketed metal containers, known as Eutectic pads, which contain calcium chloride (brine) solution of specific gravity of about 1.1, are refrigerated in a similar brine tank whose specific gravity is about 1.26, at a temperature of $-32°C$ ($-25°F$). The containers attain a temperature of $-21°C$ ($-5°F$) and are then placed around the packaged ice cream. This arrangement is used by a few ice cream factories for air-lifting ice cream in this country.

6.11 Soft Ice Cream (Softy)

There is a marked demand for the form of ice cream which has generally come to be known as 'softy'. This term has been applied largely because this product is marketed in a soft condition and is ready for consumption shortly after it is drawn from the freezer. The problems involved in the preparation of softy ice creams are somewhat different from those encountered in the manufacture of regular ice cream.

The composition of soft ice cream has been given in Table 6.7.

TABLE 6.7

Composition of soft ice cream

Constituent	Percentage
Fat	3 to 6
Milk-solids-not-fat	11 to 14
Sugar	12 to 15
Stabilizer and emulsifier	0.4 to 0.6

Note: Soft ice cream is usually drawn from the freezer at around −8 to −7°C (18 to 20°F). The overrun may be in the range of 30 to 50 per cent.

6.12 Judging and Grading of Ice Cream

A. *Score card*. This is given in Table 6.8.

TABLE 6.8

Score card of ice cream (ADSA)

Items	Perfect score
Flavour	45
Body and texture	30
Bacteria	15
Colour and package	5
Melting quality	5
	100

B. *Procedure of examination*

(a) *Sampling*. Taken at random for ice cream cups but at a later stage for bigger lots.

(b) *Tempering ice cream*. Generally, temperatures from −15°C to

—12°C (5°F to 10°F) are satisfactory. This is best done by taking the ice cream out of the hardening room and placing it in a dispensing cabinet several hours prior to judging.

(c) *Sequence of observations.* Since the condition of ice cream changes rapidly when exposed to room temperature, one should be alert and observant during sampling, so as not to miss any of its true characteristics, particularly of body and texture. Proceed in the following order:

(i) *Examine container.* Note the type and condition of container and presence of any package defects.

(ii) *Note colour of ice cream.* Observe the colour of ice cream, its intensity and uniformity, and whether the colour matches its flavour.

(iii) *Sample the ice cream.* While using the dipper for sampling, note the following: the manner in which the product cuts, the evenness of cutting, the resistance offered during cutting, the presence of ice particles, whether the ice cream is heavy or soggy, light or fluffy, etc. Set aside a sample in a petri plate/dish for observing the melting characteristics.

(iv) *Begin judging.* After obtaining the sample, take a small spoonful or bite of the frozen product, and taste. Quickly manipulate the sample between teeth and tongue and note the body and texture and flavour characteristics. (Expect delayed taste reaction.)

Note: Rinse mouth with saline water frequently.

(v) *Note the melting qualities.* Observe whether the melted liquid is creamy, curdled, foamy or watery.

(vi) Determine the bacterial count.

C. *Requirements of high grade ice cream.* An ideal ice cream should be packaged in an attractive container, possess a typically pleasant and desirable flavour, have a close, smooth and uniform body and texture, have desirable melting properties, possess an uniform natural colour, and have a low bacterial count.

6.13 Defects in Ice Cream, their Causes and Prevention

Defects in ice cream may arise due to low quality ingredients, improper mixing, or faulty methods of manufacture and storage. The common defects in ice cream, their causes and prevention are given in Table 6.9.

TABLE 6.9

Defects in ice cream, their causes and prevention

Name of defect	Causes	Prevention
(a) *Flavour*		
High	Addition of excessive amount of flavour.	Addition of correct amount of flavour.
Low	Addition of inadequate amount of flavour.	–do–
Acid/sour	Presence of excessive (developed) acidity due to: use of sour dairy products, slow cooling of mix and storage of mix at higher temperatures.	Control over developed acidity by: using fresh and sweet dairy products, prompt and efficient cooling of milk and storage of mix at 0–5°C.
Bitter	Using low quality ingredients, especially flavour, dairy products, etc.	(i) Using true flavour extract (ii) Using fresh, sweet dairy products.
Cooked	Overheating of mix during pasteurization.	Proper heating of mix during pasteurization.
Flat	Addition of inadequate amount of sugar.	Addition of correct amount of sugar.
Unnatural	Addition of not-so-typical (ice cream) flavour.	Addition of typical (ice cream) flavour.
Rancid	Fat hydrolysis due to lipase action in the individual fat-rich ingredients or in the mix.	Inactivating lipase by proper pasteurization of the individual fat-rich ingredients or mix.
Oxidized/Oily/ Metallic/Tallowy	Fat oxidation due to: direct contact of individual fat-rich ingredients or mix with copper or iron, exposure to sunlight, etc.	Storage of individual fat-rich ingredients or mix in tinned/aluminium alloy/ stainless steel vessels.
(b) *Body*		
Crumbly	(i) Low solids content (ii) Low stabilizer content (iii) Excessive overrun (iv) Improper homogenization.	(i) Optimum solids content (ii) Optimum stabilizer content (iii) Correct overrun (iv) Proper homogenization.

Name of defect	Causes	Prevention
Soggy	(i) Low overrun	(i) Optimum overrun
	(ii) High sugar content	(ii) Optimum sugar content
	(iii) Excessive stabilizer content.	(iii) Optimum stabilizer content.
Weak	(i) Low solids content	(i) Optimum solids content
	(ii) Low stabilizer content.	(ii) Optimum stabilizer content.
(c) *Texture*		
Buttery	Inadequate homogenization.	Adequate homogenization.
Coarse/Icy	(i) Low solids content	(i) Optimum solids content
	(ii) Low stabilizer content	(ii) Optimum stabilizer content
	(iii) Inadequate ageing	(iii) Adequate ageing
	(iv) Slow freezing	(iv) Rapid freezing
	(v) Slow hardening	(v) Rapid hardening
	(vi) Heat-shock	(vi) Avoiding heat-shock
	(vii) Long storage.	(vii) Short storage.
Fluffy	(i) Excessive overrun	(i) Optimum overrun
	(ii) Low solids content	(ii) Optimum solids content
	(iii) Excessive emulsifier content.	(iii) Optimum emulsifier content.
Sandy	(i) High MSNF/lactose content	(i) Optimum MSNF/lactose content
	(ii) Temperature fluctuation in retail cabinet	(ii) Avoiding temperature fluctuation in retail cabinet
	(iii) Long storage period.	(iii) Short storage period.
(d) *Melting quality*		
Curdy meltdown	Using high-acid mix.	Using fresh, sweet mix.
Foamy meltdown	(i) Excessive overrun	(i) Optimum overrun
	(ii) Excessive emulsifier content.	(ii) Optimum emulsifier content.
Slow melting	(i) Excessive stabilizer content	(i) Optimum stabilizer content
	(ii) Inadequate homogenization.	(ii) Adequate homogenization.
(e) *Colour*		
Unnatural	Wrong colour.	Proper colour.

Name of defect	Causes	Prevention
(f) *Miscellaneous*		
Shrinkage	(i) Temperature fluctuations during storage	(i) Constant temperature during storage
	(ii) Excessive overrun	(ii) Optimum overrun
	(iii) Rough transportation.	(iii) Avoiding rough transportation.

6.14 Uses of Ice Cream

(i) direct consumption as frozen dessert;
(ii) as a topping for fruit pies and fruit salad.

7 CHEESE

7.1 Introduction

Cheese, like butter, also functions as the balance wheel of the dairy industry in developed dairying countries. The world's recorded annual cheese production in 1969 (*vide F.A.O. Production Year Book* 1970) has been estimated to be 6.8 million tonnes. An insignificant amount of milk is annually converted into cheese in India, mainly of the cheddar type.

The manufacture of cheese did not develop in India during the past mainly because animal rennet could not be used by Indians (mostly Hindus), who considered cow slaughter sinful. However, they discovered a plant known as *Withania coagulans*, the seeds of which coagulated milk, and this helped in the preparation of Indian cheese or panir on a very limited scale. The non-acceptability of rennet even today by the vast majority of the population (consisting of orthodox vegetarians) together with a lack of taste for cheese, besides certain other factors, have impeded the growth of the industry in this country.

7.2 Definition

Cheese has been defined by Davis as a product made from the curd obtained from milk by coagulating the casein with the help of rennet or similar enzymes in the presence of lactic acid produced by added or adventitious micro-organisms, from which part of the moisture has been removed by cutting, cooking and/or pressing, which has been shaped in a mould, and then ripened by holding it for some time at suitable temperatures and humidities.

According to the PFA Rules (1976), (hard) cheese means the product obtained by draining after the coagulation of milk with a harmless milk coagulating agent, under the influence of harmless bacterial cultures. It shall not contain any ingredients not found in milk, except coagulating agent, sodium chloride, calcium chloride (anhydrous salt) not exceeding 0.02 per cent by weight, annatto or carotene colour; and may contain certain emulsifiers and/or stabilizers, namely citric acid, sodium citrate or sodium salts of orthophosphoric acid and polyphosphoric acid not exceeding 0.2 per cent by weight; wax used for covering the outer surface should not contain anything harmful to the health. In case the wax is coloured, only permitted food colours may be used. Hard cheese shall contain not more than 43.0 per cent moisture and not less than 42.0 per cent milk fat of the dry matter. Hard cheese may contain 0.1 per cent of sorbic acid or its sodium, potassium or calcium salts; or 0.1 per cent of nicin.

7.3 History

Cheese is one of the oldest foods of mankind. It was a prominent article of the Greek and Roman diet as much as 2500 years ago. It is referred to in the Old Testament several times. Probably cheese was made accidentally in the stomachs of animals carrying milk, when milk-clotting enzymes of the stomach converted the liquid milk into a solid mass or junket.

Until 1850, cheese was made in the 'farmhouse'. The period 1860–80 saw the introduction of the 'factory system' throughout the cheese-making world.

Cheddar cheese originated in the town of Cheddar located in the county of Somerset in south-western England. Cheddar is probably the best-known cheese in the world; many variants are now recognized, such as American, Australian, New Zealand, Canadian and Indian Cheddar.

Modern cheese-making technology has advanced through the years as shown below:

About 1870—Commercial rennet preparation was put on the market by Hansen in Denmark.

About 1900—Use of titratable acidity measurements to control acidities in cheese making.

—Introduction of pure cultures of lactic streptococci as 'starters'.

—Pasteurization of cheese milk to destroy pathogenic micro-organisms.

—Refrigerated curing of cheese.

—Processed cheese making.

In recent ⎱ —Mechanization of cheese making.
years   ⎰ —New methods of packaging.

7.4 Scientific Basis of Cheese Making

This has been stated by Davis as follows:

(a) All cheeses, irrespective of country of origin and methods of manufacture, possess certain characteristics in common:

(i) They are made from the milk of certain mammals;

(ii) the first stage is souring/ripening;

(iii) the second stage is clotting/coagulation by rennet or a similar enzyme preparation;

(iv) the third stage is the cutting or breaking up of the coagulum or junket to release the whey;

(v) the fourth stage is the consolidation or 'matting' of the curd;

(vi) the fifth stage is the maturing/curing of green cheese in some type of container.

(b) The above five stages are common to all cheeses, but the conditions vary considerably. The chief factors responsible for differences in the final cheese are:

(i) The type of milk used;

(ii) the degree of souring and the type of souring organisms added;

(iii) the temperature of renetting and subsequent 'cooking' of the curd in the whey;

(iv) the method and fineness of cutting or of breaking up the curd;

(v) the treatment of the curd after separation from the whey;

(vi) the milling and salting of the curd before placing it in the hoop or mould;

(vii) the pressure applied to green cheese,

(viii) the time, temperature and relative humidity of curing;

(ix) special treatment such as pricking or stabbing the cheese, bathing in brine, and surface treatment to produce a certain type of coat.

(c) These variables, which are under the control of the cheese maker, all exert an influence on the physical, chemical and microbiological changes which take place successively in the milk, co-agulum, curd and cheese.

(d) From the scientific point of view, cheese making is essentially the controlled syneresis of the rennet milk coagulum, the expulsion of moisture being affected by:

(i) Acid development—the pH falling from 6.6 to about 5;

(ii) warmth—the temperature being raised to 31°C (88°F) for renneting and to about 38°C for cooking the curd;

(iii) repeated cutting of the curd.

The combined effect of these factors is to decrease the moisture from 87 per cent in milk to about 40 per cent in green cheese.

Note: Earlier, cheese making was done 'by the clock'; today, it is done 'by the acidity/pH' test.

7.5 Classification

It is reported that there are probably about twenty distinct classes/types/varieties of cheese in the world today, although they are given over a thousand different names. Cheese can be classified according to the following systems:

(a) *Geographical considerations.* Country, valley, institution, town or region where first produced/marketed.

(b) *Type of milk.* Cow, sheep, goat, buffalo.

(c) *Method of manufacture.* Temperature of cooking, degree of acidity, fineness of cutting, etc.; these affect moisture retention, which in turn affects firmness (hardness/softness) and also the rate of ripening.

(d) *General appearance.* Flavour, size, colour, keeping quality.

(e) *Physical and rheological properties.* Very hard (less than 25 per cent moisture); hard (25–36 per cent moisture); semi-hard (36–40 per cent moisture); and soft (40 per cent moisture).

(f) *Chemical analysis.* Water, calcium, sodium chloride, casein, lactose, fat-acidity contents.

(g) *Microbiological properties.* Bacteria-ripened, mould-ripened, unripened, etc.

Note: The factors that influence the resultant cheese from a given lot of milk are: types of organisms added, enzymes added, acid development, temperature and time used for cooking the curd, amount of salt added, moisture content of cheese, etc.

(h) A summary of the classification of some important varieties of cheese is given in Table 7.1.

TABLE 7.1

Classification of cheese

Country of origin	Soft	Semi-hard	Hard	External mould	Internal mould
U.K.	Cream (C)	Lancashire	Cheddar Cheshire		Stilton
France	Neufchatel		Gruyere (P)	Camembert	Roquefort/ Blue (G)
Belgium		Limburger (S)			
Italy			Parmesan (VH) Romano Provolone (W)		Gorgonzola
Germany	Romadur	Munster			
Holland (Netherlands)			Edam Gouda		
USA	Cottage Cream (C)	Brick	Cheddar Swiss (P)		Blue (G)
Sweden			Herrgard (P)		
Switzerland			Swiss/ Emmental Sapsago		
Norway					Gammelost
Hungary	Liptau				

SOURCE: *Cheese* by Davis (1965 and 1976).

Remarks: C = High fat content; G = A general name; P = Propionic fermentation leading to holes (eyes); R = Ripened; S = Surface Slime; U = Unripened; W = Washed (plastic) curd; VH = Very hard.

7.6 Composition

The average composition of some of the important varieties of cheese is given in Table 7.2.

TABLE 7.2

Percentage composition of cheeses

Name	Moisture	Fat	Protein	Ash and Salt
Brick	42.5	30.7	21.1	3.0
Camembert	47.9	26.3	22.2	4.1
Cheddar	36.8	33.8	23.7	5.6
Cottage	69.8	1.0	23.3	1.9
Cream	42.7	39.9	14.5	1.9
Edam	38.1	22.7	30.9	6.2
Gorgonzola	37.3 ·	34.7	25.2	3.8
Limburger	54.8	19.6	21.3	5.2
Gruyere	30.0	28.2	33.0	4.0
Neufchatel	52.1	23.5	19.3	5.0
Parmesan	17.0	22.7	49.4	7.6
Romano	29.6	27.7	31.2	8.7
Roquefort	38.7	32.2	21.4	6.1
Sapsago	47.6	2.0	41.6	11.9
Swiss	33.0	30.5	30.4	4.2
Stilton	33.6	31.2	29.0	3.0
Gouda	38.1	24.5	29.6	6.1

SOURCE: Miscellaneous.

7.7 Food and Nutritive Value

Cheese has high food and nutritive value: (i) It is an excellent source of milk proteins; (ii) a rich source of calcium and phosphorus; (iii) an excellent source for several fat-soluble vitamins, such as A, D, E and K; (iv) a concentrated form of energy; cheddar cheese gives about 400 calories/100 g.; (v) is both palatable and digestible; there is practically no waste.

7.8 Manufacture of Cheddar Cheese

A. *Flow diagram of manufacture*

Receiving milk
|
Pre-heating (35–40°)
|
Filtration/Clarification
|
Standardization
|
Pasteurization (63°C/30 min.)
|
Adding Starter (Ripening) 31°C
|
Adding colour
|
Adding Rennet (Renneting) (31 C)
|
Coagulation/Setting
|
Cutting
|
Cooking (up to 37–39 C)
|
Drainage of whey
|
Cheddaring
|
Milling
|
Salting
|
Hooping
|
Dressing
|
Pressing
|
Drying
|
Paraffining
|
(Curing/Maturing)

B. *Details of manufacture.* Although not included in the above flow diagram, record keeping and preparation of equipment are both important.

I. *Record keeping.* The objects are:

(i) To evolve a standard process-schedule and technique for cheese manufacture and curing suitable to local factory conditions;

(ii) to study seasonal trends in the manufacture of cheese;

(iii) to assess the efficiency of manufacturing operations;

(iv) to trace backwards any variation in the manufacturing technique affecting the quality of the cured cheese;

(v) to control variations caused by climatic, biological and chemical conditions so as to obtain a standard finished product;

(vi) to collect basic data for computing the cost of cheese production.

II. *Preparation of equipment*: This refers mainly to cleaning and sanitization of cheese-making equipment and accessories. Cheese milk should be received and processed only in thoroughly cleaned and properly sanitized equipment. Insanitary conditions during manufacture will cause contamination, thereby impairing the quality of the finished cheese. All cheese-making equipment and accessories should be sterilized just before use by contact with hot water (at 82°C/180°F)or chlorine solution (having 100 ppm available chlorine) for at least 2 minutes.

III. *Receiving milk*. It is well known that: 'Only high-grade milk can yield high-grade cheese'; 'The quality of finished cheese depends upon the initial quality of the milk from which it is made'; 'Cheese is no better than the milk from which it is made'.

The milk grader in a cheese factory has to perform his task conscientiously from day to day. He should intercept any can/tanker of inferior milk and not allow it to get mixed up with high-grade milk. Successful cheese factories follow a system of daily, efficient grading of all milk received. This consists of:

(i) Determining the odour of the milk in each can/tanker. No off-flavour should be accepted.

(ii) Inspecting the appearance of the milk, which should be free from all extraneous matter.

(iii) Determining sediment, either once a week or every ten days, in each can of milk. (A minimum amount of sediment is desirable.)

(iv) Performing MBR, Resazurin and Rennet-curd tests on the milk once a fortnight or so for each producer/supplier and more frequently (weekly or even daily) on milk of doubtful quality.

(v) Determining the percentage of titratable acidity. (There should be as little developed acidity as possible.)

(vi) Examining milk for bacteriophage, antibiotics and inhibitory substances.

After the milk has been examined for quality and accepted, it is weighed; then a representative sample is taken for determination of fat and casein contents, etc.

IV. *Filtration/clarification*. The chief object of this step is to remove any visible dirt in milk so as to improve the aesthetic quality of the cheese made. The milk is usually pre-heated to 35–40°C for efficient filtration/clarification.

V. *Standardization*. In cheese making, standardization refers to adjustment of the casein/fat ratio in cheese milk to 0.68–0.70. The objects are:

(i) To regulate the fat in the dry matter of cheese;

(ii) to produce the maximum amount of cheese per kg. of fat in cheese milk.

Note: Standardization should either be done correctly, or avoided altogether.

Problem. Standardize 1000 kg. milk testing 4.5% fat and 2.7% casein so that C/F ratio is 0.70. Available: Skim milk testing 2.8% casein. (Neglect the fat in the skim milk.)

Solution. In given milk,

$$\text{Fat} = 1000 \times \frac{4.5}{100} = 45 \text{ kg.}$$

$$\text{Casein} = 1000 \times \frac{2.7}{100} = 27 \text{ kg.}$$

In standardized milk,

Casein = $45 \times 0.70 = 31.5$ kg.

Extra casein required = $31.5 - 27 = 4.5$ kg.

Hence

$$\text{Skim milk required} = \frac{4.5}{2.8} \times 100 = 161 \text{ kg. } Ans.$$

Note: This is a rough method. For an accurate but time-consuming method, consult standard books.

VI. *Pasteurization*. The usual temperature-time employed for pasteurization of cheese milk is:

1. Holder—63°C for 30 min.

2. HTST—71°C for 15 sec.

(a) *Objects*. The objects or advantages of pasteurizing cheese milk are:

(i) to destroy all pathogens;

(ii) to destroy fault-producing micro-organisms;

(iii) to produce a more uniform product of high quality;

(iv) to increase the yield.

(b) *Limitations.* The chief limitations of pasteurization are:

  (i) it destroys the typical flavour and body of cheese;

 (ii) it entails a longer ripening period;

(iii) it encourages the use of low-quality milk;

(iv) it increases the overall cost of cheese making.

Note: The advantages of pasteurization heavily outweigh its disadvantages.

VII. *Homogenization*

(a) *Advantages.* (i) Lower fat losses in whey and thereby a higher yield of cheese; (ii) reduced fat leakage of cheese at elevated temperatures; (iii) increased rate of fat hydrolysis in some cheeses, such as blue cheese.

(b) *Disadvantage.* A softer curd is formed, which necessitates modifications in the cheese-making process.

Note: Because of the disadvantage, cheese milk is normally not homogenized.

VIII. *Addition of calcium chloride.* Excessive heat-treatment causes the precipitation of a part of the calcium salts in milk. This results in slower renneting action and a weaker curd, which can be corrected by the addition of 0.01–0.03 per cent calcium chloride to milk.

IX. *Adding starter* (ripening). Ripening or souring of milk refers to the development of acidity in milk from the time it is received in the cheese vat until renneting. In cheese milk, ripening is done by the addition of starter.

The starter is the 'heart' of cheese. A bad starter is almost certain to give low-quality cheese. A good starter may make up for other defects, such as contaminated milk. There are different kinds of cheese starters, such as those producing acids, aroma, special effects (such as 'eyes'), etc. A cheddar cheese starter usually contains Str. Lactis and/or Str. Cremoris. (See 2.7 for more information on starters.)

The usual time to add the starter is before all the milk has been received in the vat. The amount of starter added is to the extent of 0.5 to 1 per cent of the milk, and the temperature of addition is 30–31°C (86–88°F). Before being added to the milk, the starter should be examined for its quality; it should then be stirred until smooth and creamy in consistency; then strained and added in the required quantity, and mixed thoroughly and uniformly into the milk.

Ripening (or addition of starter) aids in: (i) the formation of desirable curd; (ii) establishing a favourable bacterial flora (and checking the growth of undesirable micro-organisms); (iii) controlling moisture.

Note: Ripeness in milk is measured by: titration (for acidity); rennet test; and pH metre.

IX. *Adding colour.* When colour is used, it is added just before renneting. The usual amount is 30 to 200 ml. or more (for buffalo milk. for 1000 kg. milk. The colour is diluted with approximately 20 times its volume of (potable) water for even distribution. It is vigorously agitated to ensure uniform and rapid distribution. The colour of cheese is usually an alkaline solution of annatto. Rennet and colour should not be mixed together before being added to the milk.

X. *Renneting.* Adding rennet to milk in cheese making is commonly known as renneting or setting.

(a) *What is rennet?* It is the crude preparation or extract from the abomasum. Rennet contains two principal enzymes, viz., rennin and pepsin. Rennin is an extremely powerful clotting enzyme, which causes rapid clotting without much proteolysis. On the other hand, pepsin induces proteolysis, leading to bitterness in cheese. Rennet is available as a liquid or powder or as tablets.

(b) *How is it prepared?* Rennet is the preparation obtained commercially from the fourth or true stomach (abomasum) of the young calf, known as the *vell*. The lining of the stomach is washed, dried, cut into small pieces and macerated into water containing about 4 per cent boric acid at 30°C for 5 days. Milk-fed calves yield the purest rennet. Alternatively, a brine extract at 15–20°C may be prepared. A common method is to dry the *vells* by inflation and afterwards cut them into strips and extract with brine, i.e. sodium chloride solution (up to 10 per cent) for a few days. Preservatives such as boric acid are commonly added.

Note. The pioneer in the commercial manufacture of rennet was Christopher Hansen (Danish) who established his first rennet factory in 1874. The Hansen brand of rennet is world famous.

(c) *How is it stored?* The essential properties of a commercial rennet are high activity, stability (constant strength) and a reasonable bacteriological purity. Rennet is commonly supplied in barrels, stone jars or plastic containers. Commercial rennet should be stored in a closed vessel, in a dark room at below 10°C. It should not lose more than 1–2 per cent of its strength per month.

(d) *Properties of rennin.* This is a sulphur-containing protein. One part can clot about 5 million parts of milk. In cheese making, one part of liquid rennet (about 2 per cent protein) is used for about 5000 parts of milk. Being an enzyme, it is easily destroyed by heat, many chemical substances and some physical conditions. It is very sensitive to alkali. Heating to 70°C at pH 6.8–7.0 will destroy it in 14 minutes.

(e) *Factors affecting rennin action*

(i) *Temperature.* Below 20°C, rennin is almost inactive. From 30 to 48°C, it is about equally active, the optimum being 41°C. Above 50°C, the activity falls off rapidly.

(ii) *Acidity.* The rate of clotting increases rapidly with small increases in acidity. Alkalis considerably retard the clotting of milk by rennet.

(iii) *Calcium ions.* These have little, if any, effect on the first (enzymic) stage of rennin action, while the coagulation of milk (second stage) is very sensitive to changes in concentration of calcium ions. It is common practice to add calcium chloride to milk which has been severely pasteurized, e.g. at 80°C for 30 seconds. This acts in three ways by lowering the pH value, increasing the calcium ion concentration, and raising the colloidal calcium-phosphate content.

(iv) *Inhibitory substances.* Many colloidal substances interfere with rennin coagulation, e.g. albumin, serum peptone, etc. Albumin and globulin retard coagulation. (Mastitis milk clots slowly with rennet; the alkalinity of such milk also contributes to this effect.) Boiling, resulting in denaturation of the proteins, removes the inhibitory effect. Five per cent 'peptone' almost prevents clotting.

(v) *Homogenization.* This has an accelerating effect on rennet clotting, but decreases the curd tension.

(vi) *Heating of milk.* Heat not only destroys rennin but also makes clotting of the milk by the enzyme less easy. The major reason for this is the removal or precipitation of calcium ions.

(f) *Rennet preparations other than calf rennet.* These include goat and lamb rennets, plant enzymes such as *withania coagulans*, ficus, papain, etc.

(g) *Difference in behaviour between animal and vegetable rennet.*
Although vegetable rennets clot both cow and vegetable milks,
animal rennets do not clot vegetable milks even if the calcium content is raised to that of cow milk.

(h) *Bacterial rennet.* The use of enzymes from micro-organisms,
particularly aerobic spore-formers (*Bacillus Subtilis*) and some of the
gram-negative rods (*Serratia Marcescens*) is a fairly new development in cheese technology.

(j) *Adding rennet.* Rennet is added when it has been determined
that the acid is developing at the desired rate. Thus, when making
cheese from ripened milk, rennet is added when the acidity has increased from the initial level by 0.02 per cent. The ideal temperature for setting raw milk under normal conditions is 30°C (86°F),
and for pasteurized milk, 31°C (88°F). The amount of rennet extract
used should be such as to form curd that is firm enough to be cut
in 25 to 30 minutes after the addition of rennet.

The amount of rennet which should be added depends on: (i)
strength of the rennet; (ii) temperature of milk; (iii) acidity of milk;
and (iv) composition of milk. Usually, liquid rennet is added @ 15
to 25 ml. per 100 litres of milk. The rennet is diluted with 20 to 40
times its volume of (potable) water before it is added, to ensure
proper distribution for uniform coagulation. The milk is thoroughly
stirred during the addition of the rennet and also for 3 to 5 minutes
afterwards. The vat is covered as soon as the stirring is over, to
keep the surface warm and protect it from contaminating dust
particles.

(k) *Coagulation.* This refers to liquid milk changing to a semi-
solid junket. The first signs of coagulation are that bubbles of air
stirred into the milk surface take longer to break and a spatula
dipped into the milk and withdrawn shows small flakes of curd.

XI. *Cutting.* This refers to the cutting of the 'firm' coagulum into
cubes of a specific size.

(a) *When to cut curd.* When a (sanitized) glass rod inserted at a
45° angle and lifted straight up makes a clean break in the curd, it
is ready for cutting. If the curd is cut too soon, there will be a lower
yield of cheese; if cut too late, cutting will be difficult and moisture
expulsion delayed.

(b) *Curd knives.* These consist of stainless steel wires or strips,
6 or 9 mm. apart, one horizontal and the other vertical.

(c) *Method of cutting.* The curd is usually first cut with the horizontal knife lengthwise, then with the vertical knife lengthwise and widthwise.

(d) *Syneresis of cheese curd.* This refers to the expulsion of whey and contraction of the curd. From the cheese-making point of view, the factors controlling the loss of whey and contraction of the coagulum are: cutting, temperature, acidity, agitation, time and salt.

(e) *Behaviour of curd after cutting.* After the curd is cut, whey begins to appear between the cubes and a film begins to form on the outer surface of each cube. This film should not harden, i.e. become firm, too rapidly. Care has also to be taken to avoid breaking this film.

(f) *Acidity of curd after cutting.* Decreases by 0.05 to 0.08 per cent from that of milk at renneting.

(g) *Stirring curd after cutting.* During the first 2–3 minutes after cutting, the curd is not stirred. Then gentle stirring starts. The speed of stirring increases with the gradual firming of curd cubes. Matting is indicative of inadequate stirring.

XII. *Cooking.* This refers to the heating of curd cubes; it begins within 15 minutes of cutting.

(a) *Regulation of heating.* The heat is applied slowly to begin with. If the temperature is raised too rapidly, a condition similar to 'case-hardening' will result, and the curd cubes will be hard on the outside but soft and 'water-logged' inside. The rate of heating is such that the temperature rises to 32°C in about 15 minutes and thereafter to the maximum cooking temperature (37 to 39°C) at the rate of 1°C every 4 minutes.

(b) *Amount of heat required.* This depends chiefly on the type of cheese required. For cheddar, a maximum temperature of 37 to 39°C is normal. Too high a temperature can reduce the souring rate and activity of starter organisms.

Note: If acidity is developing faster, then a faster rate of heating and cooking to a higher-temperature-than-normal is necessary, and vice versa.

XIII. *Drainage of whey* (dipping): This refers to the removal of whey from the curd. When the curd cubes have been reduced to about one-half of their size at cutting, the acidity approaches a desirable limit and the cubes attain a desirable consistency (elastic feel when squeezed), stirring is stopped and the cubes are 'pitched'. (Pitching refers to the curd cubes being dropped to the bottom of the vat and piling them up together.) The curd cubes are pushed away from the gate of the vat, a strainer is inserted in the gate, a curd-pail is hung on the curd outlet and the whey is drawn from the vat. In actual practice, especially with large vats, it is desirable to remove one-half of the whey before the curd is quite ready so as to make quick removal of the remaining whey possible at the proper time.

XIV. *Cheddaring.* This refers to the combined operations of packing, turning, piling and repiling the curd cubes.

(a) *Packing.* After the bulk drainage of whey, the curd cubes are kept closely together in two heaps with a channel in between (for continuing the whey removal process). This is known as packing, and takes 5 to 15 minutes after dipping. It results in the formation of two long slabs of curd. These are cut with a cheese knife into blocks or strips 15 to 20 cm wide.

(b) *Turning.* As soon as the blocks (strips) of curd can be handled without breaking, they are rolled bottom-side up in the vat. This is called turning and is carried out every 15 minutes till the curd is ready for milling and salting.

Note: The vat is kept covered and the temperature of the curd maintained at about 32°C.

(c) *Piling and repiling.* Within 30 to 45 minutes of packing, blocks of curd are turned and laid one over another in twos or threes. This is called piling. Then the position of the curd blocks is altered and this is known as repiling.

(d) The cheddaring operation usually lasts two hours or more and is very important not only for moisture control but also for improving body and texture. After cheddaring, the curd becomes drier, more mellow and silky and changes from a sorbo rubber-like material to one resembling chicken breast-meat. In the later stages, it tends to tear apart in fibrous shreds and develops a characteristic nutty and buttery aroma. The end of the cheddaring operation is indicated by:

(i) *Titratable acidity*: 0.30–0.35 per cent *more* than at cutting.

(ii) *Hot iron test*: long threads, 12 mm or slightly more.

(iii) *pH*: About 5.4.

XV. *Milling.* This refers to the mechanical operation of cutting the blocks of cheddared curd into small pieces with the help of a cheese mill.

(a) *Objects.* These are:
 (i) To promote the further removal of whey;
 (ii) to enable quick distribution of salt in the curd;
 (iii) to prepare curd for pressing into final form;
 (iv) other benefits include: de-odourization; cooling of curd, through more rinsing if needed; and making cheese more uniform in composition.

(b) *Types of mill.* The curd mill may be hand or power-driven. Milling is done in such a way that the cut curd falls into the vat itself. The curd pieces are stirred gently to prevent matting.

Note: (i) Milling normally releases a small amount of whey from the curd.
   (ii) After milling, the curd pieces may be rinsed with water to improve their physical condition for salting and pressing.

XVI. *Salting.* This refers to the addition of common salt to the curd pieces. Salt in cheese affects flavour, body and texture, and keeping quality. Cheeses without salt are soft, ripen quickly and rapidly develop unpleasant flavours.

(a) *Objects.* These are:
 (i) the further removal of whey;
 (ii) hardening and shrinking of curd;
 (iii) retarding further formation of lactic acid;
 (iv) checking undesirable fermentation;
 (v) producing desirable quality characteristics.

(b) *Holding before salting.* Salting may be delayed (by more than 15 minutes if needed) when it seems desirable to develop more acid in the cheese curd to encourage further drainage of whey, or to aerate the curd to improve its flavour.

(c) *When done.* Cheese curd is normally salted:
 (i) about 15 minutes after milling;
 (ii) when a hot iron test shows threads 1 to 2 cm. long;
 (iii) when acidity is 0.4 to 0.5 per cent; and
 (iv) when pH is 5.4 to 5.0.

(d) *Amount of salt added.* This depends on the amount of curd in the vat and salt content desired, and generally varies from 1 to 2 per cent (average 1.5 per cent).

Note: Both under-salting and over-salting of cheese are undesirable; while under-salting produces a weak and pasty body, open texture and abnormal ripening, over-salting produces a harsh body, slow ripening, close texture and cracked rinds.

(e) *Methods*. The curd is salted in one of the following ways: (i) *Direct addition*. One-third of the calculated amount of salt is added to the curd in the vat in three applications; (ii) rubbing salt on the surface of the cheese; (iii) floating the cheese in 18–20 per cent brine.

(f) *Quality of salt*. Same as for butter. (See 4.7)

Note: After the curd has been salted, there is no danger of matting.

XVII. *Hooping*. This refers to the curd being placed in hoops or moulds in which the cheese curd is pressed into its final shape.

(a) *Condition of curd at hooping*. The salt should have dissolved completely and the curd should feel mellow and silky.

(b) *Temperature at hooping*. Should be 30–32°C. Hooping and pressing at too high a temperature cause an excessive loss of fat, decreased yield, development of abnormal flavours and exaggeration of bacterial defects. On the other hand, hooping and pressing at too low a temperature result in an open texture, imperfect rind formation and lack of whey drainage.

Note: Before filling, cheese-curd is weighed accurately enough so as to make cheeses of uniform size.

XVIII. *Dressing*. This refers to the arrangement of the cheese cloth before and after pressing.

(a) *Before pressing*. Large cheese hoops are lined with cloth before they are filled with cheese curd for pressing. Small hoops are filled with curd and pressed for 30–60 minutes without any cloth. A cloth is necessary to form a closed rind or surface. The hoops are carefully lined with cloth in order to produce a smooth surface in the finished cheese.

(b) *After (first) pressing*. To remove all wrinkles formed during pressing.

XIX. *Pressing*. This refers to the operation of forcing the particles of milled and salted curd in the hoops into the smallest possible space.

(a) *Object*. To give cheese its final shape.

(b) *Method*. The curd is pressed in two stages: (i) *Preliminary or first pressing*. This shapes the cheese and reduces it to almost its final volume. It ends after 30–60 minutes when the cheese is dressed.

(ii) *Final pressing after dressing*. This lasts for 6 to 20 hours (average 15 hours).

The average pressure applied on round hoops is around 70 psi and on square hoops 25 psi. While pressing, some whey comes out of the cheese curd. Also, the air-spaces and whey-pockets are closed up by the curd. Pressure is applied lightly and gradually at first, but rapidly enough to prevent the curd settling at the bottom of the hoops. Full pressure is reached in about 30 minutes. Too much initial pressure traps whey in the openings between the curd particles and tends to produce on open texture.

(c) *Types of press*. Cheese presses may be of the following types: (i) Screw; (ii) Pneumatic; (iii) Hydraulic; (iv) Spring—in this, full pressure is maintained all the time.

XX. *Drying*. This is done for rind formation in cheese. It involves the following steps:

(i) Taking the cheese out of the hoop. Care is taken to see that the chees remove removed from the hoop is neat, clean, uniform in size and regular in shape.

(ii) Stamping the cheese. The date, batch number, variety, name, etc., are stamped on the cheese for identification and record.

(iii) Keeping cheese in a drying room, where the temperature is maintained at 12 to 16°C (55–60°F) and the average relative humidity at 50 per cent for a few days. The cheese is turned at 24-hour intervals so that both ends and sides of the cheese can dry and form the desired rind.

Note: Mould control in the drying room is important.

XXI. *Paraffining*. This refers to the operation of dipping the cheese for a few seconds in a bath of melted paraffin, whereby a thin coating of paraffin is applied to the surface of the cheese.

(a) *Objects*. (i) To reduce loss of moisture during curing; (ii) to prevent extensive mould growth (paraffin, however, is not mould-proof); (iii) to protect it against insects (as long as the cheese is free from cracks).

(b) *Kinds of paraffin*:

(i) *Paraffin wax*. This is a product of the petroleum industry. The type used for cheese has a melting point of 51–52°C (125–127°F).

(ii) *Micro-crystalline wax*. More water and vapour-resistant.

(iii) *Flexible waxes*. These are combinations of paraffin and micro-crystalline waxes. They are frequently coloured (red, brown, black, etc.) for an identification of the cheese.

Note: The samples of cheese for analysis are taken before paraffin-ing.

(c) *Procedure*. The following steps are involved:

(i) Melting of paraffin in a steel tank. Only that quantity of paraffin is used which avoids overflow when the cheese blocks are dipped in it.

(ii) Keeping the cheese-blocks, a few at a time, on metal racks (with wooden slats) on which the blocks rest on their curved surfaces while being dipped.

(iii) Maintaining the temperature of liquid paraffin in the tank at 104–121°C (220–250°C). Both over-heating and under-heating are avoided for best results.

(iv) The cheese blocks are dipped quickly and completely, held under paraffin for about 5 seconds, and allowed to drain for 10 seconds or until they can be handled without rubbing off the paraffin coating.

7.8.1 *Moisture control in cheddar cheese.*

The following considerations are involved:

(a) *Coagulation period.* An increase in the coagulation period tends to increase the moisture content of cheese, and vice versa.

(b) *Curd particle size.* An increase in the curd particle size for cooking increases the moisture content of cheese, and vice versa.

(c) *Cooking temperature.* Although a rise in the (maximum) cooking temperature causes an increased rate of moisture expulsion, it also reduces the rate of acid production by the starter which has the reverse effect on moisture expulsion; hence the overall effect is rather variable.

(d) *Dry stirring before cheddaring.* This tends to reduce the moisture content.

(e) *Cheddaring.* The smaller the size of the cheese blocks, the greater the moisture loss during cheddaring. On the other hand piling of cheese blocks encourages moisture retention in cheese.

(f) *Salting.* More salts expel more moisture, and vice versa.

(g) *Curd treatment after salting prior to pressing.* An increase in the time between salt-addition and hooping decreases the moisture content of cheese, and vice versa.

7.9 Curing

A. *Definition.* The curing/ripening/souring/maturing of cheese refers to the storage of cheese for at least 2 to 3 months at a given low temperature (0–16°C), during which its physical, chemical and bacteriological properties are profoundly changed, resulting in the development of a characteristic flavour, body and texture.

The term 'green cheese' is usually applied to hard-pressed cheese in the early stages of ripening before the characteristic flavour, body and texture of ripened cheese have developed.

B. *Ripening agents.* These influence the rate, extent and nature of ripening in cheese and include micro-organisms (chiefly bacteria and moulds) and enzymes, including pepsin.

C. *Systems of curing.* These are detailed in Table 7.3.

TABLE 7.3

Systems of curing cheddar cheese

Particulars	Cold curing	Warm curing
Temperature	0–4°C (32–40°F) Ave. 1.5°C/35°F	10–16°C (50–60°F) Ave. 12.5°C/55°F
Humidity	75 per cent	85 per cent
Duration	3 to 12 months	½ to 2 months
Quality of cheese obtained	Mild flavour; bacterial defects minimized.	Sharp flavour; bacterial defects exaggerated.

Source: Miscellaneous.

Note: Soon after curing, the cheeses are stored at 0.5°C/33°F to prevent over-ripening.

D. *Changes during curing* (*cheddar*)

(a) *Physico-chemical*:

(i) *Flavour.* From a mildly acid taste and aroma (no real cheese flavour) in green cheese to the development of the characteristic flavour of ripened cheese. The latter is really a blend of several odours and tastes, such as diacetyl in mild cheese, to traces of odours of butyric and caproic acid, esters of alcohol, salts of propionic and acetic acids in well-aged cheese and pungent odours of compounds of ammonia and sometimes hydrogen sulfide in very old cheese.

(ii) *Body.* The cheese becomes slightly harder, due to loss of moisture. There is also a gradual change from the rubbery body in green cheese to a mellow and waxy body in ripened cheese.

(iii) *Texture.* Cured cheese tends to acquire a fairly close to close texture.

(iv) *Chemical.* The chief chemical changes which occur during the curing of cheddar cheese are: fermentation of lactose to lactic acid and small amounts of acetic acid, propionic acid and carbon dioxide; proteolysis; and a slight fat breakdown. The most obvious chemical changes are the breakdown of the proteins and the newly created solubility of about 25 per cent of total proteins in cured cheddar cheese. In addition to fat breakdown, the ammonia produced by moulds and certain bacteria may have considerable effect on the pH of the cheese and so assist in the growth of other types of bacteria.

An increase in acidity and decrease in pH takes place for the first few days. The pH is lowest in cheese on about the third or fourth day after pressing, and is normally 5.10 to 5.05. It then decreases slowly and steadily during the curing period, as shown in Table 7.4.

TABLE 7.4

pH of cheese (cheddar) in relation to age

Age of cheese	pH
3 days	5.05
7 days	5.06
49 days	5.13
9 months	5.32
24 months	5.58

SOURCE: *Cheese* by Van Slyke and Price (1952).

(b) *Microbiological changes.* All cheeses contain, or should contain, predominantly lactic streptococci during manufacture and the early stages of curing. Cheeses of the cheddar type which are low in moisture and close in texture sustain a steady changeover from streptococci to lactobacilli, some of which contribute to the flavour. Other types are of course present and the higher the proportion of miscellaneous types, the quicker is the curing and the greater the possibility of off-flavours.

E. *Precautions during curing*:

(a) *Selection of cheese*. Only the right quality of cheese should be selected for curing; a cheese which is either too sweet or too acid should be avoided. There should be no damage to the rind.

(b) *Supervision*. The cheese should be examined periodically for flavour, body and texture, finish, etc. The walls, floors, shelves/racks, etc., of the curing rooms should be regularly inspected and kept in sanitary condition. That the temperature and humidity in the curing rooms is correct should be checked, and then be maintained.

F. *Shrinkage in cheese*. This refers to the loss in weight of cheese during curing/storage. Although a slight shrinkage is natural, excessive shrinkage should be prevented. Shrinkage is caused mainly by 'loss of moisture'.

The factors causing shrinkage, i.e. loss of moisture, in cheese, are:

(i) *Temperature of curing/storage*. The higher the temperature, the higher the shrinkage, and vice versa.

(ii) *Relative humidity of curing/storage room*. The higher the humidity, the lower the shrinkage, and vice versa.

(iii) *Size (and shape) of cheese*. The larger the size, the lower the shrinkage, and vice versa.

(iv) *Moisture content of cheese*. The higher the moisture content, the higher the shrinkage, and vice versa.

(v) *Paraffining of cheese*. Paraffined cheese undergoes less shrinkage, than non-paraffined cheese.

Note: The other cause of shrinkage is loss of fat.

G. *Methods of measuring curing progress*. These are:

(a) *Judging*. This is the most practical method. The cheese is examined organoleptically at regular intervals for changes in flavour, body, texture, colour and appearance.

(b) *Physico-chemical and microbial changes*. These include: (i) rheological properties, such as hardness/firmness, elasticity, plasticity, etc.; (ii) the freezing point; (iii) enzyme content; (iv) microbial flora and content; (v) moisture, lactose, fat-acidity, pH, volatile-acidity contents; oxidation-reduction potential, salt-distribution, etc.

(c) *Protein changes*. Protein degradation measurements have been used most systematically and extensively in studying the ripening of cheese. The rate of ripening is measured by determination of the 'ripening index' as follows:

$$\text{Ripening Index} = \frac{\% \text{ soluble nitrogen}}{\% \text{ total nitrogen}} \times 100.$$

H. *Factors affecting the rate of cheese curing*:

(a) *Time*.   The rate of curing is higher in the earlier stages than in the later ones. (During the first 3 months, two-thirds of the total water-soluble protein-degradation compounds are formed.)

(b) *Temperature*.   The higher the temperature, the higher the rate of curing, and vice versa.

(c) *Moisture content of cheese*.   The higher the moisture content, the higher the rate of curing, and vice versa.

(d) *Size of cheese*.   The larger the size, the higher the rate of curing, and vice versa.

(e) *Salt content of cheese*.   The greater the salt content, the lower the rate of curing, and vice versa.

(f) *Amount of rennet added for coagulation of milk*.   The greater the amount of rennet added, the higher the rate of curing, and vice versa.

J. *Role of lactic acid in cheese making and curing*.   Lactic acid plays an important role in the manufacture and curing of cheese because of the following effects:

(i) helps in curdling milk with rennet;

(ii) helps in expulsion of whey;

(iii) helps in the fusion of curd particles;

(iv) exerts protective action against putrefactive bacteria;

(v) favours proteolytic action of rennet extract during curing.

7.10   Freezing

Freezing of cheese may damage its texture. Whereas in fresh cheese the substances dissolved in the moist portion include lactose, milk salts and sodium chloride, as the cheese cures, increasing amounts of water-soluble protein-degradation compounds are added. There is also a gradual decrease in moisture due to evaporation. Thus the percentage concentration of substances dissolved in cheese-moisture gradually increases and the freezing point is continually lowered as curing progresses. On average, the freezing point of cheddar may be $-4.5°C$ ($24°F$) in fresh cheese and $-14.5°C$ ($6°F$) in cheese more than a year old.

7.11   Yield

This is affected by: the quality of milk, nature of manufacturing operations, the skill of the manufacturer, and curing procedures. More specifically the yield of cheese depends on:

(i) composition of milk, mainly the content of cheese solids (i.e., casein and fat).

Note: An extra 1 kg. casein increases the yield of cheese by 2.5 to 2.75 kg., since each 1 kg. of casein carries 1.5 to 1.75 kg. of moisture; on the other hand, an extra 1 kg. fat increases the yield by only 1 kg.

(ii) quantity of milk constituents lost in whey;

(iii) amount of sodium chloride added during the making process (a minor part of which is lost in whey after salting);

(iv) amount of water retained in cheese.

The yield of cheddar cheese is given by the following formula (*vide* Van Slyke):

$$Y = (F + C)N,$$

where

$Y = $ kg. cheese per 100 kg. milk
$F = $ kg. fat per 100 kg. milk
$C = $ kg. casein per 100 kg. milk
$N = 1.63$ for green cheese
$\quad = 1.555$ for cured cheese.

7.12   Distribution of Milk-constituents in Cheddar Cheese and Whey

The average figures are given in Table 7.5.

TABLE 7.5

*Percentage distribution of milk consti-
tuents in cheddar cheese and whey*

Milk constituents	Cheese	Whey
	Percentage	
Fat	92.5	7.5
Protein	76.6	23.4
(i) Casein	96.0	4.0
(ii) β-lactoglobulin	7.1	92.9
Lactose	3.9	96.1
Salts	50.0	50.0
TS	51.5	48.5
SNF	33.3	66.7

SOURCE: *Cheese* by Van Slyke and Price (1952).

7.13 Cottage Cheese

A. *Definition.* This is a soft, unripened cheese usually made from skim milk. It has a mildly acid flavour. It consists of small particles or flakes of curd which have a meaty consistency (when made from rennet curd). Creamed cottage cheese has cream mixed into it so that the finished product contains not less than 4 per cent fat. Both varieties are usually salted.

B. *Types of curd.* These are: (a) Acid curd, in which the milk is coagulated by lactic acid developed by the action of a lactic starter; (b) Rennet curd, in which milk is coagulated by the action of rennet in the presence of lactic acid, developed in turn by the action of lactic starter. The character of cottage cheese resulting from these two types of curd is shown in Table 7.6.

TABLE 7.6

Character of cottage cheese in relation to type of curd

Type of curd	Character of cheese
Acid	(i) Small particles/grains,
	(ii) Extremely acid flavour (mildly acid if thoroughly washed)
	(iii) Lower yield.
Rennet	(i) Large particles/flakes
	(ii) Mildly acid flavour
	(iii) Higher yield
	(iv) Meaty body.

Rennet curd may be formed either by short setting or long setting methods, the particulars of which are given in Table 7.7.

TABLE 7.7

Particulars of rennet curd formation

Particulars	Short setting	Long setting
Setting temperature	29–32°C (85–90°F)	22°C (72°F)
Setting time	4–6 hrs	15–16 hrs
Amount of starter added to milk	4–5 per cent (up to 10 per cent)	0.3–1 per cent

C. *Method of manufacture*

(a) *Flow diagram of manufacture*

Receiving (pasteurized) skim milk
|
Adding calcium chloride
|
Adding starter
|
Adding rennet
|
Setting
|
Cutting
|
Cooking
|
Drainage of whey
|
Washing and draining the curd
|
Salting
|
Creaming
|
Packaging and storage

(b) *Details of manufacture*

(i) *Receiving skim milk.* The skim milk should be fresh, sweet, low in fat and bacterial content and clean in flavour. It should be pasteurized immediately after separation, preferably by the holder method (since higher heating temperatures result in a softer curd, which is easily broken while cutting and handling).

(ii) *Adding calcium chloride.* Calcium chloride is generally added to the skim milk at the rate of 1 ml. saturated solution per 100 litres of milk. The object is to restore the concentration of calcium ions (which is lowered due to pasteurization) to the original level, for formation of the firm curd desired. It is added after the pasteurized milk has been cooled to the setting temperature.

(iii) *Adding starter.* A high-quality lactic starter prepared from skim milk is added as indicated in Table 7.7 and thoroughly mixed into it.

(iv) *Adding rennet.* Rennet is added at 2–2.5 ml. per 1000 litres of milk. Before adding, it is diluted with 40 times its volume of (potable) water for uniform distribution.

Note: Cheese colour may be added, if desired, at 2–4 ml. per 1000 litres of milk before adding rennet.

(v) *Setting*.   The temperature and time of setting have already been indicated in Table 7.7.

(vi) *Cutting*.   The most desirable acidity of whey at cutting is approximately 0.5 per cent (pH 4.6–4.7). The whey should come from the interior of the curd and should be clear and free from curd particles. The method of cutting and the size of curd cubes are the same as for cheddar cheese.

Note: Too low an acidity at cutting causes an undesirable rubbery consistency in the curd. On the other hand, too high an acidity induces a brittle consistency in the curd; and this causes it to shatter during handling, thus decreasing the yield.

(vii) *Cooking*.   This begins soon after cutting and continues for an hour or two until the temperature reaches 46°C (115°F), or until the curd becomes firm enough to remove the whey. The temperature is increased slowly at first; and the final temperature is reached in one-and-a-half to two hours. Stirring during cooking is kept at a minimum and is very gently done in the early stages.

(viii) *Drainage of whey*.   Whey is removed when the curd cubes no longer have a 'soft centre' and when a handful of them squeezed gently show slight elasticity. The whey is removed from the curd approximately two hours after cutting. By this time the size of the curd cubes is approximately two-thirds of their original volume. The whey is drained in the same way as in cheddar cheese.

(ix) *Washing and draining*.   The curd is washed after all the whey has been removed. This treatment makes the curd firmer and hard to the touch; it also removes acid-whey from around it and helps produce the desired mildness in flavour. The wash water is applied in at least two treatments. In the first, the temperature is about 21°C (70°F) and the quantity not less than twice the volume of curd in the vat; after soaking the cubes for 15 minutes, the wash water is removed. The second (or third, if necessary) lot of wash water is at 16°C (60°F) or below, in the same quantity as above.

After it has been washed, the curd is drained. Draining should be thorough. It is best done by placing the curd cubes in a draining rack with perforations at the bottom, which can be wheeled into refrigerated rooms.

(x) *Salting*.   This is done when free moisture has been drained from the curd. Salt can be added to the curd in the vat, or it can be dissolved in the cream for creamed cottage cheese. Coarse salt is preferable. Salt is added @ 1 per cent of curd (or 15 per cent of milk).

(xi) *Creaming.* This is done immediately after draining, if the product is to be packaged at once. Holding the curd overnight in a cold room before it is creamed makes it more firm when creaming. The amount of 20 per cent cream required to give 4 per cent fat in the finished product is then homogenized before mixing so as to form thick glossy coats over the curd particles.

(xii) *Packaging and storage.* Cottage cheese, creamed or uncreamed, may be packed in waxed/polythene-coated paper cups or in polythene bags. It should be stored at 5–10°C.

D. *Yield.* The yield of cottage cheese before creaming depends essentially upon: (i) the composition of milk; (ii) manufacturing losses; and (iii) the moisture content of the cheese. While the approximate yield of uncreamed cottage cheese is 15 per cent of milk, that of creamed cottage cheese (with 20 per cent fat in cream and 4 per cent fat in the finished product) is 18.3 per cent.

E. *Keeping quality.* The keeping quality of cottage cheese, whether uncreamed or creamed, is short even under refrigerated storage (5–10°C). Uncreamed cottage cheese may be preserved for 90 days or longer by freezing or by brine storage. However, it will deteriorate in quality because freezing often leads to graininess and curd-shattering, particularly with rennet cheese.

7.14 Processed Cheese

A. *Definition.* Processed cheese may be defined as a modified form of natural cheese prepared with the aid of heat, by comminuting and blending one or more lots of cheese, except certain types such as cream, cottage cheese, etc., with water, salt, colour and emulsifier into a homogeneous plastic mass (which is usually packed while hot).

According to the PFA Rules (1976), processed cheese refers to the product obtained by heating cheese with permitted emulsifiers and/or stabilizers, namely citric acid, sodium citrate, sodium salts of orthophosphoric acid and polyphosphoric acid, with or without added condiments, and acidifying agents, viz., vinegar, lactic acid, acetic acid, citric acid and phosphoric acid. Processed cheese may contain not more than 4.0 per cent of anhydrous permitted emulsifiers and/or stabilizers, provided that the content of anhydrous inorganic salts in no case exceeds 3.0 per cent of the finished product. It should not contain more than 47.0 per cent moisture. The milk fat content should not be less than 40.0 per cent of the dry matter. Processed cheese may contain 0.1 per cent sorbic acid or its sodium, potassium or calcium salts (calculated as sorbic acid) or 0.1 per cent of nicin, either singly or in combination.

Note: Processed cheese food is cheese blended with legally limited amounts of dairy products such as cream, milk, skim milk, or whey (or their concentrates) and certain optional ingredients. Processed cheese spreads are made with cheese as a base but with the addition of optional ingredients, similar to those used in cheese foods, for desired flavour and body properties. For processed cheese foods and spreads, higher heating temperatures such as 71–82°C (160–180°F), are normally required than in processed cheese, so as to more efficiently destroy heat resistant and putrefactive organisms. This improves the keeping quality of these perishable products. They are sometimes homogenized as well, as this treatment produces an extremely smooth consistency in the finished product.

B. *Specifications*. These have been given for processed cheese, foods and spreads in Table 7.8.

TABLE 7.8

Specifications for processed cheese, foods and spreads

Characteristics	Processed cheese	Processed foods	Processed spreads
Moisture (Max.)	47.0*	44†	60†
Fat/Dry matter (Min.)	40.0*	23†	20†

* *vide* PFA rules (1976).
† *vide* IS : 2785, 1964.

C. *Merits*.

(i) Long keeping quality (so long as the package remains unopened);

(ii) uniform flavour;

(iii) no waste in consumption;

(iv) ease of purchase;

(v) sold in attractively packaged units, which are easily displayed;

(vi) subject to few marketing losses (such as spoilage, shrinkage, etc.);

(vii) utilize unacceptable raw cheeses (which are sour, gassy, etc.) in their production.

D. *Method of manufacture*

I. *Flow diagram of manufacture*

Receiving raw cheese

|

Analysing

|

Selecting for blending

|

Tempering and cleaning

|

Quartering and grinding

|

Processing

|

Packaging

|

Cooling and storage

II. *Details of manufacture*

(aa) *Receiving raw (natural) cheese.* Processed cheese manufacturers usually prefer to control the curing of their cheeses (meant for processing), so that the quality and quantity of the same meet their needs.

(bb) *Analysing.* On receipt, each block of cheese is sampled and then analysed for acidity, fat, moisture, salt, etc. The record of analysis stays with the cheese till it is all used up.

(cc) *Selection for blending.* Blending is the operation of bringing together for processing cheeses of different age-groups. It produces the desired physical characteristics and uniformity of chemical composition in the finished product. Blending is an important operation which requires judgement, experience and technical skill.

The guidelines for selecting cheeses for blending in a particular batch are as follows:

(a) It is desirable that 75 per cent of the cheese used be 0–3 months old and about 25 per cent of the cheese be 6–12 months old.

(b) If the cheese is highly acid/sour, it should make up not more than 5 per cent of the total; if gassy, not more than 2 per cent.

Note: Selection of raw cheese is determined chiefly by age, acidity and pH, flavour, body and texture, and composition of the blocks available. Relatively young cheese produces a mild flavour, smooth texture, firm body, and has good slicing properties; while older well-cured cheese produces a strong flavour, grainy texture, weak body, and has poor slicing properties. Highly acid cheese tends to produce a grainy texture.

(dd) *Tempering and cleaning.* Tempering of cheese refers to bringing it to the proper consistency or hardness. Cleaning refers to the removal of inedible portions of cheese before processing.

Cheese is brought from the curing/storage room to the blending room till it attains a temperature of 16–21°C (60–70°F) in about 48 hours. This is called tempering of cheese and has the effect of softening it, facilitating cleaning, cutting and grinding operations. The tempered cheese is cleaned shortly before it is actually required for processing. First the paraffin is removed and then all inedible portions of the cheese are scraped off or cut away.

(ee) *Quartering and grinding.* The cheese blocks are first cut into four pieces each (which is called quartering), in order to facilitate grinding. Then each quarter is conveyed to the grinder, which is similar to a meat grinder for small batches. For large batches, each quarter is first shredded and then forced through a heavy metal perforated screen.

(ff) *Processing.* This involves the following operations: addition of water, colour, salt and emulsifiers; and heating, stirring and emptying the kettle/cooker.

(a) *Addition of water, colour, salt and emulsifier.* At first a portion of the ground cheese is dropped into the cheese processing kettle/cooker; and to this are added the calculated amount of water, colour, salt and emulsifier. Then the remaining ground cheese is added.

The emulsifier has very important roles to play in processed cheese. These are: (i) to prevent separation of fat from cheese during the heating operations; (ii) to cause specific soft and smooth characteristics in the body and texture of the finished product; (iii) to produce desirable melting and slicing properties in the finished cheese.

The two most commonly used emulsifiers are di-sodium phosphate and tri-sodium citrate, and mixtures of these salts. Used to a lesser extent are rochelle salt, sodium pyrophosphate and sodium metaphosphate. The amount of emulsifier varies from 0.5 to 3.0 per cent by weight of cheese. The calculated amount of emulsifier is mixed with water and added to the kettle/cooker.

(b) *Heating, stirring and emptying of the kettle/cooker.* The kettle is used for small batches, while the cooker for large ones. The kettle initially used was open, upright, steam-jacketed with double-acting agitators. The modified kettle used today is closed and equipped to permit the use of vacuum or pressure to aid heating and emptying. It is heated by direct steam and the excess moisture has to be removed; and it is emptied through an opening at the bottom.

The cooker now generally used is horizontal and cylindrical or trough-like in shape, and closed at both ends; the cheese is stirred with one or sometimes two screws or spiral-shaped horizontally-acting conveyors. The cheese enters through a hopper at the top-rear of the cooker, and is forced towards the gate-end of the machine by conveyors; at the same time live steam is injected into it. As the charge approaches its capacity, the partially melted cheese flows back over the agitators so that complete mixing and thorough heating of the batch is accomplished in minimum time. The rapid emptying of these cookers is accomplished by the positive delivery action of the above conveyors, which force the melted cheese through the wide-mouthed gate at the end of the cooker opposite the entry side.

The optimum temperature-time relationship of processing is 65°C (150°F) for 2–5 minutes, although a higher heating temperature and a longer time span ensures more efficient microbial destruction.

(c) *Changes during heating.* When heat is first applied, the cheese becomes sticky and tends to cluster in lumps or balls. This condition is minimized by efficient agitation. Fat may separate at this stage, although a proper blend may show no visible fat separation. At about 54°C (130°F), the free fat, if any, begins to be absorbed. As the heating temperature approaches 65°C (150°F), the mass becomes more plastic, ductile, smooth, homogeneous and glossy; although it is highly viscous at this stage, it flows readily.

(gg) *Packaging.* In large-scale operations, the cheese, after being processed, is conveyed or piped to the package filler; in small-scale operations, it is drawn directly from the processing kettle into the final package. The cheese should be kept hot and well-stirred as long as a semi-fluid condition is needed for satisfactory packaging. The packaging machinery is an essential part of large-scale operations.

(hh) *Cooling and storage.* The packaged processed cheese is at first slowly cooled to 18–21°C (65–70°F) and then only afterwards kept under refrigeration at 2–4°C (35–40°F).

(jj) *Modern trend.* A modern trend has been the manufacture of cheese especially for processing. After draining out the whey, the curd is immersed in a lactic acid solution and heated with agitation to 39–43°C (102–110°F) for 6–40 minutes. The dilution is then drained off and the curd washed with cool water, salted, hooped, pressed and stored for 2 days at 5–6°C, when it is ready for processing.

7.15 Continuous Cheese Making (Cheddar)

(a) *Introduction.* It is generally agreed that the conventional batch process of cheese making is time-consuming and laborious, involving back-breaking manual work. Further, the rise in present-day labour and manufacturing costs in cheese making countries has made it necessary to look for ways of mechanizing cheese making.

A study of the time-schedule adopted for making cheddar cheese from pasteurized ripened milk will show that the total time required from receiving milk to first pressing is about $6\frac{3}{4}$ hours, with the following break-up:

	Hrs	*Mts*
(i) Setting, cutting and cooking	4	15
(ii) Drying and cheddaring curd	1	45
(iii) Milling, salting and hooping	0	40
	6	40

Although in the process itself there has been little change in the last century, a considerable amount of mechanization has been successfully introduced in all phases of cheese-making operations over the past thirty years. Since 1950, much progress has been made in the mechanization of the manufacturing process of several varieties of cheese, and more recently, continuous methods have been introduced. Continuous cheese-making, as distinct from the conventional batch method, implies a steady and continuous treatment of the curd to expel whey until a 'green' cheese or filled mould is obtained.

(b) *Advantages.* Continuous cheese-making has the following advantages over the traditional batch method:

(i) it is more economical, since power is usually much cheaper than hired labour;

(ii) processing is more uniform and should be more reliable, provided mechanical breakdowns can be avoided.

(c) *Basic principles.* The cheddar cheese-making process can be divided into 4 phases, which can most rationally be mechanized and automated along the following lines:

(i) *Phase I. Setting, cutting and cooking.* This begins with the addition of starter to the milk in the vat and extends to the removal of the bulk of the whey from the curd. In the batch method, this phase is carried out in rectangular jacketed vats which are equipped with mechanically-driven agitators and can be heated by injection of steam into the jacket. The cheese maker cuts the curd, operates the agitators and the steam valves, determines the titratable acidity of the whey at intervals, and at the required acidity, first draws off a half and later all the remaining free whey.

The above operation has been considerably mechanized and can be automated by equipping the vats with temperature and pH regulating devices. An important approach to improving this phase has been continuous precipitation of curd using cold renneted whole milk (Berrige—U.K.; NIZO/Nicoma-Netherlands) and cold renneted concentrate (Stenne-Hutin-French). Although there have been some commercial applications of these processes to soft cheese, the same is not yet true for hard pressed cheeses. Until this is done, the best approach seems to be to automate deep round-ended horizontal vats and pump the curd and whey to a suitable continuous cheddaring system.

(ii) *Phase II. Drying and cheddaring curd.* This could be mechanized by a machine that would convert the granular curd into a fibrous slab. This stage is a laborious one when carried out in the vat and mechanization will reduce the back-breaking work involved. There have been a number of approaches to mechanizing the cheddaring of cheese and these can be classified as: Cheddar Towers; Batch cheddaring or Cheddar-box systems; and Continuous cheddaring.

In cheddar towers (developed by NIRD in the U.K.), the normal curd is placed in an elongated vertical cylinder tapered at the top with its upper portion perforated to facilitate whey drainage. The curd is forced downwards by the pressure of the succeeding curd. As it progresses down the enlarging cylinder, it expands or flows and produces the stretch required for a desirable cheddar texture. The matted curd is removed by a cutter that cuts off layers from the bottom. In the cheddar-box system (developed in Australia, New Zealand and the Netherlands), the traditional batch method of cheddaring, i.e. the formation of curd blocks with regular turning to allow for curd flow, is initiated in a machine and the whole period takes at least one-and-a-half hours. In the continuous cheddaring system (developed in the U.S.A. and Australia), the curd and whey are pumped to a vibrating screen for separation. The curd falls into a vertical curd-fusing section where some further drainage takes place and it mats together. At the bottom of the fusing section, the curd flows on to a cheddaring belt and is slowly moved in a continuous stream to the curd mill.

(iii) *Phase III. Milling, salting and hooping.* This needs large amounts of labour by traditional methods, involving strenuous manual work. Mechanization would not only reduce the labour force, but also take a shorter time and increase efficiency. The operation is better performed away from the coagulation vat. With modern milling machines, the curd is not damaged much and fat losses are reduced. There is no manual handling of the curd after it is placed inside the curd mill; this reduces the possible pick-up of coliforms and other undesirable organisms and extraneous matter. The accuracy of mechanical salting is better than that obtained by hand salting. The filling of curd into hoops has been considerably mechanized, as also the operations of cheese washing, drying, brine salting and waxing.

(iv) *Phase IV. Pressing and packaging.* This stage of the cheese manufacturing operation uses the largest percentage (nearly 40 per cent) of the total cheese labour requirements and, therefore, its mechanization should receive much more attention in the future than it has done in the past. It could be dealt with under the following headings:

1. Rectangular film wrapped cheese;
2. brine salted cheese;
3. large block pressing;
4. continuous pressing and extrusion;

5. continuous pre-pressing of 40 or 60 lb. blocks;

6. vacuum pressing.

There has been a gradual change from round blocks to rectangular ones all over the world; the latter can be film-wrapped conveniently by machine, thereby much reducing packaging costs. Mechanized brine salting reduces labour costs considerably. Several countries have adopted large block pressing in an endeavour to reduce capital and labour costs. The continuous pressing and extrusion of cheese, and continuous pre-pressing of 40 or 60 lb. blocks are both time-saving processes. Vacuum pressing is catching on all over the world, since it caters principally to the demand for close-textured cheese by consumers in their cut and wrapped pieces. Considerable work has been done in the mechanization of the cheese mould and hoop handling from the filling point to the packing room.

(d) *Methods.* Only those dealing with cheddar cheese will be discussed here. With the development of the 'short-time process' of cheddar cheese-making by adding more starter, or by increased syneresis or the drying off of curd, there has been greater scope for large-scale mechanization. A great deal of intensive research in this regard has been carried out in Australia, New Zealand, U.K. and the U.S.A. One method of continuous cheese-making developed in each of the above countries is briefly described below:

(i) *CSIRO (Australia).* The latest cheese making and cheddaring unit has been called the 'Bell-Siro Cheese maker 2, Mark 2', while the milling, salting and hooping unit is known as the 'Bell-Siro Cheese maker 3'. The Cheese maker 2, Mark 2 is capable of handling between 6000-10,000 lb. of curd an hour. The curd and whey mixture is pumped on to a rotating perforated cylinder to separate the curd, which moves along an endless belt on which it is compressed. The compacted curd is sliced and deposited into cheddaring boxes. After cheddaring, the blocks are automatically transferred into the milling, salting and hooping machines.

(ii) *DRI (New Zealand).* Here, the cheese making equipment has been called the Cheese-master. In this, the curd and whey are pumped from the vat to a draining conveyor, which consists of a slow-moving belt with perforated stainless steel slats. Four sets of drums fitted with peg stirrers prevent matting during the draining period. The drained curd is delivered by gravity into stainless steel cheddaring boxes, each holding 400 lbs of curd which are turned through 90° every 15 minutes. This results in the cheddaring of curd in due course. The large cheddar blocks are milled by a rotary mill and deposited on a belt similar to the one described above. The milled curd is mellowed for 5–10 minutes before it undergoes mechanical salting and hooping.

(iii) *NIRD (UK)*. The essential feature of this method is cheddaring in a tall vertical tube, which widens towards the bottom and is insulated. Whey drains between the curd and the wall of the tube; or if a perforated tube is used, it goes through the holes and out by a separate outlet. The weight of the curd assists the cheddaring process in all these different methods. A cutting disc at the bottom supports the curd mass and cuts off slices or chips of curd, which are collected at a controllable rate and passed on for direct salting, as further milling is no longer required. To initiate the process, the tube must be filled with curd. This naturally does not receive the proper cheddaring treatment and must subsequently be handled separately. When the supply of curd is used up, pressure can conveniently be applied to the last batch by compressed air blown in with the top of the cylinder sealed. It is claimed that in a factory operating 12 vats, the man-hours can be reduced from 48 to 8 at the cheddaring stage.

(iv) *Ched-O-Matic (USA)*. In this case, the curd is handled normally* in regular cheese vats until dipping. Afterwards a curd and whey mixture is pumped into an inclined rotating perforated drum for whey removal. The dried curd is deposited on the top of a large rectangular pressing unit provided with channels to permit the whey to escape. After cheddaring, the curd is cut and milled automatically. The milled curd is mechanically sprayed with brine and conveyed to the hooping device.

7.16 Packaging

A. *Definition*.   Packaging of cheese refers to its being placed in a protective wrapper or container for transport or storage.

B. *Requirement*.   Any material to be used for packaging natural cheeses should: (i) afford general protection; (ii) prevent moisture loss; (iii) improve its appearance; (iv) protect it against micro-organisms; and (v) prevent oxygen transmission.

---

* This process has been modified to produce a continuous curd, using natural milk and a cold renneting-cum-heat application.

C. *Modern packaging materials and forms*

(a) *Materials.* The basic ones for cheeses are paper (usually coated or lined); vegetable parchment; foil (usually aluminium); and plastics such as polyethylene (polythene), polypropylene, treated cellulose and cellulose acetate (cellophane), polystyrene, polyester, polyamide (nylon), rubber hydrochloride (pliofilm), polyvinyl chloride, polyvinyledene chloride (cryovac) and saran (a mixed polymer). Laminates are now more common.

(b) *Forms.* The common forms for cheeses are cans (lacquered or lined with plastics), bags/pouches, glass jars, etc.

D. *Film packaging.* This is synonymous with rindless cheese.
Green cheeses of uniform size and shape are ripened in bags made of plastic films; these cheeses may be placed in wooden boxes to preserve their shape.

(a) *Merits*

(i) It affords a considerable saving in labour required for paraffining, turning while curing, etc.;

(ii) it protects the cheese from attacks by moulds, insects, rodents and fault-inducing micro-organisms;

(iii) it is easily applied, and the method can be readily mechanized;

(iv) there is practically no shrinkage while curing;

(v) the method is suitable for packaging small quantities, which makes handling and retail trade easier;

(vi) the method is most easily applied to rectangular blocks;

(vii) it is cheap and convenient;

(viii) humidity control is not necessary during ripening and storage;

(ix) more cheese can be stored in a given volume;

(x) turning is not necessary during ripening;

(xi) it permits rindless curing so that the whole cheese can be eaten. (When rind is formed as in the traditional method, the loss can be as high as 10 per cent.)

(b) *Demerits*

(i) Not all technical problems in film packaging have been solved. For example, the new methods fail to obtain a perfect seal and to remove all air, which may in turn result in mould growth.

(ii) The moisture content of the cheese at packaging must be smaller than that for traditional packaging and must be carefully standardized. Failure to do so may lead to the growth of taint-producing organisms.

(iii) The ripening process in some cheeses (such as camembert) may be affected.

(iv) The film does not always give the same mechanical protection to cheese as traditional methods.

(v) The most careful attention to detail is necessary in film packaging.

E. *Packaging of raw and processed cheese.* Broadly speaking, there are two main types of packaging requirements, viz., the 'long-term' wrap for factory packaging and the 'short-term' wrap for retail sale. For the former, waxed cellulose and nylon films, and cellulose-pliofilm, cellulose-polythene, pliofilm-polythene, polythene-polyester laminates have found favour; for the latter, pliofilm, cryovac, saran, polyvinyl and chloride are suitable.

Due to improved keeping quality, the packaging requirement for processed cheese is less critical. Wax-coated cellophane, laminates with a heat-sealable layer and foil-composite with cellophane or paper laminated on the outer surface are generally used. Hot cheese is poured into pre-formed pouches and the sealed package is tight, mould-resistant and inexpensive. Canning is rather expensive. Processed cheese spreads are packaged in glass jars, paper-board cartons with foil overwraps and rigid vacuum-formed polythene tubs.

Automatic packaging machinery has allowed cheese packers to eliminate all hand wrapping, and cheese packages may be formed from either rollstock or pre-fabricated pouches.

7.17 Storage

Natural cheeses should be stored at low temperatures, preferably 0 to 1°C (32 to 34°F), to ensure good quality. A high temperature leads to evaporation of moisture, growth of unwanted moulds and taint-producing bacteria, and other faults. A very low temperature also leads to mould growth (because of the relatively high humidity usually associated with it) and may result in damaged texture. Processed cheese may be stored at 5–10°C (40–50°F).

7.18 Judging and Grading of (Cheddar) Cheese

A. *Score card.* This is given (for cheddar cheese) in Table 7.9.

TABLE 7.9

Score card for cheddar cheese (ADSA)

Items	Perfect Score
Flavour and aroma	45
Body and texture	30
Finish and appearance	15
Colour	10
Total	100

B. *Procedure of examination*

(a) *Tempering cheese.* Before judging, cheese should be tempered by holding it at 10–15°C (50–60°F) for a sufficient length of time, so as to enable determination of its true body and texture characteristics.

(b) *Sampling.* Take a sample with a cheese trier and hold it under the nose immediately. Then break the upper 2–3 cm. of the sample-plug (to be replaced flush with the surface of the cheese and later brushed with melted paraffin).

(c) *Sequence of observations*

(i) *Appearance.* Before sampling, look for a neat, attractive appearance, evenness of surface, smoothness of paraffin coating, mould spots, cracks in rind, etc., on the cheese-block.

(ii) *Colour.* Observe the colour of the cheese-plug: whether bright and clear, dull and lifeless, uniform and free from mottles, etc.

(iii) *Body and texture.* Note the body by bending the plug and observing the nature of the break; then take one of the broken pieces and work it up between thumb and forefingers. Observe whether the mass feels smooth, silky, waxy, sticky, pasty, mealy or crumbly. Observe the texture by noting the nature and size of the opening and whether they are regular, rounded, large or small.

(iv) *Flavour.* Observe the flavour and aroma by placing the worked-up mass under the nose and noting its aroma; compare this with the aroma observed during sampling. Then place a small portion of the unworked plug into the mouth, chew it to a semi-liquid, and note the flavour (smell and taste).

Note. Rinse mouth with saline water frequently.

C. *Requirements for high-grade cheddar cheese.* The 'ideal' requirements for high-grade cheddar cheese are:

   (i) *Colour.* Uniform; light amber to ivory; not artificially coloured.

   (ii) *Finish and appearance.* Smooth; unbroken rind; a neat, clean, attractive appearance.

   (iii) *Body.* Slightly elastic; breaks slowly when plug is bent; firm but not hard when crushed between the fingers.

   (iv) *Texture.* Compact; continuous and homogeneous; free from openings, holes, breaks, cracks or fissures.

   (v) *Flavour.* Clean, pleasing aroma; mildly salted in taste; when fully aged, causes a pleasant tingling sensation within the mouth; after cheese is swallowed, leaves pleasing after-taste resembling the flavour of sweet nuts.

7.19 Defects in (Cheddar) Cheese, their Causes and Prevention

Defects in cheese may arise due to low quality milk and faulty methods of manufacture and storage of cheese. Their causes and prevention are given in Table 7.10.

TABLE 7.10

Defects in cheddar cheese, their causes and prevention

Name of defect	Causes	Prevention
(a) *Colour*		
Acid cut/ bleached/faded	Excessive acid development in cheese curd.	Optimum acid development in cheese curd.
High/ Unnatural	Excessive addition of colour to cheese milk.	Optimum addition of colour to cheese milk.
Mottled	(i) Combining cheese curd from two vat-lots	(i) Not combining cheese curd from two vat-lots
	(ii) Uneven acid development in cheese curd.	(ii) Even acid development in cheese curd.
Seamy	(i) Incorrect method of addition of salt to curd cubes	(i) Correct method of addition of salt to curd cubes
	(ii) Pressing curd cubes too soon after salting.	(ii) Pressing curd cubes with sufficient time-gap after salting.
Uneven/wavy	Pressing layers of curd cubes from two different vat-lots.	Not pressing layers of curd cubes from two different vat-lots.

Name of defect	Causes	Prevention

(b) Finish and appearance

Name of defect	Causes	Prevention
Cracked paraffin	Excessive thickness of paraffin coating on cheese.	Optimum thickness of paraffin coating on cheese.
Scaly paraffin	Insufficient thickness of paraffin coating on cheese.	Correct thickness of paraffin coating on cheese.
Lopside/ hillside/ misshapen	Incorrect filling and pressing of curd cubes.	Correct filling and pressing of curd cubes.
Cracked rind	(i) Incorrect cheddaring of cheese curd (ii) Incorrect drying of cheese.	(i) Correct cheddaring of cheese curd (ii) Correct drying of cheese.
Rind rot	Excessive acidity and/or moisture in cheese before curing.	Optimum acidity and/or moisture in cheese before curing.
Mouldy surface	(i) Excessively high humidity during curing and storage (ii) Excessively high temperature of curing and storage (iii) Insanitary condition of curing and storage rooms (iv) Delayed turning and inspection of cheese blocks during curing and storage.	(i) Optimum humidity during curing and storage (ii) Correct temperature of curing and storage (iii) Sanitary condition of curing and storage rooms (iv) Frequent turning and inspection of cheese blocks during curing and storage.
Huffed/	Excessive gassy fermentation in cheese.	Avoiding gassy contamination in cheese.

(c) Body

Name of defect	Causes	Prevention
Corky/dry/ hard	(i) Insufficient fat content in cheese (ii) Excessively slow acid development in cheese curd (iii) Insufficient moisture in cheese before curing.	(i) Optimum fat content in cheese (ii) Optimum acid development in cheese curd (iii) Optimum moisture in cheese before curing.
Crumbly	Excessive acid development in cheese curd.	Optimum acid development in cheese curd.

Name of defect	Causes	Prevention
Curdy/rubbery	(i) Low moisture content in cheese before curing	(i) Optimum moisture content in cheese before curing
	(ii) Low acid development in cheese curd	(ii) Optimum acid development in cheese curd
	(iii) Insufficient cheddaring of cheese curd	(iii) Proper cheddaring of cheese curd
	(iv) Over-salting of cheese	(iv) Optimum salting of cheese
	(v) Excessively low temperature of curing cheese.	(v) Optimum temperature of curing cheese.
Greasy	High fat content in cheese.	Optimum fat content in cheese.
Mealy/salvy	Excessive acid development in cheese curd.	Optimum acid development in cheese curd.
Pasty/watery/ wet	Excessive moisture content in cheese.	Optimum moisture content in cheese.
Weak/soft	(i) High fat content in cheese	(i) Optimum fat content in cheese
	(ii) High moisture content in cheese.	(ii) Optimum moisture content in cheese.
(d) *Texture*		
Fish eyes/ yeast holes	Contamination with yeast.	Avoiding contamination with yeast.
Pin holes/ Gassy	Contamination with gas-producing micro-organisms.	Avoiding contamination with gas-producing micro-organisms.
Mechanical holes (openings)	Incorrect cheddaring of cheese curd.	Correct cheddaring of cheese curd.
Swiss holes/ shot holes	Contamination with *Propionic Bacterium Shermanii.*	Avoiding contamination with *Propionic Bacterium Shermanii.*
(e) *Flavour*		
High acid/ sour	High acid development in cheese curd.	Optimum acid development in cheese curd.
Bitter	(i) Low quality milk	(i) Good quality milk
	(ii) Low quality starter	(ii) Good quality starter
	(iii) Excessive acid and/or moisture in cheese	(iii) Optimum acid and/or moisture in cheese

Name of defect	Causes	Prevention
	(iv) Insanitary condition of equipment and surroundings	(iv) Sanitary condition of equipment and surroundings
	(v) Excessive amount of rennet.	(v) Optimum amount of rennet.
Mouldy	(i) Selection of wrong cheese for curing	(i) Selection of right cheese for curing
	(ii) Adopting warm curing conditions	(ii) Adopting cold curing conditions
	(iii) Insanitary conditions of curing and storage rooms	(iii) Sanitary conditions of curing and storage rooms
	(iv) Inadequate supervision during curing and storage.	(iv) Proper supervision during curing and storage.

7.20 Uses of Cheese

(i) Direct consumption as such or in sandwiches;

(ii) in the preparation of special dishes (added in cut or grated form);

(iii) in the preparation of sauce.

8 CONDENSED MILKS

8.1 Introduction and Development

The advent of condensed milks belongs to the nineteenth century. In 1809, Nicholas Appert (1749–1840), a French Food Scientist, announced his discovery of a means of preserving milk (without the admixture of sugar or other preservatives) by the following method: the milk was condensed by heating it in an open vessel placed in a waterbath over fire, to about two-thirds of its original volume. The condensed milk was strained, cooled and poured into glass bottles, filling them to the brim and corking them tightly. The bottles so filled and sealed were then held in a boiling waterbath for two hours. The milk so treated was found to have very good keeping quality.

The commercially successful manufacture of condensed milk was initiated by the American, Gail Borden (1801–74), who is known as 'the father of the process of milk condensing'. Borden is said to have experimented for some ten years before he finally decided that a semi-fluid state, produced by evaporation *in vacuo*, was the best form of preservation. In 1856, he received a patent both from the U.S.A. and England. Records show that Borden manufactured sweetened condensed milk sold under the famous Eagle Brand label as early as 1856.

About 1860, the Anglo-Swiss Condensed Milk Co. was organized in Switzerland by the American brothers Charles A. Page and George H. Page, with the assistance of Swiss and English capital. This company prospered and grew rapidly in Europe. About 1880, it extended its operations to the U.S.A., but in 1902 it sold its American interests to Borden. In 1904, it consolidated with Henry Nestlé of Switzerland forming the Nestlé-Anglo-Swiss Condensed Milk Co.

The basic principle in the process of preserving unsweetened condensed milk by heat-sterilization was introduced by John B. Meyenberg, a Swiss, who was an operator in the original plant of the Anglo-Swiss Condensed Milk Co., Switzerland. He migrated to the U.S.A. in 1884, and in the same year was granted a basic patent on his invention of a sterilizer. Later in 1884 and in 1887, he was granted patents on his process of preserving milk. His process patents provided sterilization by steam under pressure at a temperature not exceeding 116°C (240°F), while the sealed cans were continuously agitated by the revolving reel. This innovation provided the basis for a new industry.

The fundamental equipment used in the early days of the industry has not changed very much in principle. Condensation is still largely done in the vacuum pan or vacuum evaporator under the Gail Borden process, and sterilization is done by steam under pressure in sterilizers embracing the principles introduced by John B. Meyenberg.

In India, the Amul Dairy is credited with the first-ever commercial production of sweetened condensed milk under standard techniques, in 1961. The total annual production of sweetened condensed milk in 1974 was estimated at 6000 tonnes.*

8.2 Definition

Condensed milks are the products obtained by evaporating part of the water of whole milk, or fully or partly skimmed milk, with or without the addition of sugar. The term 'condensed' milk is commonly used when referring to 'full-cream sweetened condensed milk', while the term 'evaporated milk' is commonly used when referring to 'full cream unsweetened condensed milk'. Skimmed milk products are known as 'sweetened condensed skim milk' and 'unsweetened condensed skim milk' respectively. The ratio of concentration of milk solids is about 1:2.5 for full-cream products and 1:3 for sweetened condensed skim milk.

According to the PFA Rules (1976) the various condensed milks have been specified as follows:

Unsweetened condensed milk (*evaporated milk*) is the product obtained from cow or buffalo milk or a combination thereof, or from standardized milk, by the partial removal of water. It may contain added calcium chloride, citric acid and sodium citrate,

---

*Source: *Dairying in India*, an IDSA Publication, XIII Dairy Industry Conference, Ludhiana, 1976.

sodium salts of orthophosphoric acid and polyphosphoric acid not exceeding 0.3 per cent by weight of the finished product. Such additions need not be declared on the label. Unsweetened condensed milk should contain not less than 8.0 per cent milk fat, and not less than 26.0 per cent milk solids.

Sweetened condensed milk is the product obtained from cow or buffalo milk or a combination thereof, or from standardized milk, by the partial removal of water and after addition of cane sugar. It may contain added refined lactose, calcium chloride, citric acid and sodium citrate, sodium salts or orthophosphoric acid and polyphosphoric acid not exceeding 0.3 per cent by weight of the finished product. Such additions need not be declared on the label. Sweetened condensed milk should contain not less than 9.0 per cent milk fat, not less than 31.0 per cent total milk solids and not less than 40.0 per cent cane sugar.

Unsweetened condensed skim milk (*evaporated skimmed milk*) is the product obtained from cow or buffalo skim milk or a combination thereof by the partial removal of water. It may contain added calcium chloride, citric acid and sodium citrate, sodium salts of orthophosphoric acid and polyphosphoric acid not exceeding 0.3 per cent by weight of the finished product. Such additions need not be declared on the label. Unsweetened condensed skimmed milk should contain not less than 20.0 per cent total milk solids. The fat content should not exceed 0.5 per cent by weight.

Sweetened condensed skim milk is the product obtained from cow or buffalo skimmed milk or a combination thereof by the partial removal of water and after addition of cane sugar. It may contain added refined lactose calcium chloride, citric acid and sodium citrate, sodium salts of orthophosphoric acid and polyphosphoric acid not exceeding 0.3 per cent by weight of the finished product. Such additions need not be declared on the label. Sweetened condensed skimmed milk should contain not less than 26.0 per cent of total milk solids and not less than 40.0 per cent cane sugar. The fat content should not exceed 0.5 per cent by weight.

8.3 Composition and Standards

(a) The gross composition of condensed milks, sweetened or unsweetened, whole or skim, is given in Table 8.1.

TABLE 8.1

Gross composition of condensed milks (percentage)

Type of condensed milk	Fat		TMS	
	UK	USA	UK	USA
Condensed milk	9.0	7.9	31.0	25.9
Evaporated milk	9.0	8.5	31.0	28.0
Skim sweetened	—	—	20.0	20.0
Skim unsweetened	—	—	26.0	24.0

(b) The detailed composition of condensed milks is given in Table 8.2.

TABLE 8.2

Detailed composition of condensed milks (percentage)

Type of condensed milk	Water	Total solids	Fat	Milk-solids-not-fat	Protein	Lactose	Ash	Total milk solids	Sucrose
Condensed milk	26.0	74.0	9.0	22.0	8.3	12.2	1.5	31.0	43.0
Evaporated milk	31.0	69.0	9.0	22.0	8.3	12.2	1.5	31.0	—
Skim sweetened	29.0	71.0	0.5	25.5	9.3	14.0	2.2	26.0	45.0

Note: Composition of unsweetened condensed skim milk has not been included, as this product is rarely manufactured.

(c) The Indian Standard specifications for sweetened condensed milks, whole or skim, are given in Table 8.3.

TABLE 8.3

Indian Standard specifications for condensed milks
(vide IS : 1166, 1973)

Characteristics	Requirements for	
	Condensed milk	Skim sweetened
Total milk solids (% wt.) Min	31.0	26.0
Fat (% wt.)	Not less than 9.0	Not more than 0.5
Sucrose (% wt.) Min	40	40
Acidity (% lactic) Max	0.35	0.35
Bacterial count (per g.)	500	500
Coliform count (per g.)	—ve	—ve
Yeast and mould count (per g.) Max	10	10

8.4 Food and Nutritive Value of Condensed and Evaporated Milks

Both have high nutritive value. Both are rich in fat and fat-soluble vitamins A, D, E and K, body-building proteins, bone-forming minerals and energy-giving lactose. Further, while condensed milk is especially high in energy-giving sucrose, evaporated milk is suitable for infant feeding since it makes a soft curd which is easily digested.

Note: There is some loss of vitamin B_1 (30–50%) and vitamin C (60–100%) caused by sterilization in evaporated milk. However, milk is a poor source of vitamin C. Sterilization is reported to have a minor effect on the biological value and digestibility of milk-proteins.

8.5 Physico-chemical Properties

(a) *Specific gravity/density*. Evaporation of water in the manufacture of condensed milks raises their specific gravity/density, which is universally employed to control their composition. Baume hydrometers are widely used for this purpose. Table 8.4 gives some of the figures for specific gravity and Baume readings.

TABLE 8.4

Specific gravity and Baume readings of condensed milks

Type of condensed milk	Fat	Milk-solids-not-fat —Percentage—	Sucrose	Specific gravity 16°C (60°F)	Specific gravity 49°C (120°F)	Baume' Reading 16°C (60°F)	Baume' Reading 49°C (120°F)
Condensed milk	9.0	22.0	43.0	1.303	1.282	33.7	31.9
Evaporated milk	9.0	22.0	—	1.083	1.072	11.2	9.7
Skim sweetened	—	26.0	45.0	1.355	1.333	38.0	36.2

(b) *Freezing point*. The figures for condensed and evaporated milks are given in Table 8.5.

TABLE 8.5

Freezing point of condensed and evaporated milks

Type of condensed milk	Fat	Milk-solids-not-fat —Percentage—	Sucrose	Freezing point (0°C)	Freezing point (0°F)
Condensed milk	9.0	22.0	43.0	−14.9	5.1
Evaporated milk	9.0	22.0	—	−1.3	29.6

(c) *Colour and flavour.* The exposure to heat during manufacture and storage of condensed milks tends to darken their colour and develop a cooked flavour. The darkening of colour, commonly referred to as browning-discolouration, results from the interaction of the amino-compounds with sugar (principally casein with lactose) and has been called Maillard-type browning. The brown pigment is called melanoidin. The cooked flavour is attributed to sulfydryl compounds, which are formed during heat treatment. The rate of development and the intensity of these defects are cumulative. Further, the development of browning-discolouration is usually accompanied by the development of a cooked flavour, and vice versa. The above reactions also continue during storage.

The development of a brown colour in milk and milk products is objectionable. Although pasteurized milk exhibits no tendency to brown, certain condensed and dried milk products which are processed at high temperatures and stored at room temperatures for an appreciable time are subject to browning. Evaporated milk is particularly susceptible to this defect.

The principal factors affecting browning-discolouration and cooked flavour production in fluid milk systems are:

(i) *Heat-treatment.* Most important. The higher the intensity of heating, the greater the tendency for production of browning-discolouration and cooked flavour, and vice versa.

(ii) *Total solids concentration.* The higher the concentration of milk solids (especially proteins and lactose) the greater the effect with any given level of heat-treatment, and vice versa.

(iii) *pH.* The higher the pH (due to the increased level of added stabilizer) the greater the effect, and vice versa.

(iv) *Storage temperature and time.* The higher the temperature and/or time of storage the greater the effect, and vice versa. (Refrigerated storage exhibits an inhibitory effect on colour development.)

(v) *Oxygen content.* The higher the oxygen content in the headspace of the container the greater the effect, and vice versa.

(vi) *Various added compounds.* Reducing sugars (such as lactose and glucose) favour browning to a much greater extent than sucrose.

Note: Besides amino-sugar or Maillard-type browning in milk and milk products, non-amino browning or caramelization occurs due to heat-decomposition of sugars in the absence of amino-compounds.

(d) *Viscosity*. This refers to the resistance offered by a liquid to flow. The viscosity of condensed/concentrated milks seems to be influenced by the following factors:

(i) *Concentration*. The higher the degree of concentration of the milk solids the greater the viscosity, and vice versa.

(ii) *Composition*. The higher the percentages of casein and fat (and also added sugar in the case of condensed milk) the higher the viscosity of condensed milks, and vice versa.

(iii) *State of protein and fat*. The higher the instability of milk proteins (especially casein), the higher the viscosity upon heating, and vice versa.

(iv) *pH and salt-balance*. The more disturbed the salt-balance (due to lower pH, as a result of developed acidity) the greater the viscosity, and vice versa.

(v) *Temperature of forewarming/pre-heating*. The lower the temperature the greater the viscosity, and vice versa.

Viscosity control during the manufacture and storage of condensed milks is highly important for successful marketing. To the trade and to the consumer, a viscosity sufficient to give the product a nice, full body symbolizes richness of milk. Neither an abnormally low (due perhaps to age-thinning) nor an excessively high viscosity (due perhaps to age-thickening) is desired. Low viscosity suggests low nutritive value to the consumer; it also tends to leave an objectionable sugar sediment in condensed milk and fat separation in evaporated milk; excessive viscosity causes gel-formation and mineral deposit in evaporated milk.

Note: Practically the same factors which control heat-stability during sterilization, also influence viscosity. However, the effect is in the opposite direction; in other words, an increase in heat-stability results in a decrease in viscosity, and vice versa.

8.6 Role of Milk Constituents in Condensed Milks

(a) *Milk-fat*. Imparts a rich and pleasing flavour, soft body and smooth texture to both condensed and evaporated milks. Affects viscosity. Significant in flavour problems, such as rancidity, tallowiness, etc.

(b) *Milk-proteins*. Technologically of great importance. Their physico-chemical reactions to processing-heat largely determine the heat-stability and viscosity of condensed milks.

(c) *Milk-sugar.* Plays an important role in the successful control of the texture of condensed milk. The size of lactose crystals determines the relative smoothness of condensed milk, and is controlled by the procedure used for the cooling and crystallization of this product.

(d) *Mineral salts.* These—particularly calcium and magnesium together with citrates and phosphates—control the salt-balance and heat-stability of milk. A disturbed salt-balance causes objectionable heat-coagulation of milk.

8.7 Method of Manufacture, Packaging and Storage of Condensed Milk

A. *Flow diagram of manufacture*

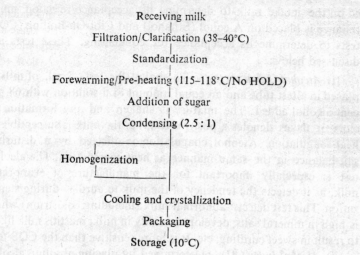

Receiving milk

Filtration/Clarification (38–40°C)

Standardization

Forewarming/Pre-heating (115–118°C/No HOLD)

Addition of sugar

Condensing (2.5 : 1)

Homogenization

Cooling and crystallization

Packaging

Storage (10°C)

B. *Details of manufacture*

Basic principle. The basic principle in the production of condensed and evaporated milks is that high quality milk is filtered/clarified, standardized, forewarmed and condensed/evaporated to the desired level. The concentrated product is preserved by the addition of sugar for condensed milk and by heat-sterilization for evaporated milk.

(aa) *Receiving milk.* The quality of the incoming milk is one of the indispensable corner-stones upon which rest the quality and marketability of every form of concentrated milk. It is well known that the sanitary quality of the milk on the receiving platform depends on its background on the farm, viz., healthy cows, clean milk production, clean utensils, freedom from colostrum, prompt cooling and refrigerated transport. However, all milk supplies must be systematically and thoroughly inspected each day by conscientious and experienced milk-graders.

When milk is received at the plant, its temperature should be at 10°C (50°F) or below. The milk should be clean, sweet, free from off-flavours and odours and reasonably free from extraneous material. Contamination by antibiotics, pesticides and other chemical residues and metals is highly undesirable. No abnormal milk should be accepted. Acid development is objectionable, for not only does this indicate an excessive bacterial count, but it also reduces the heat-stability of milk.

Among the various platform and laboratory tests usually performed on the intake milk to determine its acceptance/rejection, much reliance is placed on Alcohol (Ethanol) and Clot-On-Boiling (COB) tests to determine its acceptance for condensing. These tests are discussed below:

(i) *Alcohol (Ethanol) test.* To make this test, 5 ml. of milk is placed in a test tube and an equal amount of a solution with 68 per cent alcohol added. The mixture is shaken and any formation of clots or flakes denotes a positive test, i.e. the milk is susceptible to heat-coagulation. Alcohol coagulation is affected by a disturbed salt-balance in the same manner as heat-coagulation. The alcohol test is especially important for the manufacture of evaporated milk, as it detects the tendency of the milk to curdle during sterilization. This test detects: abnormal milk (including colostrum) which is high in mineral salts; developed acidity in milk; mastitis milk likely to result in sweet curdling; etc. It is more sensitive than the COB test.

(ii) *Alcohol Index (AI).* Determined by placing absolute alcohol in the burette and 10 ml. milk in a beaker. The number of ml. of alcohol required for flake formation is known as the Alcohol Index (AI). An AI of 7 is indicative of good stable milk for acceptance, while 3 or less shows that the milk is fit for rejection.

(iii) *Alcohol-Alizarin test.* This test not only determines the heat-stability of milk but also the pH. (Milk is coagulated if the pH is 5.6 or below.)

Note: Under Indian conditions today, where any developed acidity in milk is invariably neutralized by the addition of sodium bicarbonate by unscrupulous dealers resulting in a disturbed salt balance, acceptance of milk on the basis of Alcohol Tests alone may prove impractical since the bulk of the daily milk supply may then have to be rejected.

(iv) *Clot-On-Boiling test.* In this test, 5 ml. of milk is placed in a test tube and kept in a boiling water-bath for 5 minutes. Afterwards it is removed and examined for precipitation. If curd is observed, the milk is said to fail the COB test and should be rejected.

Note: After the milk has been accepted on the basis of the above tests, it is weighed, sampled and tested for fat, SNF, etc.

(bb) *Filtration/Clarification.* This is done in order to remove visible foreign matter, which is unsightly and may cause consumer complaints, from the milk. The milk is generally pre-heated (in warm-milk clarifiers) to 35–40°C to increase the efficiency of the operation. Afterwards, it is cooled so as to preserve its quality.

(cc) *Standardization.* This is done so as to conform to legal standards in the finished product. The standardization of raw milk is normally carried out in three stages:

(a) the first standardization, which establishes the desired ratio of Fat : SNF (usually 1 : 2.44);

(b) the second, which establishes the desired ratio of added sugar to the total milk-solids;

(c) the third, which adjusts the concentration of the finished condensed milk to the desired percentage of total solids.

The fat/SNF ratio in raw milk is adjusted by adding a calculated amount of cream or skim milk to it, depending on whether there is a fat shortage or fat surplus, as shown in the examples below:

(i) *Correcting fat shortage in the batch by the addition of cream*:

Problem. Wanted 9.05% fat and 31% total milk-solids in condensed milk. On hand, 10,000 kg. milk testing 3.60% fat and 12.50% TS, and cream (from the same milk) testing 40% fat. How much 40% cream must be added to provide the desired ratio of fat to SNF?

Solution.

$$\% \text{ SNF in cream} = \frac{(100 - \% \text{ fat in cream})}{(100 - \% \text{ fat in milk})} \times \% \text{ SNF in milk}$$

$$= \frac{100 - 40}{100 - 3.60} \times 8.9 = 5.54\%$$

In raw milk:

$$\frac{SNF}{fat} = \frac{12.50 - 3.60}{3.60} = 2.47$$

In condensed milk·

$$\frac{SNF}{fat} = \frac{31 - 9.05}{9.05} = 2.43.$$

Hence there is a fat shortage; to be corrected by adding cream (C kg).

Total fat in mixture $= \dfrac{10,000 \times 3.6}{100} + \dfrac{C \times 40}{100} = 360 + 0.4C$

Total SNF in mixture $= \dfrac{10,000 \times 8.9}{100} + \dfrac{C \times 5.54}{100} = 890 + 0.0554C$

$$\frac{SNF}{fat} = \frac{890 + 0.0554C}{360 + 0.4C} = 2.43$$

$$890 + 0.554C = 2.43(360 + 0.4C)$$

$$C = 16.6 \text{ kg.} \quad Ans.$$

(ii) *Correcting fat surplus in the batch by the addition of skim milk.*
Problem. Wanted 9.05% fat and 31% total milk solids in condensed milk. On hand 10,000 kg. milk testing 6.5% fat and 16.08 TS, and skim milk testing 0.1% fat. How much skim milk must be added to provide the desired ratio of fat to SNF?
Solution.

$$\% \text{ SNF in skim milk} = \frac{\% \text{ SNF in whole milk}}{100 - \% \text{ fat in whole milk}} \times 100$$

$$= \frac{9.58}{100 - 6.5} \times 100 = 10.25$$

In raw milk:

$$\frac{SNF}{fat} = \frac{16.08 - 6.5}{6.5} = 1.47$$

In condensed milk:

$$\frac{SNF}{fat} = \frac{31 - 9.05}{9.05} = 2.43.$$

Hence there is a fat surplus, to be corrected by adding skim milk (S kg).

Total fat in mixture

$$= \frac{10,000 \times 6.5}{100} + \frac{S \times 0.1}{100} = 650 + 0.001S$$

Total SNF in mixture

$$= \frac{10,000 \times 9.58}{100} + \frac{S \times 10.25}{100} = 958 + 0.125\ S$$

$$\frac{SNF}{fat} = \frac{958 + 0.1025\ S}{650 + 0.001\ S} = 2.43$$

$$958 + 0.125\ S = 2.43\ (650 + 0.001\ S)$$

$$S = 6,210.6\ Kg.\ Ans.$$

(dd) *Forewarming/pre-heating.* This refers to the heating of milk before it is condensed, and serves the following purposes:

(i) To ensure that the finished product is free from micro-organisms and enzymes;

(ii) to ensure uninterrupted boiling in the vacuum pan;

(iii) to provide an effective means of controlling objectionable age-thickening in the finished product.

The temperature-time of forewarming/pre-heating extends over a wide range, such as 82 to 93°C (180 to 200°F) for 5 to 15 minutes; or 116 to 149°C for 0.5 to 5 minutes. The modern trend is towards high-temperature short-time heating, such as 115 to 118°C (239 to 248°F), for No-Hold/Flash. The exact temperature-time of heating is so controlled as to provide optimum viscosity in the manufactured product without inducing excessive thickening or thinning during storage.

Tubular heat-exchangers are commonly used for forewarming; either double-tube or shell-and-tube heat-exchangers are preferred. The several systems of forewarming may be grouped as below:

Equipment	Principle of heat-exchange
Hot well	Either direct heating by injection of live steam, or indirect steam-in-jacket heating
Continuous flow heaters (plate or tubular)	Indirect steam-heating in alternate plates or concentric tubes
Closed pressure heater (tank or tubular)	Indirect steam-heating in a closed tank or in concentric tubes under pressure.

(ee) *Addition of sugar*

(a) *Purpose.* Sugar is added for the purpose of preserving the condensed milk without resorting to sterilization by heat.

(b) *Kind.* Generally sucrose is added as it has proved most suitable. It is either highly refined cane or beet sugar. Other sweetening agents, such as corn syrup solids, glucose and dextrose, have been used to replace sugar by 5 to 25 per cent. The disadvantages of these sweetening agents are their reduced sweetening capacity compared to sucrose and their adverse effects on colour and the rate of thickening in storage.

(c) *Amount.* This ranges from 40 to 45 per cent in the finished product, which requires 18 to 20 per cent sugar on milk basis. Hunziker advocated a Sugar Ratio (sugar-in-water concentration) of 62.5 to 64.5 per cent; this amount not only ensures proper protection against microbial growth, but also prevents sugar crystallization.

(i) *Determination of sugar ratio (SR).* Either of the two formulae may be used:

$$\% \text{ SR} = \frac{\% \text{ sugar}}{100 - \% \text{ TMS}} \times 100 \tag{I}$$

$$\% \text{ SR} = \frac{\% \text{ sugar}}{\% \text{ sugar} + \% \text{ water}} \times 100 \tag{II}$$

Problem. Condensed milk contains 31% total milk solids and 43.1% added sugar. What is the sugar ratio?

Solution. $\text{SR} = \dfrac{43.1}{100 - 31} \times 100$

$\qquad\qquad = 62.5\%$ *Ans.*

(ii) *Determination of percentage of sugar in condensed milk for desired sugar ratio.* The following formula should be used:

$$\% \text{ sugar in condensed milk} = \frac{(100 - \% \text{ TMS}) \times \text{SR}}{100}$$

Problem. Using the same values as above, what should the percentage of sugar in condensed milk for a SR of 62.5 be?

Solution.

$\qquad$ Sugar in condensed milk $= \dfrac{100 - 31}{100} \times 62.5$

$\qquad\qquad\qquad\qquad = 43.1\%.$ *Ans.*

(iii) *Determination of sugar in milk to give 43.1% sugar in condensed milk.* Determine ratio of concentration by dividing % total milk solids in condensed milk by % total milk solids in fresh milk. Then divide percentage of sugar in condensed milk by the ratio of concentration.

Problem. Fresh milk contains 12.3% total solids and condensed milk contains 31% total solids. How much sugar should be added to milk to give 43.1% sugar in condensed milk?

Solution.

$$\text{Ratio of concentration} = \frac{\% \text{ TMS in condensed milk}}{\% \text{ TMS in milk}}$$

$$= \frac{31}{12.3} = 2.5$$

$$\text{Sugar in milk} = \frac{\% \text{ sugar in condensed milk}}{\text{ratio of concentration}}$$

$$= \frac{43.1}{2.5} = 17.2. \quad Ans.$$

(d) *Quality.* Sucrose in granulated or syrup form must be of good quality. Liquid sugars (approximately 65 per cent sucrose) should be subjected to a high pasteurizing temperature to destroy the micro-organisms before they are added to condensed milk.

(e) *Method.* The temperature and time at which sugar is added to the milk in the batch have a definite effect on the keeping quality and physical stability (age-thickening) of the finished product. Sugar is added at the end of the condensing process. The dry sugar is dissolved in the least possible quantity of water. If added before condensing, an increase in viscosity and greater difficulty in the evaporation of moisture result. Further, the presence of added sugar in the fresh milk during forewarming increases the heat-resistance and survival capacity of the micro-organisms, thereby adversely affecting keeping quality. In order to ensure freedom from extraneous material, the sugar syrup may be passed through a pressure filter or a centrifugal clarifier.

(ff) *Condensing.* The basic principle consists in the removal of water from the standardized milk by boiling it under partial vacuum at a low temperature till the desired concentration is reached. This operation is carried out in an evaporator, which should preferably be of the single-effect type (also known as a vacuum pan). The chief advantages of condensing milk in vacuum are: economy of operation, rapidity of evaporation and protection of milk against heat damage. Vacuum condensing achieves the object of obtaining a finished product which is free from any cooked flavours and can be readily reconstituted into the original milk.

(a) *Description of a vacuum pan.* The vacuum pan or evaporator is the heart of the milk condensary. It is used in the manufacture of every type of concentrated milk product. It consists essentially of five major parts and numerous accessories, as given below:

(i) *Heating surface.* This determines the evaporative capacity of the vacuum pan. It is provided with either a steam jacket, or a series of steam coils, or both; or with product-tubes enclosed in a steam chest or calandria; or a series of plates with low pressure steam and product in alternate plates; etc.

(ii) *Vapour space.* This refers to that portion of the body of the pan which extends above the level of milk. It is here that the water contained in boiling milk is converted into vapour. The walls of the vapour space are equipped with a manhole, thermometer, vacuum gauge, vacuum break, observation glass and illumination glasses with lights. The milk intake pipe also enters through the wall of the condenser. This pipe connects with the forewarmer and discharges the hot fresh milk into the pan.

(iii) *Entrainment separator.* The purpose of this is to reclaim particles of milk entrained by the vapour currents that pass from the vacuum pan to the condenser at a high velocity—so as to prevent excessive entrainment losses of valuable milk solids and to minimize the danger of troublesome pollution of milk-factory wastes. The latest designs of efficient entrainment separators are capable of reducing entrainment losses to a small fraction of one per cent. These may be of the centrifugal, deflector or reverse-flow types.

(iv) *Condenser.* The purpose of this is to condense the milk vapour and to cool the entrained air and non-condensable gases. The condensing of milk vapours is essential for maintaining the desired vacuum in the pan; the cooling of the entrained air and non-condensable gases is necessary for smooth pan operation.

Condensers may be either surface or spray types. The spray type condenser is used exclusively in the milk condensery and may be jet or cataract, parallel or counter-current, with the condenser installed either inside or outside the vacuum pan. The condenser water is removed either by pumps or a barometric drain/leg (usually 10.4 metre/34 ft. or more in length to remove water by gravity).

The counter-current condenser makes highly efficient use of the water supply, makes possible the advantageous use of a water-cooling tower or spray pond, and is therefore recommended in the tropics.

The efficiency of spray condensers depends on the volume and temperature of the available water, surface area of water spray and the duration of contact of hot vapours with the cooling water spray.

The amount of cooling water required in the condenser is determined by the temperature of the water supply, the pan operating temperature and the temperature of the condenser water discharge. On average, it requires 20 kg. of cooling water to remove the vapours of 1 kg. of water contained in the milk, in the tropics. It is obviously desirable to use potable water in the condenser because it may get into the milk in the vacuum pan at any time.

(v) *Vacuum pump.* The purpose of this pump is to produce and maintain a partial vacuum, so as to make possible the condensing of milk in the vacuum pan under reduced pressure and at a correspondingly reduced temperature. Instead of a vacuum pump, the partial vacuum may be produced and maintained by a steam ejector, thereby eliminating all moving mechanisms. It also has the advantages of simplicity of construction, low cost of initial installation and absence of maintenance costs. There are two principal classes of vacuum pumps, viz., the wet and the dry vacuum pump. The former removes the condenser discharge water as well as the air and non-condensable gases while the dry vacuum pump disposes of the air and non-condensable gases only.

(vi) *Accessories.* An important accessory is the condensed milk sampler. Its purpose is to draw samples representative of the boiling milk in the pan for determination of its density, without interrupting pan operation. The sampler may be either a batch type, or capable of continuous pan operation; the latter is preferably installed near the pan platform so that the operator can continuously observe the density of the finished product by means of a hydrometer freely floating in the sampler.

(b) *Evaporator classification*

I. *Basis.*

The evaporators may be classified on the following basis:

   (i) *Source of heat.* Steam, direct-fire, etc.;

   (ii) *Position of heating tubes.* Horizontal, vertical or inclined;

   (iii) *Method of circulation of product.* Forced, natural;

   (iv) *Length of tubes.* Long, short, medium;

   (v) *Direction of flow of film of product.* Upward, downward, (rising film, falling film);

   (vi) *Number of passes of product.* One, two or more;

   (vii) *Shape of tube assembly for heat-exchanger.* Coil, basket, straight;

(viii) *Location of steam*.   Inside or outside the tube, or both;

(ix) *Location of tubes*.   Internal, external.

II. *Nomenclature*

The classification of a few well-known evaporators with their particulars is briefly given below:

(i) *Vertical short-tube evaporator*. Known popularly as a Calandria Evaporator. Commonly used throughout the world. The tubes, carrying steam internally, are placed vertically at the bottom of the cylindrical evaporating chamber. The calandria has a large central downcomer to allow vigorous natural circulation. Cleaning and inspection are easy.

(ii) *Vertical long-tube evaporator*. This uses natural circulation, the flow of the product being either upward or downward. With upward flow, it is known as a rising/climbing film evaporator; and with downward flow, it is called a falling film evaporator.

(iii) *Forced circulation evaporator*. Used for viscous liquids, with the help of either a centrifugal or positive pump.

(iv) *Plate evaporator*. This uses an arrangement of gasketed plates, in place of calandria, and operates on a single pass climbing and falling principle. It is characterized by the short heat-contact time of the product.

(v) *Multiple-effect evaporator*. Most commonly used. The vapour from the first vacuum-pan/effect, which contains considerable latent heat, may be used to heat the second, and so on. Thus two or more effects can be utilized in the evaporator to improve economy of operation, as shown in Table 8.6.

TABLE 8.6

Steam requirements of different-effect evaporators

Type of evaporator	Steam required to evaporate 1 kg. of water from milk (Ave.)
Single effect	1.2 kg.
Double effect	0.6 kg.
Triple effect	0.4 kg.
Quadruple effect	0.3 kg.

Note: The temperature of the first effect is comparatively higher with an increase in the total number of effects. Hence, in order to prevent heat-damage, the use of the double-effect evaporator alone is preferred for milk processing.

(vi) *Centrifugal evaporator* (Centri-therm). In this, centrifugal force is used not only in applying the product on steam-heated cones but also in removing the condensed product, steam condensate and vapour.

(vii) *Expanding-flow evaporator*. Operates on the same principle as the Centri-therm, but use of inverted cones and counter-current flow of the product as well as heating medium is believed to increase efficiency of evaporation.

(viii) *Vapour recompression*. Heat-energy is added to the vapour removed from the first-effect by a mechanical compressor of steam jet (thermo-compressor) for heating the second-effect.

(ix) *Low-temperature evaporator*. This is particularly useful for removing water from a heat-sensitive product.

(c) *Important operating points for evaporators*. These have been listed below:

(i) The evaporator may be operated either as a batch or continuous system;

(ii) it should be sanitized before admitting the product to the pan;

(iii) the product should cover the heating tubes (coils) before steam intake, so as to prevent scorching;

(iv) the product should be maintained at a uniform level in the evaporator. This is made possible by controlling the rate of fresh product intake so that the volume of water removed is replaced;

(v) excessively rapid boiling is avoided as it is likely to increase entrainment;

(vi) air leaks in the system should be avoided;

(vii) single-effect evaporator (vacuum pan) is normally operated for milk at 54–60°C (130–140°F), or 63.5 cm. of mercury vacuum;

(viii) in order to stop the evaporator, the following steps should be taken in the sequence given: turn off steam; turn off water to the condenser; stop the vacuum pump; and open the vacuum relief;

(ix) dry saturated steam is more desirable for vacuum pan operation than wet or super-heated steam.

(d) *Striking the batch*. When the boiling milk approaches the desired concentration, there are visual indications which show that the final stage has been reached, viz., the milk 'settles down' to a quiet boil, its surface assumes a glossy and glistening lustre, there is a heavy roll from the periphery towards the centre, etc. These signs should warn the operator as to the right time for 'striking the batch'. (This term indicates that the correct concentration, as determined by specific gravity/density tests, has been reached.) The sampling of the condensed milk should, however, begin sufficiently early to permit taking and testing for density several successive samples without the risk of objectionable over-condensing. The standard testing temperature is 49°C (120°F), close to which the pan temperature usually drops towards the end of the condensing period.

The most practical density tests usually applied are:

  (i) Pycnometer test;
 (ii) Hydrometer test;
(iii) Refractometer test;
(iv) Viscosimeter test.

The Baumé Hydrometer test is most commonly used for density tests of pan samples of condensed milk. The hydrometer scale may record the density either directly or indirectly, or both. For condensed milk, the Baumé Hydrometer ranges from 30' to 37 Bé. The temperature correction factor is 0.03 for each °F of deviation from the standard (120°F); for temperatures above the standard, 'add' and for those below the standard, 'subtract'. However, for the most dependable results, the sample should be brought to the standard temperature adopted for density tests.

The specific gravity of condensed milk is obtained by the formula:

Specific gravity of condensed milk at 16°C (60°F)

$$= \frac{100}{\dfrac{\% \text{ Fat}}{\substack{\text{Sp. Gr.} \\ (0.9)}} + \dfrac{\% \text{ MSNF}}{\substack{\text{Sp. Gr.} \\ (1.6)}} + \dfrac{\% \text{ Sugar}}{1.6} + \% \text{ Water}}$$

The specific gravity of liquids heavier than water is converted to the Baumé degree by the formula:

$$\text{Baumé at } 16°C \ (60°F) = 145 - \frac{145}{\text{Sp. Gr. at } 16°C \ (60°F)}$$

This is then corrected to the standard temperature used for the hydrometer test of the pan sample by the temperature correction factor given earlier.

(e) *Finishing the batch.* On 'striking the batch' when the desired density has been reached, the condensing process is stopped. All steam to the pan is shut off, the valve in the water-line to the condenser is closed, the vacuum pump is stopped and the vacuum relief is opened. The above operations should be carried out in the order stated to prevent milk from burning on to the heating surface and condenser water from flooding the pan. When the vacuum has been dissipated, the condensed milk is drawn from the pan. This should be done promptly.

(f) *Third standardization.* Some manufacturers prefer to slightly over-condense the milk and then standardize it back to the exact concentration desired by the addition of the correctly calculated amount of water. The following examples explain the method:

Problem I. The batch sample tests 9.2% fat. The fat desired in condensed milk is 9.0%. The batch weighs 450 kg. How much water must be added to reduce the fat content to 9.0%?

Solution I. The % fat of the batch is *9.2* or 1.022 times the amount desired. Hence the amount of water to be added is 450 × 0.022 or 9.9 kg. water.

Problem II. (No means to weigh the batch.)

Weight of standardized fresh milk	650 kg.
Fat in standardized fresh milk	3.50 %
Fat desired in condensed milk	9.00 %
Fat test of batch	9.20 %

How much water must be added to reduce the fat in the batch to 9.00%?

Solution II.

Condensed milk desired $= \dfrac{3.50}{9.00} \times 650 = 252.2$ kg.

Condensed milk in batch $= \dfrac{3.50}{9.20} \times 650 = 247.3$ kg.

Water required $= (252.2 - 247.3) = 4.9$ kg.

(gg) *Homogenization.* Although not mentioned in text-books, hot condensed milk is invariably homogenized before it is cooled and crystallized by standard manufacturers of the product throughout the world. The object is to obtain a uniform fat emulsion and reduce fat separation to a minimum during storage. A special type of homogenizer suitable for handling a highly viscous product is used at a total pressure of 2500 psi (2000 psi in the first stage and 500 psi in the second stage).

(hh) *Cooling and crystallization*

(i) *Importance.* The cooling process occupies an important place in the manufacture of a marketable condensed milk. Prompt cooling is desirable to delay the tendency of age-thickening and discolouration, which is accelerated by prolonged exposure to heat. In addition, and even more importantly, on the method of cooling depends in a large measure the smoothness of texture of the finished product and its freedom from an objectionable sugar deposit.

(ii) *Role of lactose.* Lactose plays an important role in the successful control of the texture of condensed milk, which constitutes a highly concentrated solution of lactose. A considerable portion of the lactose content in the condensed milk held at ordinary temperature is present in crystal form. The size of these crystals determines the relative smoothness of the product. Crystal size is also one of the factors upon which depends the presence or absence of sugar sediment in the container. The size of the lactose crystal is controlled by the procedure used for cooling the condensed milk.

(iii) *Effect of cooling process on texture of condensed milk.* The relative smoothness of condensed milk is controlled by the number and size of the lactose crystals it contains. It is the treatment which the hot sweetened condensed milk receives during the cooling process that determines very largely the number and permanent size of the lactose crystals. The correlation of the number and corresponding size of lactose crystals with degree of sandiness is given in Table 8.7.

TABLE 8.7

Correlation of lactose crystal size with degree of sandiness

Condensed milk contains: 9% fat, 22.5% SNF, 42.5% sucrose, 26% water, 12.2% lactose

No. of crystals per cubic mm.	Length of longest edge of crystal in micron	Scale of sandiness
4,00,000	9.3 (9)	Excellent
3,00,000	10.25 (10)	Good
2,00,000	11.7 (11)	Slightly pasty
1,50,000	12.9 (13)	Pasty
1,00,000	14.75 (15)	Fine mealy
75,000	16.2 (16)	–do–
50,000	18.6 (19)	Mealy
25,000	23.4 (23)	Fine sandy
12,500	29.4 (29)	Sandy
7,500	34.9 (35)	Very sandy

SOURCE: *Condensed Milk and Milk Powder* by Hunziker (1949).

(iv) *Mechanism of lactose crystallization.* Under the temperature conditions that prevail in the manufacture of condensed milk, only α-lactose-hydrate will crystallize. The crystallization proceeds slowly because maintenance of the status of supersaturation of α-hydrate in solution requires the continued mutation from the highly soluble β-lactose anhydride to the less soluble α-hydrate form. In condensed milk, the rate of lactose-crystallization is further impeded by the presence of milk colloids and the high viscosity which reduces the rate of diffusion. For normal condensed milk of average composition, the temperature of maximum rapidity of crystallization is approximately 30°C (86°F).

(v) *Importance of mass crystallization in cooling of condensed milk.* The problem of ensuring a permanently smooth texture in the finished product is not to prevent the formation of lactose crystals during the cooling process, but to prevent the crystals that are present at the end of this process from subsequently growing larger. This is done by providing conditions in the cooling process that cause mass crystallization.

(vi) *The forced crystallization period.* The purpose of this is to produce mass crystallization of lactose. It is the period in batch cooling when condensed milk has reached, and is then held, at the temperature which helps mass crystallization. This temperature is optimum for seeding. After seeding, the milk should be held at this temperature for at least an hour under vigorous agitation after which it should be cooled rapidly to the final temperature (for packaging). For the best results at the end of the condensing period, the hot condensed milk should be cooled from pan temperature as rapidly as possible to the seeding temperature.

(vii) *Determination of optimum temperature for forced crystallization.* The optimum temperature for mass crystallization varies chiefly with the ratio of lactose to water in the condensed milk. For milks of fairly normal concentration, the variations are usually limited to an approximate range of about 30–40°C (86–104°F). The optimum temperature for forced crystallization for any particular batch of condensed milk can be determined by reference to the standard forced-crystallization curves.

(viii) *Seeding condensed milk.* 'Seeding' refers to the introduction of lactose in very fine powder form during the cooling process to provide nuclei for crystallization. The purpose of seeding is to give the lactose present in the supersaturated state an added incentive to crystallize. Further seeding at an optimum temperature for mass crystallization, with properly prepared seed lactose in the presence of vigorous agitation, yields crystals of uniform size. The seed material commonly used is powdered lactose of commerce (α-lactose-hydrate) or pulverized non-fatty dry milk, or sweetened condensed milk from a previous batch. For best results, the seed lactose should be able to pass through a 200-mesh screen consistent with the preservation of sharp crystal edges. Since the standard powdered lactose of commerce does not normally have particles of a sufficiently fine size, it has to be re-ground. This should prefer- ably be carried out by an Impact-Mill or Hammer-Mill type grinder.

If sterilization of the resulting lactose dust is desired, the follow- ing procedure (suggested by Whittier) is recommended: heat the powdered lactose of commerce to 93°C (200°F), preferably under vacuum. This converts the α-lactose hydrate to the α-anhydride form. Then grind the α-anhydride using an impact pulverizer mill. Fill the resulting lactose dust into cans, preferably with a friction top. Seal the cans and sterilize them at approximately 130°C (266°F) for one to two hours. The lactose dust is now ready to be used.

(ix) *Amount of seed material to use.* It is good practice not to use more seed material than is necessary for optimum mass crystal- lization. This ensures superior smoothness of texture in the finished product. The seed lactose usage rate is about 375–500 gm. per 1000 kg. of the original fluid milk, or 0.1 to 0.3 per cent of con- densed milk. Twice as much non-fat dry milk and condensed milk is required when it is used as the 'seed'.

(x) *Method of adding seed lactose to the batch.* The seed lactose should not be added to the batch in dry form. Such a practice causes it to lump together into large aggregates which do not dis- integrate readily. In this condition the seed material is incapable of inciting mass crystallization. A means of ensuring uniform disper- sion of the seed material is essential. One procedure consists of blending the 'seed' into a small amount of condensed milk and then adding this to the batch during vigorous agitation. The agitation must continue while crystallization takes place, in order to stimulate the formation of numerous small crystals of lactose (rather than a few larger ones). The above operation must be carried out under strict hygienic conditions.

(xi) *Lactose crystal formation.* Rapid crystallization leads to the formation of a large number of small crystals, giving a smooth texture to the condensed milk; on the other hand, slow crystallization creates a small number of large crystals which produce a sandy or gritty texture. After 'seed' lactose is uniformly dispersed, cooling of the product may be continued slowly to 24°C (75°F). This should take approximately an hour. Then the cooling is completed to 13–18°C (55–65°F) with continued agitation. The rate of crystal formation is controlled by the amount of agitation, number of nuclei, total solids in the product, temperature and viscosity. Vigorous agitation (stirring) during cooling is highly important; it increases the rate of crystallization, besides ensuring uniform small-sized lactose crystals in the batch system.

(xii) *Finishing the cooling process.* After seeding and forced crystallization, cooling is resumed under constant agitation, as rapidly as possible, until the final temperature is reached. Agitation is then generally continued for another hour or longer, when the product is ready for packaging. A line diagram of cooling and crystallization of condensed milk is given as follows:

Condensed milk
(Discharged from vacuum pan)
|
Quickly cooled to 30°C (86°F)
|
Seeded with 0.1–0.3% lactose
|
Vigorous stirring and slow cooling for 1 hour
|
Temperature of 15°C (59°F) reached
|
Stirring continued until packaged

(ii) *Systems of cooling.* These are: Batch: Continuous flow; Combined Batch and Continuous; and Vacuum.

(a) *Batch.* The equipment for cooling and crystallization consists of an especially designed tank or vat, with water-jacketed sides and bottom, and a powerful rotary agitator. These coolers are provided with nylon/rubber scrapers of special design that press closely to the cooling surface. The cooling is done by controlled circulation of refrigerated water through the jacket. The milk is seeded at the proper temperature for mass crystallization and the cooling resumed at the end of the forced crystallization period. Some of the batch coolers are operated under vacuum.

(b) *Continuous-flow.* This system is represented by the internal tube counter-current. This type of cooler is used in large-scale operations, particularly when condensed milk is the main product of the plant.

(c) *Combined batch and continuous.* A common combination is to use the continuous internal tube cooler from the pan to seeding temperature, and finish the operation in a crystallizer tank. Alternatively, the batch is run from the pan into the crystallizer tank, then cooled to seeding temperature, seeded, and the cooling finished by means of the continuous-flow internal-tube cooler.

(d) *Vacuum cooling*

I. *Principle.* This system utilizes a high vacuum as the cooling medium; in other words, the temperature of milk in this cooler is reduced by evaporation under vacuum.

II. *Equipment.* This consists mainly of a vacuum pan without a heating surface. The vapours arising from the milk are condensed in a counter-current condenser. The non-condensable gases and air are compressed and eliminated by multi-stage ejectors with intermediate condensers. The water from the main condenser is discharged over a barometric leg, or by a centrifugal pump. To accelerate the circulation of the increasingly viscous milk, the cooler is equipped with a powerful rotary agitator, which assists proper thermo-circulation, promotes uniform cooling throughout the batch and expedites the rate of evaporation and cooling.

III. *Operation.* The milk is condensed in the regular vacuum pan or evaporated to a predetermined point, after making due allowance for the additional evaporation that will occur in the cooler. The batch is dropped from the pan directly into the vacuum cooler. When the temperature in the cooler has been lowered to about 32°C (90°F), the batch is seeded (by blowing lactose 'dust' through the side of the cooler, using pressure difference as the motivating force). This causes mass crystallization. At the end of the forced crystallization period, the milk is further cooled to 10°C (50°F). Agitation is continued throughout until the product is packaged.

IV. *Advantages over other systems*

(i) The time required for cooling is relatively short;

(ii) the cooling is uniform throughout the batch;

(iii) this cooling system yields mass crystallization; the size of most of the lactose crystals ranges from 5 to 8 microns;

(iv) the finished product has an exceptionally smooth and velvety texture;

(v) it enhances the keeping quality of the finished product.

(jj) *Packaging.* The condensed milk is now ready for packaging. Bulk packaging may be done in barrels of various sizes, drums with polythene liners, or tin-containers. For the retail market, fillers are used to package condensed milk in cans. After filling, the cans are sealed, labelled and packed in cases for storage and distribution.

The retail cans are filled with automatic filling machines. In general, the filling machine consists of multiple-piston pumps. The cylinder charge can be adjusted to the size of the cans to be filled. It is important to fill the cans fully in order to exclude as much of the air from the container as possible.

Since cans filled with condensed milk do not undergo any subsequent sterilization, strict sanitary conditions should be observed during the filling process so as to prevent contamination, which will adversely affect the keeping quality of the finished product. These sanitary measures may be listed as follows:

(i) The filling machine, connecting pipe-lines, etc., should be thoroughly cleaned and sanitized before use.

(ii) The filling and sealing room should be kept in strict sanitary condition, and preferably be closed to the outside and also to visitors during operation. Its air supply should consist of efficiently filtered pure air.

(iii) It is good practice to reject the first few cans when starting the machine (returning their contents to the forewarmer).

(iv) The filling machine should be hooded when not in use to protect it from dust, stray insects and other agencies of contamination.

(v) Working personnel should wear masks, so as not to breathe contaminated air into the product during filling. The personnel should also observe sanitary habits.

(vi) The cans and lids, on their passage to the filler, should be sterilized. (This is usually done by passing them under or over a battery of suitable gas jets.)

(vii) It is important to fill the cans fully (so as to exclude as much air from the container as possible) and seal them promptly after filling.

(kk) *Storage.* The main consideration in the storage of condensed milk is the temperature of storage, which should be such as to prevent such defects as sandiness, sugar separation and viscosity changes. During storage, a wide temperature variation may increase the tendency to sandiness. A very low storage temperature such as 0°C (32°F) or below may not only cause sandiness but also sugar (sucrose) separation. Cool storage is important to prevent changes in viscosity. The trend in recent years has been to store condensed milk at 10°C (50°F) or slightly below. The humidity of the surrounding air should be low (below 50 per cent) to check spoilage of cans and labels.

8.8 Method of Manufacture and Storage of Evaporated Milk

A. *Flow diagram of manufacture*

Receiving milk

Filtration Clarification (35–40°C)

Standardization

Forewarming/Pre-heating (115–118°C/No hold)

Evaporation (1 : 2.5)

Homogenization $\left\{ \begin{array}{l} 2000 \text{ psi— I stage} \\ 500 \text{ psi—II stage} \end{array} \right\}$ (50–55°C)

Cooling (7°C)

Pilot Sterilization Test

Packaging

Sterilization (116–118°C/15 min.)

Cooling (27–32°C)

Shaking

Storage (5–15°C).

B. *Details of manufacture*
(aa) *Receiving milk*
(bb) *Filtration/Clarification* } Same as for condensed milk (See 8.7)
(cc) *Standardization*
(dd) *Forewarming/Pre-heating.* The main purpose of this is to

improve the heat-stability of milk and to ensure a medium viscosity in the finished product. (See 8.7.)

Note: The forewarming of milk during the manufacture of evaporated milk is not relied upon for destruction of micro-organisms and inactivation of enzymes; this latter is the function of sterilization.

(ee) *Evaporation.* Same as for condensed milk (see 8.7), except that no sugar is added and normally a continuous operation takes place. It is customary to slightly over-condense the milk to facilitate standardization later.

(ff) *Homogenization.* After evaporation and before cooling, the evaporated milk is thoroughly homogenized to obtain a uniform fat emulsion and reduce separation of fat to a minimum during storage. A temperature and pressure combination that will reduce the fat globules to less than 2 microns in diameter is needed. The temperature is usually about 49°C (120°F) as the product is removed from the last effect of the evaporator. Two-stage homogenization is generally recommended, 2000 psi in the first stage and 500 psi in the second.

Note: In developed countries, evaporated milk is enriched with vitamin D. This is done either through irradiation (ultraviolet radiation from artificial sources) or fortification (addition of vitamin D-rich substances).

(gg) *Cooling.* After homogenization, the evaporated milk is cooled to 7°C (45°F) if it is to be sterilized on the same day, as in small-scale handling; however, in large-scale handling it is cooled and held at 5°C (40°F). The cooled product is held in large storage tanks for re-standardization of fat or total solids. Stabilizing salts may also be added at this point if pilot tests indicate such a need.

(hh) *Pilot sterilization test*

(a) *Purpose.* To determine the amount of chemical stabilizer (trisodium citrate or disodium phosphate) to be added to any given batch of evaporated milk for the most satisfactory heat-stability.

(b) *Apparatus.* The major items needed are: (i) a pilot sterilizer with accessories; (ii) a viscosimeter; (iii) a sample can filler; (iv) a weighing balance; (v) glassware for making and measuring the stabilizer.

(c) *Preparation of stabilizer solution.* An approximate 10 per cent solution of stabilizer is prepared for use, so that 0.1 ml. of the solution is equivalent to the addition of 1 g. of dry salt for every 16 kg. of evaporated milk.

(d) *Method of adding stabilizer solution.* The amount of stabilizer to be added to any batch is determined by trial. About 8 to 10 sample cans are used. They are then individually filled first with different accurately measured amounts of the stabilizer solution and then with 170 g. (6 oz.) of evaporated milk to be tested, as shown in Table 8.8.

TABLE 8.8

Pilot sterilization test

		Can X	Can 1	Can 2	Can 3	Can 4	Can 5	Can 6
170 g./6 oz. of unsterilized evaporated milk *plus*	ml. of 10% stabilizer solution	0.0	0.0	0.2	0.4	0.6	0.8	1.0
	ml. distilled water	0.0	1.0	0.8	0.6	0.4	0.2	0.0
Rate of addition required and expressed as: g. stabilizer for every 16 kg. evaporated milk.		0	0	2	4	6	8	10

SOURCE: *Condensed Milk and Milk Powder* by Hunziker (1949).

Note: In Table 8.8, Can X represents the evaporated milk without any addition, Can 1 contains no stabilizer but represents the evaporated milk in diluted form, the rate of dilution being the same as that of all other samples. The remaining samples represent an addition of stabilizer in increasing amounts, but with the dilution in all cases equal to Can 1.

(e) *Sterilizing the samples.* The sample cans, containing measured amounts of stabilizer solution and a fixed quantity of evaporated milk, are sterilized at 117°C (242°F) for 15 minutes and then cooled rapidly to 24°C (75°F). As soon as they have been cooled, the cans are opened, examined for smoothness and colour, and tested for viscosity. According to Mojonnier and Troy, a viscosity of 150°R on the Mojonnier-Doolittle viscosimeter represents the correct viscosity of evaporated milk as it comes out of the sterilizer. Changes in viscosity during the different stages in the manufacture of evaporated milk are given in Table 8.9.

TABLE 8.9

Viscosity of evaporated milk at different stages of manufacture

Stages in the process of manufacture	Viscosity at 24°C/75°F (degrees retardation)
Fresh milk before forewarming	15.24
Fresh milk after forewarming	15.26
After condensing and cooling but before sterilization	20.20
Evaporated milk after sterilization	150.00

SOURCE: *Condensed Milk and Milk Powder* by Hunziker (1949).

(f) *Determining the amount of stabilizer to be added.* If the viscosity tests of pilot-sterilized cans show that no stability correction is necessary, the batch is ready to be filled into the cans. However, if the tests show otherwise, as in Table 8.10, stability corrections become necessary.

TABLE 8.10

Determining amount of stabilizer to be added

Can X	Can 1	Can 2	Can 3
Control	Diluted with water only	Contains 0.2 ml. stabilizer solution	Contains 0.4 ml. stabilizer solution
Curdled	Curdled	Smooth texture (150°R)	Slightly rough texture (250°R)

°R = degree retardation

In Table 8.10, it will be seen that Can 2 has come out of the sterilizer with a smooth texture and to this can 0.2 ml. of the 10 per cent solution of stabilizer was added. This amount is equivalent to 2 g. of dry disodium phosphate crystals per 32 kg. evaporated milk.

(g) *Adding stabilizer to the batch.* The calculated amount of stabilizer should be added to the evaporated milk in the form of a solution, using just enough water to dissolve it. The stabilizer solution should be added slowly, thoroughly agitating the evaporated milk both during addition and for several hours thereafter. In practice, a portion of the required amount of stabilizer is added to the milk in the forewarmer and then correction completed by adding the remainder to the evaporated milk in the storage tank. (The previous day's figures may be used as guidelines.)

(jj) *Packaging*. The cans are now mechanically filled with volumetric fillers. The types of can used for this purpose are: the sanitary can; the can with a solder seal; and the vent hole can. The cans should be able to withstand pressure changes during sterilization and the seal should be absolutely air-tight and strong. The temperature of evaporated milk when filling the cans should be neither high nor low, but around 5°C; a higher temperature causes foaming, while a lower one increases the tendency towards 'flipping'. (Flipping refers to the sudden snapping of can ends from their slightly concave contour to a convex outward bulge, which is usually accompanied by an audible sound.)

Note: The cans should be filled as nearly full as possible. Filling the cans too much also causes flipping. They should be properly sealed.

(kk) *Sterilization*. Immediately after sealing and before sterilization, each can is tested by means of a dependable leak detector, where the cans pass submerged in a hot-water bath. In case of leaky cans, air bubbles rise to the top; these cans are removed for repair. The filled and sealed cans, which have passed the test for leaks, are now ready for sterilization.

(a) *Purpose*. The primary purpose of sterilization is to destroy all germ life and enzymes present, thereby preserving the product permanently. In addition, the sterilizing process is utilized to increase the viscosity and improve the body so as to give a creamy consistency to the finished product.

During sterilization, the temperature of evaporated milk is raised rapidly to 116–118°C (240–245°F) and held at this temperature for 15 minutes. If the cans cannot be sterilized within an hour or two, they should be held under refrigeration (5–7°C/40–45°F) especially in hot weather.

(b) *Equipment*. There are two types of sterilizers in use, viz. batch and continuous. Their merits and demerits are given in Table 8.11.

TABLE 8.11
Merits and demerits of sterilizers

Type of sterilizer	Merits	Demerits
Batch	(i) Useful for both small and large plants (ii) Usable for cans of all sizes (iii) Low initial cost.	High labour cost
Continuous	Low labour cost	(i) Not useful for small plants (ii) Made for a particular can size only (iii) High initial cost.

I. *Batch*. This consists of a large boiler-like, horizontal steam drum, opening at the top or at one or both ends. Its hollow interior is equipped with a revolving frame into which the cans are loaded. A perforated steam-distributing pipe near the bottom, with a steam inlet at both ends, extends over the entire length of the sterilizer drum. Near the top, there is a water-distributing pipe with connections to the water main. At the bottom of the shell there is a drain. On the sterilizer drum are mounted a pressure-safety valve, water, steam and vacuum gauges, a high-temperature thermometer, etc.

The sterilizer rotates at a speed of 6 to 12 rpm. Rapidity and uniformity of heat distribution during sterilization are important. It has been found practicable to use just enough water in the sterilizer so that all the cans in the same position in the frame are submerged. Use of water also eliminates interfering air-pockets between cans.

The temperature-time for heating during sterilization should be such as to ensure sterility consistent with sufficient body (to prevent fat separation) without causing the formation of an unshakeable curd, objectionable discolouration or an excessively cooked flavour. A successful sterilizing routine consists of:

Coming-up time	Between 15 and 20 min.
Holding temperature	116°C and 118°C
Holding time	Not less than 15 min.
Cooling time	Not more than 15 min.

II. *Continuous*. This is so designed as to pre-heat the cans gradually by slowly moving them through progressively hotter hot-water chambers to a few degrees below boiling point. Then the cans enter the sterilizer proper where they are heated to sterilizing temperature by steam under pressure. Later, the cooling process starts with the cans gradually moving through progressively less hot hot-water chambers and finally through cold water (under air pressure). One such type of sterilizer consists of three principal parts, viz., pre-heater, sterilizer and cooler, with two leak-detectors at the can-exit of the pre-heater and cooler respectively. (For more details, refer to *Condensed Milk and Milk Powder* by O. F. Hunziker.)

(ll) *Cooling*. Immediately after the holding time is over, the evaporated milk is cooled within 15 minutes to 27–32°C (70–80°F). Rapid and uniform cooling is important. This requires, for the batch system, not only a plentiful supply of cold water but also its uniform distribution all over the sterilizer. Further, delayed cooling may cause the cans to bulge badly. Bulging can be avoided, however, by admitting a sufficient quantity of compressed air. In the continuous system, the cooler operates at 10 psi.

(mm) *Shaking*. The purpose of shaking is to mechanically break down any curd which may have formed during sterilization to a smooth homogeneous consistency. A shaking period from about one-fourth to two minutes is usually sufficient. Excessive shaking should be avoided as it decreases the viscosity.

(nn) *Storage*. In recent years, the trend has been to store evaporated milk at below room temperature. A storage temperature of 5 to 16°C (40 to 60°F) is generally used. This checks the deterioration in quality. Studies have shown that commercial evaporated milk remains acceptable for 2 years when stored below 16°C (60°F) but deteriorates rapidly at 21°C (70°F) or above. The humidity of the surrounding air should be low (below 50%) to inhibit spoilage of cans and labels. Inversion of the cans during storage will help minimize fat separation. A guideline for turning cases of cans in storage is given in Table 8.12.

TABLE 8.12

Guideline for inversion of cans of evaporated milk

Temperature of Storage °C/°F	When to invert
16°C/60°F	After 3 to 6 months
21°C/70°F	After 2 to 3 months
27°C/80°F	After 1 to 2 months
32°C/90°F	After 1 month and 15 days thereafter

8.9 Heat Stability and its Control

(a) *Introduction.* The heat-stability of milk is of tremendous importance in the successful processing of milk and the manufacture of most dairy products. The application of heat to milk becomes necessary for destruction of spore-resistant micro-organisms and the preservation of the most desirable product characteristics. However, milk should not coagulate during heating. Heat-coagulation of milk is caused chiefly by de-stabilization of the milk-proteins.

(b) *Definition.* Heat-stability of milk may be defined in terms of the time required to induce coagulation at a given temperature, such as 115°C/239°F. Alternatively, the term 'heat-stability of evaporated milk' refers to the relative resistance of the milk to coagulation in the sterilizer.

(c) *Mechanism of heat-coagulation.* The coagulation of milk revolves around the coagulation of milk proteins. Milk proteins, as already mentioned in 1.8, are composed of several proteins, notably casein (containing α, β, γ fractions) which represents 82 per cent and whey proteins (containing β-lactoglobulin, α-lactalbumin, immuno-globulins etc.) which represent 18 per cent of the total quantity. Casein exists in milk as complex colloidal particles or miscelles containing calcium, magnesium, phosphate and citrate in addition to casein proteins. This system is generally referred to as the calcium-caseinate-phosphate complex. The casein miscelles range in diameter from 30 to 300 mμ, are stabilized by an electric charge and are in constant kinetic motion. As soon as the casein particles in milk join together to form large aggregates, coagulation takes place.

(d) *Salt balance theory of heat-stability of milk.* Sommer and Hart's Salt-Balance Theory (1919) conceives that optimum heat-stability is dependent on a certain ratio/balance of calcium plus magnesium-ions to phosphate plus citrate-ions. (According to Egyptian workers, this ratio for normal cow milk is 0.37 and for buffalo milk 0.39.) Any disturbance in the salt balance, due to the excess or deficiency of either group, accelerates heat-coagulation.

(e) *Factors influencing heat-stability of milk.* The chief factors are:

(i) *Acidity and pH of milk.* The higher the acidity (and lower the pH), the lower the heat-stability, and vice versa. Addition of acid to milk, either by bacterial action or chemical means, results in an increase of ionic calcium, which in turn disturbs the salt balance and lowers the heat-stability of milk.

(ii) *Concentration of total solids.* The higher the total solids concentration, the lower the heat-stability, and vice versa Increase in concentration causes a marked shift in the salt equilibrium, increase in destabilizing ions and reduction in pH.

(iii) *Concentration of salts and ions.* Any increase in concentration of either the numerator or denominator of the ionic ratio:

$$\frac{\text{Calcium} + \text{Magnesium}}{\text{citrate} + \text{phosphate}}$$

disturbs the salt-balance, resulting in lowered heat-stability.

(iv) *Pre-heating/forewarming of milk.* The temperature-time and method of pre-heating/forewarming of milk affects the heat-stability. However, the mechanism by which this effect takes place is not yet completely understood. (The modern trend is towards high-temperature and short-time heating.)

(v) *Homogenization.* Homogenization of milk tends to slightly lower its heat-stability, which is affected by the pressure used; the greater the homogenization pressure, the greater the reduction in heat-stability.

(f) *Control of heat-stability.* This may be done by either of the following procedures:

(i) *Forewarming/pre-heating of whole milk.* The modern trend of high-temperature-short-time pre-heating/forewarming of milk appears to give much greater heat-stability than the low-temperature-long-time method used earlier.

(ii) *Heat-treatment after condensing/evaporation.* Heating the milk-concentrate to temperatures above the boiling point increases heat-stability. (However, it is advisable to determine the effect of such treatment on test samples before attempting to heat-stabilize the entire lot.)

(iii) *Addition of chemical stabilizer.* This is the basis of the Pilot Sterilization Test. In most cases the heat-stability is restored by addition of citrate or phosphate. However, some milks may require the addition of calcium-ions (as calcium chloride).

Note: The use of sodium bicarbonate as a casein stabilizer has long been discontinued because of the following objections: it tends to darken the colour and jeopardize the flavour of evaporated milk; its release of carbon dioxide under sterilization heat causes excessive bulging of the cans; and when used in large amounts, it may lower rather than raise the heat-coagulation points—the latter being desired.

(iv) *Mineral-ion-exchange treatment.* By exchange of calcium and magnesium with sodium in a portion of milk, its heat-stability increases, leading to decrease of curdling tendencies in the sterilizer. (However, from a nutritional point of view, this procedure may raise objections.)

8.10 Judging and Grading of Condensed and Evaporated Milks

A. *Score card.* This is given in Table 8.13 for condensed milk and Table 8.14 for evaporated milk.

TABLE 8.13
Score card for condensed milk (ADSA)

Items	Perfect score
Flavour and odour	30
Body and texture	25
Colour	5
Fat content	10
Milk solids	10
Bacteria	10
Sugar	10
Adulterants and preservatives—Must be absent	
	Total score: 100

TABLE 8.14
Score card for evaporated milk (ADSA)

Items	Perfect score
Flavour and odour	40
Body and texture	35
Colour	5
Fat content	10
Total solids	10
Adulterants and preservatives—Must be absent	
	Total score: 100

B. *Procedure for the examination of both condensed and evaporated milks*

(a) *Sampling.* Select a can of the product at random for examination.

(b) *Sequence of observations.* Avoid undue agitation when transporting the can to the laboratory. Place it on the table for examination in the same upright position as before. Cut more than three-fourths of the top of the can and turn it back. Then examine it in the following order:

(i) *Appearance of the can.* Look for signs of rust, etc., both outside and inside (when emptied).

(ii) *Appearance of the product.* Examine uniformity of colour: look for absence of lumps in condensed milk and cream layer/butter particles/curd in evaporated milk.

(iii) *Viscosity (body and texture).* Observe whether the viscosity is high, normal or low while pouring the contents into a beaker.

(iv) *Sediment.* Watch for presence and absence of sediment at the bottom of the container when emptied.

(v) *Flavour and odour.* Note defects, if any, by placing a small spoonful of condensed milk or of diluted evaporated milk (1 : 1 with distilled water) on the tongue.

(vi) *Laboratory tests.* Take a suitable sample aseptically and then test for fat, total solids, bacteria, sugar, adulterants and preservatives, etc.

(c) *Requirements of high grade condensed and evaporated milks.* High quality condensed milk should have a clean, pleasant aroma, a pronounced sweet taste, smooth and uniform body and texture, and a uniform light colour, which should be yellow for cow and light-greenish white for buffalo milk. High quality evaporated milk should have a mild, pleasant flavour, a relatively viscous body and uniformly smooth texture, and uniform colour as described for condensed milk.

8.11 Defects in Condensed and Evaporated Milks, their Causes and Prevention

Defects in condensed milk and evaporated milk may arise due to low quality milk and faulty methods of manufacture and storage. Their causes and prevention are given in Table 8.15.

TABLE 8.15

Defects in condensed and evaporated milks,
their causes and prevention

Name of defect	Causes	Prevention
I. Condensed milk		
(a) Microbial		
Mould buttons	(i) Contamination with, and growth of, the mould *Asperigillus Repens*	(i) Avoiding contamination with, and growth of, *Asperigillus Repens*
	(ii) Storage at high temperatures	(ii) Storage at low temperatures (10°C 50°F) or below
	(iii) Presence of air (oxygen) in the head-space of package.	(iii) Vacuum or gas packaging.
Bacterial thickening	(i) Contamination with, and growth of, species which produce a rennin-like enzyme	(i) Avoiding contamination with, and growth of, species which produce a renin-like enzyme
	(ii) Storage at high temperature	(ii) Storage at low temperature (10°C/50°F or below)
	(iii) Low sugar ratio.	(iii) Optimum sugar ratio.
Bloats (microbial)	(i) Contamination with and growth of the yeast *Torula lactis condensi*	(i) Avoiding contamination with, and growth of, the yeast *Torula lactis condensi*
	(ii) Storage at high temperature.	(ii) Storage at low temperature (10°C/50°F or below).
(b) Non-Microbial		
Sandiness due to lactose	(i) Incorrect cooling and crystallization	(i) Correct cooling and crystallization
	(ii) Excessively low temperature of storage.	(ii) Optimum low temperature of storage.
Sandiness due to sucrose	(i) Excessive sugar ratio	,i) Optimum cooling and crystallization
	(ii) Excessively low temperature of storage.	(ii) Optimum low temperature of storage.
Sugar separation (lactose)	(i) Low viscosity	(i) Adequate viscosity
	(ii) Long storage.	(ii) Short storage.

Name of defect	Causes	Prevention
Age-thickening (physico-chemical)	(i) Excessive forewarming temperature and/or homogenization pressure (ii) Adding sucrose before forewarming (iii) Storage at high temperature (iv) Low sugar ratio.	(i) Optimum forewarming temperature and/or homogenization pressure (ii) Adding sucrose only at the end of condensing (iii) Storage at low temperature (10°C/50 F or below) (iv) Optimum sugar ratio.
Bloats (physico-chemical)	Temperature shock to filled cans with non-hermetic seals.	Avoiding temperature shock to filled cans with non-hermetic seals.

Note: Fat separation is not so frequent in condensed milk.

II. *Evaporated milk*

Name of defect	Causes	Prevention
Cooked flavour	High heat-treatment during sterilization by the conventional method.	Ultra-high-temperature sterilization and aseptic packaging reduces—but may introduce the problem of more spoilage and cooked flavour.
Coagulation (curdling)	Excessively low heat-stability of milk.	Optimum heat-stability of milk.
Browning discolouration	(i) Excessively high heat-treatment during sterilization (ii) Storage at high temperature (iii) Long storage.	(i) Optimum heat treatment during sterilization (ii) Storage at low temperature (7°C/45°F or below) (iii) Short storage.
Age-thickening	(i) Excessive forewarming temperature and/or homogenization pressure (ii) Storage at high temperature.	(i) Optimum forewarming temperature and/or homogenization pressure (ii) Storage at low temperature (7°C/45°F or below).
Fat-separation	(i) Inadequate homogenization pressure	(i) Adequate homogenization pressure

Name of defect	Causes	Prevention
	(ii) Storage at high temperature	(ii) Storage at low temperature (7°C/45°F or below)
	(iii) Long storage	(iii) Short storage
	(iv) Improper handling during storage	(iv) Proper handling during storage
	(v) Improper processing (causing low viscosity).	(v) Proper processing (causing optimum viscosity).
Feathering in coffee	Excessively high viscosity.	Optimum viscosity.
Age-thinning	Not yet fully explained.	Storage at low temperature (7°C/45°F or below) reduces.
Mineral deposit	(i) Storage at high temperature	(i) Storage at low temperature (7°C/45°F or below)
	(ii) Long storage.	(ii) Short storage.
Bloats (gassy)	Improper heat-treatment (low temperature-time of heating during sterilization).	Proper heat-treatment (optimum temperature-time of heating during sterilization).

8.12 Uses of Condensed and Evaporated Milks

(a) *Condensed milk*
  (i) For reconstitution into sweet milk drinks;
  (ii) in tea or coffee;
  (iii) in ice cream preparation;
  (iv) in candy and confectionary;
  (v) in prepared foods.

(b) *Evaporated milk*
  (i) For reconstitution into milk for feeding infants and persons with weak stomachs, etc.;
  (ii) in ice cream;
  (iii) in tea and coffee.

8.13 Plain Condensed Milk

This is unsweetened condensed milk, made from whole milk, partly skim milk or entirely skim milk, and condensed to 2.5 to 4 : 1. It is used in ice cream factories and bakeries. The product is neither sterile nor preserved by sugar. Its keeping quality is similar to that of high quality, efficiently pasteurized milk.

8.14 Superheated Condensed Milk

This is plain condensed milk superheated by blowing live steam towards the end of the condensing period. The major purpose of superheating is to increase the viscosity. It is used in ice cream factories and bakeries, where it is believed to yield better results than plain condensed milk.

8.15 Frozen Condensed Milk

This is plain condensed milk frozen to give it longer storage life. It is used largely in ice cream factories.

9 DRIED MILKS

9.1 Introduction

Today, the production of dried milks and milk products has become an increasingly important segment of the dairy industry. The world's recorded annual output of dried milks and some milk by-products in 1969 (*vide FAO Production Year Book,* 1970) was 4.2 million tonnes, the contribution of India being 31.1 thousand tonnes, i.e. 0.7% of the total. There are definite indications of greater future production of dried milks and milk products due to their better keeping quality, their requiring less storage space and lower shipping costs—all of which are economically attractive. More non-fat dry milk production takes place than whole milk powder production, due to the high keeping quality of the former.

The ultimate aim of the industry is to obtain dry products which, when recombined with water, give little or no evidence of detrimental change compared to the orignal liquid product. While the reconstituted non-fat dry milk is nearly comparable in flavour to the original skim milk, much improvement needs to be made with dry whole milk. The other aims are to ensure good keeping quality and a low manufacturing cost

Dry milk provides a means of handling the excess milk supply in a dairy factory during the flush season, while in the lean season, that meant for the production of dry milk can be diverted to market

TABLE 9.1

Production of some dried milk products in India

Types of dried milk products	Production (tonnes)		
	1972	1973	1974
Milk Powder (mainly skim milk powder)	12,900	11,042	12,416
Infant Milk Food	20,540	19,500	11,143
Malted Milk Food	11,977	12,979	15,347

SOURCE: *Dairying in India,* An IDSA publication, XII Dairy Industry Conference, Ludhiana (1976).

milk. Thus dry milk may be called the balance wheel of the dairy industry today.

In India, the first-ever commercial production of spray dried milk was started by AMUL Dairy, Anand, in 1955. The production of some dried milk products in this country during the past few years, is shown in Table 9.1.

9.2 Objects of Production

The objects or purposes of drying milk (and milk products) are:

(i) To remove the moisture so as to reduce bulk, thereby effecting a saving in storage space and packaging costs;

(ii) to reduce the cost of transportation (due to reduced bulk);

(iii) to improve the storage-life of the product (due to low moisture content);

(iv) to provide a product which can be utilized for many food manufacturing operations;

(v) to conserve, as far as possible, the natural properties of the original raw material.

9.3 History and Development

Marco Polo, the celebrated Venetian traveller of the thirteenth century, reported that the soldiers of Kublai Khan, a Mongol emperor, carried dried milk when on an excursion. Before it was used, water was added to a portion of the dried material. Mixing was accomplished by the horses' movements while travelling.

Next we hear of dried milk in tablet form made in 1810 by the French scientist, Nicholas Appert, by the air-drying of milk solids concentrated to a 'doughy' consistency.

In 1855, Grimwade of Britain developed a modified dry product from highly concentrated milk to which was added sodium (or potassium) carbonate and sugar. This semi-solid material was extruded into thin streams and dried in trays.

In 1902, Just of the USA was among the first inventors of a drum drier with two rolls. Numerous other types of drum driers were invented, but most of these were used to a limited extent. Vacuum drum driers were designed between 1889 and 1909. Among the early inventors of spray drying equipment were Percy of the USA (1872) and Stauf of Germany (1901). Peebles of the USA is known for his pioneering research to improve the reconstitutability of non-fat dry milk in water.

9.4 Definition

Dried milk or milk powder is the product obtained by the removal of water from milk by heat or other suitable means, to produce a solid containing 5 per cent or less moisture. Whole milk, defatted milk or skim milk may be used for drying. The dried product obtained from whole milk is called Dried Whole Milk or Whole Milk Powder (WMP); and that from skim milk is known as Dried Skim Milk or Skim Milk Powder (SMP), or Non-Fat Dry Milk (NFDM). The various dried milk products are given specific names.

9.5 Standards

A. *PFA (Legal)*

(a) *Whole Milk Powder.* According to the PFA Rules, 1976, whole milk powder is the product obtained from cow or buffalo milk, or a combination thereof, or from standardized milk, by the removal of water. It may contain calcium chloride, citric acid and sodium citrate, sodium salts of orthophosphoric acid and polyphosphoric acids, not exceeding 0.3 per cent by weight of the finished product, and 0.01 per cent of butylated hydroxy anisole (by weight) of the finished product. Such addition need not be declared on the label. Milk powder should contain not more than 5.0 per cent moisture and not less than 26.0 per cent fat. The total acidity expressed as lactic should not be more than 1.2 per cent. The standard plate count may not exceed 50,000/g. and the Coli count may not exceed 90/g. The maximum solubility index should be 15.0 for a roller-dried and 2.0 for a spray-dried product.

Note: The process of drying must be mentioned on the label. The spray dried product must be packed in hermetically sealed containers when the net quantity exceeds 510/g.

(b) *Skim milk powder.* According to the PFA Rules (1976), skim milk powder is the product obtained from (the skim milk of) cow or buffalo milk, or a combination thereof, by the removal of water. It may contain added calcium chloride, citric acid and sodium citrate, sodium salts of orthophosphoric acid and poly-phosphoric acid, not exceeding 0.3 per cent by weight of the finished product. Such addition need not be declared on the label. Skim milk powder may not contain more than 1.5 per cent milk fat, and moisture may not exceed 5.0 per cent. The total acidity expressed as lactic acid should not exceed 1.5 per cent. The standard plate count should not exceed 50,000/g. and the Coli count must not exceed 90/g. The maximum solubility index should be 15.0 for a roller-dried and 2.0 for a spray-dried product.

Note: Same as for whole milk powder.

B. *ISI*. According to the Indian Standards Institution, the specifications for dried milks, *vide IS : 1165*, 1967 (First Revision) are as given in Table 9.2.

TABLE 9.2

Indian standards for dried milks

Characteristics	Requirement for	
	Whole milk powder	Skim milk powder
Flavour and odour	Good	Good
Moisture (% wt) (Max)	4.0	5.0
Total milk solids (% wt)	96.0	95.0
Solubility:		
(a) Solubility index (Max) ml.	15.0 (If roller-dried) 2.0 (If spray-dried)	15.0 (If roller-dried) 2.0 (If spray-dried)
(b) Solubility (% wt) (Min)	85.0 ml. (If roller-dried) 98.5 ml. (If spray-dried)	85.0 ml. (If roller-dried) 98.5 ml. (If spray-dried)
Total ash (on dry basis) (% wt) (Max)	7.3	9.3
Fat (% wt)	Not less than 26.0	Not more than 1.5
Titratable acidity (% lactic)	1.2	1.5
Bacterial count per g. (Max)	50,000	50,000
Coliform count per g. (Max)	90	90

C. *ADMI.* The American Dry Milk Institute standards are given in Table 9.3.

TABLE 9.3

ADMI standards for dried milks

Particulars	Instant	Spray		Roller	
	US extra	US extra	US stand	US extra	US stand
Skim milk powder					
Moisture (%) NMT	4.25	4.0	5.0	4.0	5.0
Milk fat (%) NMT	1.25	1.25	1.50	1.25	1.50
Titratable acidity (%) NMT	0.15	0.15	0.17	0.15	0.17
Scorched particles (mg/g.) NMT	15.0	15.0	22.5	22.5	32.5
Solubility index (ml.) NMT	1.0	1.2	2.0	15.0	15.0
Standard plate count (per g.) NMT	35,000	50,000	100,000	50,000	100,000
Coliform count (per g.) NMT	90	—	—	—	—
Whole milk powder					
Moisture (%) NMT	2.25	2.25	3.0	3.0	4.0
Milk fat (%) NLT	26.00	26.00	26.00	26.00	26.00
Solubility index (ml.) NMT	0.5	0.5	1.0	15.0	15.0
Scorched particles (mg/g.) NMT	15.0	15.0	22.5	22.5	32.5
Titratable acidity (%) NMT	0.15	0.15	0.17	0.15	0.17
Standard plate count (per g.) NMT	30,000	50,000	100,000	50,000	100,000
Coliform count (per g.) NMT	90	—	—	—	—
Copper (ppm) NMT	1.5	1.5	—	1.5	—
Iron (ppm) NMT	10	10	—	10	—
Oxygen (% vol) NMT	2	3	—	3	—
	(If gas packed)			(If gas packed)	

Legend: NMT—Not more than
NLT —Not less than

9.6 Composition

The average percentage composition of whole milk powder and skim milk powder is given in Table 9.4.

TABLE 9.4

Composition of dried milks (Percentage)

Type of dried milk	Average composition				
	Moisture	Fat	Protein	Lactose	Ash
Whole milk powder	2.0	27.5	26.4	38.2	5.9
Skim milk powder	3.0	0.8	35.9	52.3	8.0

SOURCE: *Drying of Milk and Milk Products* by Hall and Hedrick (1971).

9.7 Food and Nutritive Value

Under modern drying methods, the nutritive value of milk is preserved to a great extent. While there appears to be only a slight destruction of lysine in spray drying, the severe heat-treatment of roller drying destroys more lysine. Dry whole milk is a good source of vitamin A, calcium and phosphorus. It is also a valuable source of riboflavin.

9.8 Role of Milk Constituents

(a) *Milk fat*. This may be present in dried milks or milk products either in the original globule, i.e. in emulsion form, or as free fat, i.e. in de-emulsified form. Free fat makes the dry product greasy and leaves an oily film on the reconstituted milk.

The unsaturated fatty acids of milk fat, e.g. oleic, play a profound role in oxidative deterioration. Free fat promotes oxidation. The phospholipids of milk appear to be responsible for the oxidized flavour. The rancid flavour of milk fat is primarily due to the liberation of butyric acid as a result of hydrolysis of glycerides through lipase action.

(b) *Milk proteins*. Many of the problems of dairy technology revolve around the behaviour of the caseinate system and particularly on the aggregation of casein particles by heat, salts, acid, etc. Milk proteins are readily subject to changes during heat-processing and to some extent during storage; the changes adversely affect their solubility, i.e. dispersibility. The heat-treatment destabilizes the proteins by inducing first stage denaturation and then irreversible denaturation (coagulation) as it becomes more severe. Some destabilization also occurs slowly during prolonged storage. Some proteins, probably β-lactoglobulin, appear to be the source of sulfydryl compounds associated with a cooked and caramelized flavour.

(c) *Milk sugar.* This has an important role to play in the manufacture and storage of dried milk products. In freshly dried milk, the lactose is still present in the amorphous or glass (non-crystalline) state. In this form it is very hygroscopic and readily absorbs moisture upon exposure to the atmosphere, which induces crystallization. This absorbed humidity then causes the powder to become sticky, and then to cake. (This tendency to stickiness and caking increases in the presence of lactic acidity.)

Browning (colour defect) of dried milk products may be caused during manufacture, chiefly due to excessive temperature and long exposure to heat. Browning-discolouration may also occur during storage; especially under conditions of high moisture, high storage temperature and packaging in air-packed containers—all of which hasten and intensify browning.

(d) *Milk salts.* These play an important part in influencing the physical state and physical stability of the milk proteins, particularly the caseinates. The well-known 'salt balance' theory of Sommer and Hart holds that optimum stability depends on a certain ratio of calcium and magnesium ions to those of citrates and phosphates. Minor changes in salt balance and pH easily upset this equilibrium and tend to destabilize and precipitate the casein particles. The resulting dried milk will have a low solubility (dispersability). Copper and iron exert a catalytic action in the oxidation of milk lipids, which produces undesirable flavours in the dried milk products.

9.9 Milk Drying Systems

The systems and process of milk drying can be classified as follows:

```
                   ┌─Cold → ┌─Freezing out water and centrifuging
                   │         └─Freezing milk and sublimation
Drying by →        │
                   │         ┌─Film, roller or drum drying →┌─Atmospheric
                   └─Heat →  │                              └─Vacuum
                             │                    ┌─Compressed air
                             └─Spray drying→      ├─Pressure spray
                                                  └─Centrifugal disc
```

9.10   Drying Milk by Cold Treatment

(a) *Drying milk by freezing out the water and centrifuging.* This system was proposed and patented as early as 1884 and is now obsolete.

(b) *Drying milk by freezing and sublimation.*   This freeze-drying method, which seems to have been developed by 1945, consists of: (i) freezing the product and (ii) supplying heat, so that moisture is removed by sublimation (without passing through the liquid phase) by maintaining a vacuum in the vapourizing chamber. (For details, see standard books on the subject.)

(c) *Merits and demerits of freeze-drying process*

Merits.   (i) Can be designed for continuous operation; (ii) there is an almost complete absence of air throughout the drying cycle, (iii) moisture content of the finished product can be reduced to extremely low values; (iv) heat-damage to protein stability, flavour, solubility and colour of the finished product is minimal.

Demerits.   (i) The plant is complicated; (ii) operating costs are rather high. (Five to ten times that of conventional heat-drying, according to one estimate.)

9.11   Film, Roller or Drum Drying Systems

A. *Principle.*   The milk, preferably concentrated, is applied in a thin film upon the smooth surface of a continuously rotating steam-heated metal drum, roller or cylinder, and the film of dried milk is continuously scraped off by a stationary knife/doctor blade/scraper, located opposite the point of application of milk. The milk-film (in the form of a sheet) has to be ground to obtain the powder.

B. *Advantages and disadvantages (over Spray-Drying System)*

Advantages.   (i) Relatively low capital and operating costs; (ii) plant is movable and occupies little floor space; (iii) plant is easy to handle; (iv) suitable for operating small quantities of milk economically; (v) produces milk powder of better keeping quality.

Disadvantages.   (i) Produces milk powder with low solubility; (ii) produces a definitely cooked/scorched flavour in the reconstituted milk.

C. *Classification of drum driers (adapted from Hall & Hedrick)*

(a) *Number of hollow drums.*   (i) Single drum: (ii) Twin drum; (iii) Double drum.

(b) *Pressure surrounding the product.* (i) Atmospheric; (ii) Vacuum.

(c) *Directions for the turning of drums.* (i) Turn up at the centre and away at the top—Twin drum; (ii) turn at centre and together at top—Double drum.

(d) *Method of placing the product on the surface of drum.* (i) Trough or reservoir above for top feed; (ii) spray or splash feed; (iii) sump below for dip feeding; (iv) trough below for pan feeding.

(e) *Method of obtaining vacuum* (for a vacuum drier unit). (i) By steam ejector, (ii) by vacuum pump.

(f) *Material for construction of the drum.* (i) Steel; (ii) Alloy steel; (iii) Stainless steel; (iv) Cast iron; (v) Chrome or nickel-plated steel.

Note: (i) Cast iron is usually used. The wear is excessive on stainless steel drums. The metal used for the knife should be softer than that used for the drum.

(ii) The double-drum atmospheric drier is most commonly used in the dairy industry. Vacuum drum driers are essentially the same as atmospheric units except that the drums are enclosed so that a vacuum can be pulled on the product during drying. The single drum with top feed is more commonly used for vacuum drying. A thicker film is obtained with top feed.

D. *Flow of product.* The product may be placed in its natural form or pre-condensed in a vacuum pan/evaporator (see G(j) for advantages of pre-condensing) before it is fed to the drum drier. Milk is usually pre-condensed for a single-drum unit. The product is usually pre-heated and pumped into the reservoir between the upper portion of the drums to provide a thin film over the turning drums. The doctor blade, which is a sharp hard flexible knife, scrapes the dried material from the drum. The blade sits at an angle of 15 to 30° to the surface. The film of dry milk forms a continuous sheet from the knife to the auger trough, which is about level with the bottom of the drum. The auger for each drum discharges the product into elevators, then to a grinder which pulverizes the product, after which it is sifted. When sifted, the dried product is packaged and stored, or marketed. These steps are carried out in a continuous operation.

E. *Vapour removal.* Water vapour above the drier has a lower density than the air surrounding the unit and hence rises upwards. A hood is placed over the drums for the vapours to escape.

F. *Drums*

(a) *Description.* The drums are normally horizontal, hollow, steel cylinders, 90 to 360 cm. (3 to 12 ft.) in length and 60 to 120 cm. (2 to 4 ft.) in diameter. They are heated internally by steam, usually at 4.2 to 4.9 kg./sq. cm. (60–70 psi) with suitable arrangements for steam intake and a condensate outlet. In the case of double drums, the cylinders are mounted parallel to each other about 0.5 to 0.75 mm. apart; further, one drum is mounted on a stationary bearing, and the other on a flexible one so that it can be moved to provide the desired clearance between the drums.

(b) *Drying particulars.* In atmospheric driers, drying takes place at atmospheric pressure. In vacuum driers, however, the drier is enclosed in a vacuum chamber which is maintained at a vacuum of 68.5 to 73.5 cm. Hg. A high quality product is obtained in vacuum driers, but besides being expensive the process is complicated.

The speed of the drums is adjustable, usually averaging 14–19 rpm. The speed is important as it affects the thickness of the film and the time the product is on the roller; the speed may be varied according to the dryness desired. Both drums should turn at the same speed. The product is removed after the drum has completed $\frac{3}{4}$ or $\frac{7}{8}$ of a revolution. The product is in contact with the drum for 3 seconds or less at a temperature of about 150°C (302°F), depending on steam pressure.

(c) *Heat-transfer through the drum.* Drums must be carefully machined, both inside and outside, for a difference in thickness will alter heat transfer and prevent uniform drying. The requirement of steam is 1.2 to 1.3 kg. per kg. of water evaporated.

(d) *Operation.* The drier is started by: (i) lifting the knives; (ii) starting the drums; (iii) turning on the steam, and (iv) placing the product on the drums. The very first powder is not as good in quality as the remainder because of the tendency to be either over- or under-dried. The drums should be set in motion when the heat is applied by gradually turning on the steam to prevent warping.

G. *Important operating points*

(a) *Close control of the temperature and time of drying.* A higher temperature-time of drying tends to produce browning, a scorched flavour and reduced solubility in the powder. On the other hand a lower heat-treatment may result in incomplete drying and consequently a higher moisture content in the dried product.

Note: For a given drum size, the moisture content of the powder decreases with increased steam pressure and increases with higher drum speed. Since an increase in steam pressure hastens the drying, it makes possible a more rapid drum speed, thereby shortening the period of heat exposure.

(b) *Evenness of heating over the drum surface.* This should be maintained in order to obtain an uniformly dried product of standard quality. The condensate should be promptly removed from inside the drum.

(c) *Accurate alignment of rollers.* Drums should be properly aligned, particularly if double drum or twin drum units, and should have identical characteristics of speed, heat transfer, wear, etc., for best results.

(d) *Accurate control of the feed device.* Only accurate control will ensure uniformity of film thickness on the drum, which is essential for the maintenance of uniformity of moisture content in the finished product through the day's run. Lack of such uniformity also has an unfavourable effect on the solubility, flavour and colour of the finished product. The level of milk in the reservoir must be uniform and holes kept open in the distribution tubing. Change in the milk level affects the film thickness on the drum and thus the steam requirements.

(e) *Pre-heating of milk before drying.* As the milk feed temperature is increased, the rate of drying is proportionately increased (2.2 per cent for each 10°F from 120 to 160°F, with little increase thereafter).

(f) *Keeping the drum surface smooth.* The drum surface must be kept smooth and free of rust and pits. Pits in the drum surface get filled with milk, escape the blade and flake off gradually, resulting in scorched particles.

Note: It may be necessary to resurface the drums after 1000 to 3000 hours of operation. The surface may be smoothened by attaching sand paper beneath the scraper knife. The drums should be coated with oil or paraffin wax when not in regular use.

(g) *Keeping scraper knives sharp and reground frequently*. The scraper knives should be sharp and true for efficient film removal. The knives must be reground regularly (after approximately every 100 hours) and be uniformly sharp. They must be flexible, machined on both edges, uniformly thick and easily adjustable. A uniform knife pressure against the drum must be maintained.

Note: The knife pressure against the drum is adjusted by screws at each end of the knife, and by numerous screws along the length of the knife for local adjustment. Excessive pressure of the blade on the drum increases the operational energy of the drum and the danger of metallic shavings in the finished product. The long one-piece knife may be substituted with a series of independent short knives arranged in staggered positions for effective coverage of all parts of the drum over its entire length.

(h) *Using fresh sweet milk*. This will ensure a high quality product. Any developed acidity will lower the solubility and produce an oxidized or tallowy flavour in whole milk powder.

(j) *Using pre-condensed milk*. Normally milk which is drum-dried is pre-condensed to 2 : 1, so as to contain 16–18 per cent total solids in order to obtain the following advantages: (i) to provide satisfactory film thickness on the drum surface, especially with single drum dryers. The fluid sweet milk, because of its low viscosity, will not do so; (ii) greater thermal economy. This is actually due to the use of a double-effect evaporator for pre-condensing; (iii) increased capacity of dryers; (iv) increased bulk density, and (v) increased keeping quality.

Note: (i) The product may be damaged and scorched if there is an uneven milk supply, incomplete removal of the film, imperfect roller alignment, a rough roller, and an excessively high product-temperature (caused by an excessively high steam temperature or excessively slow drum speed).

(ii) High moisture in the product is due to low temperature, thick film, high total solids, and fast speed (rpm).

H. *Factors affecting capacity of drum driers*

(a) *Steam pressure inside the drum*. A higher steam pressure permits greater drum speed consistent with satisfactory completeness of drying.

    (b) *Temperature of milk feed* ⎫

    (c) *Level of milk in the trough* ⎬ Discussed above.

    (d) *Pre-condensing of milk* ⎭

    J. *Merits and demerits of vacuum drum drying over atmospheric drying*

    (a) *Merits.* (i) Higher solubility of powder; (ii) better keeping quality of powder.

    (b) *Demerits.* (i) Higher initial cost of plant; (ii) higher operating cost of plant; (iii) more complicated plant.

    K. *Flow diagram of drum drying system*

Milk concentrate

|

Adjustable pump

|

Feeding

|

Drying drum

|

Scraper

|

Grinder

|

Sifter

|

Dried product

9.12 Spray-Drying System

A. *Principle*

The basic principle of spray drying consists in atomizing the milk, preferably pre-heated and concentrated, to form a spray of very minute droplets (fog-like mist), which are directed into a large, suitably designed drying chamber, where they mix intimately with a current of hot air. Owing to their large surface area, the milk particles surrender their moisture practically instantaneously and dry to a fine powder, which is removed continuously.

    B. *Advantages and disadvantages* (*over roller-drying system*)

    (a) *Advantages*: (i) Yields milk powder which is markedly superior in appearance, flavour and solubility (and hence commands a higher market price); (ii) most economical when large quantities of milk are handled.

    (b) *Disadvantages*: (i) Involves large capital investment in plant and buildings; (ii) plant is complicated.

C. *Classification of spray driers* (*vide* Hall and Hedrick).

(a) *Method for atomizing spray material*:   (i) Hydraulic pressure jet (pressure spray); (ii) Pneumatic (compressed air); (iii) Centrifugal disc.

(b) *Method of furnishing heat*: (i) Steam; (ii) gas; (iii) fuel oil; (iv) electricity.

(c) *Method of heating air*: (i) Direct (gas or fuel oil); (ii) Indirect (utilizing heat exchanger plate or coils).

(d) *Position of drying chamber*:   (i) Vertical; (ii) horizontal.

(e) *Number of drying chambers.* (i) One (main only); (ii) two (main and subsidiary).

(f) *Direction of airflow in relation to product flow*:   (i) Counter-current; (ii) parallel; (iii) right-angle.

(g) *Pressure in drier*:   (i) Atmospheric (usually a very slight pressure); (ii) vacuum.

(h) *Method of separation of powder from air*: (i) Cyclone; (ii) multi-cyclone; (iii) bag filter; (iv) liquid dust collector; (v) electrical dust collector.

(j) *Treatment and movement of air*:   (i) Recirculation of air; (ii) dehydration of air; (iii) Conventional (atmospheric air used and exhausted after use).

(k) *Removal of powder from drying chamber*: (i) Conveyor; (ii) vibrator; (iii) sweep conveyor; (iv) air conveyed to cyclone.

(l) *Method of heat transfer*:   (i) Convection; (ii) radiation.

(m) *Kind of atmosphere in drying chamber*: (i) Nitrogen; (ii) air; (iii) other (usually inert gas).

(n) *Position of fan provided*: (i) Pressure in chamber; (ii) suction in chamber.

(p) *Direction of air-flow in chamber*: (i) Updraft; (ii) downdraft; (iii) horizontal; (iv) mixed.

(q) *Shape of drying chamber*: (i) Silo or cylindrical; (ii) box-like; (iii) square cross section; (iv) tear-drop.

(r) *Product being dried*: (i) Milk; (ii) other milk products; (iii) other food products.

D. *Atomization*

(a) *Object.* To reduce the milk to particles so small in size that due to their large surface area they surrender their moisture practically instantaneously.

(b) *Purpose.* To obtain many small particles, preferably uniform in size, generally ranging from 50 to 150 microns in diameter. Uniform particles provide: (i) a superior instantizing product; (ii) reduced product losses; (iii) less over- and under-drying, and (iv) more efficient drying (large drops are more difficult to dry and require a longer time or a higher temperature, or both).

(c) *Influence of type and efficiency.* This affects the desired design (size, air temperature, exposure time, evaporation rate and efficiency). The atomization also affects the product properties, such as air content, moisture, bulk density, particle size (range and average) and reconstitutability. The pattern produced by the atomizer must be so directed that the particles will be dried before hitting the surface of the drying chamber, else there will be an accumulation of partially dried product on the drier.

(d) *Methods/Systems.** There are three major methods/systems cf atomizing. These are: (i) pressure spray jet/nozzle; (ii) centrifugal (spinning) disc; (iii) compressed air.

(i) *Pressure spray nozzles.* These include the swirl nozzle (called whizzer or centrifugal pressure nozzle), the solid cone spray nozzle, and the fan nozzle. The pressure spray jet is the most common in the USA for milk and food product atomization for spray drying. Pressures from 1500–5000 psi are used. A high pressure pump, such as a three or five piston homogenizer pump, is commonly employed to ensure uniform fineness of spray. The milk is thus forced under high pressure through a small orifice and is atomized instantly. The higher the pressure or the smaller the orifice, the finer the particle size of the mist, and vice versa.

To control the spray powder satisfactorily, and ensure uniformity of moisture content, the orifice must be of the right size and shape and its edges must be smooth. On the other hand, if the milk stream flows at high velocity under high pressure, the spray discs wear out rapidly due to the intensive abrasive action of the milk solids. The new-alloy (tungsten-carbide) nozzles of today are much more wear-resistant.

Note: (i) The purpose of the swirling motion is to widen the angle of the milk fog and intensify the atomizing action.

(ii) A recent development is the use of sonics or ultrasonics to vibrate the nozzle and thereby increase the uniformity of the droplets from the spray nozzle.

---

* Adapted from Hall and Hedrick.

(ii) *Centrifugal spinning discs.* The atomizing device consists of a radial vaned disc (vanes placed between two discs), multiple discs (three or more discs), and a bowl or hemispherically shaped liquid chamber through which the product moves. The atomizing device may revolve at 50,000 rpm for a small diameter disc (approximately 5 cm.) or at 3500 rpm for a large diameter disc (approximately 75 cm.). The product may be ejected from the spinning disc/ slotted basket over a lip or through a slot, hole or other opening. The disc atomizer permits considerable variation in capacity, about $\pm$ 25 per cent of the design capacity. The pattern produced by the disc is umbrella-shaped although for very fine droplets a mist of cloud is formed. The spinning disc is particularly useful for viscous materials and for materials in suspension. The centrifugal unit is used in a vertical drying chamber.

Advantages: 1. Absence of small orifices that are subject to clogging; 2. Permits spray drying of highly concentrated milk (containing as much as 50 per cent solids), which results in high thermal economy; 3. No pump pressure is required; 4. Capable of continuous operation over prolonged periods without special attention; 5. Free from abrasive action.

Disadvantage: 1. Requires upkeep of high-speed bearings.

Note: Some European milk-drying factories (LUWA Ltd., Zurich) use centrifugal spray dryers that are equipped with twin spray discs, attached to the same shaft but at different levels. The fresh milk is separated and only the skim milk is pre-condensed. The condensed skim milk feeds one disc and the fresh cream the other. The two liquids reach their respective spray discs through separate pipes simultaneously. The resulting powder is an automatically produced mechanical mixture of the dried particles from each disc.

(iii) *Compressed air spray/Pneumatic.* A jet of high-temperature compressed air moves at high velocity through a stream/s of preheated milk. The milk streams issue from a battery of simple nozzles. The high-velocity jet of very hot air strikes the milk stream/s at a right angle/s, atomizing the milk instantly.

E. *Heating air.* A fresh supply of air is drawn through a filter by the intake fan, which blows it over the heater.

(a) *Air supply.* Invariably, fresh new air from the outside atmosphere is used. Air from the drying chamber is not re-used, since the cost of dehydrating the exhaust air is uneconomical. The supply of air, which may be derived from outside or inside the plant, should be pure, free from visible extraneous material, dust, soot and objectionable odours. Air intake may take place from the top of the building or ground level.

(b) *Air filter.* In order to ensure purity, the air to be used for drying is filtered. This removes suspended impurities and as many micro-organisms as possible. Different types of air filters may be used. Close weave filters are unsuitable. Filtering is normally done by mechanical means. Those normally used are:

(i) *Water spray type.* The air is washed by drawing it through a spray of water, or through a series of screens of wire mesh or gauze over which a film of water trickles.

Drawback: Does not remove greasy turbidity.

(ii) *Oil film type.* The air is purified by drawing it through a film of oil contained in multiple cells of expanded metal. This is most commonly used. The oil used should be odourless and sufficiently heavy to prevent it being blown off by the interior air.

(c) *Air intake fan.* This is normally installed between the air filter and air heater. Draws cool air and forces it through the air heater into the drying chamber. (The next best location for the fan is at the exit of the drying chamber.)

(d) *Air heater.* The air may be heated directly, as for instance by the furnace flame, or semi-directly by other means such as the furnace with hot air flues; or by indirect means, as by air passing over banks of fin-type coils through which are circulated steam, hot oil, etc.

The direct (and semi-direct) heaters are more efficient, for less heat is lost during heat-transfer. Fuels for direct-fired units are limited to gas and light oil to avoid soot formation; with these units, the selection of fuel is based primarily on the cost and the effect of combustion products of the fuel on the drying product. Where electricity is cheap, or in laboratory spray driers, electrical heating may be utilized. It is easier to control a uniformly low temperature with steam, which provides a relatively non-hazardous source of heat.

F. *Products moisture removal.* The atomized product is brought into intimate contact with heated air in the drying chamber, for moisture removal. The temperature and volume of heated air that will evaporate a given amount of water or that will dry a given amount of milk, vary with the temperature and humidity of the atmospheric air, the temperature and concentration of the milk to be dried and the temperature and degree of saturation of the moisture-laden air emerging from the drying chamber.

(a) *Temperature of heated air.* The higher the temperature of heated air, the lower the volume required, and vice versa. However, lower temperatures necessitate large drying chambers. It is economically advantageous to use the highest temperature that the liquid to be dried will stand without injury to its quality. Heat damage also depends on the rapidity of evaporation. Damaging overheating is avoided by mixing the milk particles with the hot air while violently agitating it, thus providing the maximum rapidity of evaporation.

The inlet-air entering the drying chamber now usually ranges in temperature from 149 to 260°C (300 to 500°F) for drying milk and milk products; the outlet-air exhausted from the drying chamber usually ranges from 100 to 105°C (212 to 221°F). The relative humidity of the drying air is also quite low, e.g. 3 to 4 per cent.

(b) *Volume of heated air.* The temperature of heated air being the same, a smaller volume of air is required in cold weather than in hot weather. This is because the former is denser than the latter. But a smaller quantity of cold air requires more calories to heat it than does the larger quantity of warmer air in order to attain the same temperature.

(c) *Velocity of air.* For economical and proper heating of the air and satisfactory performance in the drying chamber, the air should move at the right velocity. This is made possible by correctly correlating the dimensions of the various components of the drying unit.

(d) *Drying chamber designs.* All drying chambers are intended to completely mix the product droplets with the hot air, and then dry them as rapidly as possible in a space of reasonable dimensions. In practice, size and shape vary considerably, as designs are made according to the type of atomizer used and the method of recovering the powder from the outgoing air. The common ones are:

(i) *Rectangular, horizontal type.* The concentrated milk is sprayed in at one end of a long, rectangular chamber as a conical spray, usually from a pressure-jet type atomizer. The hot air is also admitted as a parallel stream to the spray and is ejected at the opposite end of the chamber. The (coarse) powder particles fall gently to the floor of the chamber, from which they are removed continuously by mechanical sweeping. The inlet air temperature is around 130 to 140°C (266 to 284°F). A large volume of drying air is used.

(ii) *Vertical, cylindrical type.* These comprise a tall cylindrical chamber with either a flat or conical base. In most designs, the concentrated product is sprayed in from the top and mixed with a strong spiral and downward stream of hot air which shakes the product violently. The exposure time is very short and high temperatures of 150 to 170°C (302–338°F) can be used with a smaller volume of air.

Note: The horizontal driers are commonly used in the USA, while the more flexible vertical ones are more common in Europe.

(e) *Flow of air.* The air must be properly and uniformly directed into and through the drying chamber, else the heat in the air will be inefficiently utilized and a partially dried product may accumulate on the inside edge of the drier. In general, the product and air either enter at opposite sides or from the top and bottom respectively and flow in counter-current directions towards each other; or they both enter in the same region, mingling together in a parallel or co-current flow.

The heated air is forced through an insulated duct at the end of which is the air disperser. This is especially designed, since on its correct shape depends the proper functioning of the entire plant. It actually spreads or distributes the hot air stream. In one design the air disperser is placed just below the atomizer, while in another it is behind it, leading to product-air co-current or parallel, or counter-current flow as the case may be.

After milk-dust recovery, the stale air is removed from the system by means of the Exhaust Air Fan and goes out to the atmosphere through the outlet duct furnished with an especially designed Exhaust Air Hood, which acts as a protecting cover in preventing dirt, dust, rain drops, etc., from falling through the duct into the system.

G. *Product recovery*

(a) *Separation of air and powder.* As the product is dried it is necessary to separate the dried product from the air, to prevent a major portion of it being carried away by the moist air being ejected from the drier (thereby resulting not only in lower yields, but also in air-pollution surrounding the drying plant). The powder may be separated from the air primarily either inside the drier (internally) or outside the drier (externally). In both cases, it is necessary to use an additional device outside the drier to remove the fines/dust or small particles, which will not normally settle inside the drier.

The particle size of spray-dried milk (or milk product) depends on several factors. Yet regardless of the type of spray drier, a certain proportion of the powder is much finer than the remainder. It has been estimated that the powder particle size may range from 10 to 100 microns. The relatively large/coarse particles, which may constitute approximately 80 per cent or more of the yield, respond to the force of gravity and get deposited on the sides or drop to the floor of the chamber. The milk-fines/dust, which constitute the remaining 20 per cent or less, become entrained in the air currents and are swept by them to the exit of the drying chamber, where they are more or less completely removed by mechanical means.

(b) *Recovery of larger particles.* The larger powder particles, which are separated within the drier, can be removed from the drier by: (i) an air-brush; (ii) a mechanical sweeper; (iii) a screw conveyor, or (iv) a gravity system. In the air brush system, air from outside the drier, either at room temperature or conditioned to a lower temperature, is used to direct a jet of air. A mechanical sweeper consists of a rake or broom which is pulled across the bottom of the drier. The screw conveyor helps to remove the powder particles by forcible ejection through screw movement, while the gravity system employs the principle of gravity settling. Vibrators are often attached to the sides of the drier to prevent, or minimize, the quantity of powder which sticks to the surface and to move the product rapidly from the drier.

(c) *Recovery of fines.* There are principally three types of devices in use for separation and recovery of milk-dust/fines:

(i) *Filter bag dust collector.* This consists of a series of filter bags equipped with mechanical shakers. The material of the bags may be cotton or wool (or plastic), of very fine weave. The bags are 180 to 300 cm. high and 20 to 25 cm. wide. The entire series of bags present a large screening surface. The air is drawn through these bags and deposits the entrained milk particles in their meshes. Intermittent shaking helps drop the powder to the bottom of the vault in which the bags are suspended. This device needs close supervision to maintain it in an approved sanitary condition. Losses generally range from 0.2 to 0.5 per cent.

(ii) *Cyclone/cyclonic separator/centrifugal milk dust separator.* The cyclone or multi-cyclone is most commonly used today. It is usually a stainless steel cylindrical container with a cone-shaped bottom. The air leaving the drying chamber at a high velocity enters the cyclone tangentially. It thus assumes a rotary motion forming a cyclonic vortex. Centrifugal force throws the solids to the peripheral wall of the cylinder, along which the material works down into the hopper.

In the past, large cyclones (diameter ranging from 150 to 600 cm.) were used, generally supplemental to filter bags and preceding the latter. However, the modern trend is to use the multi-cyclone with a smaller diameter, which increases the efficiency of milk-dust recovery.

The efficiency of separation with a cyclone unit is based on product, cyclone design and on the size of the particle to be removed, but losses range from 0.5 to 3.0 per cent (average 1 per cent). The cyclone is normally used for separation of material between 5 and 200 microns. As the size of the particle decreases, the efficiency of the cyclone also decreases.

(iii) *Liquid dust collector.* This consists of a closed tank into which the incoming fresh milk is pumped through a series of suitably distributed spray jets. The exhaust air escaping from the drying chamber passes through the fresh milk spray in the collector tank. By this method, the milk dust entrained in the spent air from the drying chamber is deposited in the incoming fresh milk.

Merits. 1. High recovery of product; 2. Pre-condenses fresh milk; 3. Utilizes a considerable portion of the heat-units contained in the exhaust air; 4. Economical; 5. Highly advantageous for skim milk, butter, whey, etc.

Demerits. Less suitable for whole milk, since oxygen and other gases removed in the drying chamber are re-introduced in the fresh incoming milk, thereby enhancing the possibilities of product deterioration and contamination.

H. *Cooling the powder.* The dried milk/milk product should be removed from the drier as quickly as possible to minimize the effect of heat-damage on the product. The product and air may be removed together from the drier and separated outside the drier to reduce heat effect. Prolonged exposure of the dried milk/product to high temperatures jeopardizes its flavour, colour and keeping quality, besides increasing the tendency towards clumping and sticking. Hence it is desirable to cool the product soon after production.

Some cooling of the product takes place in the drier when using an air-brush supplied with cool air to remove the dried product from the sides and bottom of the drier. Cooling powder outside the drier may be done by: (i) conduction cooling, in which the product is cooled when moving through a water-jacketed screw conveyor; (ii) convection cooling, by using room or refrigerated air to cool it to 38°C (100°F), or by moving conditioned air over the product or through the conveyor handling the product, and (iii) surrounding the outlet of a cyclone separator by a chamber through which cold air is moved to cool the product.

J. *Flow diagram of spray drying system*

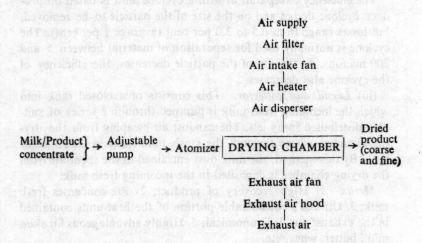

9.13 **Foam-Spray Drying**

Common dairy products such as skim milk, whole milk, buttermilk, sweet and sour cream, whey and emulsified cheese slurry can be foam-spray dried. This is done by forcing the 'gas' into the liquid product after the pump but before the atomizer. Air is commonly used as the added gas for making foam-spray non-fat dry milk, and nitrogen for foam-spray dried whole milk.

Foam-spray drying permits the use of most items of conventional spray drying equipment for: (i) drying liquids up to a maximum of 60 per cent total solids as compared to 50 per cent on a particular drier; (ii) for drying special products, such as malted milk, cottage cheese and whey, and (iii) for obtaining an instant powder.

The particles of the dried product obtained by foam-spray drying are more uniform in size. However, foam-spray non-fat dry milk has a low bulk density (about 0.35 g./ml. or less) and hence higher packaging costs.

9.14 Method of Manufacture by Drum Process of Whole Milk Powder (WMP) and Skim Milk Powder (SMP)

A. *Flow diagram = combined for WMP and SMP*

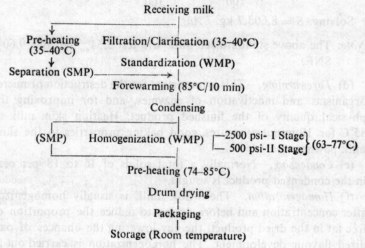

B. *Details*

I. *Whole milk powder*

(a) *Receiving milk.* Only high-grade milk should be accepted.

(b) *Filtration/clarification.* The chief object of this is to remove extraneous matter.

(c) *Standardization.* This is done to adjust the ratio of fat and solids-not-fat in raw milk to meet the legal standards for composition in dried whole milk. Raw milk is standardized by adding to it a calculated amount of skim milk or cream.

Problem. Given 10,000 kg. milk testing 6.50% fat and 9.58% SNF and skim milk testing 0.10% fat and 9.61% SNF. How much skim milk must be used for standardization so as to give whole milk powder of standard composition?

Solution.

Assuming whole milk powder to contain:

26.2% fat and 2.8% moisture.

In WMP, $\dfrac{\text{SNF}}{\text{Fat}} = \dfrac{71.0}{26.2} = 2.71$.

Let the quantity of skim milk required be S kg. Then the following equation can be framed:

$$\frac{\dfrac{10,000 \times 9.58}{100} + \dfrac{S \times 9.61}{100}}{\dfrac{10,000 \times 6.50}{100} + \dfrac{S \times 0.10}{100}} = 2.71$$

Solving, $S = 8,603.7$ kg. *Ans.*

Note: The above standardized milk will test 3.54% fat and 9.60% SNF.

(d) *Forewarming.* This is important for the destruction of micro-organisms and inactivation of enzymes, and for improving the physical quality of the finished product. Heating skim milk to 85°C for 10 minutes ensures good baking properties in the skim milk powder.

(e) *Condensing.* Normally a total solids of 16 to 18 per cent in the condensed product is sought.

(f) *Homogenization.* The whole milk is usually homogenized after concentration and before drying to reduce the proportion of free fat in the dried product, thereby lowering the chances of oxidized flavour development. The homogenization is carried out at 63–77°C (145–170°F) in two stages, 2500 psi on the first stage and 500 psi on the second.

(g) *Pre-heating.* This increases the efficiency of drum drying. It is carried out by heating the feed-concentrate to 74–85°C before pumping it into the reservoir between the drums.

(h) *Drum drying* (See 9.11).

(j) *Packaging* (See 9.17).

(k) *Storage* (See 9.18).

II. *Skim milk powder.* Same as for whole milk powder except that 'standardization' and 'homogenization' are omitted, while 'clarification' is taken care of during centrifugal cream separation.

9.15 Method of Manufacture by Spray Process of Whole Milk Powder (WMP) and Skim Milk Powder (SMP)

A. *Flow diagram = combined for WMP and SMP* (Adapted from Hall and Hedrick):

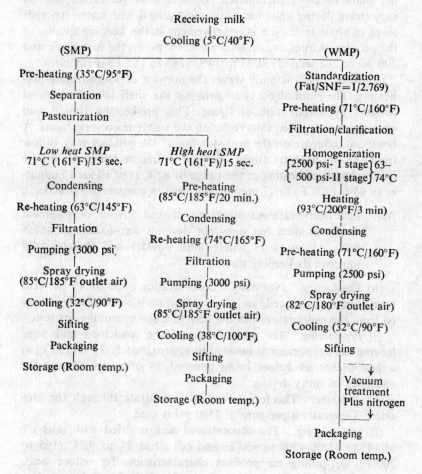

Receiving milk

Cooling (5°C/40°F)

(SMP)

Pre-heating (35°C/95°F)

Separation

Pasteurization

Low heat SMP
71°C (161°F)/15 sec.

Condensing

Re-heating (63°C/145°F)

Filtration

Pumping (3000 psi)

Spray drying
(85°C/185°F outlet air)

Cooling (32°C/90°F)

Sifting

Packaging

Storage (Room temp.)

High heat SMP
71°C (161°F)/15 sec.

Pre-heating
(85°C/185°F/20 min.)

Condensing

Re-heating (74°C/165°F)

Filtration

Pumping (3000 psi)

Spray drying
(85°C/185°F outlet air)

Cooling (38°C/100°F)

Sifting

Packaging

Storage (Room temp.)

(WMP)

Standardization
(Fat/SNF=1/2.769)

Pre-heating (71°C/160°F)

Filtration/clarification

Homogenization
$\begin{cases} 2500 \text{ psi- I stage} \\ 500 \text{ psi-II stage} \end{cases} \begin{matrix} 63- \\ 74°C \end{matrix}$

Heating
(93°C/200°F/3 min)

Condensing

Pre-heating (71°C/160°F)

Pumping (2500 psi)

Spray drying
(82°C/180°F outlet air)

Cooling (32°C/90°F)

Sifting

Vacuum
treatment
Plus nitrogen

Packaging

Storage (Room temp.)

B. *Details*

I. *Whole milk powder*

(a) *Receiving milk.* Only high-grade milk should be accepted.

(b) *Cooling.* To preserve the quality of milk.

(c) *Standardization* (See 9.14).

(d) *Pre-heating.* For efficient filtration/clarification

(e) *Filtration/clarification.* The chief object of this is to remove extraneous matter. This operation can also be done before standardization.

(f) *Homogenization.* Commonly done, if direct reconstitution of dry whole milk is contemplated. Without homogenization, the fat may churn during agitation while combining it with water. Another merit of homogenization is improvement in the keeping quality of the powder. A pressure of 3000 psi (2500 psi on the first stage and 500 psi on the second) at 63 to 74°C (145 to 165°F) is sufficient.

(g) *Heat.* This actually serves the purpose of forewarming/pre-heating. The main object is to prolong the shelf life of the dried product by inactivation of lipase. This pre-heating should also ensure pasteurization, thus reducing the viable micro-organisms. A beneficial influence on the heat-stability of the product may follow from the pre-heat treatment. Several optimum temperature-time combinations of heating in the range of 82°C (180°F) for 15 minutes to 93°C (200°F) for 3 minutes are used in commercial practice.

Note: Low heat-treatment minimizes cooked flavour development in the product but does not develop anti-oxidants, which delay oxidation in whole milk powder and thereby help improve its keeping quality.

(h) *Condensing.* Normally a concentration of 35 to 45 per cent total solids is produced, and the concentrate is continuously removed from the evaporator with the help of a continuous density teste.

(j) *Pre-heating.* The temperature of the condensed milk after leaving the evaporator is boosted to approximately 71 C (160°F) in a heat-exchanger before being pumped, in order to increase the efficiency of spray drying.

(k) *Pumping.* This forces the hot concentrate through the atomizer. Generally a pressure of 2500 psi is used.

(l) *Spray drying.* The concentrated milk is dried with inlet air at 143 to 232°C (300 to 450°F) and exit air at 74 to 93°C (165 to 200°F), depending on product characteristics. To reduce heat-damage during drying and yet obtain the desired moisture, a low exhaust air temperature is preferred.

(m) *Cooling.* The dry whole milk should be removed promptly from the hot air stream to maintain better flavour and body characteristics and also keeping quality. The higher the temperature and the longer the time the product is above the melting point of fat.

the greater the amount of free fat obtained, thus adversely effecting keeping quality. Hence it is essential to cool the powder immediately to a temperature below the melting point of fat.

(n) *Sifting.* A 12-mesh screen is used for sifting dry whole milk.

Note: The size of (powder) particles is designated by microns or mesh. A micron (μM) is one-millionth part of a metre, i.e. 0.001 mm. Mesh refers to the number of screen openings per lineal inch. The opening also depends upon the size of the wire used in making the mesh material. The Tyler sieve, the U.S. scale sieve and the B.S.S. sieve use different sizes of wire for making up the screen. A 100-mesh Tyler sieve has an opening of 0.147 mm., which is equivalent to 147 μM; the 400-mesh opening is equivalent to a 38 μM diameter. For smaller sizes, a microscopic analysis is made to determine the particle diameter.

(p) *Packaging* (See 9.17).

(q) *Storage* (See 9.18).

II. *Skim milk powder*

(a) *Receiving milk* } Same as for WMP.
(b) *Cooling*

(c) *Pre-heating and separation.* Cream can be separated with or without pre-heating the milk; special cold milk separators are required for the low-temperature method. The most important consideration is a high degree of separation efficiency (not more than 0.1 per cent fat in skim milk).

(d) *Pasteurization*

I. *Low heat skim milk powder.* Its manufacture requires that heating be carefully controlled during pasteurization so as to produce the minimum number of heat-induced changes. Control of both temperature and time is important. Higher temperature and/or longer holding time contribute directly to whey protein denaturation—which is measured by whey protein nitrogen (WPN) content per g. of powder. It should have a WPN of 6 mg. or more.

II. *High heat skim milk powder.* A higher heat treatment imparts good baking qualities to the powder. For this purpose, besides pasteurizing at 71°C (161°F) for 15 seconds, the powder is pre-heated a second time at 85°C (185°F) for 20 minutes before being condensed. Its WPN content should be not more than 1.5 mg.

(e) *Condensing* (see under whole milk powder). Normally a concentration of 40 to 42 per cent total solids is obtained.

(f) *Re-heating* (see under whole milk powder). This is done to increase the efficiency of drying.

(g) *Filtration.* This is done to remove any extraneous matter from the concentrate before atomization, so that it can function smoothly.

(h) *Pumping* (see under whole milk powder). This is done to force the hot concentrate through the atomizer.

(j) *Spray drying* (see under whole milk powder). Low heat skim milk powder is dried up to 3 to 4 per cent moisture, while high heat skim milk powder usually has not more than 3.5 per cent moisture.

(k) *Cooling.* Most milk driers have a continuous removal system to immediately separate the dry product from the hot air stream. The dry product should be cooled at once. If the skim milk powder is too hot when packaged, it may become lumpy due to 'heat-caking', and development of storage defects in flavour and colour may be rapid.

(l) *Sifting.* A 25-mesh screen is commonly used for sifting dry skim milk (see under whole milk powder).

(m) *Packaging* (See 9.17).

(n) *Storage* (See 9.18).

9.16 Instantization

(a) *Definition.* Instantization refers to the process by which dried milk and milk products are made instant-soluble.

(b) *Purpose.* The chief purpose of instantizing is to improve the rate and completeness of the reconstitutability of dry milk and milk products. The instantizing process affects wettability, sinkability, dispersability and solubility of the particles; however, total solubility is not improved.

(c) *Products.* Mainly applied to skim milk powder/non-fat dried milk. However, whole milk powder and other milk fat containing dry dairy products are also being instantized.

(d) *Characteristics.* (i) Lowers bulk density and hence increases packaging costs; (ii) increases moisture content of the finished product, which lowers the keeping quality.

(e) *Factors influencing instantization.* Dry milk that is manufactured especially for instantization usually yields the best results. Moisture content and particle size should be as uniform as possible. A minimum of fine particles, less than 20 μM in diameter, is desired, while particles in the range of 25 to 50 μM are preferred. The skim milk powder for agglomeration should be low in fat content. Low heat or medium heat skim milk powder is normally used, since high heat skim milk powder shatters much more easily in handling after instantization.

(f) *Success factors.* The success of the instantizing operation depends on:

(i) Uniform and constant rate of powder distribution into the wetting zone.

(ii) Avoiding over- or under-wetting of particles by providing uniform moisture conditions. (Over-wetted particles dissolve slowly and inadequate wetting permits excessive shattering during handling.)

(iii) Stabilizing air movement to ensure optimum particle collision. (Excess movement causes the product to adhere to the equipment lining.)

(iv) Controlling redrying air temperature and flow rate (which is necessary for adequate moisture removal without heat-damage to the instantized product).

(g) *Major systems/processes.* These are: (i) the Peebles process; (ii) the Cherry-Burrell process, and (iii) the Blow-Knox process (all American). In addition, there are NIRO and ANHYDRO Agglomerators, both Danish. The equipment of each system varies in detail.

I. *Common features.* These are: 1. *Wetting* of the surface of the particles with steam, atomized water, or a mixture of both (in a tube or chamber); 2. *Agglomeration*, which occurs because the particles collide with each other due to turbulence, and adhere to each other to form clusters (in a tube or chamber or cyclone); 3. *Re-drying* with hot filtered air (in a chamber or cyclone or deck); 4. *Cooling*; 5. *Sizing* to eliminate the very large agglomerates and the very small particles, and 6. *Sifting and packaging.*

II. *Particulars of major processes.* These are outlined in Table 9.5.

TABLE 9.5

Particulars of major processes

| Name of process | Particulars | | | Remarks |
| | Wetting | Re-drying | | |
	Moisture limit (percentage)	Hot air temp. °C/°F	Moisture limit (percentage)	
Peebles	10–15	110–121/ 230–250	4.0 (Approx.)	Wetting and re-drying in chamber
Cherry-Burrell	6–8	132–149/ 270–300	3.5–4.5	Wetting and re-drying in cyclone
Blow-Knox	7 (Approx.)	–do–	4.0–4.5	Wetting in tube and re-drying in deck

Note: The NIRO/ANHYDRO Agglomerator in an attachment fixed to the bottom of the vertical drying chamber. Milk is dried to approximately 9 per cent in the drying chamber and then the powder transported by a vibrator from the drier to the inlet of the agglomerator. The latter consists of three sections: the first for agglomeration, the second for re-drying and the third for cooling the instantized powder to room temperature. The fine particles are returned to the drying chamber.

9.17 Packaging

(a) *Introduction*. Before packaging, the sheets of roller-dried milk must be broken down to powder form. This is often done with a simple brush-type sifter totally enclosed in design, to reduce costs. If a very fine powder is desired, a ball mill can be used. With spray powder, it is only necessary to remove any coarse aggregates by passing the powder through a screen sifter.

Packaging by hand is undesirable as it is difficult to avoid dust, wastage, manual contact and general discomfort. Powder-filling machines are normally used, the type depending upon the nature of the container. Semi-automatic single-head machines may be used for large containers, while fully automatic multi-head rotary machines are available for the rapid filling of small containers.

In vacuum-operated fillers, the package (which must be rigid) is raised to the filling head and makes an air-tight joint against a rubber-faced filling nozzle. A vacuum pump withdraws air from the package through the gauze and the powder is sucked into the package from a supply hopper until the gauze is completely filled. The vacuum is then broken and the container is removed from the filler-head. Vacuum filling involves an enclosed circuit, which permits faster, dustless filling without wastage. No moving parts are required to make contact with the powder and removal of air enables a denser pack to be obtained.

The powder packaging department should be completely isolated to reduce the spread of powder dust to the drier building. A pneumatic conveying system is preferable for transferring powder from the drier to the packaging rooms; apart from the advantage of an enclosed system, the powder is cooled by the air current and can be moved over considerable distances.

A suitable container for dry milk should be impervious to moisture, light, gases, and insects; should be durable for handling; resistant to corrosion; of low cost; and be relatively easy to fill, seal, handle and empty. The retail package should have a reclosable opening. Because of the hygroscopic nature of dry milk, the packaging materials must provide a good vapour barrier. Of the several types in use, one is the fibreboard carton with an overwrap of foil laminated to paper. Another consists of a fibreboard carton with an inner lining of foil laminated to paper. A polyethylene bag inside the fibreboard carton is also used. Other combinations of layers of polyethylene, foil and paper either as lining or overwrap, are available for packaging. In India, the tin-can, though expensive, is still the most widely used retail container. Plastic-coated paper bags are the latest development in packaging technology.

Powder packaging should be carried out: (i) in a dry atmosphere between the drier and sealed package, and (ii) promptly in a hermetical, moisture-proof package. This is because lactose is present in a glass/non-crystalline/amorphous state in freshly prepared dried milks and milk products. In this state, the powder is very hygroscopic. If exposed to a humid atmosphere it will readily absorb moisture, become sticky and cake in storage.

(b) *Packaging of whole milk powder.* Fat decomposition resulting in a tallowy flavour is a major storage defect in whole milk powder, and less often in skim milk powder. The rapid flavour deterioration in whole milk powder (and other fat-containing products) due to oxidation necessitates inhibitory measures. One of these consists or packaging the product with a low oxygen content.

The general procedure is to immediately remove oxygen by subjecting the product to a vacuum of 71 cm. (28 in.) of Hg within 24 hours of drying, with final packaging within a few days. Less than 2 per cent of oxygen in the headspace gas of the package is considered satisfactory for most storage conditions. Good quality whole milk powder with a low oxygen content can be expected to withstand room temperature for six months or more without an oxidized off-flavour.

To obtain a low level of headspace-oxygen in whole milk powder, a double gassing technique is applied. The customary procedure is to collect filled, air-tight metal cans (with a small brogue hole) on trays to be conveyed into the vacuum chamber/cabinet. The air is removed rapidly (in 60 seconds) under a very high vacuum of 74 cm. (29 in.) of Hg. After a 2–5 minute hold, the pressure is restored with nitrogen to 0.5 to 1.0 psi above atmospheric pressure. Nitrogen may be replaced with a mixture of nitrogen and carbon dioxide, the latter being restricted to 5–20 per cent. Once removed from the chamber, the containers are sealed by soldering the 1–2 mm. holes on the lid. The containers are then held for oxygen desorption. When an oxygen equilibrium has been attained in the headspace, usually within a week, but at the most within ten days, the cans are punctured and the vacuum treatment, pressure restoration with nitrogen and sealing steps are repeated.

Gas packaging of whole milk powder should not be delayed after drying. Delay causes a deterioration in quality during the holding period. Warm powder directly from the drier tends to have a more rapid rate of oxygen desorption under vacuum. (If the production is not large, whole milk powder may be placed in metal drums and the air exhausted. By holding the product under partial vacuum for oxygen desorption the first gassing step in the package may be eliminated, and yet the final maximum of 2 per cent oxygen can be attained.) Gas packing is the most effective method of extending keeping quality in tropical climates.

Note: Keeping quality of dried milk and milk products can be increased by the addition of anti-oxidants such as hydroquinone, ascorbic acid, ethyl or propyl gallate, nor dihydro guiaretic acid, etc., to the liquid milk product before dehydration. Many countries prohibit the use of anti-oxidants. In

India, butylated hydroxy anisole at 0.01 per cent by weight of the finished product is permitted for use in dried milks.

(c) *Packaging of skim milk powder.* For industrial use and storage, skim milk powder may be packed in barrels, drums and bags; for retail purposes in metal cans, glass jars or cartons. A 2-mil polythene bag inside a 4-ply kraft paper bag is a common package for domestic commercial trade. Cartons of fibreboard, foil and plastics have largely supplanted glass and metal as retail containers.

(d) *Packaging/Marking.* The following particulars are expected to be marked or labelled on each container of dried milks and milk products:

  (i) Name and type of the material (Trade/Brand name, if any);
 (ii) name of manufacturer and address;
(iii) batch or code number;
 (iv) net weight;
  (v) process of manufacture (spray or roller-dried);
 (vi) date of manufacture and/or expiry date;
(vii) directions for use;
(viii) composition, etc.

9.18 Storage

Since high storage temperatures are detrimental to the keeping quality of dried milks and milk products, temperatures lower than 24°C (75°F) are desirable.

To ensure maximum keeping quality, the dried product should be stored in a vapour-proof, moisture-proof, sealed package in a dark, cool, dry place. Refrigerated storage should be used for long storage in warm climates. Retail distribution should be done in the original container.

9.19 Yield

The yield of milk powders (whole or skim) will depend on the per cent total solids in the raw material, moisture retained in the finished product and losses in manufacturing.

Problem. Given 10,000 kg. milk testing 7.0% fat and 9.5% SNF. Calculate the yield of whole milk powder.

Solution. According to the PFA standard, whole milk powder shall contain not more than 5.0% moisture and not less than 26.0% milk fat.

Assuming whole milk powder to contain 2.0% moisture and 27.0% milk fat

% TS in whole milk powder = 100 − 2.0 = 98.0%

% SNF in whole milk powder = 98.0 − 27.0 = 71.0%

In whole milk powder, $\dfrac{\% \text{ SNF}}{\% \text{ Fat}} = \dfrac{71.0}{27.0} = 2.63$.

Assuming 3.5% fat in standardized milk and 40% fat in cream. the Pearson's Square may be drawn up as shown below:

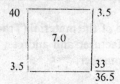

Hence, Cream (C) removed is given below:

3.5 : 36.5 = C : 10,000

Therefore $C = \dfrac{3.5 \times 10,000}{36.5}$

Standardized milk = 10,000 = 958.9 = 9041.1 kg. In standardized milk:

% SNF = 3.5 × 2.63 = 9.21

% TS = 3.5 + 9.21 = 12.71

TS content = $\dfrac{9041 \times 12.71}{100}$ = 1149.1 kg.

Assuming 1.5% loss in total solids during manufacture,

Amount of TS loss = $\dfrac{1149.1 \times 1.5}{100}$ = 17.2 kg.

TS content used for production of whole milk powder
= 1149.1 − 17.2 = 1131.9 kg.

Yield of whole milk powder = $\dfrac{1131.9 \times 100}{98}$

= 1155 kg.
Cream (40% fat)   = 958.9 kg. $\Big\}$ *Ans.*

9.20 Properties

The properties of dry milks may be divided into two categories, viz., physico-chemical and sensory. The relevant physico-chemical properties include: particle size, surface and shape, structure, density, flowability, dustiness and reconstitutability. The sensory characteristics of chief importance are flavour, colour and appearance, and tactual sensations in dry or reconstituted forms.

Note: The dry product characteristics and their changes are influenced to a large extent as a result of the above properties and their interactions. Further, every item from the milk supply to the equipment, processing, packaging and storage, will influence the properties of dry milk products.

A. *Drum vs Spray-dried milks.* The physico-chemical and sensory characteristics of drum and spray-dried milks have been briefly compared in Table 9.6.

TABLE 9.6

Comparison of physico-chemical properties of drum-dried and spray-dried milks

Properties	Drum-dried	Spray-dried
Particle size	8–20 μM	10–250 μM
Surface	Wrinkled	Normally smooth
Shape	Irregular; angular with rough edges	Regular; usually spherical
Air cell	Normally absent	Normally one or more present
Bulk density (g./ml.)	0.3–0.5	0.5–0.6
Flowability	Slightly lower (than spray-dried)	Slightly higher (than roller-dried)
Dustiness	–do–	–do–
Reconstitutability	Lower (than spray-dried)	Higher (than roller-dried)
Flavour	Definitely cooked	*Low heat*: same as pasteurized milk *High heat*: definitely cooked
Colour and appearance	Usually of slightly darker shade (than spray-dried)	*WMP* Normally light yellow for cow and creamy white for buffalo milk. *SMP* Normally yellowish-white for cow and chalky-white for buffalo milk.

Note: (i) Pre-concentration of milk before drying yields particles of larger size for both processes.

(ii) The greater the pre-concentration, the smaller the amount of entrapped air within the spray-dried particle.

B. *Structure.* Dry milks have a dual structure, viz., primary and secondary. The primary structure comprises the milk solids in which are dispersed the moisture and air cells. The physical mass of the particle, both in skim milk powder and whole milk powder, is dominated by the lactose in which presumably the protein, fat and minerals are more or less dispersed. The bulk of the particles surrounded by air (whole particles are not in contact) constitute the secondary structure. The size and shape of the particles and the degree of uniformity of these characteristics affect the secondary structure.

(a) *State of lactose.* Lactose in dry milk and milk products generally exists in an amorphous or glass (non-crystalline) state. It is very hygroscopic and readily absorbs moisture when the relative humidity of the surrounding air is 50 per cent or above. As sorption occurs, the lactose becomes sticky and this initiates the adherence of the milk particles to each other. Then solidification, commonly known as caking, occurs.

Note: No crystallization of lactose-glass occurs in dry milks with a moisture of 5 per cent or less. The critical moisture level for crystallization is 7 per cent or more.

(b) *State of protein.* The heat-treatment given to milk during the drying process destabilizes the milk proteins (casein and serum proteins) by first inducing reversible denaturation and then irreversible coagulation

(c) *State of fat.* The fat may exist in dry milks as globules surrounded by a membrane covering of proteinous nature or as 'free' fat. It is considered de-emulsified in the free state. Free fat makes the dry product greasy and produces an oily film on reconstituted milk. In drum-dried whole milk powder, most of the fat (85 to 95 per cent to total) exists in the free state and much of it is on the surface of the particles. This high percentage may be caused by the rupturing of the globule-membrane by the hot drum and the scraping action of the knife when removing the film. In spray-dried whole milk powder, deviations from the standard drying operation or improper storage increase the free fat. Free fat promotes oxidation, especially free fat on the particle surface.

(d) *Moisture content.* The normal satisfactory range of moisture content is 3–4 per cent for skim milk powder and 2–3 per cent for whole milk powder. The rate of several deteriorative changes is influenced by the moisture content of dry milks.

C. *Density*

(a) *Importance.* The density of dry milks and milk products has several practical implications. The chief one is its pronounced influence on packaging costs. Recovery of milk particles in cyclone separators is also affected, and density directly contributes to the proportion of the milk-dust nuisance.

(b) *Classification.* Densities are classified into: bulk/apparent density, particle density and true density.

(i) *Bulk/Apparent density.* This is regarded as weight per unit volume and generally expressed as g./ml. It is divided into packed and loose density. The packed bulk density of skim milk powder is generally 0.50–0.60 g./ml. for a spray-dried product. Whole milk powder has a slightly lower bulk density than skim milk powder. Foam spray-dried has the least, drum-dried the next and spray-dried the highest. The degree of pulverizing drum-dried milk in the hammer will affect bulk density. Agglomeration reduces it roughly by 40 to 60 per cent. Dry milk from a centrifugal spray has a slightly lower density than a pressure-spray product.

The manufacturing process and conditions greatly influence bulk density. Steps to reduce occluded air will increase bulk density. One method is to minimize the air content of the concentrate before drying; increasing the total solids of the concentrate is another.

(ii) *Particle density.* This is chiefly influenced by the amount of entrapped air. Centrifugal spray-dried milks contain more entrapped air than pressure-spray products and hence have a lower particle density.

(iii) *True density.* This refers to the density of air-free solids and may be calculated by the formula:

$$\text{True density} = \frac{110}{\dfrac{\% \text{ Fat}}{0.93} + \dfrac{\% \text{ SNF}}{1 \cdot 58} + \dfrac{\% \text{ Water}}{1}}$$

The true density of skim milk powder is 1.44–1.48 and whole milk powder 1.26–1.32 g./ml. The moisture content and the ratio of solids-not-fat : fat are the two chief factors affecting it. In a dry high-fat product, an increase in moisture reduces density and the opposite is true for skim milk powder. A decrease in fat will increase true density.

(iv) *Increasing density.* With air within and around the dried particles, there is scope for compression. The application of 7–10.5 kg./sq. cm. (100–150 psi) pressure to whole milk powder can reduce its volume by half. The densities of dried milks are given in Table 9.7.

TABLE 9.7

Densities of dried milks

Category	Approximate density (g./ml.)
Uncompressed drum powder	0.3–0.5
Uncompressed pressure spray powder	0.5–0.6
Compressed drum and spray powder	1.1–1.2
Air-free whole milk powder	1.31–1.32
Air-free skim milk powder	1.44

SOURCE: *Condensed Milk and Milk Powder* by Hunziker (1949).

D. *Flowability.* This is affected by size, shape, density and the electrostatic charge of the dried milk particles. The following properties improve flowability: (i) agglomeration; (ii) spherical shape; (iii) high particle density; (iv) smooth surface; (v) dryness.

Note: Addition of free-flowing agents, such as calcium silicate @ 1.5 per cent, sodium-aluminium silicate @ 0.5–1.0 per cent, etc., improves flowability.

E. *Milk dustiness.* Small, light dry milk particles, otherwise called milk dust, easily become air-borne. They cause higher entrainment losses, are a health hazard to people allergic to protein and create sanitation problems in the factory. Milk dustiness is increased by low solids in precondensed milk, low moisture content, etc.

F. *Reconstitutability.* This refers to the sum total effect of solubility, dispersability, sinkability and wettability. Lactose, undenatured serum protein and a portion of the salts are the most soluble. The casein is dispersible. Sinkability refers to the ability of the dried particles to penetrate the surface tension of water. Wettability is the penetration of water into the particles. Reconstitutability includes all those functions which take place in the process of recombining dried milk with water. The ideal dry milk is one which rapidly recombines with water without agitation to give the characteristics of regular milk.

The factors affecting reconstitutability include: (i) *Physical properties*, viz., size, shape, density, uniformity, air content, composition (especially ratio of solids-not-fat : fat of the particles) and presence of additives; (ii) *chemical properties*, viz., extent of protein denaturation (by heat or storage), and (iii) *conditions of recombination*, viz., the temperature of water and dried milk, the nature and extent of hardness in water, and the time and nature of agitation.

Note: The physico-chemical properties of milk powder, which influence reconstitutability, are affected by various factors discussed earlier. These may be grouped into two, viz., equipment and processing conditions: equipment includes the drier and system of atomization; and processing conditions include heat-stability of the milk, pre-heat treatment of the milk and the concentrate, total solids percentage of the concentrate, outlet-air temperature and contact time, recycling of fines, selectivity of screening, agglomeration, and storage temperature and time.

(a) *Dispersability*. This is affected by the total heat-treatment on the casein during processing. Higher heat-treatment with a higher percentage of total solids causes a greater degree of irreversible denaturation; and the denatured casein under normal reconstitution procedures does not form a stable dispersion. Drum drying causes a higher degree of denaturation than spray drying; however, heating the milk concentrate too much or for too long, or subjecting milk particles to above-normal temperatures in the drier in spray drying (when attempting to obtain production above the normal capacity of the drier) will increase percentage denaturation. Large particles of dry milks are generally recognized as being good for dispersability.

(b) *Wettability*. The tendency of dry milks to form lumps upon addition of water indicates lack of wettability. The factors which favour wettability are large-sized and irregularly shaped particles (which provide more space in the interstices for water penetration for wetting); agglomeration favours wetting by providing both the above conditions.

The amount and dispersion of fat influences wettability. The milk dried with low melting point fats has better wettability. The addition of up to 25 per cent sugar (sucrose) to milk before it is dried, or dry blending the sugar in granulated form (powdered sugar is less effective), improves wettability and dispersion.

(c) *Sinkability*.   This is closely related to wettability. The amount of occluded air within the particle has a pronounced influence on sinkability. Foam spray-dried milk has very poor sinkability. Agglomeration of regular spray-dried milk improves sinkability by increasing the aggregate weight. The effect of agglomeration on sinkability is greater in skim milk powder than whole milk powder.

G. *Flavour*.   When made from high-grade milk. the flavour of dried whole milk should be clean, rich, sweet and very pleasant; and that of dried skim milk similar, when reconstituted, to that of fresh skim milk. However, in practice, there is some degree of burnt flavour, which is greater in drum-dried milks than in spray-dried ones. Normally, drum-dried milks always possess a distinct cooked flavour.

The intensity with which milk is heated (mainly the pre-heating temperature-time combination) considerably influences the development of a cooked and caramelized flavour in spray-dried milks. 'Low-heat' and 'medium-heat' powders give the reconstituted milk a flavour close to that of pasteurized milk; however, 'high-heat' powder, when reconstituted, gives a definite cooked flavour.

Note: In practice, during the storage of milk powders, various flavour defects occur which are of concern to the user.

H. *Colour and appearance*.   The colour of whole milk powder should be uniformly light-yellow for cow and creamy-white for buffalo milk; while that of skim milk powder should be uniformly yellowish-white for cow and chalky-white for buffalo milk. The yellow colour varies in intensity with the season of the year. Small errors in operation during drum drying can readily produce a darker shade of colour. Discolouration, often associated with a cooked or caramelized flavour, results from high heat-treatment. A more common defect in appearance is the presence of burnt particles, commonly in drum drying and seldom in spray drying. A general brown discolouration may develop as a storage defect of both roller and spray powders (mainly when a powder with a high moisture content is exposed to high temperatures).

9.21 Keeping Quality

A. *Definition.* Keeping quality or shelf-life of dried milk or milk product refers to the time (in days or months) it retains its edible qualities after production.

B. *Factors influencing keeping quality.* Generally the deterioration occurring during storage involves flavour, colour and solubility index. The rate of spoilage is influenced by the following factors: (a) composition; (b) quality of milk used in production; (c) care during production; (d) care during handling and storage; (e) manufacturing conditions, especially heat-treatment; (f) moisture content; (g) metallic contamination; (h) packaging conditions (materials and methods), and (j) storage conditions.

Note: In commercial practice, the three most important factors influencing keeping quality are: fat content, moisture percentage and storage temperature. Since milk fat deteriorates rapidly, its content in skim milk powder should be restricted to 1.25 per cent or less. Likewise, moisture adversely affects storage life as the content increases above 4 per cent. To prevent absorption of moisture during storage, the package should be relatively impervious to moisture vapour. High storage temperatures are detrimental to the keeping quality. Hence temperatures lower than 24°C (75°F) are desirable. If possible, refrigerated storage should be used for long term storage in tropical countries.

C. *Major changes during storage.* Micro-organisms do not generally proliferate in dried milks and storage defects are purely chemical in nature. There are two major types of storage deterioration, viz., one affecting fat and the other affecting lactose-protein.

I. *Fat decomposition.* This may be divided into oxidation and rancidity (hydrolytic).

(a) *Oxidation.* Whole milk powder and other dry high-fat milk products undergo oxidative deterioration (resulting in production of tallowy flavour) in storage. Chemical changes occur due to the addition of oxygen to the double bonds of unsaturated glycerides, producing first peroxides and later aldehydes, ketones and various carbonyl compounds. Assuming average conditions of milk quality and processing, an oxidation off-flavour (oxidized flavour) becomes noticeable by sensory tests in roughly three months when the dry whole milk/milk product is held at 21–24°C (70–75°F) under air-packed conditions.

Various factors influence the rate of milk-fat oxidation. These are:

(i) *Storage temperature.* The higher the storage temperature, the higher the rate of oxidation, and vice versa. (Hence low storage temperature is recommended.)

(ii) *Presence of copper and iron.* The higher the copper and iron content, the higher the rate of oxidation, and vice versa. Both act as catalysts. To prevent a rapid oxidized flavour development, not more than 1.5 ppm of copper and 10 ppm of iron are recommended in dried milk and milk products. (Hence milk/milk product should come in contact only with stainless steel/aluminium surfaces during production, handling and processing.)

(iii) *Acidity.* The higher the acidity, the higher the rate of oxidation, and vice versa. (Hence, use of fresh, sweet milk is desirable.)

(iv) *Sunlight.* Accelerates fat oxidation. (Hence transparent packaging materials should be avoided.)

(v) *Pre-heating.* Proper pre-heating/forewarming of milk will delay oxidative changes during storage of dry whole milk/fat-rich products. This beneficial effect of pre-heating has been attributed to the release of sulfydryl compounds, which act as anti-oxidants. The improvement may also be due to the more complete inactivation of lipase with the higher temperature-time required for pre-heating.

(vi) *Addition of anti-oxidants.* When added in small amounts to the liquid product before dehydration, anti-oxidants increase the keeping quality of the dried product. Under the PFA rules (1976) butylated hydroxy anisole may be added to whole milk powder at the rate of 0.01 per cent by weight of the finished product.

(vii) *Gas-packing.* This is the most practical commercial procedure for increasing the keeping quality of dried products. By reducing the oxygen content to 2 per cent or less (by volume) in the headspace gas, the keeping quality is roughly doubled. The product may be vacuum-packaged with the low oxygen level. However, replacing the partial vacuum with nitrogen is more common in the dry milk industry.

(b) *Rancidity (Hydrolytic)*. True rancidity may be due to the hydrolysis of fat through lipase enzymes, leading to the production of free fatty acids, such as butyric. However, this defect is of minor importance in fat-rich dried products.

II. *Lactose-protein changes*. During storage, the dry milk/milk products may develop an off-flavour, off-colour and insolubility, all due to lactose-protein changes.

(a) *Staleness*. This storage defect is increased by a high moisture content and/or a high storage temperature. (Hence a low moisture content and a low storage temperature are recommended.)

(b) *Off-colour*. The principal change in colour is called browning-discolouration, which is attributed to the Maillard Reaction (lactose-protein reaction). The higher the moisture content and/or storage temperature, the faster the browning, and vice versa. Delayed cooling of the dry milk/milk product after drying is a contributing factor. (Hence, a low moisture content, prompt removal of the dried product from the drying chamber and a low storage temperature are recommended.)

(c) *Insolubility*. This is measured by determining the solubility index, which measures the extent of protein-denaturation. The higher the storage temperature and moisture content of the dry milk and the longer the storage period, the higher the rate of increase of the solubility index, and vice versa. (Hence a low moisture content and low storage temperature are recommended.)

9.22 Recent Developments

The manufacture of dried milks/milk products has increased more than that of any other milk product in the world in recent years. Not only have new uses for dried milks been found, but it has also been suggested in leading dairying countries that instant milk powder will, to a great extent, be a substitute for fresh milk in the future.

The dry milk industry today has become far more sophisticated than it was before. In the larger plants, automation has set in. Control of the air-inlet and air-outlet temperature of a spray drier is usually provided. The feed rate to the atomizer is adjusted automatically to give a constant air-outlet temperature (which controls the moisture content of the powder). A new important development is to place the drying chamber externally, i.e. in the open air. This saves building costs. The external insulation of the chamber is increased up to 20 cm. thickness and the chamber looks like a silo.

9.23 Judging and Grading of Whole Milk Powder and Skim Milk Powder

A. *Score card.* This is given jointly for both whole milk powder and skim milk powder in Table 9.8.

TABLE 9.8

Score card for dry milks (ADSA)

Items	Perfect score
Flavour	45
Appearance	20
Package	5
Laboratory tests	30
Total score	100

B. *Procedure of examination (canned product)*

(a) *Sampling.* Select a can of the product at random for examination.

(b) *Sequence of observations.* Cut more than three-fourths of the top of the can and turn it back. Then examine it in the following order:

(i) *Appearance of the can.* Look out for signs of rust, etc., both outside and inside (when emptied).

(ii) *Flavour.* Note the smell (odour) immediately on opening the can. Then reconstitute with distilled water to the original concentration (according to directions given on the can-label), and after about an hour examine flavour (smell and taste) by tasting 5–10 ml. on the tongue.

(iii) *Appearance of the product.* Examine uniformity of colour and absence of lumps, foreign specks, scorched/burnt particles, etc.

(iv) *Fineness and homogeneity (body and texture).* Pour the product from the can into another container and note the flow characteristics.

C. *Requirements of high-grade whole milk powder and skim milk powder*. The physical (sensory) qualities of high-grade milk powder will chiefly depend on the method of drying, viz., roller or spray, and also to some extent on whether they have been prepared from cow or buffalo milk and whole or skim milk.

Spray-dried whole milk should be clean, rich, sweet and very pleasant in flavour; fine, smooth and homogeneous in body and texture; uniform in colour—which should be normally light yellow for cow and creamy white for buffalo—and devoid of foreign specks, and scorched or burnt particles.

Skim milk powder, when reconstituted, should be similar in flavour to that of fresh skim milk for a spray product, although it may possess a slightly cooked or heated flavour for a roller-dried product; it should be fine, smooth and homogeneous in body and texture if produced by the spray process, but may be coarse and less homogeneous if produced by the roller process. If not finely pulverized, it should be uniformly yellowish white for cow and chalky white for buffalo milk; foreign specks, and scorched or burnt particles should be absent.

9.24 Defects in Whole Milk Powder and Skim Milk Powder, Their Causes and Prevention

Defects in whole milk powder and skim milk powder may arise due to low quality milk and faulty methods in the manufacture and storage of these products. Their causes and prevention are given in Table 9.9.

TABLE 9.9

Defects in whole milk powder and skim milk powder, their causes and prevention

Name of defect	Causes	Prevention
(a) Flavour		
Stale/Old	(i) Long storage	(i) Short storage
	(ii) Storage at high temperature	(ii) Storage at low temperature (24°C/75°F) or below
	(iii) Excessively high pre-heating temperature	(iii) Optimum pre-heating temperature

Name of defect	Causes	Prevention
	(iv) Delayed cooling-and-removal of dried product from drying chamber	(iv) Prompt cooling-and-removal of dried product from drying chamber
	(v) High moisture content during storage.	(v) Optimum moisture content during storage.
Oxidized/Tallowy	(i) Storage at high temperature	(i) Storage at low temperature (24°C/75°F) or below
	(ii) Action of sunlight (because of transparent packaging material)	(ii) Avoiding action of sunlight (by using opaque packaging material)
	(iii) High acidity in milk	(iii) Using fresh, sweet milk
	(iv) Metallic (copper and iron) contamination (due to direct contact with milk)	(iv) Using stainless steel/aluminium alloy milk contact surface only
	(v) Excessively high pre-heating temperature	(v) Optimum pre-heating temperature
	(vi) Delay in cooling-and-removal of dried product from drying chamber	(vi) Prompt cooling-and-removal of dried product from drying chamber
	(vii) Higher oxygen content in the headspace of the container.	(vii) Vacuumizing and/or gas-packaging (to reduce oxygen content in the headspace to 2 per cent or less)
		(viii) Use of (permitted) anti-oxidants.
Rancid	Low pre-heating temperature (lipase not inactivated).	Optimum pre-heating temperature (so as to inactivate lipase).
Scorched/Burnt	(i) Excessively high temperature of drying (in drum process)	(i) Optimum drying temperature (in drum process)
	(ii) Drum surface has pits	(ii) Drum surface kept smooth
	(iii) Scraper knives dull (in drum process).	(iii) Scraper knives kept sharp (in drum process).

Name of defect	Causes	Prevention
(b) Body and Texture (*Fineness and homogeneity*)		
Lumpy	(i) Insufficient drying	(i) Sufficient drying
	(ii) Absorption of moisture (due to exposure to humid atmosphere)	(ii) Preventing absorption of moisture (by using moisture-impervious package)
	(iii) Drippage from pressure spray nozzle.	(iii) Using centrifugal disc atomizer.
Caked	Absorption of moisture (due to exposure to humid atmosphere).	Preventing absorption of moisture (by using moisture-impervious package).
(c) Colour and appearance		
Browning/ Darkening of colour	(i) Long storage	(i) Short storage
	(ii) Storage at high temperature	(ii) Storage at low temperature (24°C/75°F) or below
	(iii) Delayed cooling-and-removal of dried product from drying chamber	(iii) Prompt cooling-and-removal of dried product from drying chamber
	(iv) High moisture content during storage	(iv) Optimum moisture content during storage.
Scorched/Burnt appearance	Same as Scorched/Burnt flavour	
Lack of uniformity in appearance	(i) Partial scorching during manufacture (in drum process)	(i) Careful control of operations (in the drum process)
	(ii) Partial discolouration after packaging.	(ii) Careful control of storage conditions influencing discolouration.

9.25 Uses

(a) *Skim milk powder*

(i) In the preparation of toned, double toned and recombined milks;

(ii) in tea and coffee (during milk shortage);

(iii) in ice cream manufacture;

(iv) in candy and confectionary;

(v) in prepared foods;

   (vi) in breads and rolls, biscuits, etc.:

  (vii) in cultured products;

 (viii) in the preparation of a few Indian sweets.

Note: A spray-dried product is preferred where complete reconstitution is required; if not, a roller-dried product, being cheaper, is used.

 (b) *Whole milk powder*

   (i) In the preparation of reconstituted milk;

  (ii) in tea and coffee;

 (iii) in baby-food preparation;

 (iv) in candy and confectionary, bakery products, etc.

Note: The production and consumption of whole milk powder is normally very low compared to that of skim milk powder throughout the world. This is mainly due to the much shorter shelf-life of the former as compared with the latter.

10 DRIED MILK PRODUCTS

10.1 Introduction

Dried milk products are manufactured for the same purposes as dried milks, viz. to reduce bulk so as to effect a saving in storage space, to reduce packaging and transportation costs, to improve the storage life of the product, etc. Over the last two decades, a large number of milk products and by-products have been successfully dried and more are in the offing. Several challenging problems of production, handling and storage are being tackled through painstaking research all over the world, with the ultimate object of conserving, as far as possible, the natural properties of the original raw material.

10.2 Buttermilk Powder

Dried buttermilk or buttermilk powder may be prepared from sweet, sour and high-acid buttermilks.

(a) *Composition.* The average chemical composition of buttermilk powder is given in Table 10.1.

TABLE 10.1

Composition of buttermilk powder (percentage)

Type of buttermilk	Moisture	Fat	Protein	Lactose	Ash	Lactic acid
Sweet	2.8	5.3	34.3	50.0	7.6	—
Sour (Acid)	4.8	5.7	37.6	38.8	7.4	5.7

SOURCE: *Fundamentals of Dairy Chemistry* by Webb and Johnson (1974).

(b) *Food and nutritive value.* Both sweet and sour/acid buttermilk powders are high in protein, lactose and minerals; acid powders are also high in lactic acid.

(c) *Method of manufacture*

From sweet buttermilk. The method of manufacture by either the spray or drum process is similar to that of skim milk powder. The buttermilk should be cooled immediately to 5°C (40°F) on drainage from the churn, and stored in stainless steel lined tanks when intended for human consumption. A common practice is to pre-heat it to 32–49°C (90–120°F) and separate it, so as to reclaim a portion of the fat. The pre-heating is then continued to 85°C (185°F) for 15 minutes. Then it is condensed to 16 per cent of the total solids for the drum process or 40–45 per cent for the spray process. The concentrate is re-heated to 71–79°C (160–175°F) and dried to a moisture content of 3 to 4 per cent.

(ii) *From sour (ripened-cream) buttermilk.* In developed dairying countries, since the dried product is used for animal and poultry feeding, the question of the solubility of the finished product does not arise. Hence the buttermilk is dried by means of the atmospheric drum dryer, which requires the least initial investment and is simple to operate. However, a few drying difficulties and storage problems are encountered:

1. Because of the high acidity, the concentrate tends to form an unmanageable smear on the drying drums.

2. The buttermilk, liquid or concentrate, constantly tends to whey-off, dropping its curd to the bottom of the container. (This tendency to whey-off increases when the buttermilk is heated preparatory to drying; and when it reaches the hot drying drum without the curd, it produces an abnormally thin film.)

3. Due to the high lactose content (about 40 per cent), the dried powder readily absorbs moisture and becomes sticky and cakes due to the crystallization of amorphous lactose glass into a hard mass of α-lactose hydrate.

Note: (i) The above drying difficulty can be minimized by neutralizing the sour buttermilk to about 0.2 per cent acidity, using calcium hydroxide as neutralizer.

(ii) The whey-off problem can be solved by vigorous agitation to ensure uniform distribution of the curd particles in the body of the buttermilk when it reaches the drying drums.

(iii) The caking problem can be prevented by: inducing copious pre-crystallization between dryer and grinder/

sifter; and drying to a low moisture content (below 5 per cent) and packaging in a dry atmosphere in air-tight moisture-proof containers.

(iii) *From high-acid buttermilk.* Sweet buttermilk is pasteurized at 82°C/180°F for 16 seconds or longer and then concentrated to 30 per cent total solids. After lowering its temperature to 46°C (115°F), it is inoculated with 1-5 per cent *lactobaccillus bulgaricus* and agitated during incubation to produce a smooth curd. (Homogenization after incubation at low pressure will achieve the same result.) When the acidity has developed sufficiently, equivalent to 10–12 per cent in the dry product, the buttermilk, without preheating, is spray-dried to 3.5–4 per cent moisture. The dry product should be removed continuously, cooled immediately and sifted. Care should be taken to control the outlet drying air temperature, else there will be excessive browning and a high solubility index.

(d) *Packaging and storage.* Dried buttermilk is usually packed in kraft paper bags with plastic (polythene) liners or in fibre drums with or without plastic liners. It is usually stored at room temperature.

(e) *Keeping quality.* The storage life of sweet buttermilk powder is relatively short, e.g. 1 to 3 months. However, a few commercial samples have been reported to have a shelf-life of more than a year at room temperature.

(f) *Uses*

(i) Sweet/cream buttermilk powder may be used for enriching the nutritive value of prepared foods, bread, etc.; it can also be used in ice cream.

(ii) Sour cream buttermilk powder is intended for animal and poultry feeding.

(iii) High-acid buttermilk powder is used for special purposes; under Indian conditions it may also be used for reconstitution into a 'lassi' beverage. (For 'lassi', see 11.16.)

10.3 Whey Powder

Dried whey or whey powder presents several production and storage difficulties. The high lactose content of whey-solids creates difficulties in the manufacture of dry whey. Heat causes the lactose to become sticky. Caking from moisture absorption is particularly objectionable during storage. Lastly, the low solids content plus the difficulty and expense of drying means there are limited monetary returns.

(a) *Composition.* The average chemical composition of whey powder is given in Table 10.2.

TABLE 10.2

Composition of whey powder (percentage)

Type of whey	Moisture	Fat	Protein	Lactose	Ash	Lactic acid
Cheddar cheese whey (sweet)	4.5	0.9	12.9	73.5	8.0	2.3
Cottage cheese whey (acid)	3.2	0.0	13.0	66.5	10.2	8.6

SOURCE: *Fundamentals of Dairy Chemistry* by Webb and Johnson (1974).

(b) *Food and nutritive value.* Both sweet and acid whey powders are fairly high in protein, high in minerals and very high in lactose.

(c) *Method of manufacture.* Both drum and spray processes are common. The drum drying of a whey concentrate may be complicated by the formation of a sticky mass. Numerous patents and methods have been reported for the spray drying of whey to obtain a non-caking flowable product. One such spray process may be described as follows: the whey is passed through a separator to reclaim the fat, unless it is derived from skim milk. The separated whey, with or without neutralization, is pre-heated to 77–104°C (170–220°F) and then condensed in a multiple-effect evaporator to 40–70 per cent total solids. The whey concentrate is cooled to 2–27°C (35–80°F), seeded with lactose and then held for 24 hours for lactose crystallization. It is then spray-dried by the usual technique employed for skim milk powder.

Note: Whey for animal feed can be drum or spray-dried by mixing 15–50 per cent skim milk, buttermilk or certain cereal products, e.g. wheat bran, which reduces the problem of a high lactose content. The procedure is similar to that for drum-dried skim milk.

(d) *Packaging and storage.* Dry whey is usually packed in conventional bags with polythene liners. Since lactose in the amorphous form is very hygroscopic, the liner of the bag must be reasonably impervious to moisture vapours. Methods of production that cause a maximum degree of lactose crystallization reduce the tendency of dry whey to cake in storage, which is usually at room temperature.

(e) *Keeping quality*. When stored at 10–15°C in air-tight polythene bags, the shelf-life is usually 6 to 12 months.

(f) *Uses*. (i) As poultry and livestock feed; (ii) in the manufacture of frozen desserts, processed cheese products, bakery products and candy—all from sweet whey.

10.4 Cream Powder

Dried cream or cream powder refers to a dried milk product which has a higher fat content than whole milk powder. The usual range for milk powder is 40–70 per cent fat.

(a) *Composition*. The average chemical composition is given in Table 10.3.

TABLE 10.3

Composition of cream powder
(percentage)

Moisture	Fat	Protein	Lactose	Ash
0.8	65.0	13.4	18.0	2.9

SOURCE: *Fundamentals of Dairy Chemistry* by Webb and Johnson (1974).

(b) *Food and nutritive value*. Cream powder is fairly high in protein and lactose and very high in fat.

(c) *Method of manufacture*. Good quality cream is standardized to a ratio of fat : solids-not-fat of 1 : 1. The cream is pasteurized at 74°C (165°F) for 16 seconds and homogenized at 3000 psi. It is then concentrated to 40–50 per cent total solids, re-heated to 65–71°C (150–160°F) and spray-dried to 1–2 per cent moisture. The outlet air temperature is lower than that used for drying skim milk powder. (An alternate procedure consists of pre-heating the skim milk, concentrating it and adding pasteurized, homogenized cream; homogenization may be done at 65°C (150°F) using a pressure of 2000 psi in the first stage and 700 psi in the second stage. Re-heating and spray-drying follow.)

Note: Dry cream has a tendency to stick to the sides of the drying chamber. Immediate continuous removal and cooling of the dried product is certain to result in a better product. During removal, rubbing action should be kept to a minimum, especially when the dry cream is hot, i.e. when the fat is in the liquid state. The rubbing will cause the melted fat to 'oil off' and become free fat; the free fat in the dry product increases stickiness during handling and produces a greasy body and texture; also, a greater quantity of the product is lost, and lumpiness causes problems.

(d) *Packaging and storage.* Normally dried cream is packed in bags with polythene liners or in fibre drums with or without a polythene liner, preferably small in size. It may be stored at room temperature or in a cooled room (10–15°C/50–60°F) with or without gas-packing. Oxidized flavour development and lumpiness are the main storage problems.

(e) *Keeping quality.* At room temperature, the storage life of air-packed dry cream is limited to 2–3 months. However, gas packing increases the shelf-life considerably; oxidation is delayed by 12 months or more when stored at 32°C (90°F) with not more than 0.75 per cent oxygen in the package. Storage of dry cream below the melting point of fat is certain to reduce lumpiness, while storage at 10–15°C is certain to reduce oxidative changes and thereby considerably prolong its keeping quality, especially when gas-packed.

(f) *Uses.* The industrial uses of dry cream have so far not been extensive because of its chalky flavour, lack of free-flowing character and tendency to form lumps. It has the following uses:

  (i) in the confectionary and baking industries;

 (ii) in the preparation of cream cheese;

(iii) in the preparation of chocolate ice cream.

10.5 Butter Powder

Butter with modifications has been dried successfully by Australian scientists. The fat content of the dried product is the same as in regular butter, but other components differ.

(a) *Composition.* The average chemical composition of butter powder is given in Table 10.4.

TABLE 10.4

Composition of butter powder (percentage)

Moisture	Fat	Solids-not-fat	Caseinate-citrate	Emulsifier	Free flowing agent	Anti-oxidant
0.60	81.98	6.70	6.70	3.50	0.50	0.02

SOURCE: *Drying of Milk and Milk Products* by Hall and Hedrick (1971).

(b) *Food and nutritive value.* Butter powder is a rich source of butter fat.

(c) *Method of manufacture.* The following ingredients are used in the quantities mentioned:

Ingredients	Amount (kg.)
Pasteurized cream (32% fat)	132.0
Dry acid casein	6.0
Sodium citrate	1.0
Skim milk (9% TS)	20.0
Sodium hydroxide (2%)	7.0
Glycerol mono-stearate (36%)	3.5
Sodium aluminium silicate	0.5
Butylated hydroxy anisole	10.9

SOURCE: *Drying of Milk and Milk Products*
by Hall and Hedrick (1971).

During production, pasteurized cream is separated to 62 per cent fat. Sodium citrate is dissolved in the cream and the product is homogenized at 43°C (110°F) and 1000 psi in the first stage and 500 psi in the second. High grade casein is dispersed in skim milk at 65–82°C (150–180°F) and sodium hydroxide added slowly. Glycerol mono-stearate (GMS) is melted and the anti-oxidant butylated hydroxy anisole (BHA) added. The mixture is blended into the caseinate solution. This is added to the cream solids. After heating it to 65°C (150°F), the product is spray-dried, cooled immediately and dry-blended with a free-flowing agent composed of 80 per cent sodium aluminium silicate and 20 per cent calcium phosphate.

(d) *Packaging and storage.* Normally butter powder is packed in bags with polythene liners or in fibre drums with or without polythene liners, preferably small in size. It may be stored at room temperature or in a cooled room (10–15°C/50–60°F), with or without gas-packing.

(c) *Keeping quality.* Air-packed butter powder is expected to have a storage life of 2–3 months at room temperature. However, a combination of gas-packing (with a low oxygen level in the package) and low temperature storage (10–15°C) is expected to raise the shelf-life to 6 months or more. Fat oxidation is the chief storage defect.

(f) *Uses*

  (i) In ice cream manufacture;

 (ii) in bakery products;

(iii) in dry mixes, sauces, icings and fillings.

10.6 Ice Cream Mix Powder

Dried ice cream mix or ice cream mix powder has become popular in India in recent years and a few dairy factories are already producing it on a regular basis.

(a) *Composition.* The average chemical composition of dried ice cream mix is given in Table 10.5.

TABLE 10.5

Composition of ice cream mix powder (percentage)

Moisture	Fat	Serum solids	Sugar	Stabilizer+ emulsifier
1.0 to 2.5	25.0 to 29.0	25.0 to 30.0	37.0 to 42.0	0.5 to 1.2

SOURCE: *Drying of Milk and Milk Products* by Hall and Hedrick (1971).

(b) *Food and nutritive value.* Ice cream mix powder is high in fat, protein and sugars (sucrose and lactose).

(c) *Method of manufacture.* The ice cream mix is prepared in the usual manner by proper selection of ingredients; the percentages of fat and serum solids (milk-solids-not-fat), sugar, stabilizer and emulsifier, and total solids, are standardized to ensure proper composition of the dry product; the mix is made, pre-heated to 65–71°C (150–168°F) and homogenized at 2500 psi in the first stage and 500 psi in the second. The prepared mix is heated to 82–88°C (180–190°F) for 5–10 minutes, spray-dried to a coarse particle with 2–2.5 per cent moisture, cooled at once to 32–38°C (90–100°F), sifted and packaged.

Note: (i) Sugar used in preparing the ice cream mix is mainly sucrose, although 1–25 per cent may be replaced with corn syrup solids or dextrose. The product may be dried with 0–100 per cent of the required sugar, although usually 20 per cent of the required amount is added; the remaining percentage may be dry-blended in the form of a finely granulated sugar or the buyer may like to add the additional sugar himself.

(ii) Flavours are usually added when reconstituting the powder, and before freezing the mix.

(d) *Packaging and storage.* Normally ice cream mix powder is packed in bags with polythene liners or in fibre drums with or without polythene liners, preferably small-sized. It may be stored at room temperature or in a cooled room (10–15°C/50–60°F) with or without gas-packing.

(e) *Keeping quality.* Air-packed ice cream mix powder with not more than 2 per cent moisture is expected to have a storage life of 3–4 months at room temperature. The product, when gas-packed with a 2 per cent oxygen level in the container, is expected to have a shelf-life of 6–12 months at 10–15°C. Browning, oxidation and staleness are common defects that develop during storage.

(f) *Uses.* For reconstitution into ice cream mix to be frozen into ice cream.

10.7 Cheese Powder

Commercially produced dried cheeses or cheese powders are of two principal types: grated and tray/belt-dried cheeses, chiefly Parmesan cheese; and spray-dried cheeses, mainly Cheddar.

(a) *Composition.* An average chemical composition of dried Cheddar cheese is given in Table 10.6.

TABLE 10.6

Composition of Cheddar cheese powder (percentage)

Moisture	Fat	Protein	Carbohydrates	Ash
2 to 5	50 to 54	36 to 42	3 to 4	3 to 4

SOURCE: *Drying of Milk and Milk Products* by Hall and Hedrick (1971)

(b) *Food and nutritive value.* Dried cheese powder is high in fat and protein and fairly high in mineral content.

(c) *Method of manufacture (spray drying).* Aged and medium-aged cheeses are selected by standard methods. These are cut and ground and then placed in a processing kettle, which consists of a steam-jacketed stainless steel vat equipped with a powerful agitator. Sufficient water at 27–32°C (80–90°F) is added to the vat to make a 35–40 per cent slurry. Stabilizer (usually sodium citrate and/or disodium phosphate) is added at 1.5–2.5 per cent of the weight of cheese in the form of an aqueous solution. Cheese colour may be added to meet market demand. The addition of 0.5 per cent sodium chloride is optional. The cheese slurry is heated to pasteurization temperature and held for the required time (66°C/150°F for 2–5 minutes). Thereafter the temperature is lowered to 60°C (140°F) and the product is homogenized at 1500–2500 psi during the first stage and 500 psi in the second. The cheese slurry is spray-dried to 2.5–3.5 per cent moisture and the dry product is continuously removed from the drying chamber and immediately cooled to 29–32°C (85–90°F).

(d) *Packaging and storage.* Normally cheese powder is sifted through a 12-mesh screen prior to packaging in bags with polythene liners, or occasionally in fibre drums, with or without polythene liners, at room temperature or preferably at 10°C (50°F) o below.

(e) *Keeping quality.* The keeping quality of dry cheddar cheese is relatively short. Air-packed cheddar cheese powder should be held at 10°C (50°F) or below to ensure longer storage life. Gas-packing with nitrogen, replacing the oxygen, will prolong the keeping quality. The addition of anti-oxidants also slightly delays oxidation.

Note: One problem in the production of cheddar cheese powder is loss of cheese flavour from the product during spray drying. Reconstituted cheddar cheese with the same moisture content as the original cheese prior to dehydration is much milder in flavour.

(f) *Uses*
  (i) For reconstitution into cheese;
 (ii) in the preparation of (cheese) sauce;
(iii) for enriching the flavour of cooked food.

10.8 Malted Milk Powder

(a) *Introduction.* The process of manufacture of malted milk powder was invented by William Horlick of the USA in 1883 and the product was first placed on the market in 1887. The convenience, nutritive value, palatability and digestibility of this product made it an instant success.

(b) *Definition.* The US Federal Standard provides that dried malted milk or malted milk powder shall contain not less than 7.5 per cent milk fat and not more than 3.5 per cent moisture; and that each kg./lb. of malted milk powder shall contain the total solids of approximately 2.2 kg./lb. of whole milk.

According to the PFA Rules (1976), malted milk food is the product obtained by mixing whole milk or partially skimmed milk or milk powder with malt extract and cereal grain flour in such a manner as to secure complete hydrolysis of the starchy material. It should not contain added sugars, foreign fat and added colours and preservatives. It may contain cocoa powder. Malted milk food should be in the form of a powder.

(c) *PFA standard.* This is given in Table 10.7.

TABLE 10.7

PFA standard for malted milk food

Characteristics	Requirements		
Moisture	Not more than 5.0%		
Total ash	–do–	5.0%	on dry basis
Ash insoluble in dil. HCl	–do–	0.1%	–do–
Milk fat	Not less than	7.0%	–do–
Nitrogen	–do–	2.0%	–do–
Solubility	–do–	80.0%	
Starch	1 g. dissolved in 5 ml. of boiling water, cooled and treated with 0.5 ml. of 0.05% iodine solution in KI does not develop any blue colour		
Bacterial count	Not more than 50,000/g.		
Coliform count	–do–	10/g.	

(d) *Indian standard.* This is given in **Table** 10.8.

TABLE 10.8

Requirements for malted milk food
(IS : 1806, 1961)

Characteristics	Require-ment
Moisture (% wt.) (Max)	3.5
Total protein (% wt.) (Min)	14.0
Milk fat (% wt.) (Min)	7.5
Total ash (% wt.) (Max)	5.0
Total insoluble ash (% wt.) (Max)	0.1
Solubility (% wt.)	85.0 ml
Bacterial count (per g.) (Max)	50,000
Coliform count (per g.) (Max)	10
Test for starch	Negative

(e) *Composition.* An average chemical composition is given in Table 10.9.

TABLE 10.9

Composition of malted milk powder (percentage)

Moisture	Fat	Protein	Lactose etc.*	Ash
3.29	7.55	13.19	72.40	3.66

* Also includes maltose and dextrin.

SOURCE: *Condensed Milk and Milk Powder* by Hunziker (1949).

(f) *Food and nutritive value.* Malted milk powder is high in protein and very high in sugars, both of which are present in readily digestible form. It has a pleasant flavour and is used for feeding children, invalids and convalescents.

(g) *Method of manufacture*

(i) *Principle.* The liquid, separated from a mash of ground barley malt and wheat flour, is combined with whole milk in such a proportion and manner as to ensure not only full enzymic action of the malt extract but also the prescribed US standards in the final dehydrated product.

(ii) *Flow diagram*

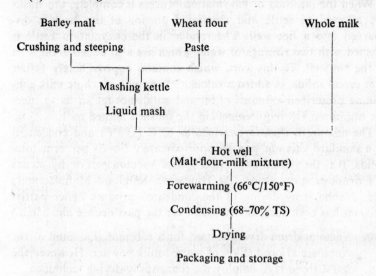

(iii) *Details.* Barley malt may be obtained in dry form from a company specializing in its production, or can be prepared by the factory making malted milk powder. Barley malt is crushed (run through a roller-type mill) and then steeped in a separate kettle in about six to seven times its weight of water at 32°C (90°F) for 30 minutes. The purpose of steeping is to put the enzymes (diastase, etc.) in solution. Simultaneously, wheat flour, which is rich in protein content besides being a source of starch, is prepared for the mash in a separate kettle. It is mixed with approximately 1.3 times its weight of water and the mixture cooked at 93°C (200°F) for 2 hours to make a paste. Generally the ratio of barley malt to wheat flour is 2.5 : 1.

The barley malt and its steeping water and the cooled flour paste are then transferred to a large mashing kettle where they are mixed. The mixture is held at 45°C (113°F) for 30 minutes; then the temperature is raised gradually to 70°C (158°F) in 30 minutes and held at that level for 2 hours. This mashing or enzymation process ensures the complete conversion of starch to maltose and dextrin, together with the breakdown of the wheat-proteins into simpler and more readily digestible compounds. The characteristic pleasant flavour of barley malt is conveyed to the liquid extract from the barley husk.

When the mashing or enzymation process is complete, the husks are allowed to settle and the liquid portion of the mash is discharged into a hot well. The residue in the enzymation kettle is washed with two rinsings of water which are also added to the wort in the hot well. To this wort, which contains approximately 11 per cent cereal solids, is added a calculated amount of whole milk containing prescribed amounts of fat and solids-not-fat so as to meet the minimum US requirements in the finished malted milk.

The mixture is then forewarmed to 65°C (150°F) and condensed in a standard vacuum pan to approximately 68–70 per cent total solids. It is then dried either in a special vacuum pan or by means of a drum or spray drier. (At Hindustan Milkfood Manufacturers Ltd., Nabha, tray drying of the condensed product under partial vacuum has been successfully used over the past decade and a half.)

Note: Vacuum drum drying is used for a substantial amount of the commercial production of malted milk powder. However, the latest trend is to employ the foam spray-drying technique.

(h) *Packaging and storage.*   The finished product, if obtained as a porous firm mass (as in pan drying), is broken into chunks and manually removed. The chunks are milled and the malted milk powder is promptly packaged. Since freshly dried malted milk is very hygroscopic, the milling and packaging are carried out in an atmosphere of controlled low humidity. For packaging, glass bottles with screw-type metal lids, or some containers impervious to moisture, are used. The product is stored at room temperature.

(j) *Keeping quality.*   Malted milk powder, properly made and packed, can be depended upon for long keeping quality even at room temperatures. This is ascribed to a film or layer of gluten (provided by the wheat), sugars and salts, that protects the surface of the fat globules against the quality-deteriorating influence of contact with air.

(k) *Uses.*

(i) As a beverage at home and soda fountains after proper reconstitution;

(ii) in the confectionary industry.

10.9   (Dried) Infant Milk Food

A. *Introduction.*   It has been estimated that in most developing countries including India, nearly 30–50 per cent of the children suffer from malnutrition. Although during the early months of infancy the child normally gets its mother's milk. it is deprived of this nutritious food soon thereafter. Unless a substitute is found from other sources, malnourishment will set in, damaging the child's health with consequences which may prove fatal.

Human milk is universally regarded as ideal food for the feeding of infants, or children below one year of age. Yet, owing to various causes, an infant may not derive adequate nutrition from the mother and it may become necessary to feed the infant either wholly or partly with milk from other sources. The average composition of a few such milks is given in Table 10.10.

TABLE 10.10

Composition of milks used for infant feeding (percentage)

Species	Water	Fat	Protein	Lactose	Solids-not-fat	Calcium
Human	86.4	4.6	1.2	6.9	9.0	0.03
Cow	86.7	4.5	3.4	4.9	8.8	0.13
Buffalo	83.7	6.5	3.8	5.1	9.8	0.20
Goat	86.8	4.5	3.3	4.4	8.7	0.13
Sheep	81.6	7.5	5.6	4.4	10.9	0.20

Note: It will be observed from Table 10.10 that human milk is characterized by a lower protein and calcium content (both of which contribute towards the formation of soft-curd, which is easily digestible) and a higher lactose content. Other milks are generally modified for infant feeding by dilution with water and the addition of sugar. For the past few decades, modified cow milk has been successfully dried in developed dairying countries for infant feeding. In India, investigations were undertaken jointly by the Central Food Technological Research Institute, Mysore, and Amul Dairy, Anand, in 1957, and a standardized process was evolved for the commercial production of Amul infant/baby food from buffalo milk in 1960 by the Roller Process. Since 1967, Amulspray babyfood has been in the market.

B. *Definition.* (Dried) Infant milk food or baby food, according to the PFA Rules (1976). is the product obtained by drying cow or buffalo milk or a combination thereof or by drying standardized milk, with the addition of specific carbohydrates (cane sugar), dextrose and dextrins, maltose (or lactose), iron salts and vitamins. It should contain no starch and anti-oxidants. Its moisture content should not exceed 5.0 per cent, milk fat content should not be less than 18.0 per cent and not more than 28.0 per cent; total carbohydrates not less than 35 per cent; milk proteins not less than 20 0 per cent; total ash not more than 8.5 per cent; ash insoluble in dilute hydrochloric acid not more than 0.01 per cent; iron (as Fe) not less than 4.0 mg. per 100 g.; and vitamin A not less than 15 I.U. per g. The drying process used should be indicated on the label. Infant milk food must not have a Standard Plate Count of more than 50,000 per g. The solubility index of a roller-dried product may be a maximum of 15.0 ml., and that for a spray-dried product, 2.0 ml. The product should be packed in hermetically sealed containers and the label should bear the date by which the product is to be consumed.

C. The Indian Standard Specifications for infant milk foods are given in Table 10.11.

TABLE 10.11

Indian Standard Specifications for infant milk foods
(vide IS : 1547, 1968)

Characteristics	Requirement
Moisture (% Wt) (Max)	4.5
Total milk protein (% Wt) (Min)	20.0
Milk fat (% Wt)	18.0 to 28.0
Total carbohydrates, including sucrose, dextrose and dextrins, maltose or lactose (% Wt) (Min)	35.0
Total ash (% Wt) (Max)	8.5
Acid insoluble ash (% Wt) (Max)	0.01
Solubility: (a) Solubility index (ml.) (Max)	15.0 (if roller dried)
	2.0 (if spray dried)
OR	
(b) Solubility (% Wt) (Min)	85.0 (if roller dried)
	98.5 (if spray dried)
Vit. A, I.U. per 100 g (Min)	1500
Added vit. D, I.U. per 100 g.	400 to 800
Iron, mg. per 100 g. (Min)	4.0
Bacterial count per g. (Max)	50,000
Coliform count per g. (Max)	10

Note: The addition of vitamin C to infant milk food is necessary. The normal vitamin C requirement of an infant is 30 mg. per day.

D. *Composition.* The chemical composition of a few Indian brands of infant foods as printed on the label is given in Table 10.12.

TABLE 10.12

Composition of some infant foods (percentage)

Brand Name	Moisture	Fat	Protein	Carbohydrate*	Ash
Amul	3.0	18.0	22.0	52.0	5.0
Glaxo	2.9	26.5	24.9	38.5	5.6
Lactogen	3.0	19.0	21.6	50.8	4.8
Nestogen	3.3	12.0	20.2	60.0	4.7
Vijayaspray	—	19.0	22.0	50.0	—
Parag	—	18.0	24.0	49.0	—

* Includes sucrose, dextrose or dextrins, maltose or lactose.

E. *Method of manufacture* (*Amul*)

(a) *Principle.* The successive steps in the production of Amul babyfood are: (i) reduction of the fat content of buffalo milk to 2.5 per cent; (ii) addition of phosphate buffer salt to react with ionized calcium and thus reduce the curd tension of infant food: (iii) addition of sugar (sucrose) so as to reduce the protein content to about 22 per cent and the fat content to about 18 per cent in the dried product; (iv) concentration; (v) homogenization; (vi) drying; (vii) fortification with amino-acids, vitamins and minerals, and (viii) packaging in tin-cans under inert gas (nitrogen).

(b) *Flow diagram*

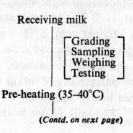

Receiving milk

⌈ Grading ⌉
| Sampling |
| Weighing |
⌊ Testing ⌋

Pre-heating (35–40°C)

(Contd. on next page)

(Contd. from prev. page)

Filtration/Clarification
|
Chilling and storage (5°C)
|
Standardization
|
Addition of ferrous sulfate and sugar
|
Pre-heating (80°C/No hold)
|
Condensing
|
Homogenization ⎰50 kg./sq. cm.— I stage⎱
⎱25 kg./sq. cm.—II stage⎰
|
Chilling and storage (5°C)
|
Pre-heating (70°C)
|
Drying (Roller or Spray)
|
Grinding and sifting
|
Fortification with amino-acids, vitamins and minerals
|
Gas packing
|
Storage

(c) *Details*

(i) *Receiving milk.* Only high grade raw milk is accepted and used.

(ii) *Pre-heating.* For efficient filtration/clarification, the milk is pre-heated to 35–40°C.

(iii) *Filtration/clarification.* To remove extraneous matter which would cause consumer complaints.

(iv) *Chilling and storage.* The milk is promptly cooled to 5°C or below and held at this temperature so as to preserve its quality.

(v) *Standardization.* This is done with the initial milk so that the dried product conforms to legal standards. Generally the Fat : SNF ratio is kept at 1 : 3.227 (Amul) and the standardized milk contains: Fat 2.9 to 3.05 per cent; SNF 9.6 per cent.

(vi) *Addition of ferrous sulfate and sugar.* Ferrous sulfate is added to provide iron for blood formation, while sugar (sucrose) is added to increase the palatability of infant food. (The aqueous solution of each is filtered before addition.)

(vii) *Pre-heating.* The milk is pre-heated to 80°C/No hold for efficient destruction of all pathogenic, and almost all other harmful, micro-organisms and enzymes, so as to make the finished product safe for infant feeding.

(viii) *Condensing.* The milk is concentrated in a double effect evaporator to a total solids content of usually 25–30 per cent for roller drying and 43–48 per cent for spray drying.

(ix) *Homogenization.* In order to obtain uniform fat dispersion and other advantages in the finished product, the concentrated milk is homogenized, using a pressure of 50 kg./sq. cm. during the first stage and 25 kg./sq. cm. during the second.

(x) *Chilling and storage.* In order to preserve the quality of the concentrate till it is dried, it is chilled to 5°C and held at this temperature. The pH of the concentrate is adjusted to 7.0 with sodium bicarbonate; disodium phosphate is also added, if required.

(xi) *Pre-heating:* The concentrate is pre-heated to 70°C before it is dried, so as to increase the capacity of the drier.

(xii) *Drying:* Either the roller or spray process is used.

(xiii) *Grinding and sifting.* The roller-dried product has to be ground before it is sifted. A proper mesh-size screen is used for both processes.

(xiv) *Fortification with amino-acids, minerals and vitamins.* The dried product is generally sucked up by vacuum in a silo, where it is mixed with the required amino-acids, minerals and vitamins in the correct proportions by a mechanical mixer.

(xv) *Gas packing.* Only after the Quality Control Laboratory approves the quality of the finished infant food, it is nitrogen-packed in properly labelled and pre-sterilized tin-cans under strict sanitary conditions, and immediately sealed with pre-sterilized lids.

(xvi) *Storage.* The (dried) infant milk food is normally stored at room temperatures.

F. *Keeping quality.* Dried infant/baby milk food, properly made and packed, can be kept for a long time even at room temperatures.

G. *Uses.* For infant/baby feeding after proper reconstitution according to the manufacturer's instructions printed on the label.

10.10 Dry Sodium Caseinate

(a) *Composition.* The average chemical composition of dry sodium caseinate is given in Table 10.13.

TABLE 10.13

Composition of dry sodium caseinate
(percentage)

Moisture	Fat	Protein	Lactose	Ash
4.5	1.5	85.5	4.0	4.5

SOURCE: *Drying of Milk and Milk Products*
by Hall & Hedrick (1971).

(b) *Method of manufacture.* High-grade edible casein is first prepared by taking the required precautions in the selection of raw material and adoption of standard manufacturing technique (see 12.6). Then the casein-curd is dispersed in a 0.5 per cent sodium hydroxide solution at 65°C (150°F) and the pH adjusted to 7.0. The solids content of the slurry is usually controlled to 15–20 per cent for spray drying. Precautions should be taken for complete curd dispersion. The material is then spray dried, using an outlet air drying temperature which reduces moisture to 3.5–4.5 per cent.

Note: Dry sodium caseinate should normally be yellowish white for cow and chalky white for buffalo milk. Its bulk density is 0.2–0.3 g./ml. A high grade product should have a pH of 6.5 to 7.2 and should be free from off-flavours.

(c) *Packaging and storage.* Dry sodium caseinate, after it has been sifted through a screen of the appropriate mesh-size, is usually packaged in kraft paper bags with a plastic liner or in a fibre drum with or without a plastic liner for industrial use. It is normally stored at room temperatures.

(d) *Uses*
 (i) As a binder-emulsifier and whipping agent in food products:
 (ii) to increase the overrun in ice cream;
 (iii) as a coffee whitener;
 (iv) in sausages;
 (v) in special foods for infants and diabetics.

10.11 Srikhand Powder*

(a) *Introduction.* Srikhand is an indigenous (Indian) whole milk

* See footnote (54) in Chapter 11.

product prepared from lactic-curd (dahi) and popular in the western region of the country. The curd is strained through cloth for several hours and the solids obtained are kneaded with sugar to a buttery mass. This is called 'srikhand' and is used for direct consumption (see 11.11). It is usually prepared under household conditions. However, the preparation of srikhand is time-consuming and a supply of ready-to-reconstitute dried srikhand or srikhand powder will indeed be helpful to the housewife.

(b) *Composition.* The average gross composition of dried srikhand or srikhand powder is given in Table 10.14.

TABLE 10.14

Composition of Srikhand powder (percentage)

Type of milk	Composition			
	Moisture	Fat	Total solids	Lactic acid
Cow	3.5	22.9	96.5	0.25
Buffalo	2.8	32.8	97.2	0.26

(c) *Food and nutritive value.* Dried srikhand has a high fat content. It is expected to have a high protein and sugar (sucrose) content, a fairly high mineral content, and also to contain appreciable amounts of lactic acid.

(d) *Method of manufacture.* At first, the srikhand base (i.e., Chakka) is prepared under standardized conditions (see 11.11). Then good-grade ground sugar is added to the base @ 18 per cent and thoroughly mixed into it by kneading. A calculated amount of water at 20–25 per cent of the mix is now added to it and well stirred to give a smooth slurry. The slurry is homogenized at 100 kg./sq. cm. pressure and spray dried under standard techniques using an inlet air temperature of 180–200°C and an outlet air temperature of 100°C. The powder is promptly removed from the drying chamber, cooled, packaged and stored at room temperature with or without gas-packaging.

Note: The technology of large-scale production of srikhand, which is an essential prerequisite to its conversion into powder, is yet to be developed.

(e) *Packaging and storage.* Srikhand powder may be packaged in paper bags with polythene liners or fibre drums, with or without polythene liners, with or without gas-packing, for storage at room temperature.

(f) *Keeping quality*. Dried srikhand seems to have a marketable life of over 3 months at room temperature storage, when gas-packed in hermetic containers.

(g) *Uses*. For reconstitution into srikhand for direct consumption.

10.12   Chhana Powder*

(a) *Introduction*. Chhana is an indigenous (Indian) whole milk product, which constitutes an important base and filler for the preparation of milk sweets. It is prepared by lactic or citric acid coagulation of boiled, hot milk and the subsequent straining of whey; the milk solids thus obtained are called chhana (see 11.13). Since it has a very low keeping quality—this being 1–2 days at room temperature—inter-state trade in chhana presents many problems. Efforts to increase its storage life in the original form have so far proved unsuccessful. Hence the production of dried chhana, which by virtue of its low moisture content is expected to have a much longer shelf-life than the original product. (The large-scale production of chhana is an essential prerequisite before its conversion into powder. Hence the development of a continuous chhana-making machine merits attention.)

(b) *Composition*. The average composition of dried chhana or chhana powder is given in Table 10.15.

TABLE 10.15
Composition of chhana powder (cow)
(percentage)

Moisture	Fat	Protein	Lactose	Ash
3.5	41.6	46.3	4.2	4.4

(c) *Food and nutritive value*. Dried chhana has a high fat and protein content and a fairly high mineral content.

(d) *Method of manufacture*. Fresh cow milk, standardized to 4.0 per cent fat and filtered, is heated to first boil, preferably in a stain-

* See footnotes (71) and (72) in Chapter 11.

less steel jacketed steam-heated kettle of the rotary type, with constant stirring-cum-scraping to prevent the milk from scorching. The steam intake is then stopped. Sodium citrate at 0.02 per cent of milk is now added as an aqueous solution and thoroughly mixed into the milk, which is then covered and left undisturbed at $80 \pm 2°C$ for $2 \pm \frac{1}{2}$ hours.

The milk is coagulated at about 70°C by the rapid addition of a 1–2 per cent lactic or citric acid solution till the whey is clear. (Alternatively, sour lactic-whey of similar acidity may be used as a coagulant.) The mixture of coagulated mass and whey is strained through a bleached muslin cloth, and the milk-solids (chhana) obtained are cooled to room temperature by submerging the chhana—tied with a cloth without being pressed, in the form of a bundle—in running cold water.

The chhana is deposited in a separate vessel and broken up into small particles, either manually or, better still, with a suitable mechanical device. Then a calculated amount of water is added to it so as to give 19–21 per cent total solids in the mixture. It is pre-heated to about 60°C and passed through a micro-pulverizer so as to give a smooth slurry This is pre-heated to $80 \pm 5°C$ before spray drying under standard techniques, using an inlet air temperature of $195 \pm 5°C$ and an outlet air temperature of $102 \pm 2°C$. The chhana powder is promptly removed from the drying chamber, cooled, packaged and stored at room temperature, preferably under gas-packing.

(e) *Packaging and storage.* Chhana powder may be packaged in paper bags with polythene liners or fibre drums with or without polythene liners, with or without gas-packing, for storage at room temperature.

(f) *Keeping quality.* Dried chhana appears to have a marketable life at room-temperature storage of 2 and 4 months under air-tight and gas-packed conditions, respectively.

(g) *Uses.* For reconstitution into chhana for the preparation of indigenous sweetmeats, etc.

10.13 Khoa Powder*

(a) *Introduction.* Khoa is an indigenous (Indian) whole milk pro-

* See footnote (30) in Chapter 11.

duct, which constitutes an important base and filler for the preparation of milk sweets. It is prepared by the continuous heating of milk in an open pan with constant stirring-cum-scraping till it reaches a semi-solid consistency. This partially dehydrated solid product is called khoa (see 11.6). Since it has a low keeping quality, this being 4–5 days under normal conditions of atmospheric storage and ordinary packaging, inter-state trade is not feasible. Efforts to increase its storage life in the original form have so far met with limited success. Hence the production of dried khoa, which by virtue of its low moisture content, is expected to have a much longer shelf-life than the original product. (The large-scale production of khoa, which is an essential prerequisite before its conversion into powder, is already under development.)

(b) *Composition.* The average composition of dried khoa or khoa powder is given in Table 10.16.

TABLE 10.16

Composition of khoa powder (buffalo)
(percentage)

Moisture	Fat	Protein	Lactose	Ash
3.1	33.8	27.2	30.6	5.3

(c) *Food and nutritive value.* Dried khoa has a high fat, protein and lactose content, and a fairly high mineral content.

(d) *Method of manufacture.* Fresh, sweet buffalo milk, standardized to 5 per cent fat and filtered, is pre-heated to 65–70°C and homogenized at 2500 psi. It is then subjected to heat-dehydration as in the normal khoa-making process up to the stage when the heat-coagulation of milk-proteins is just completed. A calculated amount of water is now added, so as to yield 16–18 per cent total solids in the mixture. This is pre-heated to about 60°C and passed through a micro-pulverizer to make it smooth. The slurry is now drum-dried under standard techniques with a steam pressure (inside the drum) of 50±5 psi. When the drier is properly set for working, the powder is collected, ground as required, and packaged and stored at room temperature, with or without gas-packing.

Note: Increasing the total solids in the slurry (for drum drying) consistent with the physical properties of the dried product, with a view to improving the economics of the process, merits further study.

(e) *Packaging and storage.* Khoa powder may be packaged in paper bags with polythene liners or fibre drums with or without polythene liners, with or without gas-packing, for storage at room temperature.

(f) *Keeping quality.* Dried khoa seems to have a marketable life at room-temperature storage of 3 and $3\frac{1}{2}$ months under air-tight and gas-packed conditions, respectively.

(g) *Uses.* For reconstitution into khoa for the preparation of indigenous sweetmeats, etc.

11 INDIAN DAIRY PRODUCTS

11.1 Introduction

The term 'Indian dairy products' refers to those milk products which originated in undivided India*. The importance of milk and milk products in this country has been recognized since Vedic times (five thousand years ago), and the variety of ways in which milk is used for the preparation of indigenous products has developed more or less as an art. Only recently have these methods been studied on scientific lines.

Until the year 1940, there was very little published information on the method of preparation and use of these products. The credit for the first publication on the subject goes to Dr W. L. Davies, the first Director of Dairy Research, Indian (now National) Dairy Research Institute, Bangalore. Within the span of three or four decades since Dr Davies' book appeared, considerable research has been conducted at the National Dairy Research Institute and other places on indigenous dairy products.

11.2 Statistics of Production and Consumption

The type of indigenous dairy products prevalent in an area chiefly depends upon such factors as: (a) quantity of milk available; (b) traditional practices; (c) dietary habits of the people; (d) market demand; (e) purchasing power of the consumer, and (f) other local conditions (such as a regional and seasonal ban on production, etc.). Out of an estimated annual milk production of 19 million tonnes in India (1966), nearly 47 per cent was believed to be converted into Indian dairy products (see Table 1.6).

11.3 Comparison with Western Dairy Products

Broadly speaking, Indian dairy products (with the exception of ghee) have a lower keeping quality than Western dairy products. Further,

which includes India, Bangladesh and Pakistan.

Indian products are invariably prepared on a small scale (at present), while the reverse is true of Western products. The various Indian dairy products and their corresponding Western counterparts have been presented in Table 11.1.

TABLE 11.1
Indian dairy products and their Western counterparts

Indian dairy product	Corresponding Western product	Principle of manufacture of Indian product	Method of utilization of Indian product
(a) Concentrated whole milk products			
(i) Kheer/ Basundi	Condensed milk	Partial dehydration in open pan with sugar, and occasionally rice, etc.	For direct consumption
(ii) Khoa/ Mawa	Evaporated milk	Open-pan dehydration to a semi-solid consistency	As a base for traditional sweetmeats
(iii) Rabri	Clotted cream	Partial dehydration in open pan with sugar	For direct consumption
(iv) Kulfi	Ice cream	Concentrated milk, sugared and frozen.	For direct consumption.
(b) Coagulated milk products			
(i) Dahi	Curd/Yoghurt	Fermentation	For direct consumption
(ii) Srikhand	Curd (sweetened)	Fermentation and straining, and kneading with sugar	–do–
(iii) Paneer	Soft cheese	Rennet coagulation, draining and salting	–do–
(iv) Chhana	Lactic coagulated green cheese	Acid coagulation and draining.	As a base for traditional sweetmeats.
(c) Products of the clarified butter fat industry			
(i) Makkhan	Butter	Churning of fermented whole milk	For table use or clarified into ghee
(ii) Ghee*	Butteroil	Clarification of butter or cream	For table use or as a frying medium
(iii) Lassi	Buttermilk	By-product of makkhan	As a beverage
(iv) Ghee-residue†	—	Heat-denatured SNF of butter or cream.	At present wasted.

* Samna (or Masli) in Egyptian.
† Mourta in Egyptian.

11.4 Flow Diagram of Manufacture from Whole Milk

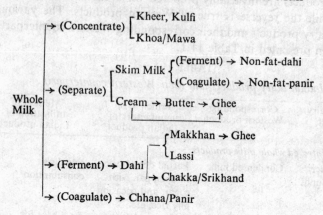

11.5 Kheer

11.5.1 Definition. Kheer, also known as *Basundi*, is an Indian dessert prepared by the partial dehydration of whole milk in a karahi* over a direct fire together with sugar and usually rice or occasionally semolina. It is popular throughout the country.

11.5.2 Chemical composition. The average chemical composition of laboratory-made kheer (prepared under standardized conditions in a stainless steel kettle) is given in Table 11.2.

TABLE 11.2

Chemical composition of kheer (percentage)

Moisture	Fat	Protein	Lactose	Ash	Sugar (added)
67.02	7.83	6.34	8.45	1.41	8.95

11.5.3 Food and nutritive value. Containing all the solids of milk in an approximately two-fold concentration plus additional sugar, the food and nutritive value of kheer is fairly high.

11.5.4 Standardized method of preparation. (1) Fresh, sweet, cleaned milk (cow or buffalo) is standardized to 4.0 per cent fat and

---

* A shallow, open, round-bottomed (iron) pan, fitted with two loop-handles.

(1) S. De, D. K. Thompkinson, D. K. Gahlot and O. N. Mathur: *Indian J. Dairy Sci.*, 29(4), 316 (1976).

vigorously boiled in a jacketed stainless steel pan or kettle† for 3 to
5 minutes accompanied by constant stirring-cum-scraping with a
khunti‡. High grade (preferably *basmati*) rice @ 2.5 per cent of
milk, pre-cleaned and washed with cold water before use, is now
added. The mixture is gently boiled, with periodical stirring-
cum-scraping. When the concentration is about 1.8 : 1, clean, good
quality sugar (preferably ground) is added @ 5 per cent of milk.
Gentle heating is continued for another 3 to 5 minutes till a final
concentration of about 2 : 1 is obtained. Heating should be stopped
somewhat before this stage, depending on the manufacturer's judgement. The kheer should now be packed and then stored under
refrigeration.

11.5.5 Yield. The yield of kheer is highly variable depending
on the percentage total solids in milk, the amount of rice/semolina
and sugar added and the ratio of concentration of the mixture
required to arrive at the desired consistency (adjudged by experience) in the finished product. If the ratio of concentration is about
2, the yield of the finished kheer should be about 50 per cent of the
milk used.

11.5.6 Keeping quality. The average shelf-life of kheer is 2 to 3
days at 37±1°C and 10 to 15 days at 4±1°C. Its storage-life could
be increased significantly by the addition of nicin (to the hot product at the end of the manufacturing process and before packaging).

11.5.7 Uses. For direct consumption as a dessert.

11.6 Khoa/Mawa

11.6.1 Introduction. Khoa constitutes one of the two chief bases
(the other being chhana) for preparing indigenous sweets. The production of khoa in India in 1966 was estimated to be about 4.9 per
cent of total dairy production and 8.7 per cent of the milk used for
manufacture of milk products (see Table 1.6). Today, the total
khoa production may be estimated at over 300 million kg., valued
at Rs 300 crores at the present rates. The preparation and use of
khoa are confined mostly to the northern and western regions of the
country. By far the largest amount is contributed by Uttar Pradesh,

† Provided with steam and cold water lines in a jacket, steam control valve,
steam pressure gauge, steam trap and condensate outlet, with arrangements for
tilting the pan as well.
‡ An (iron) stirrer, flattened at one end for scraping the bottom of the pan.

where nearly 36 per cent* of the country's total khoa production takes place.

11.6.2 Definition. Khoa/Khava/Mawa refers to the partially dehydrated whole milk product prepared by the continuous heating of milk in a karahi over a direct fire, while also constantly stirring-cum-scraping by using a khunti till it reaches a semi-solid (doughy) consistency. Thereafter, the pan-contents are removed from the fire and worked up into a solid mass known as khoa-pat.

According to the PFA Rules (1976), khoa is the product obtained from cow or buffalo (or goat or sheep) milk, or a combination thereof, by rapid drying. The milk fat content should not be less than 20 per cent of the finished product. (The Indian Standard Specification for khoa is given in *IS : 4883*, 1968).

11.6.3 Classification. Three main types/varieties of khoa, viz., Pindi, Dhap and Danedar (2), are received in Delhi, which is the biggest khoa marketing centre in the country. These types differ in quality and also in price (3–4). All of these varieties are in demand and are required for specific types of sweets, as shown in Table 11.3.

11.6.4 Composition. The chemical composition of khoa depends

TABLE 11.3

Classification of khoa

| Type | Gross composition (percentage) | | Specific sweets prepared | Remarks |
	Fat	Moisture (Total solids)		
Pindi	21–26	31–33 (67–69)	Burfi (plain, pista, chocolate, coconut), Peda, etc.	
Dhar	20–23	37–44 (56–63)	Gulabjamun, Pantooa, etc.	
Danedar	20–25	35–40 (60–65)	Kalakand, Gourd Barfi, etc.	Milk of high acidity produces a granular khoa

* Fourth Dairy Industry Conference Souvenir, 1967.

(2) M. R. Srinivasan and G. S. Rajorhia: *Indian Dairyman*, **28**(1), 11 (1976).

(3) V. K. Arora and R. K. Patel: *Indian J. Dairy Sci.*, **29**(2), 147 (1976).

(4) V. K. Arora, R. K. Patel and G. S. Rajorhia: *Indian Dairyman*, **28**(8), 365 (1976).

mainly on the initial composition of milk, the degree of concentration of the milk solids and the losses or gains in handling. An average chemical composition of fresh, laboratory-made whole-milk khoa is given in Table 11.4 (5-6). A few workers have also reported on the chemical composition/quality of market samples of khoa (7-11).

TABLE 11.4

Chemical composition of khoa (percentage)

Type of milk	Composition of khoa					
	Moisture	Fat	Protein	Lactose	Ash	Iron (ppm)
Cow	25.6	25.7	19.2	25.5	3.8	103
Buffalo	19.2	37.1	17.8	22.1	3.6	101

Note: (i) In the above table, the average composition of cow milk used for making khoa was: fat 4.8 per cent, total solids 13.8 per cent, and ratio of concentration 5.4; while that of buffalo milk was: fat 8.4 per cent, total solids 18.2 per cent, and ratio of concentration 4.5.

(ii) The high iron content in khoa may be ascribed to its removal from the surface of the (iron) karahi and incorporation of some of this iron into the finished product during the vigorous stirring-cum-scraping to which milk is subjected in the khoa-making process. (Milk normally contains only 2-4 ppm of iron.)

11.6.5 Food and nutritive value. Containing all the milk solids in an (approximately) four-fold concentration, the food and nutritive value of khoa is very high. It contains fairly large quantities of muscle-building proteins, bone-forming minerals and energy-giving fat and lactose. It is also expected to retain most of the fat-soluble

(5) S. De and S. C. Ray: *Indian J. Dairy Sci.*, **5**(3), 147 (1952).

(6) S. C. Ray and S. De: *Indian Dairyman*, **4**(2), 27 (1952).

(7) J. V. Bhat, K. Sethna and F. Fernandes: *Indian J. Dairy Sci.*, **1**(3), 49 (1948).

(8) S. G. Iyer, A. Kanan and K. P. Basu: *Indian J. Dairy Sci.*, **1**(4), 117 (1948).

(9) N. N. Dastur and A. G. Lakhani: *Indian J. Dairy Sci.*, **24**(4), 223 (1971).

(10) G. S. Rajorhia: *Indian J. Anim. Res.*, **5**(1), 25 (1971).

(11) I. T. Zariwala, U. P. Sharma and K. S. Gaikwad: *Indian J. Dairy Sci.*, **27**(1), 76 (1974).

vitamins A and D and also fairly large quantities of water-soluble B-vitamins contained in the original milk.

11.6.6   Methods of production

(a) *Existing trade practices.*   Normally 2 to 3 kg. or more of milk (preferably buffalo) is taken per batch and boiled in a karahi (of different sizes and shapes) over a brisk non-smoky fire. The milk is stirred vigorously and constantly with a circular motion by a khunti. During this operation all parts of the pan with which the milk comes into contact are lightly scraped to prevent the milk from scorching. Constant evaporation of moisture takes place and the milk thickens progressively. So far the process is similar to kheer-making. However, no sugar is added and milk-dehydration continues. At a certain concentration (cow milk 2.8; buffalo milk 2.5), heat-coagulation of milk proteins begins and the concentrate becomes progressively 'insoluble' in water(5). This stage is marked by an abrupt change in colour. The heating is continued with greater control hereafter and the speed of stirring-cum-scraping increased. Soon the viscous mass reaches a semi-solid/pasty consistency and begins to dry up. Very close attention is paid to the last stages. The final product is ready when it shows signs of leaving the bottom and sides of the karahi and sticking together. The khoa-pat is invariably made after removing the pan from the fire and working the contents up and down into a single compact mass; it is generally marketed in different sizes and shapes.

(b) *Improved method.*   This involves consideration of: equipment; conditions of dehydration, and quality of milk.

(i) *Equipment.*   The karahi and open-fire combination can conveniently be substituted (in organized dairies) by a stainless steel jacketed-pan/kettle, in the jacket of which either steam or water may be circulated as required. This will not only provide greater control over the dehydration process, but also a non-smoky heating medium.   The standard iron-stirrer, flattened at one end for stirring-cum-scraping, is normally used.

(ii) *Conditions of dehydration.*   The physico-chemical quality of khoa is influenced by the conditions of dehydration which include: temperature of dehydration; speed of stirring during dehydration; extent of dehydration, and amount of milk taken per batch for dehydration.

In order to obtain a desirable body and texture in khoa, the milk should be kept boiling till it assumes a pasty consistency and then the temperature lowered to $85\pm3°C$ till the pat-formation stage. During the entire dehydration process, milk should be stirred at 96–100 rpm. The dehydration should be stopped when the pan-contents start leaving the pan-surface and show a tendency to stick together. The amount of milk handled per batch should vary between one-fourth to one-fifth of the total capacity of the pan used.

(iii) *Quality of milk.* This also influences the quality (body and texture) of khoa. Under this factor are included: type of milk; fat level of milk; acidity of milk; adulteration of milk, and homogenization of milk.

For khoa production, buffalo milk is preferred since it yields a product with a soft, loose body and smooth, granular texture—both of which make it highly suitable for the preparation of top-quality khoa-sweets. Buffalo milk also gives a greater yield of khoa when compared with cow milk. A minimum fat level of 4 per cent in cow milk and 5 per cent in buffalo milk is necessary in order to obtain a desirable body and texture in the khoa, so as to make it acceptable for use in sweet-making. A fat level lower than the above results in an undesirably hard body and coarse texture in the finished product; on the other hand, a higher fat level improves the quality of khoa made. Fresh sweet milk yields the best results, while developed acidity in milk progressively tends to produce an undesirably sour flavour and coarse texture in the khoa, which is thereby rendered unsuitable for sweet preparation. Neutralization or stabilization of acid milk improves the texture, but does not improve the flavour of khoa made (12). Adulteration of milk with starch hardens the body of the finished product (which is rendered less suitable for sweet-making due to an overall excessive starch content). Homogenization of cow/buffalo milk produces a softer body in khoa as against unhomogenized milk; the khoa from homogenized milk also shows lower fat leakage, less browning and a reduced patting tendency as compared to that obtained from unhomogenized milk (13).

(c) *Continuous method.* In order to overcome the drawbacks of the existing batch method of khoa-making, a continuous khoa-making machine for large-scale production of khoa was designed and developed (1968) (14). The preliminary trials with a prototype

(12) S. De and S. C. Ray: *Indian J. Dairy Sci.*, 6(2), 47 (1953).
(13) C. A. Mulay and B. G. Ladkani: *J. Fd. Sci. Technol.*, 10(3), 110 (1973).
(14) A. K. Banerji, I. S. Verma and B. Bagchi: *Indian Dairyman*, 20(3), 81 (1968).

machine have shown promising results (1970) (15). The machine is undergoing further improvement.

(i) *Equipment prototype.* This consists of the following essential parts: 1. A steam-jacketed drum heater with a rotary scraper and milk outlet valve; 2. Two open steam-jacketed pans with outlet valves; 3. Two sets of scrapers for the pans, and 4. A power drive for the scrapers. A cover is provided over the pans to prevent any dust or dirt falling into it.

Whereas the rotary scraper works on the principle of centrifugal force, the pan scrapers are of the spring-loaded reciprocating type. The steam supply line is connected to the drum heater and the pans. There are three separate regulating valves to control and supply steam to the heater and pans, which are in turn provided with separate steam inlets and condensate outlets. A pressure gauge is provided in the steamline. The whole equipment is supported by stands.

(ii) *Principle.* The milk is continuously heated in the steam-jacketed drum heater, wherein it is partially concentrated. This is followed by further heating and concentration of the milk in open steam-jacketed pans till a viscous semi-solid consistency is obtained and the khoa is removed mechanically. Power-driven scrapers provided in the drum heater and in the open steam-jacketed pans, scrape the milk vigorously to prevent it from scorching and burning.

(iii) *Operation.* The equipment is first cleaned and sanitized, the safety valve pre-set at a prescribed pressure (3.5 kg sq. cm.), all bearing points lubricated with a vegetable oil (or ghee), the scraper-springs properly tightened for smooth operation and all scrapers run for a few seconds with water to test performance.

The milk outlet valve of the drum heater is then closed and its milk inlet valve opened to admit 10–12 litres of milk. The rotary scraper is started and the steamline valve for the drum jacket opened gradually. The milk is boiled vigorously for 10–12 minutes, when it is concentrated about 2.5 times. Now the milk outlet valve is opened and the concentrate flows into the first pan. Simultaneously, more milk is drawn into the drum heater for boiling.

In the first pan, the reciprocating scraper is switched on and the steamline valve in the pan-jacket opened gradually. The milk is heated here for 7–8 minutes, when the total concentration reached is

(15) S. De and B. P. Singh: *Indian Dairyman*, 22(12), 294 (1970).

about 3–5 times. Now the first pan outlet valve is opened and the milk concentrate advances to the second pan, through the pushing action of the scrapers. The second pan works on the same principle as the first. In the second pan, the milk is heated for 6–7 minutes and a final concentration of about 4.5 times obtained. The khoa outlet valve of the second pan is opened and the viscous semi-solid mass of khoa is pushed out mechanically by the scrapers and collected in a container held underneath. The process is continuous.

Note: The finished khoa usually has a moisture content of 33–37 per cent; a lower moisture level comes in the way of mechanical removal.

(iv) *Advantages claimed*

1. Khoa can be made on a large scale under hygienic conditions;

2. considerable saving in man-hours and human drudgery is made possible.

Note: The economics of khoa-production with the prototype continuous khoa-making plant have been worked out (15–16).

(d) *Miscellaneous methods*

(i) The utilization of aged atmospheric roller-dried skim milk powder and white butter or ghee for the production of khoa of an 'acceptable' quality has been standardized (17).

(ii) The feasibility of using vacuum-concentrated milk for khoa-making has been worked out. It was found that a milk concentrate containing up to 31 per cent total solids produced satisfactory khoa (18).

11.6.7 Physico-chemical changes in milk on conversion into khoa. These are:

(a) *Change of state.* From liquid milk to solid khoa (due to considerable dehydration).

(b) *Change in intensity of colour.* From 'light' to a 'more intense' shade of colour (with a tinge of brown).

(c) *Homogenization of milk fat.* The fat globules are appreciably subdivided (due to the vigorous agitation of milk at high temperatures).

(16) S. De and K. C. Tyagi: *NDRI Publication*, No. 91 (1972).

(17) S. De and M. R. Srinivasan: *Indian Dairyman*, 19(5), 151 (1967).

(18) S. De and M. R. Srinivasan: *Indian Dairyman*, 20(4), 99 (1968).

(d) *Free-fat formation.* Considerable free fat is produced (due to the rupturing of the fat globule membrane by the vigorous scraping action of the stirrer).

(e) *Heat-coagulation of milk proteins.* The serum proteins are coagulated by the action of heat, and casein is coagulated by the combined action of heat and concentration.

(f) *Super-saturated solution of lactose.* From a dilute solution in milk, lactose is present in khoa as a super-saturated solution.

(g) *Partial precipitation of milk salts.* A portion of the milk salts are precipitated by the action of heat.

(h) *Increase in iron content.* From 2 to 4 ppm in milk, the iron content in khoa exceeds 100 ppm (due to the incorporation of additional quantities of iron from the pan-surface into the finished product by the vigorous scraping of the stirrer).

11.6.8 Market quality. This may be subdivided into (a) physical, (b) chemical, and (c) microbiological qualities.

(a) *Physical quality.* This includes: (i) colour and appearance; (ii) body and texture; (iii) flavour, and (iv) suitability for sweets. These have been presented for cow and buffalo khoa in Table 11.5.

TABLE 11.5

Physical quality of cow and buffalo khɔa

Particulars	Cow	Buffalo
Colour	Straw/pale-yellow, with a tinge of brown	Whitish (dull/light greenish white), with a tinge of brown
Appearance	'Moist' surface	'Slightly oily/greasy' surface
Body	Slightly hard	Soft
Texture	Slightly sandy	Smooth, granular
Smell	Rich, nutty	Rich, nutty
Taste	Slightly salted	Slightly sweet
Suitability for sweets	Suitable	Highly suitable

The physical quality of khoa will depend mainly on the type of milk used, viz. cow, buffalo or mixed, and the method of manufacture followed. In general, market khoa, which is normally made from buffalo milk, should have a uniform whitish colour with perhaps a tinge of brown, a slightly oily or granular texture, and a rich nutty flavour which is generally associated with a mildly cooked and sweet taste.

Good quality khoa should be a compact mass of very small uniformly-sized granules, which shows no signs of fat and/or water leakage. Even if kept for over 24 hours, it should not taste gritty. The material, when fresh, should be able to produce a smooth, homogeneous paste on working—which indicates that it is 'suitable' for sweet-making.

(b) *Chemical quality.* (See *Composition*). It may be pointed out that khoa offered for sale should not contain any constituents foreign to milk and should not be adulterated with any type of starchy material, etc.

(c) *Microbiological quality.* This has yet to be prescribed. Although the milk is subjected to drastic heat-treatment during khoa-making, yet a large and varied microbial count has been reported in market samples of khoa by various workers (7)(19–23). Obviously these include the surviving spore-formers (which multiply during subsequent storage) and the contaminating micro-organisms (which gain entry during manufacture, handling, packaging and storage).

11.6.9   Yield and overrun

(a) *Yield.* The yield of khoa is rather variable and is influenced by: (i) the type of khoa; (ii) the type of milk; (iii) the quality of milk; (iv) the extent of dehydration (ratio of concentration of milk solids), and (v) losses in handling.

The type of khoa which contains a higher moisture content is certain to have a higher yield. The type of milk, viz., cow or buffalo, influences the yield by virtue of its total solids content; thus, buffalo milk with a higher total solids content gives a higher yield of khoa than cow milk with a lower total solids content. The quality of milk refers to the total solids content; good or high quality milk refers to a high total solids content, which yields larger quantities of khoa as compared to poor or low quality milk with a

(19) K. A. Naidu and B. Ranganathan: *Indian J. Dairy Sci.*, **18**(1), 4 (1965).

(20) M. M. Ahmed and B. Ranganathan: *Indian J. Dairy Sci.*, **20**(4), 157 (1967).

(21) G. R. Sharma, D. R. Saraswat and S. D. Sharma: *Indian J. Dairy Sci.*, **25**(1), 30 (1972).

(22) D. R. Ghodekar, A. T. Dudani and B. Ranganathan: *J. Milk Food Technol.*, **37**(3), 119 (1974).

(23) K. Singh, J. L. Ogra and Y. S. Rao: *Indian J. Dairy Sci.*, **28**(4), 304 (1975).

low total solids content. The extent of dehydration refers to percentage moisture retained in the khoa; the more the dehydration, the lower the yield, and vice versa. Losses in handling which include accidental overflow, etc., obviously lower the yield of khoa. Normally the yield of khoa (with 28 per cent moisture) ranges from 17 to 19 per cent from cow milk and 21 to 23 per cent from buffalo milk.

(b) *Overrun.* The overrun in khoa refers to the excess weight of khoa over the amount of total (milk) solids used in its production. The overrun is chiefly influenced by the moisture retained in khoa and the losses of milk solids. It is usually expressed as a percentage. The formula for calculating overrun (OR) in khoa is:

$$\% \text{ OR} = \frac{K - TS}{TS} \times 100,$$

where

K = weight of khoa (in kg.)
TS = weight of total solids in milk (in kg.).

Note: It may be mentioned here that in the market-place, the quality and purity of milk is judged by what is known as the 'khoa test'. In performing this test, a predetermined amount (usually 1 kg) of milk is converted into khoa in the normal manner by the intending purchaser; and the price paid for milk to the supplier is in direct ratio to the amount of khoa obtained.

11.6.10 *Packaging, storage and marketing*

(a) *Packaging.* Normally individual khoa-pats are not packaged. However, the following modern packaging materials and forms can be profitably used: Vegetable parchment paper wrappers; plastic (polythene) film bags/pouches, laminated (preferably aluminium coated) pouches; tin-plate cans, etc. The pack size usually varies from 0.5 to 1.0 kg., although packs smaller than 0.5 kg. are also available.

(b) *Storage.* Khoa has a low keeping quality at room temperature, and storage at low temperatures (5–10°C) has been found to extend its shelf-life. Hence refrigerated storage is preferable.

(c) *Marketing.* At present, khoa is generally marketed soon after production in an unpacked or crudely packed condition, depending on the distance of the market.

11.6.11 *Keeping quality.* The keeping quality of khoa is chiefly

influenced by tne following factors: (a) temperature of storage; (b) quality of the raw material (milk); (c) initial moisture content; (d) sanitary conditions observed during manufacture; (e) type of package, and (f) method of packaging.

(a) *Temperature of storage*. The higher the storage temperature the lower the keeping quality, and vice versa. The average storage life of khoa (100 g. pack in a butterpaper wrapper) made either from cow or buffalo milk at $37 \pm 1°C$, 23–24°C and 5–10°C was 7, 10 and 25 days respectively(6)(12). Khoa samples from mixed milks (500 g. lots packed while hot in laminated pouches and heat-sealed immediately) showed an average shelf-life at $37°C$, $8 \pm 1°C$ and −20°C of 5 days, 30 days and 75 days respectively (24).

(b) *Quality of the raw material (milk)*. The quality of milk used for the production of khoa has a direct influence on the keeping quality of the finished product. Any developed acidity in milk lowers the keeping quality of khoa made from it. Hence only fresh, sweet milk, produced under sanitary conditions, should be used for khoa making.

(c) *Initial moisture content*. The lower the initial moisture content of khoa, the higher the keeping quality, and vice versa.

(d) *Sanitary conditions observed during manufacture*. Since khoa is made in the open under the existing system of production, the sanitary conditions observed during manufacture will certainly play an important role in influencing its keeping quality. The better the sanitary conditions, the higher its storage life, and vice versa.

(e) *Type of package*. The type of package, as specified by the packing material, influences the keeping quality of khoa (24). Thus khoa samples (500 g. lots packed while hot in their respective pre-sterilized pouches) showed an average shelf-life at $8 \pm 1°C$ of 14 days and 30 days for parchment paper/polythene film and 4-ply aluminium-coated laminates, respectively.

(f) *Method of packaging*. This refers to whether khoa has been packed hot or cold, air-tight or loosely wrapped, etc. Hot packaging of khoa (in unsterilized cans) has been found to ensure a longer keeping quality than cold packaging. It has been reported that khoa (with an initial moisture content of 20–25 per cent) had an average shelf-life of 14–21 days when packed hot (80–90°C) and less than 7

(24) A. Kumar, G. S. Rajorhia and M. R. Srinivasan: *J. Fd. Sci. Technol.*, 12(4), 172 (1975).

days when packed cold (25–30°C) (25).

Note: Efforts to preserve khoa, i.e. to extend its keeping quality, have not been very successful so far. Heat-sterilization of canned khoa was found to adversely affect its sensory qualities and render the product unmarketable. The addition of potassium sorbate and butylated hydroxy anisole in permitted quantities did not extend the shelf-life of khoa (25). Although irradiation of khoa with ultra-violet rays for 90 minutes was found to extend its storage life from 5 to 25 days, the irradiated product soon developed a disagreeable oxidized flavour so that it lost consumer acceptability (26). The addition of nicin was observed to extend the storage life of the canned product by more than one month at 10°C and by 2 and 3 weeks at 30 and 22°C, respectively (27). Standardized khoa with an addition of potassium sorbate (in quantities greater than those tried earlier) showed a keeping quality of 10–11 days at 30°C and 40 days at 5°C; the addition of nicin (nisaplin) and anti-oxidants in permitted amounts did not increase its shelf-life (28).

11.6.12 Type of spoilage. The spoilage in khoa at $37 \pm 1°C$ and room temperatures (24–30°C) is characterized by a rancid flavour, while at low temperatures (5–10°C) it has a stale/sour flavour; at room and refrigerated temperatures, there is a mouldy growth on the surface (6)(12)(19)(22)(25)(29).

Note: Although during the manufacture of khoa, milk is subjected to drastic heat-treatment, the aerobic spore formers are known to survive such heat-treatment and may outnumber other types of micro-organisms, thereby suggesting that the survivors might have multiplied during subsequent storage. The possibility of contaminants gaining entry into these products during subsequent handling also cannot be ruled out (22).

(25) K. G. Rudreshappa and S. De: *J. Fd. Sci. Technol.*, 8(2), 50 (1971).

(26) K. Sethna and J. V. Bhatt: *Indian J. Dairy Sci.*, 2(1), 12 (1949).

(27) M. S. Kalra, H. Laxminarayana and A. T. Dudani: *J. Fd. Sci. Technol.*, 10(3), 92 (1973).

(28) Y. K. Jha, S. Singh and Surjan Singh: *Indian J. Dairy Sci.*, 30(1), 1 (1977).

(29) B. D. Narang, K. S. Dhindsa and S. P. Kohli: *Indian J. Dairy Sci.*, 22 (4), 211 (1969).

11.6.13 Judging and grading of khoa
(a) *Score card.* A tentative scord card of khoa is given in Table 11.6.

TABLE 11.6

Score card of khoa (tentative)

Items	Perfect score
Flavour	45
Body and texture	35
Colour and appearance	15
Package	5
Total	100

(b) *Procedure of examination*
 (i) *Sampling.* Obtain a representative sample with the help of a sharp-bladed knife.
 (ii) *Sequence of observations.* Note the sanitary condition of the package (if any). Before taking the sample, observe the surface of the khoa-pat and examine the uniformity of colour on the outside and inside. Observe the body and texture: note hardness/softness of body and sandiness/smoothness/coarseness/granularity/grittiness of texture; also note moisture and/or fat leakage. Take a small piece from the khoa sample and taste on the tip of the tongue. Chew until melted and then roll the melted mass within the mouth. Note flavour (smell and taste). Expectorate the sample and note the after-taste.
 (c) *Requirements of high-grade (buffalo) khoa.* This should have a uniform whitish (dull/light-greenish white) colour; soft body and smooth granular texture; and a rich, nutty flavour (which is generally associated with a slightly cooked smell and sweetish taste); and should be free from any off-flavours and surface dryness.
 11.6.14 Defects, their causes and prevention. Defects in khoa arise due to low quality milk and faulty methods of production, handling and storage. The defects in khoa, their causes and prevention are given in Table 11.7.

TABLE 11.7

Defects in khoa, their causes and prevention

Defects	Causes	Prevention
(a) *Flavour*		
Smoky	Smoky fire used for boiling and dehydration of milk.	Using non-smoky fire for boiling and dehydration of milk.
Sour/Acid	Excessively high acidity in milk used.	Using fresh sweet milk.
Rancid	Fat hydrolysis due to lipase action in khoa during storage (at room temperature and above).	Storage of khoa at low temperature (5–10°C).
Stale	Excessively long period of storage of khoa at low temperature (5–10 C).	Early disposal/marketing of khoa.
(b) *Body and Texture*		
Hard body	(i) Excessively low fat content of milk used	(i) Using milk of optimum fat content
	(ii) Excessively low moisture content of khoa, due to faulty production technique	(ii) Optimum moisture content of khoa by adopting correct production technique
	(iii) Adulteration of milk with starch.	(iii) Using unadulterated milk.
Coarse texture	(i) Excessively high acidity in milk used	(i) Using fresh sweet milk
	(ii) Excessively low fat content of milk used	(ii) Using milk of optimum fat content
	(iii) Excessively high temperature of dehydration, especially in the last stages	(iii) Optimum temperature of dehydration, especially in the last stages
	(iv) Excessively low speed when stirring milk/pan-contents.	(iv) Optimum speed when stirring milk/pan-contents.
Gritty texture	(i) Presence of sand-like particles due to incorrect straining of milk	(i) Correct straining of milk

Defects	Causes	Prevention
	(ii) Presence of large crystals of lactose due to incorrect method of manufacture.	(ii) Correct method of manufacture.
(c) *Colour and appearance*		
Dry surface	Excessively low fat content of milk used.	Using milk of optimum fat content.
Visible dirt/ foreign matter	(i) Incorrect or no straining of milk used	(i) Correct straining of milk
	(ii) Heating-pan and/or stirrer not cleaned	(ii) Heating-pan and/or stirrer well cleaned
	(iii) Dirty/windy surroundings during manufacture and/or handling of khoa	(iii) Clean surroundings during manufacture and/or handling of khoa
	(iv) Transport of unpacked khoa.	(iv) Transport of properly packed khoa.
Browning and/ or presence of burnt particles	(i) Excessively high heating-temperature, especially in the last stages	(i) Optimum heating temperature, especially in the last stages
	(ii) Excessively low speed when stirring-cum-scraping pan-contents.	(ii) Optimum speed when stirring-cum-scraping pan-contents.
Mouldy surface	(i) Excessively high moisture content of khoa in storage	(i) Optimum moisture content of khoa in storage
	(ii) Excessively high humidity of storage room	(ii) Optimum humidity of storage room
	(iii) Air-leaky packaging of khoa.	(iii) Air-tight packaging of khoa.
Fat and/or water leakage	Incorrect method of manufacture of khoa.	Correct method of manufacture of khoa.

11.6.15   Uses

(i) As a base and filler for the preparation of a large number of indigenous milk-sweets such as gulabjamun, peda, barfi, kalakand, pantooa, etc.

(ii) for direct consumption with added sugar (optional).

11.6.16   Khoa powder (See 10.13) (30).

(30) A. A. Patel and S. De: *Indian J. Dairy Sci.*, **30**(4), 325 (1977).

11.7 Khurchan

11.7.1 Definition. This is a concentrated, sweetened whole-milk product prepared by simmering milk without stirring it in a karahi, so as to allow for the simultaneous formation of a thick creamy layer of skin on the surface of the milk and the slow evaporation of water, after which sugar is added to the concentrated product. This is followed by a thorough mixing of the product. It is quite popular in the northern region of the country.

17.7.2 Composition. The average chemical composition of laboratory-made samples of khurchan has been given in Table 11.8. The microbial quality of laboratory-made khurchan has also been reported. (23)

TABLE 11.8

Chemical composition of khurchan (31) *(percentage)*

Moisture	Fat	Protein	Lactose	Sugar	Ash	Iron (mg %)
27.9	23.6	15.4	14.9	15.2	3.0	25.3

11.7.3 Food and nutritive value. As khurchan contains all the milk solids in an approximately five-fold concentration, together with an addition of sugar, its food and nutritive value is very high.

11.7.4 Method of preparation. Khurchan is normally prepared by heating 3–4 kg. milk in a karahi to simmering temperature (85–90°C) and then carefully maintaining it at this temperature by controlled heating. In no case is the milk allowed to boil; nor is it stirred (until sugar is admixed). This helps in the formation of a thick creamy layer on the upper surface of the milk. When the volume of milk gets reduced by the evaporation of water to one-fourth to one-sixth (average one-fifth) of the original, good quality ground sugar is added to the concentrated mass at 5–6 per cent by weight of the original milk and dissolved in it. The finished product has a slightly cooked flavour, which is relished. Buffalo milk is invariably used for the production of khurchan, as it gives a higher yield than cow milk.

11.7.5 Yield. The yield of khurchan depends on the percentage of total solids in milk, the ratio of concentration of the milk solids and the amount of sugar added.

11.7.6 Uses. For direct consumption.

(31) M. P. Gupta and Y. S. Rao, *Indian J. Dairy Sci.*, **25**(2), 70 (1972).

11.8 Rabri

11.8.1 Definition. This is an especially prepared concentrated and sweetened whole milk product, containing several layers of clotted cream. While the milk is slowly evaporated (without being stirred) at simmering temperature in a karahi over an open fire, pieces of skin which form on the surface of the milk are continuously broken up and moved to the cooler parts of the karahi. When the volume of milk has been considerably reduced, sugar is added to it; then layers of clotted cream are immersed in the mixture and the finished product obtained by heating the whole mass for another short period. Rabri is quite popular in the northern and eastern regions of the country.

11.8.2 Composition. The composition of rabri depends on the initial composition of milk, the degree of concentration of milk solids and the percentage of sugar added. An approximate composition of rabri is given in Table 11.9. The microbiological and chemical quality of rabri has also been reported (23).

TABLE 11.9

Chemical composition of rabri (percentage)

Moisture	Fat	Protein	Lactose	Ash	Sugar
30	20	10	17	3	20

SOURCE: *Milk Products of India* by Srinivasan and Anantakrishnan (1964).

11.8.3 Food and nutritive value. As rabri contains all the milk solids in an approximately five-fold concentration, plus additional sugar, its food and nutritive value is very high.

11.8.4 Method of preparation. Rabri is normally prepared by heating 3–4 kg. of milk in a karahi over an open fire to simmering temperature (85–90°C), and then maintaining the temperature by controlled heating. The milk is neither stirred nor allowed to boil. The surface of the milk may be gently fanned to help the process of skin formation. A piece of this skin, about 3–4 cm. square, is continuously broken with a thick wooden stick (or bamboo/cane splints) and moved to the cooler parts of the karahi. This operation requires considerable skill and constant attention. Simultaneously, as slow evaporation reduces the milk to about one-fifth of its original volume, good quality ground sugar at 5–6 per cent by weight of the original milk is added to the milk concentrate and dissolved in it. The layers of skin collected on the karahi surface are then immersed in the mixture and the finished product obtained by gently heating the whole mass for another brief period. Buffalo milk is invariably used as it produces a more creamy consistency and a higher yield.

Note: The finished product consists of non-homogeneous flakes covered and floating in a milk-sugar-syrup. By beating the concentrate slightly at the end, a more homogeneous, honey-comb textured mass is obtained.

11.8.5　Yield. The yield of rabri will depend on the percentage of total solids in milk, the ratio of concentration of the milk solids and the amount of sugar added.

11.8.6　Uses. For direct consumption.

11.8　Kulfi/Malai-ka-Baraf

11.9.1　Kulfi. This is an indigenous ice cream frozen in small containers. While the milk is boiling, it is sweetened by an addition of sugar and the product is concentrated to approximately 2 : 1. To this concentrate, when it has cooled, are added malai (indigenous cream), crushed nuts and a flavour (commonly rose or vanilla). The mix is placed in triangular, conical or cylindrical moulds of various capacities made of galvanized iron sheets. The moulds are closed on top by placing a small disc over them and the edges made airtight with wheat-dough. (Modern moulds are made of plastic, generally conical in shape with screw-cap plastic tops.) The mix-in-moulds is frozen in a large earthen vessel containing a mixture of ice and salt in the ratio of 1 : 1.

Note: Malai refers to the creamy layer formed on the surface of milk, which has usually been heated, very slowly, to boiling temperature and then left to cool undisturbed. This creamy layer is then skimmed off and finds various uses, viz. for direct consumption with sugar, as a source of cream in sweets, puddings and fruit, in the preparation of kulfi or malai-ka-baraf, etc. Owing to its higher fat content and larger fat globules, buffalo milk gives higher yields and is used for the preparation of malai. According to the PFA Rules (1976), malai refers to the product rich in butter fat prepared by boiling and cooling cow or buffalo milk or a combination thereof. It should contain not less than 25.0 per cent milk fat.

11.9.2 Malai-ka-baraf. This term is loosely applied to a variety of frozen products in which sweetened milk or malai may form the chief ingredient. They may also be prepared from diluted milk thickened with some fruit pulp, etc., with a dash of colour and flavour. (The latter kind is usually sold in the market.)

A compact cast-iron freezing-unit, which is generally an imported one and consists of a retort connected to an especially designed condenser, is used for freezing the mix. In rough outline, the method of freezing (in a closed system) consists in first heating the retort containing some crude ammonium salts over an open fire, while the condenser is kept immersed in a tub of cold water. This heating goes on for nearly 3 hours. Thereafter, the condenser is taken out of the tub and the vessel containing the mix is placed in the annular space in cold water provided in the condenser and the retort. Some wet cloth or gunny is put on the vessel containing the mix. The freezing takes about 3 hours. The frozen product is then taken out of the vessel, wrapped with an insulating material such as paper-and-felt, and sold by chipping out slices with a sharp knife.

Note: In the first stage when the retort containing ammonium salts is heated, ammonia gas is liberated. This changes into liquid ammonia as it reaches the cooler parts of the condenser. In the second stage, when the condenser comes in contact with atmospheric air, the liquid ammonia evaporates; while doing so, the latent heat for vaporization is extracted from the mix, which then freezes.

11.9.3 Comparison with ice cream. A comparison of (standard) ice cream with the indigenous product has been made in Table 11.10.

TABLE 11.10

Comparison and contrast between ice cream and kulfi/malai-ka-baraf

Particulars	Ice cream	Kulfi/malai-ka-baraf
Type of frozen product	Western	Indigenous
Composition	Standard	Variable
Scale of manufacture	Usually large	Usually very small
Freezer used	Modern batch or continuous	Crude indigenous or imported
Sequence followed	Freezing first, packaging later	Packaging first, freezing later
Sanitary conditions followed	Usually high	Usually low
Overrun	Standard	Practically nil
Body and texture	Usually soft and smooth	Usually hard and coarse
Food and nutritive value	High	Low

11.10   Dahi

11.10.1   Introduction.   Indian curd, known as dahi, is a well-known fermented milk product consumed by large sections of the population throughout the country, either as a part of the daily diet or as a refreshing beverage. In 1966, the production of dahi was estimated to be about 7.8 per cent of the total milk production in India and 14.0 per cent of the milk used for the manufacture of dairy products. (See Table 1.6.)

Since conversion of milk into dahi is an important intermediary step in the manufacture of indigenous butter and ghee, it can be said that over 40 per cent of the total milk production in India today is converted into dahi.

An extensive all-India survey project on dahi was carried out nearly three decades ago (32–34). It revealed that there are, broadly speaking, two types of dahi prevalent in the country for direct consumption, viz. a sweet/mildly sour variety with a pleasant flavour, and a sour variety with a sharp, acid flavour. The microorganisms responsible for these two types were also identified, and are maintained in selected centres as freeze-dried cultures for sale to the industry and public alike.

11.10.2   Definition.   According to the PFA Rules (1976), dahi or curd is the product obtained from pasteurized or boiled milk by souring, natural or otherwise, by a harmless lactic acid or other bacterial culture. Dahi may contain additional cane sugar. It should have the same percentage of fat and solids-not-fat as the milk from which it is prepared. Where dahi or curd, other than skimmed milk dahi, is sold or offered for sale without any indication of the class of milk, the standards prescribed for dahi prepared from buffalo milk shall apply.

The Indian Standard Specifications for designation of fermented milk products based on the types of culture used are given in Table 11.11, and requirements in Table 11.12.

(32) H. Laxminarayana and K. K. Iya: *Indian J. Vet. Sci.*, **22**(1), 1 (1952).

(33) H. Laxminarayana, V. K. N. Nambudripad, N. V. Lakshmi, S. N. Anantaramiah and V. Sreenivasamurthy: *Indian J. Vet. Sci.*, **22**(1), 13 (1952).

(34) H. Laxminarayana, V. K. N. Nambudripad, N. V. Lakshmi, S. N. Anantaramiah, V. Sreenivasamurthy and K. K. Iya: *Indian J. Vet. Sci.*, **22**(1), 27 (1952).

TABLE 11.11
Designation of fermented milk products

Designation	Culture used
Sweet dahi	*Str. lactis* ⎫ *Str. diacetilactis* ⎬ Single or in combination with or without *Str. cremoris* ⎭ *Leuconostoc* species
Sour dahi	Same as above, along with *Lact. bulgaricus* or *Str. thermophillus* or both

TABLE 11.12
Requirements for fermented milk products

Characteristics	Requirement	
	Sweet dahi	Sour dahi
Acidity, lactic (% wt) (Max)	0.70	1.0
Yeast and mould count per g. (Max)	100	100
Coliform count per g. (Max)	10	10
Phosphatase test	—ve	—ve

SOURCE: *IS* : *7035*, 1973.

11.10.3 Classification. Broadly speaking, dahi may be classified into two types:

I. For churning into desi (or indigenous) butter (makkhan);

II. For direct consumption.

Dahi for direct consumption may be further classified into:

(a) (i) Whole milk dahi; (ii) skim milk dahi.

(b) (i) Sweet (or mildly sour) dahi; (ii) sour dahi; (iii) sweetened dahi.

11.10.4 Food and nutritive value. It has been established that fermented milk products including dahi increase in food and nutritive value as compared to the original milk. The following points are cited in their favour:

(i) Dahi is more palatable, and those who usually do not like drinking milk would consume it readily;

(ii) dahi is more easily digested and assimilated than milk;

(iii) dahi seems to exert a possible therapeutic value in the stomach and during intestinal disorders, due possibly to its content of antibiotics (35).

11.10.5   Composition.   An average composition of (whole) milk dahi is given in Table 11.13.

TABLE 11.13

Composition of (whole) milk dahi (percentage)

Water	Fat	Protein	Lactose	Ash	Lactic Acid
85–88	5–8	3.2–3.4	4.6–5.2	0.70–0.72	0.5–0.11

Note: There is a slight increase in the concentration of milk solids to the extent of 5–10 per cent in dahi as compared with the initial milk.

11.10.6   Method of production
A. *For churning into desi butter (makkhan).*   (See 11.14.)
B. *For direct consumption*
I. *Sweet/Sour dahi*
(aa) *Traditional method.*   This invariably involves production on a small scale, either in the consumer's household or in the sweet-meat-maker's (halwai's) shop in urban areas. In the household. the milk is boiled, cooled to body temperature, inoculated with 0.5–1 per cent starter (previous day's dahi or buttermilk) and then allowed to set undisturbed overnight. In cooler weather, the dahi-setting vessel is usually wrapped up with woollen cloth to maintain warmth. In the shops, the method is more or less the same except that the milk is concentrated somewhat before inoculation and the dahi is usually set in a circular earthenware mould.

(bb) *Standardized method*
(a) *Need.*   The quality of market dahi presently sold in halwai shops in the country is generally sub-standard and variable. The factors responsible for this are:
  (i) use of low-quality milk;
  (ii) use of unsuitable starter cultures;
  (iii) unfavourable temperatures of incubation;
  (iv) contamination from badly-cleaned utensils.

In view of the nutritional and economic importance of dahi, it has long been realized that this product should be produced on scientific

(35) D. N. Gandhi and V. K. N. Nambudripad: *Indian J. Dairy Sci.*, **28**(1), 72 (1975).

lines in the organized sector of the Indian dairy industry (36–38). The conditions of production, packaging and distribution should be standardized so as to ensure the supply of an uniformly good quality product from day to day.

(b) *Technique*

(i) *Flow diagram of production*

Receiving milk

|

Pre-heating (35–40°C)

|

Filtration/Clarification

|

Standardization

|

Pre-heating (60°C)

|

Homogenization (176 kg/sq. cm.)

|

Pasteurization (80–90°C/15–30 min.)

|

Cooling (22–25°C)

|

Inoculation

|

Packaging

|

Incubation (22–25°C/16–18 hrs.)

|

Dahi

|

Cooling and Storage (5°C)

(ii) *Details of production.* Fresh, sweet, good-quality milk (cow, buffalo or mixed) is received, pre-heated to 35–40°C, and subjected to filtration/clarification. It is then standardized to 2.5–3.0 per cent fat and 10 per cent solids-not-fats (in order to improve the body), pre-heated to 60°C and homogenized single-stage at a pressure of 176 kg/sq. cm. The milk is pasteurized at 80–90°C for 15–30 minutes, cooled to 22–25°C and inoculated with 1–3 per cent of specific starter culture (see Table 11.10). It is then filled in suitable containers (glass bottles/plastic cups, etc.) of the required capacity and

(36) K. K. Iya and H. Laxminarayana: *Indian Farming*, 2(1), 18 (1953).

(37) K. S. Rangappa: *Indian Dairyman*, 14(8), 251 (1962).

(38) H. Laxminarayana and V. K. N. Nambudripad: *NDRI Publication No. 54* (1971).

incubated at 22–25°C for 16–18 hours, during which period the acidity reaches 0.6–0.7 per cent and a firm curd is formed. The curd is cooled to less than 12°C in about 1 hour (by circulating chilled water or air around the containers) and then stored at about 5°C in a cold room.

Note: During overnight storage, the acidity may increase slightly.

II. *Sweetened dahi.* In the eastern region of the country, especially West Bengal, a sweetened variety of dahi known as *misti* dahi, *lal* dahi or *payodhi* (the trade name of one particular manufacturer in Calcutta) is quite popular. It has a characteristic brown colour, a cooked and caramelized flavour and a firm body. It is prepared commercially by adding 6.25 per cent cane sugar to milk (cow or mixed) either before boiling or at the time of setting. The pronounced and intense heating causes the milk to brown and get partially concentrated. (The volume gets reduced to about three-fourths of the original.) Artificial colour, sugar-caramel and *gur* (jaggery) are also added during production. After heat-treatment, the milk is cooled to room temperature and then seeded (in variable amounts) with the previous day's product. It is usually set in earthenware basins and the finished product obtained after 15–16 hours. The method for the production of sweet dahi has been standardized (39).

Note: Studies have been made on: (i) utilization of colostrum for the preparation of dahi (40); (ii) development of dahi-making equipment (41), and (iii) production of new varieties of dahi (42). A suggestion has also been made for a new product named dahi-kusum (43).

11.10.7 Market quality. The desirable qualities in dahi offered for sale for direct consumption have been given in Table 11.14.

(39) H. P. Ray and R. A. Srinivasan. *J. Fd. Sci. Technol.*, 9(2), 62 (1972).

(40) S. N. Anantaramiah and K. K. Iya: *Indian J. Dairy Sci.*, 5(1), 33 (1952).

(41) A. K. Banerji, I. S. Verma and B. C. Bagchi: *Indian Dairyman*, 19(5), 177 (1967).

(42) D. C. Bhattacharya and M. R. Srinivasan: *Indian Dairyman*, 19(1), 35 (1967).

(43) K. S. Rangappa: *Indian Dairyman.* 17(1), 13 (1965).

TABLE 11.14
Market quality of dahi

Qualities	Requirements
Colour	Yellowish creamy-white for cow and creamy-white for buffalo milk; free from browning.
Appearance	Smooth and glossy surface; creamy layer on top (with whole milk product); free from extraneous matter.
Flavour	Mild, pleasant smell, clean acid taste, free from off-flavours.
Body	Soft and firm, free from gas-holes and whey-pockets.
Acidity (per cent lactic)	0.75 to 0.85.

Note: The effect of different salts and chemical additives on the quality of dahi has been observed (44). The effect of starter cultures and incubation (period and temperature) on the acidity and quality of dahi has been ascertained (45–47) and the survival of pathogens in dahi investigated (48–49).

11.10.8 Packaging and storage. The traditional container for dahi is an earthenware cup. However, modern packaging includes glass bottle and plastic/plastic-coated cup. The recommended storage temperature is around 5–10°C.

11.10.9 Keeping quality. When prepared in the conventional manner, dahi has a short keeping quality at room temperature; on prolonged storage, it becomes highly acidic; this is accompanied by whey formation, making the product unfit for human consumption. Under refrigerated storage (5–10°C), it usually keeps well for a maximum period of one week.

11.10.10 Increasing keeping quality. Efforts to increase the keeping quality of dahi at room temperatures have led to the development of a carbonated product, which has a storage life of 15–30 days without refrigeration. It is prepared as follows: good-quality

(44) R. K. Baisya and A. N. Bose: *J. Fd. Sci. Technol.*, **11**(2), 70 (1974).
(45) C. K. Sharma and S. C. Jain: *J. Fd. Sci. Technol.*, **11**(6), 277 (1974).
(46) C. K. Sharma and S. C. Jain: *J. Fd. Sci. Technol.*, **12**(2), 81 (1975).
(47) R. K. Baisya and A. N. Bose: *Indian J. Dairy Sci.*, **28**(3), 179 (1975).
(48) N. P. Tiwari and I. P. Singh: *Indian J. Dairy Sci.*, **17**(3), 97 (1964).
(49) N. P. Tiwari and I. P. Singh: *Indian J. Dairy Sci.*, **19**(3), 162 (1966).

milk, after heat-treatment (preferably boiling for 3–5 minutes) is cooled to 30–35°C. It is then inoculated with a starter culture @ 1 per cent and mixed well. The culture may consist of lactic acid producers such as *Str. lactis* and/or *Str. cremoris*, together with an aroma producer such as *Str. diacetilactis*. The inoculated milk is filled up to the neck of each glass bottle. Now carbon dioxide gas is bubbled through the milk at 1 psi for 1 minute and the bottles are crown-corked. The milk is then incubated at 25–30°C for 16–18 hours until a firm curd is obtained.

Note: The role of contaminating yeasts in the spoilage of dahi has been reported.

   11.10.11   Dahi powder. Studies have been conducted on the dehydration of dahi on a laboratory scale (50) and by various methods (51–53).
   11.10.12   Uses of dahi
   (a) *Whole milk dahi*
   (i) For direct consumption: either as such with salt/sugar; or as a beverage after beating the curd and mixing it with water, salt/sugar, etc.;
   (ii) for the preparation of chakka and srikhand (see 10.11);
   (iii) for the preparation of makkhan.
   (b) *Skim milk dahi*
For direct consumption: especially by heart patients since it is low in fat, and by the low-income group of the population because it is cheap yet nutritious.

11.11   Srikhand

11.11.1   Definition. Srikhand is a semi-soft, sweetish-sour, whole milk product prepared from lactic fermented curd. The curd (dahi) is partially strained through a cloth to remove the whey and thus produce a solid mass called chakka (the basic ingredient for srikhand). This chakka is mixed with the required amount of sugar,

(50) K. N. Srinivasan and B. Ranganathan: *J. Fd. Sci. Technol.*, **9**(2), 69 (1972).
   (51) B. S. Bhatia, V. K. Mathur and P. K. Vijayaraghavan: *Indian Fd. Packer*, **23**(1), 14 (1969).
   (52) R. K. Baisya and A. N. Bose: *J. Fd. Sci. Technol.*, **11**(3), 128 (1975).
   (53) R. K. Baisya and A. N. Bose: *J. Fd. Sci. Technol.*, **12**(6), 306 (1975).

etc., to yield srikhand. The srikhand is further desiccated over an open pan to make the srikhand wadi sweet. (All three products are quite popular in the western region of the country.)

11.11.2 Composition. The composition of chakka will depend on the initial composition of milk, the degree of fermentation (i.e. acidity developed) and the extent of whey removed. These three factors, together with the amount of sugar added, influence the composition of srikhand. The composition of srikhand wadi depends upon the extent to which srikhand is desiccated. The average composition of chakka (laboratory-made samples from buffalo milk), srikhand and wadi are given in Table 11.15. (54–56)

TABLE 11.15

Composition of chakka and srikhand wadi* (percentage)

Product	Composition						
	Moisture	Fat	Protein	Lactose	Ash	Sugar	Lactic acid
Chakka	63.2	14.7	—	—	—	—	0.80
–do–	59.6	22.4	10.3	4.4 (By diff.)	1.0	—	2.3
Srikhand Wadi	6.5	7.4	7.7	15.9	0.8	62.9	(1.0)

* Laboratory-made samples from buffalo milk.

Note: A microbiological study of market samples of srikhand has been made. (57)

11.11.3 Method of preparation. The standardized method of preparation may be described as follows: fresh, sweet buffalo milk, which has been standardized to 6% fat, is pasteurized at 71°C for 10 minutes and then cooled to 28–30°C. It is then inoculated @ 1 per cent with lactic culture (*Str. lactis*), which is mixed well, and incubated at 28–30°C for 15–16 hours (overnight). When the curd

(54) B. M. Mahajan: M.Sc. Thesis, Punjab University (1971).

(55) S. Ganguly, T. J. Boman, N. N. Dastur and S. M. Vaccha: *Indian J. Dairy Sci.*, **12**(3–4), 121 (1959).

(56) W. B. Date and D. S. Bhatia: *Indian J. Dairy Sci.*, **8**(2), 61 (1955).

(57) K. G. Upadhyay, S. H. Vyas, J. M. Dave and P. N. Thakar: *Indian J. Dairy Sci.*, **28**(2), 147 (1975).

has set firmly (acidity 0.7–0.8 per cent lactic), it is broken and placed in a muslin cloth bag and hung on a peg for the removal of whey for 8–10 hours. During this period, the position of the curd may be altered, or the curd gently squeezed, to facilitate whey drainage. The solid mass thus obtained is called chakka, which is the srikhand base. This chakka is then admixed with sugar (crystal or ground) and well kneaded for uniform mixing; colour and flavour may also be added. The product now obtained is known as srikhand. When the srikhand is further desiccated to a hard mass by heating on an open pan over a direct fire, srikhand wadi is obtained (54)(58).

11.11.4 Uses. (i) Chakka is used for the preparation of srikhand; (ii) srikhand is used either for direct consumption or for the preparation of the srikhand wadi sweet; (iii) srikhand wadi is used for direct consumption.

11.11.5 Srikhand powder. See 10.11.

11.12 Panir

11.12.1 Definition. Panir refers to the indigenous variety of rennet-coagulated, small-sized, soft cheese. Examples are: surati panir, bandal cheese, etc.

11.12.2 Composition. The approximate composition of fresh, laboratory-made surati panir is given in Table 11.16.

TABLE 11.16

Composition of surati panir (59)

(percentage)

Type of milk used	Moisture	Total solids	Fat
Cow	71.2	28.8	13.5
Buffalo	71.1	28.9	13.1

Note: The above products were prepared from standardized milk containing 4.0 per cent fat and 13.2 per cent total solids for cow and 4.7 per cent fat and 14.5 per cent total solids for buffalo.

(58) K. G. Upadhyay and J. M. Dave: *Indian Dairyman,* 29(8), 487 (1977).

(59) D. C. Bhattacharya, O. N. Mathur, M. R. Srinivasan and O. Samlik: *J. Fd. Sci. Technol.*, 8(3), 117 (1971).

11.12.3 Method of preparation of surati panir

A. *Introduction.* Surati cheese or panir is the best known of the few indigenous varieties of cheese. It seems to have been a commercial product for over a century in the western region of the country (presently Gujarat and Maharashtra States). The name surati appears to have been derived from the town of Surat, where it was probably first prepared or marketed. It is made chiefly from buffalo milk with the addition of crude rennet and salt and is generally not coloured. It is steeped in whey in earthern pots after preparation and during storage, transport and distribution. The improved conventional method and a commercial method adaptable in organized dairies have been discussed below.

B. *Improved conventional method* (60). This is for use on cottage-industry scale, using indigenous utensils and wicker baskets.

(a) *Materials required*
  (i) Milk coagulating water-jacketed pan;
  (ii) basketing ladle;
  (iii) bamboo wicker baskets;
  (iv) draining rack;
  (v) whey collecting tray;
  (vi) cheese-soaking basin;
  (vii) salt sprinkler;
  (viii) other accessories, such as a thermometer, acidity testing outfit, weighing scale, starter, rennet, etc.

(b) *Technique of production.* Fresh buffalo milk, standardized to 6 per cent fat, is pasteurized by heating it to 78°C (172°F) for 20 seconds and promptly cooling it to 35°C (95°F). About 0.5 to 2 kg. of this milk is placed in the coagulating pan and the temperature maintained at 35°C (95°F) by circulating warm water in the jacket. Good quality lactic starter @ 0.5 per cent of milk is now added to the milk and thoroughly mixed into it. This is followed by the addition of rennet @ 6–7 ml./100 lit. milk, the rennet being previously diluted with about 20 times its volume of water. (The quantity of rennet added should be such as to give a clean cut in the curd at the end of about 60 minutes.) After mixing it adequately, the renneted milk is allowed to set till a firm coagulum fit for basketing is obtained. The temperature during this time is maintained at 35°C/95°F.

(60) Zal R. Kothavalla and H C. Verma: *Indian J. Vet. Sci. and A. H.*, 12(4), 297 (1942).

The curd is then ladled out with a vertical slant in thin slices, and filled into especially made bamboo/wicker baskets. These baskets are previously prepared by cleaning them with scalding water, keeping them soaked in a 10 per cent lukewarm salt solution for about 10 minutes, and then thinly dressed with salt. Each successive layer of curd put into the baskets is uniformly sprinkled with salt. Salting is done @ 4–5 per cent of the green cheese (which works out to approximately 2 per cent of the milk taken). After they have been filled, the baskets are placed on the draining rack to allow for drainage of whey, which is collected in a tray placed underneath. Generally, at the end of 50 to 60 minutes, the individual pieces of cheese are firm enough to be handled without breaking. At this stage, they are carefully turned upside down in their respective baskets. This is known as the 'First Turning'. After draining them for a further 30–40 minutes, the cheeses, on attaining the desired firmness and consistency, are subjected to their 'Second Turning'. The collected whey is then strained through a muslin cloth and kept in the cheese-soaking basin. The pieces of cheese are removed from the baskets and carefully submerged in the whey. They are then left steeped in whey for 12–36 hours till disposed of or used.

Note: It is believed that some sort of 'ripening' takes place while the cheeses are kept steeped in whey, whereby their acceptability is increased; the best temperature for ripening is considered to be 20–25°C.

C. *Commercial method* (59)(61). This is for large scale production in organized dairies using modern cheese-making equipment. The standardized method of manufacture of surati panir may be described as follows: milk (cow, buffalo or mixed) is standardized to a casein/fat ratio of 0.7, the average percentage of fat and total solids being kept at about 4.00 and 13.25 for cow milk and 4.70 and 14.50 for buffalo milk, respectively. The milk is pasteurized at 71.5°C for 5 minutes and then cooled to 35°C in the cheese-vat itself; or separately pasteurized and cooled as above and then received in the cheese vat. Good-quality lactic starter is now added at 0.04 per cent and thoroughly mixed into it. This is followed by

(61) D. C. Bhattacharya, O. N. Mathur, B. D. Tiwari and M. R. Srinivasan: *Indian Fd. Packer*, 26(4), 28 (1972).

an addition of rennet (@ 7.5 g./100 lit. milk), which is pre-diluted with about 20 times water. After it has been thoroughly mixed, the milk is allowed to set at 35°C. The amount of rennet should be such that the setting time of curd is about 30 minutes.

When the curd is ready to be cut, as determined by the usual tests, it is cut into cubes with standard cheese knives. Five minutes after cutting the curd, dry cheese salt @ 2.5 per cent of milk is added and mixed by agitating it gently. The whey is drained off after 30 minutes of cutting the curd, by the standard procedure. The curd cubes are then put in standard brick-cheese hoops without any application of pressure. The first turning is given after 30 minutes of hooping and the second turning after 30 minutes of the first. After 30 minutes of the second turning, the cheese is taken out of the hoop. It is then sliced into the desired size, steeped in whey and stored at 4–6°C.

11.12.4 Yield. The yield of surati panir is approximately 28.5 per cent for cow and 34.0 per cent for buffalo milk.

11.12.5 Market quality. When kept steeped in whey, surati panir has a fairly firm body and smooth texture with no internal cracks, striations or loose moisture droplets. It has a slightly salted, mild acid-curd flavour.

11.12.6 Keeping quality. This is normally 1–2 days for the traditionally-made product; and up to 6 days for the standardized product under refrigerated storage (5–10°C), although the freshness is lost after 3 days.

11.12.7 Uses. For direct consumption.

Note: Bandal cheese is the other variety of panir in this country. (Dacca cheese now belongs to Pakistan.) Its name seems to have derived from the town of Bandal in West Bengal. This is also a small, soft type of panir made from either cow milk or low-fat cream. It is prepared in a more or less similar manner as surati panir, but is normally 'smoked' under crude indigenous conditions. Bandal cheese seems to have only a local importance at present.

11.13 Chhana

11.13.1 Introduction. Chhana, also called paneer in certain parts of the country, constitutes one of the two chief bases (the other being khoa) for the preparation of indigenous sweetmeats. It was estimated in 1966 that nearly 1.2 per cent of India's total milk production and 2.2 per cent of the quantity converted into milk products was utilized for the production of about 35 million kg. of chhana (see Table 1.6). The preparation and use of chhana are confined mainly to the eastern region of the country, notably West Bengal, which produces the maximum quantity.

11.13.2 Definition. Chhana refers to the milk-solids obtained by the acid coagulation of boiled hot whole milk and subsequent drainage of whey. The acids commonly used are lactic or citric, in both natural and chemical forms.

According to the PFA Rules (1976), chhana or paneer is the product obtained from cow or buffalo milk or a combination thereof by precipitation with sour milk, lactic acid or citric acid. It should not contain more than 70 per cent moisture, and the milk fat content should not be less than 50.0 per cent of the dry matter.

Skim milk chhana or skim milk paneer is the product obtained from cow or buffalo skim milk by precipitation with sour milk, lactic acid or citric acid. It should not contain more than 70 per cent moisture. The milk fat content of the product should not exceed 13.0 per cent of the dry matter. (The Indian Standard Specification for chhana is given in *IS : 5162*, 1962.)

11.13.3 Composition. The chemical composition of chhana depends mainly on the initial composition of milk; the conditions of coagulation, the technique of straining (which, in turn, determines the percentage moisture retained) and the losses of milk-solids in the whey. An average chemical composition of fresh, laboratory-made wholemilk chhana is given in Table 11.17.

TABLE 11.17
Chemical composition of chhana (62) (*percentage*)

Type of milk	Moisture	Fat	Protein	Lactose	Ash
Cow	53.4	24.8	17.4	2.1	2.1
Buffalo	51.6	29.6	14.4	2.3	2.0

Note: In the above table, the average composition of cow milk used for chhana making was: fat 4.5 per cent and total solids 13.0 per cent, while that of buffalo milk was fat 8.4 per cent and total solids 17.9 per cent.

(62) S. C. Ray and S. De: *Indian Dairyman*, 5(1), 15 (1953).

11.13.4   Food and nutritive value.   As chhana has a fairly high fat and protein content, and also contains some minerals, especially calcium and phosphorus, its food and nutritive value is fairly high. It is also a good source of fat-soluble vitamins A and D. (With its high protein and low sugar content, chhana is highly recommended for diabetic patients.)

11.13.5   Methods of production

A.   *Existing trade practices* (63).   Broadly speaking, there are two methods for making chhana which are adopted by commercial manufacturers, viz. the batch and the bulk methods.

I.   *Batch method.*   Usually all the milk for chhana-making is brought to boil by heating it directly in a large iron karahi over an open fire, all the while stirring it with a khunti, and later keeping it simmering hot in the karahi. This hot milk is ladled out in batches of 0.5 to 1 kg. into a separate coagulation vessel, either already containing, or to which is promptly added the required quantity of the coagulant. The latter is normally cleansed sour chhana-whey, which is maintained in a large earthen vessel from day to day. The mixture of milk and whey is stirred with the ladle; and when it has completely coagulated, the contents are poured over a piece of clean muslin cloth stretched over another vessel (for receiving the whey). The process is repeated till all the milk is used up. The cloth containing the coagulated solids is then removed, tied up into a bundle without applying pressure and hung up not only to drain out the whey completely but also to cool the chhana-pat.

II.   *Bulk method.*   All the milk (5–15 kg.) is brought to boil as above in the karahi, which is then removed from the fire. The coagulant is then added slowly and gradually in the required quantity to the entire lot of milk and stirred with the ladle so that it mixes properly and clear coagulation takes place. The chhana is collected by straining it through a cloth as described above for the batch method.

Note: (i) The chhana obtained by either of the above methods is removed, after cooling it down to atmospheric temperature, for storage/marketing or immediate use for preparation of sweets.

(ii) The supply of chhana for the Calcutta market from neighbouring areas is usually transported in shoulder slings carrying freshly prepared 'wet' chhana placed in

(63) S. De: *NDRI Publication No. 114* (1973).

tiers of earthenware vessels by the producer. From the manufacturer/producer, it goes to the nearest railway station, to be carried to that city by an early morning train called the 'Chhana Special'. The vessels containing chhana, to which some whey is also added to prevent surface drying, are rushed from the city railway stations to the chhana markets for immediate sale. The chhana supply from distant areas (Bihar and even Uttar Pradesh) also arrives in the morning at the railway station after an overnight journey, usually packed in bamboo baskets with a leaf lining to hold the whey.

B. *Improved method* (62–65). This involves consideration of: (a) equipment; (b) conditions of coagulation; (c) quality of milk, and (d) method of straining.

(a) *Equipment (and procedure)*. The heating-cum-coagulation of milk can be done in a stainless steel jacketed-kettle, capable of rotating sideways around a fixed axis. The milk is heated in the kettle by admitting steam into the jacket, the stirring-cum-scraping usually being done with a khunti. When the milk reaches first boil, the steam-intake is stopped, the condensate removed and cold water circulated in the jacket. Coagulation is simultaneously effected by adding the requisite amount of coagulant in a thin stream within 0.5 to 1 minute and mixing it into the milk with the stirrer. When the whey is clear, it is removed by straining it through a cloth and the chhana is collected (as already described).

(b) *Conditions of coagulation*. The body and texture of chhana is influenced by the conditions of coagulation which include: (i) pH (and acidity) of coagulation; (ii) temperature and time of coagulation; (iii) strength of the coagulating acid solution; (iv) type of acid, and (v) speed with which the milk is stirred for mixing the coagulating acid.

In order to obtain a desirable body and texture in chhana (with cow milk) the pH of coagulation should be around 5.4, the temperature of coagulation about 82°C and the time in which coagulation should be effected about 0.5 to 1 minute. A satisfactory strength of the coagulating acid solution is 1–2 per cent. While lactic acid

(64) S. De and S. C. Ray: *Indian J. Dairy Sci.*, **7** (3), 113 (1954).
(65) S. De: *Indian Dairyman*, **28** (3), 105 (1976).

tends to produce a granular texture (suitable for rossogolla), citric acid tends to produce a pasty one (suitable for sandesh). The speed with which the mix is stirred has but an insignificant effect on the body and texture of chhana; however, slow stirring is preferable, so as to avoid foam formation—which obstructs the visibility of the clear coagulation stage first time reached.

Note: (i) The acids commonly used for effecting coagulation are lactic or citric, either in their chemical or natural forms. Thus the citric acid group consists of chemical citric acid and lime-juice, whereas the lactic acid group consists of chemical lactic acid and sour-whey. Commercial manufacturers generally use sour-whey, as it is cheap. (Occasionally, sour buttermilk/curd can be used instead.)

(ii) Normally 2–2.5 g. citric/lactic acid is required to coagulate 1 kg. of fresh, sweet milk. With acid milk, less coagulating acid will be needed.

(c) *Quality of milk.* This also influences the body and texture of chhana. Under this factor are included: (i) the type of milk; (ii) fat percentage of milk; (iii) acidity of milk; (iv) adulteration of milk, and (v) presence of colostrum.

For chhana production, cow milk is preferred since it yields a soft-bodied and smooth-textured product—both of which factors make it highly suitable for the preparation of high-grade chhana sweets (such as rossogolla and sandesh). The channa from buffalo milk (without any pre-treatment) has a slightly hard body and a greasy and coarse texture, and does not produce good quality chhana sweets. A minimum fat level of 4 per cent in cow milk and 5 per cent in buffalo milk is necessary for producing a desirable body and texture in chhana tor sweet-making. Whereas a lower fat level than the above in milk results in a hard body and coarse texture in chhana, a higher fat level is also not desirable (unlike khoa) since it produces greasiness in the chhana sweets (such as rossogolla and sandesh) prepared therefrom. Fresh, sweet milk produces the best chhana; any developed acidity tends to produce an undesirably sour smell and a bitter taste, which makes it unsuitable for sweet preparation. The addition of neutralizer/stabilizer to slightly acid milk, however, helps in obtaining chhana which can make sandesh of an acceptable quality. The adulteration of milk with starch results in a gelatinous mass on coagulation, which is unfit for sweet preparation. The presence of colostrum in milk tends to produce a pasty texture in the coagulated mass, which jeopardizes its suitability for sweet-making.

Note: With acid-milk, the higher the initial acidity, the lower the amount of (coagulating) acid required to be added for effecting coagulation (pH 5.4). If the initial acidity is sufficiently high, the milk may coagulate on boiling without the addition of any acid; obviously this coagulated mass should not be called chhana.

(d) *Method of straining.* This factor affects the body and texture of chhana by influencing the moisture retained in the same. The straining may be of two types, viz. immediate or delayed. In the former, the coagulated mass is subjected to immediate straining for the removal of whey and the cooling of chhana, while in the latter this straining operation takes place at a later stage. Immediate straining is carried out by promptly gathering the coagulated mass and tying it up in a piece of cloth—without applying pressure—in the form of a bundle which is then hung up for draining out the whey and cooling the chhana. The delayed straining process consists, essentially, of leaving the coagulated mass in the whey, either as such or loosely enclosed in a piece of cloth, so as to cool it to ambient temperatures; at this stage or later, the whey may be removed by a similar process as that described above. Delayed straining causes the chhana to retain more moisture than immediate straining.

Note: In chhana markets, the 'wet' chhana is invariably wrapped in a piece of cloth on arrival and pressed between two circular stone weights to remove the excess whey, before being offered for sale to prospective buyers.

C. *Large-scale/Continuous method.* It is being increasingly realized that mechanization of chhana-making for large-scale production is a prerequisite to its adoption in organized dairies. Thus, the development of a continuous method for the manufacture of chhana is needed, especially if it is to be dehydrated into powder.

D. *Mechanization of paneer-making* (66). It has already been mentioned that in certain parts of India (such as Punjab, Haryana. etc.), chhana is more commonly known as paneer. Traditionally

(66) V. K. Arora: *NDRI Publication No. 84* (1972).

paneer has been a variety of pressed chhana, used mainly for preparing cooked vegetable dishes. The standardized method for its large-scale production may be described as follows: fresh, sweet, buffalo milk is filtered and standardized to 6 per cent fat. It is heated in a cheese vat to 82°C for 5 minutes and then cooled to 70°C. The milk is coagulated by the addition of the requisite amount of acid solution sour whey in the usual manner described earlier. When it has coagulated completely (as indicated by clear whey), the stirring is stopped and the curd allowed to settle for 5 minutes; the whey is then drained out through a muslin cloth. During this period the temperature of the whey is not allowed to fall below 63°C. The coagulated mass is collected and filled in hoops with cloth linings and then pressed (with a weight of 45 kg. placed over wooden planks measuring $35 \times 28 \times 10$ cm. sitting over the filled hoops) for 15–20 minutes. The pressed paneer is now removed from the hoop, cut into the required sizes for sale and immersed in chilled water (4–6°C) for 2–3 hours to make it firm. The chilled pieces are then removed from the water and placed on wooden planks to remove the free water. Later, they are wiped with a clean cloth and packaged in polythene bags for refrigerated storage (5–10°C) or marketing.

The average composition of paneer (made from milk with 6 per cent fat) is given in Table 11.18.

TABLE 11.18

Gross composition of paneer
(percentage)

Moisture	Total solids	Fat	pH
54.7	45.3	26.0	6.0

E. *Production of paneer from high-acid milk* (67). The standardized method of production of paneer of an acceptable quality from high-acid milk may be described as follows: the milk, with a titratable acidity of up to 0.28 per cent, is filtered and received in a cheese vat. It is then standardized with fresh, sweet, clean skim milk

(67) S. De, D. C. Bhattacharya, O. N. Mathur and M. R. Srinivasan: *Indian Dairyman*, **23**(11). 224 (1971).

to 3.5–4.0 per cent fat; the standardized milk should have an acidity of 0.20–0.23 per cent. This milk is heated to 71°C and coagulated with warm (62°C) coagulating acid, preferably a 1 per cent citric acid solution. After clear coagulation, the curd is allowed to remain in the whey for about 5 minutes. The whey is then drained out through a muslin cloth. The curd is now washed 2 or 3 times with hot water (65–70°C). The amount of wash water used each time is about one-third of the standardized milk with the curd remaining in the wash water for 10–15 minutes. After removing the final wash water, the curd is collected and pressed as before. The pressed curd is removed and cut into pieces in the required sizes, which are immersed in a cold (4–6°C) brine solution (5 per cent sodium chloride) for 2–3 hours. The salted and chilled paneer pieces are then removed, drained, wiped with a clean cloth, and packaged for cold storage or marketing as described earlier.

Note: The use of acid milks with an initial titratable acidity of more than 0.28 per cent produces an undesirable sour flavour in the finished product, while acidities lower than this in the milk produce an acceptable product.

F. *Chhana production from buffalo milk* (68). The technique for the production of chhana from buffalo milk so as to obtain a product which will be highly suitable for the preparation of rossogolla may be summarized as follows: fresh (sweet) buffalo milk is filtered, standardized to 5 per cent fat, pre-heated to 60°C and then homogenized at 176 kg./sq. cm. pressure. After bringing it to first boil, it is promptly cooled to 70°C and then coagulated in the normal manner to a pH of 5.7. Subsequently, the chhana should be separated from whey by the delayed straining technique.

11.13.6 Distribution of milk-constituents in chhana and whey. The average percentage distribution of the milk-constituents in chhana and chhana-whey, prepared under the standard technique from whole cow and buffalo milks, is shown in Table 11.19.

(68) S. S. Kundu and S. De: *Indian J. Dairy Sci.*, **25**(3), 159 (1972).

TABLE 11.19

Percentage distribution of milk-constituents in chhana and whey

Milk constituents	Percentage distribution			
	Cow		Buffalo	
	Chhana	Whey	Chhana	Whey
Fat	90	10	85	15
Protein	89	11	91	9
Lactose	7	93	12	88
Mineral salts	48	52	60	40
Total solids	58	42	65	35
Solids-not-fat	42	58	48	52

Note: (i) The average composition of cow milk is: fat 4.5 per cent and total solids 13.0 per cent; while that of buffalo milk is: fat 8.4 per cent and total solids 17.9 per cent.

(ii) Compared to Cheddar cheese (see Table 7.12), there is a greater recovery of protein in chhana. This happens because boiling the milk coagulates the whey-proteins, which are then recovered in the chhana.

(iii) The higher the fat level in milk, the higher the fat leve in channa-whey (69). This explains the reason for the low recovery of fat in chhana from buffalo milk in the above table.

11.13.7 Market quality. This may be considered under: (a) physical, (b) chemical, and (c) bacteriological qualities.

(a) *Physical quality.* This includes: (i) colour and appearance; (ii) body and texture; (iii) flavour, and (iv) suitability for sweets. These have been presented for cow and buffalo chhana in Table 11.20.

TABLE 11.20

Physical quality of cow and buffalo chhana

Particulars	Cow	Buffalo
Colour	Light yellow	Whitish
Appearance	Moist surface	Greasy surface
Body	Soft	Slightly hard
Texture	Smooth	Slightly coarse
Flavour	Mildly acid	Mildly acid
Suitability for sweets	Highly suitable	Not suitable (when made without any pre-treatment of milk).

S. C. Ray and S. De: *Indian Dairyman*, 5(5), 89 (1953).

The physical quality of chhana will depend primarily on the type of milk used, viz. cow, buffalo or mixed, the method of coagulation, and the straining technique adopted. It may be pointed out that, broadly speaking, two types of chhana are available in the market, viz. soft and hard. The former is classified as soft because it is soft to the touch on account of its higher moisture content. The reverse is the case with hard chhana, which is hard to the touch because it has a lower moisture content. In general, market chhana, which is normally made from cow milk, should have an uniform light-yellow colour, a slightly moist surface, a soft body and smooth texture and a mildly-acid flavour.

Note: (i) The physical quality of 'wet' chhana can be accurately judged only after pressing out the excess whey.

(ii) Homogenization of milk has been reported to reduce appreciably the hardness of chhana (62).

(b) *Chemical quality* (see *Composition*). It may be pointed out that chhana offered for sale should neither contain any constituent foreign to milk nor be adulterated.

(c) *Microbiological quality*. This has yet to be prescribed.

Note: The market samples of chhana should be free from off-flavours, extraneous matter and moulds.

11.13.8 Yield. The yield or output of chhana is rather variable, being influenced by: (a) the total solids content in milk, especially chhana-solids, viz. fat and casein; (b) the amount of moisture retained in the chhana, which in turn depends on the method of production and the straining technique followed, and (c) losses of milk solids in whey. Normally the yield of chhana containing 49 to 54 per cent moisture ranges from 16 to 18 per cent for cow milk and from 22 to 24 per cent for buffalo milk.

Note: The homogenization of milk for chhana-making was observed to give not only a higher yield but also a higher percentage recovery of milk-solids in chhana, without affecting it quality (70).

10.13.9 Packaging, storage and marketing

(a) *Packaging*. Hardly any chhana sold in the market is satis-

(70) G. E. Jagtap and P. C. Shukla: *J. Fd. Sci. Technol.*, **10**(2), 73 (1973).

factorily packaged at present. On overnight journeys, the chhana is usually transported in bamboo baskets with leaf linings; while there appears to be no packaging at all during short journeys. Modern packaging materials and forms, which can be profitably used, include: plastic (polythene) film bags/pouches, laminated pouches, etc. These could be placed in bamboo baskets for protection.

(b) *Storage*. Since chhana stored at room temperature has a very low keeping quality, refrigerated storage (5–10°C) is preferable.

(c) *Marketing*. This is at present generally done soon after production in an unpacked or crudely packed condition, depending on the distance of the market.

11.13.10 Keeping quality. The keeping quality of chhana/paneer is mainly influenced by: (a) the storage temperature; (b) quality of the raw material (milk); (c) initial moisture content, and (d) sanitary conditions observed during manufacture.

The keeping quality of chhana under ordinary packing is on average 2, 3 and 12 days at 37°C, 24°C and 7°C, respectively. The character of spoilage is guided by the storage temperature: at low temperatures, there is a heavy growth of moulds on the surface together with the development of a stale flavour; on the other hand, at high temperatures the stored product develops a sour smell and bitter taste, while also being sparsely covered with moulds (62).

The keeping quality of paneer made from fresh, sweet milk has been reported to be 5–6 days at 5–10°C (66); while that made from acid-milk seems to have a storage life of 3–4 days at the same temperature.

11.13.11 Judging and grading of chhana

A. *Score card*. Same as for khoa (see 11.6.13).

B. *Procedure of examination*

(a) *Sampling*. Obtain a representative sample with the help of a spoon.

(b) *Sequence of observations*. Note the sanitary condition of the package, if any. Before taking the sample, observe the surface of the chhana-pat and examine the uniformity of colour on the inside and outside. Observe the body and texture: note hardness/softness of the body and coarseness/smoothness of texture. Take a small piece of the chhana sample and place it on the tip of the tongue. Chew until melted and then roll the melted mass inside the mouth.

Note the flavour (smell and taste). Expectorate the sample and note the after-taste.

C. *Requirements of high-grade (cow) chhana.* This should have an uniform light-yellow colour, soft body and smooth texture, a mildly-acid flavour, and should be free from any off-flavour and surface dryness.

11.13.12 Defects, their causes and prevention. Defects in chhana arise due to low quality milk and faulty methods of production, handling and storage. The defects in chhana, their causes and prevention are given in Table 11.21.

TABLE 11.21

Defects in chhana, their causes and prevention

Defects	Causes	Prevention
(a) Flavour		
Smoky	Smoky fire used for boiling and simmering of milk.	Using non-smoky fire for boiling and simmering of milk.
Sour	(i) Excessive acidity in milk used	(i) Optimum acidity in milk used (preferably fresh, sweet milk)
	(ii) Excessive amount of co-agulating acid/sour-whey used.	(ii) Using proper amount of coagulating acid/sour whey.
Rancid	Fat hydrolysis due to lipase action in chhana during storage (at room temperature or above).	Storage of chhana at low temperature (5–10 C).
Stale	Excessively long period of storage of chhana at low temperature (5–10°C).	Early disposal/marketing of chhana.
(b) Body and texture		
Hard body	(i) Inadequate fat content in milk used	(i) Optimum fat content in milk used
	(ii) Inadequate moisture content of chhana, due to faulty production technique.	(ii) Proper moisture content of chhana by adopting correct production technique.
Coarse texture	(i) Excessive acidity in milk used	(i) Proper acidity in milk used (preferably fresh, sweet milk)

Defects	Causes	Prevention
	(ii) Inadequate fat content in milk used	(ii) Optimum fat content in milk used
	(iii) Improper (too-high) temperature of coagulation	(iii) Optimum temperature of coagulation
	(iv) Improper (too-low) pH of coagulation.	(iv) Proper pH of coagulation.
(c) *Colour and appearance*		
Dry surface	Excessive fat content in milk used.	Optimum fat content in milk used
Surface skin	Surface of chhana exposed to atmospheric air.	(i) Chhana kept steeped in whey
		(ii) Air-tight packing used.
Visible dirt/ foreign matter	(i) Incorrect or no straining of milk	(i) Correct straining of milk
	(ii) Milk-boiling and/or coagulation vessel not cleaned	(ii) Milk-boiling and/or coagulation vessel well cleaned
	(iii) Dirty/windy surroundings during manufacture and/or handling of chhana	(iii) Clean surroundings during manufacture and/or handling of chhana
	(iv) Transport of unpacked chhana.	(iv) Transport of packed chhana.
Mouldy surface	(i) Long storage of chhana, especially in humid atmosphere	(i) Early disposal/marketing of chhana
	(ii) Excessive moisture content in chhana.	(ii) Optimum moisture content in chhana.

11.13.13 *Uses*

(i) As a base and filler for the preparation of a large number of indigenous milk-sweets such as rossogolla, sandesh, chhana-kheer (kheer-paneer), pantooa, etc.

(ii) for direct consumption with an addition of sugar or salt—the latter being recommended for diabetic patients;

(iii) for the preparation of cooked vegetable dishes (such as matar paneer, sag paneer, etc).

11.13.14 *Chhana powder* (see 10.12) (71–72).

(71) B. D. Tiwari and S. De: 'Standardization of the Industrial Method of Production of Dried Chhana', *Indian J. Dairy Sci.*, 29(3), 212 (1976).

(72) S. De: 'Dried Chhana', *Indian Dairyman*, 28(9), 389 (1976).

11.14 Makkhan

11.14.1 Introduction. See under *Ghee* (11.15.1).

11.14.2 Definition. This refers to the country/desi butter normally obtained by churning whole milk curd (dahi) with crude indigenous devices.

According to the PFA Rules (1976), desi (cooking) butter refers to the product obtained from cow or buffalo milk or a combination thereof, or curd obtained from cow or buffalo milk or a combination thereof without the addition of any preservative, including common salt, any added colouring matter or any added flavouring agent. It should be free from other animal fats, wax and mineral oils, and vegetable oils and fats. It should contain not less than 76.0 per cent of milk fat by weight. Except in those cases where butter is sold or offered for sale without any indication as to whether it is table butter or desi butter, the standards of quality prescribed for table butter shall apply.

11.14.3 Composition. The chemical composition of makkhan is variable and depends on the method of manufacture. However, a standard-quality makkhan meant for sale may conform to the specifications given in Table 11.22.

TABLE 11.22

Proposed specifications of makkhan
(percentage)

Moisture	Butter fat	Non-fatty solids	Lactic acid
18–20	78–81	1.0–1.5	Not more than 0.2

11.14.4 Food and nutritive value. Makkhan is very high in butter fat (and is expected to be high in fat-soluble vitamins if prepared under the improved method).

11.14.5 Methods of production

(a) *Introduction.* The art of isolating milk fat in the form of makkhan is as old as the Vedas. The existing method of country butter making is born out of experience and tradition rather than any scientific appreciation of the factors involved.

This age-old process, because of its simplicity in equipment and technique, is still followed more or less throughout the country.

The obvious reason for this *status quo* is the small and scattered nature of milk production and its unorganized utilization. The isolation of milk fat in the form of table butter requires specialized equipment and techniques and can be adopted only on an industrial scale.

(b) *Existing village method.* In the villages, whole milk is invariably employed for makkhan making; buffalo milk is usually preferred, although small amounts of cow, goat and sheep milk are also admixed. The raw material, i.e. milk, is often unprocessed. The usage of a mixture of boiled and unprocessed milks is common, while that of simmered milk (i.e. milk kept heated below its boiling point) is also prevalent.

Usually, the milk is not properly inoculated, and therefore what results is a self-soured curd of indifferent quality. The setting period for dahi is often 48 hours or more; and in some cases, dahi is successively collected for even 8–12 days so as to gather a sizeable quantity for churning.

The village method of churning curd and isolating makkhan is characterized by: (i) agitation ununiform, uncontrolled and in alternate directions; (ii) no temperature control, and (iii) addition of water in different amounts. These result in lumpy butter which cannot be washed properly and has a low keeping quality. The fat loss in the buttermilk is also greater.

Whenever makkhan is stored in the villages, the receptacles generally used are either porous mud pots at the producers' households or old rusty kerosene tins used by middlemen, who collect and transport village makkhan to the ghee refineries.

Note: It will be obvious that all the above factors ultimately result in a poor quality makkhan. Since almost the entire quantity of makkhan forms an intermediate product for the preparation of desi ghee, it will be natural to expect a ghee of an inferior quality from the above raw material.

(c) *Improved village method* (73). Since the country method of butter and ghee making still handles over 90 per cent of the total ghee produced today and is expected to occupy an important place in the ghee industry for years to come, it is worthwhile to introduce improvements in the same. Indian work on improving the method

(73) M. R. Srinivasan and S. De: *Indian Dairyman*, 6(4), 75 (1954).

of makkhan making may be summarized as follows:

(i) *Raw material (milk)*. Whole buffalo milk (fresh and sweet) is desirable as by virtue of the higher fat content and larger fat globules it yields a greater quantity of makkhan, which is also firmer and therefore easier to handle than that obtained from cow milk. Milk selected for makkhan-making should be passed through a clean muslin cloth.

(ii) *Processing*. The purpose of this is to destroy all undesirable micro-organisms in the milk and thus leave a clean field for the growth of desirable starter (dahi) organisms. Under village conditions, the best form of processing has been found to be heating each lot of milk to first boil and promptly cooling it to atmospheric temperature.

(iii) *Setting of curd*. The above milk should be inoculated with a good starter (free from gas holes, whey pockets, moulds, etc.), or good quality buttermilk not more than 24 hours old. The amount of starter used should vary with the season and may range from 2 to 2.5 per cent in winter and 0.5 to 1.0 per cent in summer, depending on the time allotted and the prevailing atmospheric temperature when setting the curd. If need be, the dahi-pot may be of brass but should be heavily tinned on the inside. If the collection of dahi for churning purposes is indispensable, the total period of accumulation should not exceed 48 hours.

(iv) *Churning*. Instead of indigenous wooden beaters (mathani), an improved desi metal-churn equipped with suitable gear-driven wooden beaters and fitted with a drain tap may profitably be used. This will provide control over the direction as well as the speed of agitation when churning. It will also make possible the formation of butter grains which, after being washed, will have a minimum curd content. By adding a controlled quality of cold water at different stages and churning the curd in the cool hours of the morning, the maximum yield of makkhan can be obtained. The total quantity of water added during the churning should be equal to the amount of dahi handled. When the churning is over, the buttermilk should be removed through the tap, and the butter grains washed with cold water equal in quantity to the buttermilk removed. The makkhan should then be removed, preferably by a perforated wooden scoop, for storage or early conversion into ghee.

(v) *Storage*. It is always best to convert makkhan into finished ghee without the least delay. When this cannot be done, the next

best thing is to convert the daily production of butter into *kachcha**
ghee. When, however, even this is not possible and butter has to be
stored, the following must be done:

At producer's household. A glazed earthenware vessel with a
threaded neck and lid may be used for storage. Before being used,
the vessel should be thoroughly cleaned, scalded with hot water and
finally rinsed on the inside with saline water (1 per cent salt solution). It should then be almost half-filled with the same saline water.
The freshly-made makkhan thus produced is stored by floating it in
the saline water, which is replaced every other day.

During collection and transport. The receptacle used may be a
tin-container which should be clean, rust-free, and have a tight-fit-
ting lid. Before being filled, the inner surface of the container may
be coated with a thin layer of corn flour paste (one part corn flour
in about five parts water) and the applied film dried up completely.
Makkhan is then filled by spreading it evenly in layers. When the
entire quantity is packed, the top of the makkhan is covered by
dusting it with a thin layer of corn flour before fixing the lid.

Note: By the improved method outlined above—which consists of
using good quality buffalo milk, controlling the processing of
milk, using a satisfactory starter culture, correctly setting the
milk, regulating the churning of curd for isolating the
makkhan and correctly storing the makkhan before its conversion into ghee—it is possible not only to obtain a higher
yield of makkhan, but also one of a better quality than that
obtained under existing rural practices.

11.14.6 Market quality

(a) *Physical quality*

(i) *Colour.* The makkhan produced from cow milk should be
yellow, while that from buffalo milk, light greenish-white.

(ii) *Body and texture.* The makkhan made from buffalo milk
should have a harder firmer body and a more granular texture than
that made from cow milk.

(iii) *Flavour.* This should be pleasant and mildly acid (when
fresh) for both, and free from any objectionable taint or rancidity.

(b) *Chemical quality.* See *Composition*.

---

* *Kachcha* hee refers to a partially clarified product generally obtained by
melting the makkhan and resolidifying it, then draining out the underlying
serum.

11.14.7 Yield. The yield of makkhan is influenced by the fat content of the initial milk, the moisture content of makkhan and the fat loss in lassi (buttermilk). The fat content of milk depends primarily on its type; buffalo milk has a higher fat content than cow milk, while mixed milk indicates an intermediate value. The moisture content of makkhan usually varies from 25 to 35 per cent and samples have been reported to contain as much as 60 per cent. However, the improved method should normally yield a product containing 18 to 20 per cent moisture. The fat losses in lassi can be kept at a minimum by strictly adhering to the various steps for the improved method as outlined above.

Assuming that the fat contents of buffalo, cow and mixed milks are 7 per cent, 4.5 per cent and 5.8 per cent respectively, the moisture content in makkhan 18 per cent and the fat recovery in makkhan 85 per cent of the original fat content in milk, the approximate yield of makkhan from the various types of milk should be as given in Table 11.23.

TABLE 11.23

Yield of makkhan from different types of milk

Type of milk	Fat (%)	Yield of makkhan from 100 kg. of milk (kg.)	Amount of milk required to produce 1 kg. of makkhan (kg.)
Buffalo	7.0	7.0	14
Cow	4.5	4.5	22
Mixed	5.8	5.8	17

Note: In the above table, the yield of makkhan is shown to be the same as the fat level of milk, since the loss of fat in lassi is more or less compensated for by the overrun in makkhan.

11.14.8 Keeping quality. This is very low for makkhan prepared and stored under existing rural conditions. The keeping quality can be slightly increased by adopting the improved method of production and storage. (The question of refrigerated storage of makkhan does not arise under present rural conditions.)

11.14.9 Uses

(i) For conversion into ghee (main use);

(ii) for direct consumption with chapaties;

(iii) for preparation of Ayurvedic and Unani medicines (cow makkhan only);

(iv) as a sacrificial offering, etc.

11.15 Ghee

11.15.1 Introduction

(a) Beginning from almost Vedic times (3000 to 2000 B.C.), there is ample recorded evidence to show that makkhan and ghee were extensively used by the early inhabitants of India both in their dietary and religious practices. Thus, the Rigveda (the oldest of the Vedas) contains the following translations of the Sanskrit passages: (74)

(i) 'Give us food of many kinds dripping with "butter" (i.e. makkhan).'

(ii) 'The stream of "ghee" descended on fire like deer fleeing from hunger.'

(iii) 'The streams of "ghee" fall copious and rapid as the water of a river.'

(b) It is worth noting that the utilization of milk fat in the form of ghee, so admirably suited to this country, should have been hit upon in such early times. This unique position occupied by ghee may be ascribed to its being not only the best form for the preservation of milk fat under a tropical climate, but to its constituting, in addition, the only source of animal fat in an otherwise predominantly vegetarian diet. The large production of ghee is due to:

(i) concentration of milk production in rural areas which are far away from the nearest urban consuming centres;

(ii) lack of all-weather and refrigerated transport facilities;

(iii) unfavourable climatic conditions, i.e. high temperature and humidity, for most parts of the year, causing rapid spoilage of milk;

(iv) its long keeping quality under tropical storage conditions and ordinary packing;

(v) market demand. (As already noted, it is the only source of animal fat in the otherwise predominantly vegetarian diet of most Indians.)

(74) A. K. Yegna Narayana Aiyer: *Indian Dairyman*, 5(4 & 5), 63 and 77 (1953).

11.15.2 Definition. Ghee may be defined as clarified butter fat prepared chiefly from cow or buffalo milk. (Sheep or goat milk is also employed, although rarely, in the preparation of special-designated ghee.)

Note: To clarify means 'to make clear' a liquid or something lique-fied, by removing unwanted solid matter or impurities.

According to the PFA Rules (1976), ghee is the pure clarified fat derived solely from milk or from desi (cooking) butter or from cream to which no colouring matter is added. The standard of quality of ghee produced in a State or Union Territory specified in column 2 of Table 11.24 should be as specified against the said State or Union Territory in the corresponding columns 3, 4, 5 and 6 of the said Table.

TABLE 11.24
PFA standard for quality of ghee

Sr. No.	Name of State/ Union territory	Butyro-refractometer reading at 40°C.	Minimum Reichert Value	Percentage of	
				Free fatty acid as oleic acid (max. limit)	Mois-ture (max. limit)
1.	Andhra Pradesh	40.0 to 43.0	24	3.0	0.3
2.	Assam	40.0 to 43.0	26	3.0	0.3
3.	Bihar	40.0 to 43.0	28	3.0	0.3
4.	Delhi	40.0 to 43.0	28	3.0	0.3
5.	Gujarat:				
	(a) Areas other than the territories of the erstwhile States of Saurashtra and Kutch	40.0 to 43.0	24	3.0	0.3
	(b) Territories of erstwhile States of Saurashtra and Kutch	41.5 to 45.0	21	3.0	0.3
6.	Himachal Pradesh	40.0 to 43.0	26	3.0	0.3
7.	Kerala	40.0 to 43.0	26	3.0	0.3
8.	Madhya Pradesh:				
	(a) Areas other than the erstwhile States of Bhopal, Vindhya Pradesh and cotton tract areas	40.0 to 43.0	26	3.0	0.3

Sr. No.	Name of State/ Union territory	Butyro-refractometer reading at 40°C	Minimum Reichert Value	Percentage of	
				Free fatty acid as oleic acid (max. limit)	Mois-ture (max. limit)
	(b) Territories of the erstwhile States of Bhopal and Vindhya Pradesh	40.0 to 43.0	28	3.0	0.3
	(c) Cotton tract areas	41.0 to 45.0 40.0 to 43.0	21	3.0	0.3
9.	Madras	40.0 to 44.0	24	3.0	0.3
10.	Manipur	40.0 to 43.0	26	3.0	0.3
11.	Mysore:				
	(a) Areas other than Belgaum District	40.0 to 44.0	24	3.0	0.3
	(b) Belgaum District	40.0 to 44.0	26	3.0	0.3
12.	Maharashtra:				
	(a) Cotton tract areas	41.5 to 45.0	21	3.0	0.3
	(b) Other areas	40.0 to 43.0	26	3.0	0.3
13.	Orissa	40.0 to 43.0	26	3.0	0.3
14.	Punjab:				
	(a) Areas other than Mahendragarh	40.0 to 43.0	28	3.0	0.3
	(b) Mahendragarh	40.0 to 43.0	26	3.0	0.3
15.	Rajasthan:				
	(a) Areas other than Jodhpur Divn.	40.0 to 43.0	26	3.0	0.3
	(b) Jodhpur Divn.	41.5 to 45.0	21	3.0	0.3
16.	Tripura	40.0 to 43.0	26	3.0	0.3
17.	Uttar Pradesh	40.0 to 43.0	28	3.0	0.3
18.	West Bengal:				
	(a) Areas other than Bishnupur Sub-Division	40.0 to 43.0	28	3.0	0.3
	(b) Bishnupur Sub-Division	41.5 to 45.0	21	3.0	0.3

Note. Baudouin test shall be negative for all.

Explanation. 'Cotton tract' refers to the areas in the States where cotton seeds are extensively fed to the cattle and so notified by the State Government concerned.

11.15.3 Statistics of production and consumption. The production of ghee in India in 1966 was estimated to be about 32.7 per cent of the total milk production and 58.9 per cent of the milk used for the manufacture of dairy products (see Table 1.6). Today, the total annual ghee production may be estimated at over 500 million kg. with a value of Rs 1.250 crores at the present rates.

The percentage conversion of milk into ghee varies from State to State. The largest ghee-producing States are: Uttar Pradesh, Andhra Pradesh, Punjab, Rajasthan, Madhya Pradesh, Bihar, Haryana etc. Buffalo milk is preferred for the manufacture of ghee because, being richer in fat content than other types of milk, it gives a larger yield of ghee. The production of ghee is higher in winter and lower in summer corresponding to months of higher and lower milk production. The bulk of the ghee sold in the market is mixed (cow and buffalo).

Of the total production, on an average, less than one-fifth is retained by the producers for their own use, and the remainder is released for market sale. However, this proportion varies from place to place depending upon the status of the producer, his financial standing, dietary habits, proximity to the market, approaching festivals, season, etc.

The demand for ghee is mainly concentrated in the urban areas. The per capita consumption largely depends on the market price and availability of ghee substitutes, family income and habits, etc. The average per capita consumption of ghee today works out to less than 1 kg. per annum for the whole country.

11.15.4 Composition. The general chemical composition of ghee is shown in Table 11.25.

TABLE 11.25
Chemical composition of ghee

Characteristics	Requirements	
	Cow	Buffalo
Milk fat	99 to 99.5 per cent	
Moisture	Not more than 0.5 per cent	
Unsaponiable matter		
(a) Carotene (µg./g.)	3.2–7.4	—
(b) Vit. A (I.U./g.)	19–34	17–38
(c) Tocopherol (µg./g.)	26–48	18–37
Free fatty acid (% oleic)	Max. 2.8 (Agmark)	
Charred casein, salts of copper and iron, etc.	Traces	

SOURCE: *Milk Products of India* by Srinivasan and Anantakrishnan (1964).

11.15.5 Physico-chemical constants. Ghee, as in the case of other fats and oils, is characterized by certain physico-chemical properties, which have been found to be the basis for the fixation of certain physico-chemical constants for defining the chemical quality of the product. These properties, however, show some natural variations depending on such factors as: method of manufacture, age and condition of the sample, species, breed, individuality and the animal's stage of lactation, the season of the year, region of the country, feed of the animal etc. (75). Some of the important analytical constants or standards of mixed ghee produced under standard conditions are given below:

(i) *Melting and solidifying points.* The melting point varies from 28°C to 44°C, while the solidifying point varies from 28°C to 15°C. (Being a mixture of glycerides, ghee does not have sharp melting or solidifying points.)

(ii) *Specific gravity.* This varies from 0.93 to 0.94.

(iii) *Refractive Index.* The Butyro-Refractometer (B.R.) reading (at 40°C) varies from 40 to 45.

(iv) *Reichert-Meissl (RM) value (also known as Reichert value).* This should normally be not less than 28 (except for ghee from cotton-seed feeding areas, where the limit is 20).

(v) *Polenske (P) value.* This should normally be not more than 2 (except for cotton-seed feeding areas, where the limit is 1.5).

(vi) *Saponification value.* This should normally be not less than 220.

(vii) *Iodine value.* This should normally vary from 26 to 38.

Note: The above 'standards' are all determined under standard analytical conditions.

11.15.6 Food and nutritive value. Ghee is the richest source of milk fat of all Indian dairy products. When prepared by the traditional country method, it is normally very low in fat-soluble vitamins A and D, and contains an appreciable quantity of these only under certain prescribed conditions. (The losses of these nutrients from ghee during handling, storage and cooking; ghee as a source of nutrient in the Indian diet; the digestibility and absorption of ghee in the human system; the superiority of ghee as a food fat; ghee in the diet and Atherosclerosis—all these and other aspects of

(75) N. S. Doctor, B. N. Bannerjee and Z. R. Kothavalla: *Indian J. Vet. Sci.,* **10**(1), 63 (1940).

the food and nutritive value of ghee have been the subjects of early investigation by various research-workers).*

11.15.7   Methods of production

A. *Introduction.* Even today, the country or desi method of ghee-making contributes more than 90 per cent of India's ghee production, the remaining quantity being manufactured by the organized sector of the industry which employs modern methods. In the earlier days of dairy research in India, ghee attracted the maximum attention by virtue of its economic importance—more than two-fifths of the total milk production was converted into ghee at that time. Various workers (76–83) have studied the traditional country (desi) process of ghee-making in India and their recommendations have been summarized earlier (see 11.14.5), and in Table 11.25.

With the growth of the organized sector of the dairy industry and establishment of modern dairy plants, the emphasis shifted to conducting investigations on newer and larger-scale methods of ghee manufacture which could profitably be adopted for routine ghee production by these dairies. Various reports (84–93) on ghee-

*Refer to *Indian Dairy Products* by Rangappa & Achaya (1974).

(76) K. S. Rangappa and B. N. Banerjee: *Indian J. Vet. Sci.*, **16**(2), 65 (1946).

(77) M. R. Srinivasan and B. N. Banerjee: *Indian J. Vet. Sci.*, **16**(2), 72 (1946).

(78) K. S. Rangappa, M. R. Srinivasan and B. N. Banerjee: *Indian J. Vet. Sci.*, **16**(2), 83 (1946).

(79) K. S. Rangappa and B. N. Banerjee: *Indian J. Vet. Sci.*, **16**(2), 98 (1946).

(80) K. S. Rangappa and B. N. Banerjee: *Indian J.*   *Sci.*, **1**(1 & 2), 45 (1948).

(81) B. M. Patel, C. N. Dave and S. C. Ray: *Indian J. Dairy Sci.*, **2**(3), 122 (1949).

(82) M. P. Srivastava, H. Narasimhaswamy, M. R. Srinivasan and S. C. Ray: *Indian J. Vet. Sci.*, **18**(3), 203 (1948).

(83) T. M. Paul and C. P. Anantakrishnan: *Indian J. Dairy Sci.*, **2**(1), 39 (1949).

(84) K. V. Ghurye, M. R. Srinivasan, K. K. Desai and S. C. Ray: *Indian J. Dairy Sci.*, **2**(2), 77 (1949).

(85) A. M. El-Sokkary and M. A. Ghoneim: *Indian J. Dairy Sci.*, **2**(4), 160 (1949).

(86) B. Bahadur, M. R. Srinivasan and S. C. Ray: *Indian J. Dairy Sci.*, **3**(3), 94 (1950).

(87) M. R. Srinivasan, G. S. Mani and S. C. Ray: *Indian J. Dairy Sci.*, **6**(3), 127 (1953).

(88) G. S. Mani, M. R. Srinivasan and S. C. Ray: *Indian J. Dairy Sci.*, **7**(2), 69 (1954).

making by creamery or desi-butter-ghee and direct cream-ghee processes appeared at that time; a few (94–99) have also appeared in recent years.

B. *Flow diagram.* Ghee may be prepared either from butter or cream. Butter may be either desi or creamery. The pre-stratification and continuous methods (under development) also use butter. The flow diagram of the manufacture of ghee by these various methods, starting with milk, is given below:

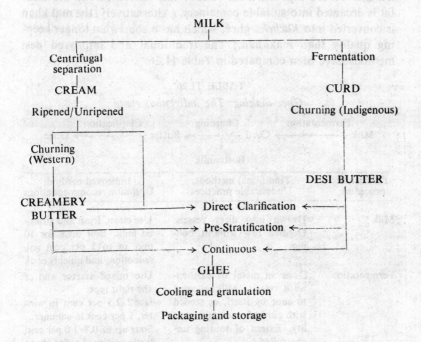

(89) M. S. Pherwani: M.Sc. Thesis, University of Bombay (1954).

(90) K. C. Nayar: M.Sc. Thesis, University of Bombay (1954).

(91) S. C. Ray: *Research Series Bulletin No. 8*, ICAR, New Delhi (1955).

(92) S. C. Ray: *Indian Dairyman*, 9(6), 221 (1957); 9(7), 263 (1957).

(93) S. De and M. R. Srinivasan: *Indian Dairyman*, 10(6), 156 (1958); 10(8), 216 (1958).

(94) R. C. Misra and N. S. Kushwaha: *Indian J. Dairy Sci.*, 23(2), 115 (1970).

(95) G. S. Rajorhia: *Food Ind. J.*, 4(3), 12 (1971).

(96) J. S. Punjrath: *Indian Dairyman*, 26(7), 275 (1974).

(97) Madan Pal and G. S. Rajorhia: *Indian J. Dairy Sci.*, 28(1), 8 (1975).

(98) M. R. Srinivasan: *Indian Dairyman*, 28(7), 279 (1976).

(99) N. C. Ganguli and M. K. Jain: *J. Dairy Sci.*, 56(1), 19 (1973).

C. *Country/desi method.* The preparation of makkhan has already been described (see 11.14.5). Both makkhan and ghee are essentially prepared on a cottage industry scale at the producer's household. The lot of makkhan, fresh or accumulated over a few days, is usually taken in a suitable open mud-pot or metallic vessel, and heated and stirred on a low fire to drive out the moisture. When practically all the moisture has been removed, a stage judged by experience, further heating is stopped and the vessel removed from the fire. On cooling, when the residue has settled down, the clear fat is decanted into suitable containers. (Alternatively, the makkhan is converted into *Kachcha* ghee, which has a somewhat longer keeping quality than makkhan.) The traditional and improved desi methods have been compared in Table 11.26.

TABLE 11.26*

Ghee-making: The indigenous route

Milk ——Fermentation——→ Curd ——Churning——→ Butter ——Clarification——→ Ghee
↓
Buttermilk

Product or procedure	Traditional methods: Undesirable practices	Improved method: Optimum recommendations
Milk	Drawn into dirty vessels. Curdled raw without boiling.	Use clean, fresh and strained milk. Boil once for 10 min. or to 5 per cent vol. reduction, and quickly cool.
Fermentation	Done in metal or earthenware vessels. Milk allowed to sour by itself, or seeded with curd of uncertain quality. Extent of souring uncontrolled.	Use mixed starter and of the right type. Use 2–2.5 per cent in winter, 1 per cent in summer. Sour up to 0.8–1.0 per cent lactic acidity, i.e. for about 12–15 hrs. in winter and 8–10 hrs. in summer.
Curd	Stored for long periods before churning.	Do not accumulate beyond one day.
Churning	Performed in mud-pots or copper vessels. Carried out with inefficient churning devices.	Perform in gear-driven wooden beater fixed on a draining device at the bottom.

* Table 12.1 reproduced from *Indian Dairy Products* by Rangappa and Achaya (1974).

Product or procedure	Traditional methods: Undesirable practices	Improved method: Optimum recommendations
	Water too warm when added, or in insufficient quantity. Washing of butter granules not done.	Carry out in the cold. Add cold water if desired, but not more than the volume of curd. After butter granules are fully formed, drain buttermilk, add cold water, and gently churn again to wash butter.
Butter (Makkhan)	Stored for long periods in mud pots or metallic vessels. Floated in lumps in buttermilk which is steadily going acid with storage.	Do not store before melting; if unavoidable, float in a 1 per cent soln. of common salt in enamel or glazed porcelain vessel.
Clarification	Done in mud pots or metallic vessels. Temperature either too high or too low. Heating prolonged, or insufficient, according to flavour preferences.	Hold at 80°C for 30 min. Remove lowest watery layer. Clarify upper layers of fat and curd by heating in an enamel, glass or stainless steel vessel. When crackling due to water-removal stops, heat for a few minutes without overburning.
Ghee	Stored in mud pots or metallic vessels. Melted frequently for use.	Store in stoneware, glazed porcelain or enamel jars filled to the top in a cool place. Withdraw small quantities for use in a small container.

Merits. Desirable flavour, body and texture.

Demerits. (i) Extremely small-scale production causing collection and marketing problems; (ii) low keeping quality and vitamin content.

D. *Creamery butter method.* This is the standard method adopted in almost all organized dairies, where the raw material used is unsalted creamery butter, commonly known as ghee or white butter.

The butter is heated in an improved ghee boiler, which consists of a stainless steel jacketed pan (vessel) provided with a manual stirrer. There may be provision for a movable, hollow, stainless steel tube, centrally bored through the bottom of the pan for emptying the pan-contents when required; alternatively, the pan may be emptied by providing a simple pan-tilting device. A steam control valve, pressure and temperature indicator, etc., are also provided in the boiler.

In the beginning, the solid mass of butter (which may be cut into small pieces to facilitate melting) is heated over a low fire and carefully stirred so that it melts. Later, the steam pressure in the jacket is raised so that the liquid mass starts boiling, with a removal of the water vapour from the pan-contents at a temperature of over 90°C. This temperature remains constant as long as the moisture is being driven out. The contents are constantly agitated throughout the process of conversion of butter into ghee, to prevent scorching.

The scum which gathers on the top surface of the boiling mass is removed from time to time by a perforated ladle. Usually, there is profuse effervescence (1st), accompanied by a crackling sound in the early stages of boiling, but both gradually decrease if the moisture content is reduced.

When practically all the moisture has been driven out, the temperature of the liquid mass suddenly shoots up and the heating at this stage has to be carefully controlled. The endpoint is indicated by the appearance of effervescence (2nd), which is much finer than the first, together with a browning of the curd particles. At this stage a characteristic ghee flavour also emanates, and this is an indication that it has been heated sufficiently. The final temperature of heating/clarification usually ranges from 110 to 120°C, depending upon the region. (In some parts of the country, it is finally heated to a still higher temperature, which yields a burnt or over-cooked flavour relished in those areas; a recent trend in other parts of the country is to use lower heating temperatures, around 107°C.) After cooling and sedimentation, the ghee is filtered through a muslin cloth so as to separate it from the sediment·known as ghee-residue (consisting mostly of burnt casein). It then goes on for granulation and packaging.

Merits. Saving in labour, physical exertion and exposure to uncomfortably high temperatures and humidity during actual ghee making compared to the direct-cream heating method (because a much lower quantity of water has to be removed).

E. *Pre-stratification method*

(a) *Introduction.* Clarification of butter into ghee by country or creamery methods has certain obvious demerits. Thus, in country methods, there is a much greater possibility of obtaining a finished product characterized by an over-heated and smoky flavour. In the creamery method, as also in the country method, the high acidity of the raw material (especially true of makkhan) at high clarifying temperatures, makes the product greasy and also reduces its shelf-life. Research work has led to the evolution of a modified technique capable of yielding a higher grade product at lower cost of clarification.

(b) *Principle.* When butter is left undisturbed at a temperature of 80–85°C for 15 to 30 minutes, it stratifies, i.e. separates into 3 distinct layers, viz., a top layer of floating denatured particles of curd, a middle layer of fat, and a bottom layer of buttermilk. This separation into layers has been called pre-stratification. The bottom layer of buttermilk contains 60–70 per cent of solids-not-fat and also over 80 per cent of the moisture originally present in the butter. The buttermilk is mechanically removed without disturbing the top and middle layers. Afterwards, the temperature of the remaining two upper layers (of denatured curd and fat) is raised to the usual clarifying temperature of 110–120°C.

Merits. (i) Economy in fuel consumption as compared to direct clarification; (ii) production of ghee with a lower acidity and longer shelf-life (acid removed in buttermilk).

Note: Desi butter with a higher moisture content is likely to be more economical in its fuel consumption as compared to creamery or white butter by this method.

F. *Direct-cream method.* In this direct-cream heating method, the cream usually obtained by normal separation of milk is heated in the same ghee boiler described for the creamery-butter method. The procedure for heating and moisture removal, final temperature of clarification, cooling and sedimentation, granulation and packaging also remain the same.

Merits. Overall economy in labour compared to the creamery-butter method, since one stage, viz. cream to butter, is eliminated.

Demerits. (i) Lower percentage of fat recovery in ghee due to greater fat loss in ghee residue—the amount of which is higher in this method than by the butter methods; (ii) slightly greasy texture in ghee.

Note : (i) As pointed out above, one of the important drawbacks of the direct-cream-ghee process is a lower percentage recovery of ghee as compared with the creamery-butter process. This is because 'normal' cream (40–50 per cent fat) contains much more solids-not-fat (about 4.5 to 5.5 per cent) than desi or white butter (1 to 1.5 per cent). This higher solids-not-fat content in cream contributes to a larger ghee-residue, which in turn causes a greater fat loss in the same. Earlier workers (82) (85–86) have shown that the non-fatty milk solids of cream can be reduced by what has been termed the 'cream washing' process. This process consists of diluting the cream with lukewarm water (40°C) equal to the volume of the original milk. After thoroughly mixing it by gentle stirring, the diluted cream is then separated without altering the conditions of normal cream separation. This washed cream contains 1–2 per cent solids-not-fat. When converted into ghee in the usual manner as indicated above, it gives a higher yield. However, the ghee has a flat flavour, although the product also has a longer shelf-life. Artificial ripening of the washed cream with lactic starter to an acidity level of 0.20 per cent lactic, or acidification of the cream with citric acid to the same level prior to clarification as above, improves the flavour of the finished ghee.

(ii) An alternative to cream washing is the use of plastic cream, containing 65–85 per cent fat and a very low solids-not-fat content. This requires a special cream separator called a plastic cream separator. It is understood that a few ghee manufacturers in India have been using the direct-cream heating method and plastic cream for their routine production.

G. *Continuous method.* This is under development.

(a) *Objects.*

(i) To manufacture ghee on an industrial scale as a continuous process, to ensure uniform quality, and greater economy.

(ii) To reduce human labour, drudgery and fatigue by introducing as much automation as feasible or dseirable under Indian conditions.

(b) *Advantages claimed*

(i) Suitability for large-scale handling;

(ii) utilization of machines for a large number of production-processes feasible;

(iii) uniform demand on services;

(iv) high fat recovery;

(v) possibility of in-place cleaning;

(vi) no stirring, no scraping and no laborious effort on the part of the ghee operators required.

H. *Comparison of the different methods.* This has been shown in Table 11.27.

TABLE 11.27

Comparison of different methods of ghee making

Particulars	Desi Method (D.C.)	Creamery butter method (D.C.)	Direct cream method (D.C.)	Pre-stratification method	Continuous method
Adaptability	Small scale	Large scale	Large scale	Large scale	Very large scale
Stages involved (from milk)	three (milk-cream butter-ghee)	three (milk-cream butter-ghee)	two (milk-cream ghee)	three (milk-cream/curd-butter/makkhan-ghee)	three (milk-cream/curd-butter/makkhan-ghee)
By-products produced	Buttermilk Ghee-residue	Skim milk Buttermilk Ghee-residue	Skim milk Ghee-residue	Skim milk and/or buttermilk Ghee-residue	Skim milk and/or buttermilk
Ghee-quality :					
Aroma	Strong and nutty	Pleasantly rich	Mild	Mild	Mild
Taste	Acid	Slightly flat	Definitely flat	Flat or acid	Flat or acid

Particulars	Desi method (D.C.)	Creamery butter method (D.C.)	Direct cream method (D.C.)	Pre-strati-fication method	Continuous method
Texture	Large grains	Fine grains	Slightly greasy	Fine grains	Greasy
Keeping quality	Poor	Good	Excellent	Fair to Good	Good
Remarks	Useful as a cottage industry	Most popular in organized dairies	Advantage-ous with plastic cream	Adopted by a few manufac-turers	Under-development

Note: D.C. means direct clarification.

J. *Final temperature of clarification* (100). In general. a temperature range from 110 to 120°C is preferred. However, the final temperature to which ghee is heated during manufacture depends upon the region of the country; normally the temperature is around 110°C (or below) in north India and 120°C (or even higher) in south India.

Note : A lower heating temperature improves the colour but decreases the keeping quality of the ghee obtained due to its greater residual moisture content; a higher temperature, on the other hand, tends to reduce the vitamin A content (with acid butter), and darken the colour, but increases the keeping quality of the finished product.

K. *Cooling and granulation (crystallization).* Granularity in ghee is considered by the average Indian buyer to be an important criterion of quality and even purity. It may be pointed out that the partly granular form assumed by ghee is primarily due to a certain content of glycerides of higher-melting saturated fatty acids, especially palmitic and stearic. In this regard buffalo ghee, which is usually more saturated, crystallizes more effectively than cow ghee.

The desi method produces large crystals in ghee. On the other hand, the ghee obtained by creamery-butter on direct-cream processes need not necessarily have large crystals. It has been observed that heating ghee to 60–100°C, followed by rapid cooling, yields

(100) K. Sethna and J. V. Bhatt: *Indian J. Dairy Sci.*, 3(2), 39 (1950).

small grains in ghee; however, if the above ghee is held for crystallization at a temperature about 1°C above the melting point of ghee (cow ghee—29°C; buffalo ghee—31°C), a large number of big grains result (101).

Note : Cold storage of ghee should be avoided, since it leads to a loss of granularity and the development of a waxy consistency in the stored product.

L. *Packaging and storage.* Since milk fat is susceptible to deterioration due to exposure to light, air and metals, ghee (which is made up almost entirely of milk fat) should be properly packaged promptly after production so as to retain its initial flavour and nutritive value; it should also be properly stored so that its body and texture do not deteriorate. The various problems of ghee-packaging have also been highlighted (102).

(a) *Selection of container.* The container is selected on the basis of the following considerations:

   (i) Non-toxic and non-tainting character;
  (ii) availability;
 (iii) cost;
 (iv) resistance to rough handling.

Based on the above criteria, tin-containers are the obvious choice. They are also impervious to the action of light and air. The tin-containers should, however, be new and free from any trace of rust. They should preferably have a minimum tin-coating weight corresponding to 50 ETP (electrolytic tin plate). Since the cost of tin containers has been rising steadily, cheaper plastic containers have appeared in the market. They are being tested to determine their suitability for the packing and storage of ghee.

(b) *Size of containers.* Most ghee is at present packed in 16 kg. containers for retail sale, which it may take two to three weeks to dispose of. In such large containers, the moisture in ghee tends to gravitate downwards. Thus the lower layers of ghee are likely to deteriorate because of an increase in the peroxide value and acidity. Hence for retail sale, ghee should be packed in smaller-sized containers with a capacity of not more than 4 kg. each.

(c) *Filling and sealing.* Since air (oxygen) exerts an adverse effect

(101) T. M. Paul and K. S. Suri: *Indian J. Dairy Sci.,* **2**(3), 94 (1949).
(102) M. R. Srinivasan: *Indian Dairyman,* **11**(5), 111 (1959).

on the quality of ghee during storage, the tin-containers should be filled to the brim, with no air gap. If the ghee is filled while hot there is usually enough dissolved air to cause appreciable oxidative spoilage. The use of vacuum-packaging in an inert atmosphere may be effective, but is prohibitive in cost. Under the circumstances, the next best alternative is to pack the ghee at a suitable temperature, viz. 30–32°C (which will limit the dissolved air to the minimum possible), up to the brim of the container, and then seal it. Only rust-free containers and lids should be used.

(d) *Storage* (103).   The storage of ghee in different types of containers has been studied. It is well known that the development of an oxidized flavour or tallowiness in ghee is accelerated at higher storage temperatures, especially with ghee which has an appreciable initial acidity. Under the existing conditions of handling, the storage temperature of ghee may vary from 5 to 38°C throughout the country depending on the season of the year. Although refrigerated storage of ghee delays acid-development and thereby prolongs its keeping quality, it renders the stored product greasy and pasty. A storage temperature of around 21°C is usually recommended.

11.15.8 Market quality.   This refers to the physico-chemical properties of ghee offered for sale in the market. The physical properties include colour and flavour (smell and taste) and texture (grain and consistency), while the chemical properties include chemical composition, etc. The physico-chemical constants are also included under market quality. The quality of ghee is dependent on the type of milk (viz. cow, buffalo or mixed) feed of the animal, season and region, and the method by which it is produced (viz., desi, creamery-butter or direct-cream method).

(a) *Physical quality*

(i) *Colour.*   The colour of ghee manufactured from either cow and buffalo milks is definitely influenced by the method of production (104). The colour of cow ghee by the desi method is deep yellow, while that of buffalo ghee is white with a characteristic yellowish or greenish tinge. When prepared by the creamery-butter method, the colour of the product is similar to that resulting from the desi method, although of a somewhat lower intensity. By the direct-cream method, the colour of cow ghee is again deep yellow, but that of

(103) T. M. Paul, V. R. Bhalerao and C. P. Anantakrishnan: *Indian J. Dairy Sci.*, **2** (1), 7 (1949).

(104) K. R. Lalitha and N. N. Dastur: *Indian J. Dairy Sci.*, **9**(4), 143 (1956).

buffalo ghee is waxy-white. Ghee from mixed milk (cow and buffalo) has a shade of colour proportional to the components of the mixture. The colour of ghee also depends on whether it is in the solid or liquid state.

(ii) *Flavour (smell and taste).* This is the most important characteristic looked for in ghee by the trade. The smell is ascertained by rubbing a small quantity of the sample briskly on the back of the palm and inhaling it. Normally, a well-prepared sample of ghee has a pleasant, cooked and rich flavour. The taste is usually sweet and characteristic of the milk fat, although a slight acidic flavour is preferred.

Note: Numerous publications have appeared in the country during the last decade on the means of identifying the flavour of ghee, for which research journals may be consulted.

(iii) *Texture (grain and consistency).* Grains of a large and uniform size, and a firm and non-greasy consistency, are preferred. The grain-size in ghee depends mainly on the following factors: rate of cooling; fatty acid make-up (which is influenced by species of animal, nature of feed, season and region etc.), and subsequent heating and cooling treatment.

(b) *Chemical quality.* See 11.15.4 and 11.15.5.

Note: In spite of the low moisture content in ghee, micro-organisms may flourish in market samples of ghee. (105)

11.15.9 Yield

(a) The yield of ghee from milk/cream/butter is influenced chiefly by:

(i) *The fat content of the raw material used for ghee making.* This is calculated by multiplying the amount of raw material used (viz., milk, cream or butter) by the fat percentage in the same. The higher the fat content, the higher should be the yield, and vice versa.

(ii) *The percentage of fat recovered in ghee.* This depends on the method of manufacture (see Table 11.29).

(b) The items of fat loss in the different methods of ghee making, starting from milk, are given in Table 11.28.

(105) J. V. Bhatt and K. Sethna: *Indian J. Dairy Sci.* 1(1), 12 (1950).

TABLE 11.28

Items of fat loss in different methods of ghee making

Methods of ghee making	Items of fat loss	
Country (desi)	(i) Lassi (ii) Ghee-residue (iii) Handling.	
Creamery-butter	(i) Skim milk (ii) Buttermilk (iii) Ghee-residue (iv) Handling and packaging.	
Direct-cream	(i) Skim milk (ii) Ghee-residue (iii) Handling and packaging.	
Pre-stratification	*Creamery butter* (i) Skim milk (ii) Buttermilk* (iii) Ghee-residue (iv) Handling and pack- aging	*Desi butter* (i) Lassi (ii) Buttermilk† (iii) Ghee-residue (iv) Handling and pack- aging.
Continuous	Same as above	Same as above

* Includes that produced when churning cream and also after the butter melt has stratified.

† Refers to that produced after stratification of the butter melt only.

(c) The approximate fat recovery in ghee by different methods, starting from milk, is shown in Table 11.29.

TABLE 11.29

Percentage fat recovery in ghee by different methods

Method of ghee making	Percentage fat recovery in ghee
Country (desi) = traditional	80–85
–do– = improved	88–90
Creamery-butter	88–92
Direct-cream = 40 to 50 per cent fat	85–86
Direct-cream = 65 to 85 per cent fat	90–95

Note: The higher fat recovery in ghee with a higher testing cream is due to the lower fat loss in a ghee-residue (which in turn is due to its lower non-fatty solids content).

(d) The percentage fat recovery in ghee by three different methods is given in Table 11.30.

TABLE 11.30

Percentage fat recovery of ghee by different methods (94)

| Method of ghee making | Percentage fat lost | | | | Percentage fat recovery (Ave.) |
	Skim milk	Buttermilk	Ghee-residue	Handling	
Country (Indigenous/ desi)	—	13.20	1.87	2.49	82.4
Creamery-butter	1.40	0.82	1.43	4.54	91.6
Direct-cream	1.40	—	9.00	1.70	87.7

Note: 1. In an earlier work (81), the percentage fat recovery figures in ghee were reported to be 87, 93 and 86 for desi, creamery-butter and direct-cream methods, respectively.

2. The possibility of recovering a higher percentage of ghee from high-fat cream or washed-cream has also been reported (95) (97).

(e) *Comparative study of fat recovery in ghee from butter, and creams of varying fat contents* (106). This is presented in Table 11.31.

TABLE 11.31

Fat recovery in ghee from butter and cream

Raw material used for ghee making	Fat content (%)	Amount of ghee-residue per 100 kg. butter/cream (Ave.) (kg.)	Percentage fat recovery in ghee (Ave.)
Butter	83 $\pm$ 2	1.6	98.3
Cream	40 $\pm$ 2	10.4	85.0
	45 $\pm$ 2	9.9	89.4
	50 $\pm$ 2	8.3	90.0
	55 $\pm$ 0	7.7	91.7
	60 $\pm$ 2	6.7	93.7
	65 $\pm$ 2	6.2	94.2
	70 $\pm$ 2	5.5	94.7
	75 $\pm$ 2	4.9	95.6
	80 $\pm$ 2	3.0	96.6

(106) S. De, K. P. Unnithan and J. L. Guglani: *Indian J. Dairy Sci.*, **31**(4), 376 (1978).

Note: The higher the fat level in cream used for ghee making, the lower the resultant ghee residue and the higher the percentage fat recovery in ghee.

11.15.10 Keeping quality

(a) Unlike all other indigenous milk products, ghee has a remarkably long keeping quality. Under optimum conditions of production, packaging and storage (viz., when prepared either by the direct heating of sweet cream or sweet cream butter, packed up to the brim in a new rust-free container and stored under sealed conditions at around 21°C), ghee is expected to have a storage life of 6–12 months. The keeping quality of ghee is adversely affected by increase in acidity and development of fat off-flavours, viz. rancidity, oxidation, tallowiness, etc. (107–110). The factors influencing the keeping quality or shelf-life of ghee are :

(i) *Temperature of storage*. The higher the temperature of storage, the lower the keeping quality, and vice versa.

(ii) *Initial moisture content*. The higher the initial moisture content, the lower the keeping quality and vice versa.

(iii) *Initial acidity content*. The higher the initial acidity content, the lower the keeping quality, and vice versa.

(iv) *Initial sediment content*. The higher the initial sediment content, the lower the keeping quality, and vice versa.

(v) *Copper and iron content*. The higher the copper and iron contents, the lower the keeping quality, and vice versa. (Copper and iron content act as a catalytic agent in fat-oxidation.)

(vi) *Method of packaging*. The higher the air-content in the head-space in packaging, the lower the keeping quality, and vice versa.

(vii) *Exposure to light* (*especially sunlight*). The greater the exposure to light, the lower the keeping quality, and vice versa.

(b) *Extending keeping quality*. The keeping quality of ghee can be extended by the addition of artificial anti-oxidants. Under the PFA Rules (1976), butylated hydroxy anisole in a concentration

(107) T. M. Paul and C. P. Anantakrishnan: *Indian J. Dairy Sci.*, **2**(3), 108 (1949).

(108) N. N. Dastur, A. Rahman and N. B. Shroff: *Indian J. Vet. Sci.*, **20**(2), 131 (1950).

(109) K. R. Lalitha and N. N. Dastur: *Indian J. Dairy Sci.*, **7**(1), 1 (1954).

(110) R. Soundararajan: *Indian J. Dairy Sci.*, **11**(2), 93 (1958).

not exceeding 0.02 per cent is permitted at present. The action of anti-oxidants in prolonging the shelf-life of ghee is similar to that of butteroil. Numerous studies* were carried out nearly two decades ago on the preservative action of anti-oxidants, natural or artificial, on ghee. A few studies have been carried out in recent years (111–113). It is claimed that ghee-residue acts as a good anti-oxidant when added to ghee—this may be due to its higher phospholipid content. Alternatively, the phospholipids can be extracted from the ghee-residue (through a simple process of solvent extraction) and added at 0.1 per cent of ghee; such addition has been found to increase the keeping quality of ghee by two or three times as compared with that of untreated ghee.

(c) *Accelerated oxidation test to determine the shelf-life of ghee.* There is yet no reliable test for measuring the developed rancidity and correlating the same with the keeping quality of ghee. Determination of the Induction Period (IP) for oxygen absorption at an elevated temperature of 79°C for ghee has been observed to be helpful in predicting its shelf-life. An Induction Period of 20 hours or more appears to correspond to a marketable life of 6 months.

Note: The Induction Period is the period measured in hours, after which the rate of increase in the peroxide value of a ghee sample shoots up.

11.15.11 Renovation of ghee. This refers to the market practice of attempting to improve old and rancid ghee, so as to make it marketable as a product of secondary quality. Some of the methods employed for the renovation of ghee include:

(i) Re-heating inferior ghee with curd, betel or curry leaves, etc., and subsequently filtering it;

(ii) adding a yellow substance, such as saffron, annatto, turmeric juice, etc., to make it appear that it is cow ghee;

(iii) blending an inferior ghee with a superior quality product.

Note: The above practices are generally carried out in a crude manner.

* Refer to *Indian Dairy Products* by Rangappa and Achaya (1974).

(111) M. K. Ramamurthy, K. M. Narayanan and V. R. Bhalerao: *Indian J. Dairy Sci.*, **22**(1), 57 (1969).

(112) T. Kuchroo and K. M. Narayanan: *Indian J. Dairy Sci.* **25**(4), 228 (1972).

(113) T. Kuchroo and K. M. Narayanan: *Indian Dairyman*, **25**(10), 405 (1973).

11.15.12   Neutralizing high-acid ghee.   Market ghee sometime; develops large quantities of free fatty acid (predominantly oleic), which result from faulty methods of preparation and storage. This high-acid ghee produces harmful effects in the body system. The problem was tackled nearly three decades ago when two processes of neutralization were developed (114). In one, the neutralizer used was sodium hydroxide, while in the other it was lime. The latter process, which is more suitable for small operators, is as follows: ghee which is to be refined, is heated to 60–70°C. Finely ground, good quality lime (preferably shell-lime), powdered to 60 mesh, is then sprinkled on the surface @ 3 per cent of ghee. The temperature is quickly raised to 108°C with gentle stirring, and the mass is cooled and filtered at 60°C. By both the above neutralization treatments, the flavour, granularity and keeping quality of high-acid ghee are all improved.

11.15.13   Marketing*

(a) At present there is no organized system for the production and marketing of ghee in India. Ghee is produced, by and large, on a small and scattered scale. It is assembled for marketing through middlemen. Adulteration at all stages of assemblage is a rule rather than an exception.

(b) The various agencies engaged in the assembling and distribution of ghee are:

  (i) Producers;
 (ii) village merchants;
(iii) itinerant traders;
 (iv) commission agents (*Arhatyas*) and wholesale merchants;
  (v) co-operative societies,
 (vi) retailers.

(c) The itinerant traders and brokers collect desi butter or *kachcha* ghee and make it over to wholesale merchants. The latter carry out what is known in the trade as the 'refining' of ghee. This process consists in mixing and blending different lots of makkhan/ *kachcha* ghee in large karahis and then heating the mixture to a certain temperature in order to remove all traces of lassi. This product is then transferred to settling tanks. The clear ghee is packed

---

* Refer to 'Report on the Marketing of Ghee and Other Milk Products in India', *Marketing Series No. 85* (1957).

(114) M. S. Samuel, K. C. Sen, Z. R. Kothavalla and N. N. Dastur: *Indian J. Vet. Sci.*, **16** (1), 11 (1946).

in tin-containers and stored in a cool place for a couple of days for proper crystallization or grain formation.

(d) At present, most ghee producers in India are financially dependent on unscrupulous money-lenders or wholesale merchants, who impose stringent conditions. Very often makkhan or *kachcha* ghee collectors make interest-free advances to the producers on the condition that the latter will sell to the former a specific quantity of ghee at a predetermined price, which has no relation to the prevailing market price.

11.15 14 *Problems of adulteration*

(a) The adulteration of ghee in India today is indeed most appalling. Being the most expensive of the edible fats, ghee offers itself as easy prey to admixture with cheap adulterants by the numerous middlemen through whose hands it has necessarily to pass. The natural variations in the analytical constants of ghee (enumerated earlier) make adulteration difficult to detect. Numerous studies* were carried out two or three decades ago on the adulteration of ghee and its detection. A simple yet quick method for the detection of vegetable fats in ghee by a thin-layer chromatographic technique has been developed (115).

(b) The main adulterants of ghee are:

(i) *Vanaspati* (*hydrogenated vegetable oil*). This is by far the most widely used today, because of its close resemblance in texture, grain and colour and other characteristics of ghee.

(ii) *Refined* (*de-odourized*) *vegetable oils*. Examples are: groundnut, coconut, cottonseed oils, etc.

(iii) *Animal body fats*.

(iv) *Miscellaneous*. The addition of minute quantities of rice, potatoes, plantain, etc., for improving the consistency of liquid ghee and inducing better grain formation has also been reported.

(c) Enquiries reveal that adulteration takes place at all stages of production, assemblage and marketing; however, the maximum adulteration takes place at the last stage. Although concerted attempts are being made by the government to insist on legal standards for market ghee, the lack of a well-organized system of food inspection, availability of laboratory facilities and easy methods for

---

* Refer to *Indian Dairy Products* by Rangappa and Achaya (1974).

(115) M. K. Ramamurthy, K. M. Narayanan, V. R. Bhalerao and N. N. Dastur: *Indian J. Dairy Sci.*, **20** (1), 11 (1967).

detection of adulteration have all contributed towards the continuance of adulteration in ghee on a wide scale.

(d) The Government of India has made it compulsory that all *vanaspati* must contain a maximum of 5 per cent of sesame oil, which can be identified in ghee by a simple colour test (known as the Baudouin Test). By means of this test, adulteration of ghee with *vanaspati* to an extent as low as 3 per cent can be detected. However, the possibility remains that hydrogenated fats sold under different names for special purposes may still be used as adulterants. Further, since the legislation does not apply to refined oils, it has not been possible to completely eliminate the adulteration of ghee with such materials.

(e) Apart from the compulsory addition of sesame oil to *vanaspati* in order to facilitate its detection in adulterated samples of ghee, attempts had been simultaneously made to evolve a suitable colour for *vanaspati*, which will enable the consumer to detect the addition of *vanaspati* in ghee at first sight. The pink extract from the roots of *rattanjot* (*onosma echioides*), grown in some parts of Uttar Pradesh had been tried out nearly three decades ago for colouring *vanaspati* (116). Extracts of turmeric and chlorophyll had also been suggested for producing an easy-to-detect colour in adulterated samples. But these attempts have not so far been wholly successful, as most vegetable colours which are acceptable to the *vanaspati* trade, can easily be bleached by simple treatment. The problem is one of evolving a harmless dye with a pleasing colour acceptable to *vanaspati* manufacturers, which produces at the same time a permanent colour and is amenable to quick detection when present in small amounts in adulterated ghee samples. Food laboratories in the country have been engaged in these problems and it is hoped that a satisfactory colour will be evolved in due course of time.

11.15.15   Grading-AGMARKING

(a) *Need for grading.*   The quality as well as purity of ghee can be judged only by detailed physical and chemical analysis. Contrary to general belief, it is not possible for an average customer to judge the purity of a sample of market ghee by its appearance, taste or smell, at the time of purchase. Under existing trade practices, a limited effort to grade ghee for marketing takes place at different

(116) N. N. Dastur, A. Kannan and Z. R. Kothavalla: *Indian J. Vet. Sci.*, **17** (3), 171 (1947).

stages of its assembly, by thumb-rule methods. Grading, i.e. classification according to quality, assures the customer of quality and purity of the ghee and its need, therefore, is obvious.

(b) *The AGMARK ghee grading scheme.* Literally, Agmark is an insignia—AG for 'Agricultural' and MARK for 'marking'. With a view to developing the orderly marketing of agricultural produce on an all-India basis, the Indian legislature had passed the Agricultural Produce (Grading and Marking) Act, 1937. This Act, which is permissive in nature. provides for the grading of ghee on a voluntary basis.

The agmark ghee grading scheme was initiated by the Agricultural Marketing Department as early as 1938. Under the scheme, recognized ghee dealers (individuals, groups of individuals, co-operative organizations and similar bodies) can market ghee in standard containers bearing the seal of authority of Agmark, and designating the quality of the product.

(c) *Objectives.* The Agmark (ghee) grading scheme was introduced mainly to achieve the following objectives:

(i) To assure the consumer a produce of pre-tested quality and purity;

(ii) to enable manufacturers of a high-grade product to obtain better returns, and

(iii) to develop an orderly marketing of the commodities by eliminating malpractices when transferring them from the producer to the consumer.

(d) *Prerequisites for using the Agmark label.* It has already been mentioned that grading under the Act is voluntary. Applications from interested parties for the issue of a certificate of authorization for the grading of ghee should be submitted on a prescribed form through the State Marketing Officer to the Agricultural Marketing Adviser to the Government of India. If on receipt of the application, the party is considered suitable, then the necessary permission is granted.

The bonafides of the ghee manufacturer or packer are determined by the following considerations: it is essential that while the ghee manufacturer should have the full facilities of a modern dairy factory for ghee-making and storing, the ghee packer should have a modern refinery and spacious godown; and both should have a well-equipped laboratory, a qualified ghee-chemist, etc.

The refinery of a ghee packer should consist of a heating furnace provided with a suitable chimney as an outlet for smoke, one or more heating pans, a settling pan or tank, and godowns where ghee tins can be kept in safe custody prior to analysis. There should be enough space for receiving butter or *kachcha* ghee and the testing of the same.

The ghee-testing laboratory should have precise equipment, apparatus, glassware and chemicals for the complete examination of ghee for its physico-chemical constants, free fatty acids, and performance of the baudouin test and phytosterol acetate test. The Agricultural Marketing Department provides all necessary assistance in the setting up and working of such a laboratory.

(e) *Procedure for using Agmark label.* The ghee manufacturer, who usually makes ghee from purchased milk or cream after thorough grading and testing, examines these records to certify the fitness of these raw materials for production of standard quality ghee.

For the ghee packer, the lot of raw ghee is examined for general characteristics and butyro-refractometer reading before purchase, and also examined for baudouin test and acid value. On passing the preliminary examinations, the same is heated at the refinery, usually to a temperature of 60–70°C, and the scum removed. Thereafter it is transferred to settling tanks and allowed to stand for a few hours so that the suspended impurities settle down.

A sample of each lot of freshly made ghee at both places (dairy factory and refinery) is drawn by the respective chemist and divided into 3 parts. One is analysed by the chemist himself. The other is sent for check analysis to one of the control laboratories maintained by the Agricultural Marketing Department. These are: the Central Control Laboratory, Kanpur (Uttar Pradesh) and the Subsidiary Control Laboratory, Rajkot (Gujarat). The third part is sealed and handed over to the packer for future reference.

After drawing the sample, the ghee is filled in new tins which have been previously marked with the following particulars: melt number, date of packing, place of packing, name of authorized packer, etc. If on analysis the melt satisfies the specification, the chemist arranges for the fixation of Agmark labels of the appropriate grade. All the above operations should be carried out under the supervision of the chemist. Ghee, filled in tins, should remain in the custody of the chemist till the labels are fixed on to them.

Agmark ghee is packed under two grades, viz. 'Special' and 'General', which are represented by two differently coloured labels. The only difference in the grades is in the maximum limit of free fatty acids (oleic), which in special grade (Red label) ghee is limited to 1.4 per cent and in general grade (Green label) to 2.5 per cent.

Agmark labels are printed under security conditions on watermark paper bearing the words 'Government of India' in micro-tint to avoid counterfeiting. These are affixed on the tins with a special adhesive supplied by the Agricultural Marketing Adviser to the Government of India.

(f) *Quality control checks.* If the Control Laboratory finds that a melt sample does not conform to the specifications, immediate intimation is sent to the authorized packer and the chemist to remove the Agmark label from all the tins filled from the melt in question, and the ghee rejected from Agmark grading.

A check on the quality and purity of ghee is also exercised by frequent inspection of the grading stations by the State and Central Marketing staff. Samples of graded ghee are collected from the grading centres and consuming markets (both retail and wholesale) through especially authorized officers. If, on analysis, a sample is found to be below specifications, the entire melt is declared misgraded and the packer has to arrange for the removal of the Agmark labels from the tins pertaining to that melt.

To ensure that graded ghee is not stored for an indefinite period so as to impair its quality, the chemists are also periodically required to draw representative check samples from stored tins of Agmark ghee and to send them for analysis to the Control Laboratories. This ensures that the ghee contained therein has not developed an acidity in excess of the limit prescribed on the label. In the event of its exceeding this limit, it is downgraded from Special to General, or rejected, and the Agmark labels removed from the tins, as the case may be.

(g) *Agmark ghee specifications.* The original specifications introduced in 1938 have been modified and amended from time to time. It may be noted in passing that Agmark ghee can be freely marketed in any part of the country even though the Agmark specifications of ghee may differ from those prescribed by the constituent States of the Indian Union. The current specifications are shown in Table 11.32.

TABLE 11.32

Agmark standards for ghee

Tests	All-India	Regional* Winter	Summer
1. Baudouin		— Negative —	
2. Phytosterol acetate		— Negative —	
3. B. R. reading (40°C)	40.0–43.0	41.5–44.0	42.5–45.0
4. R. M. Value	Not less than 28.0	Not less than 23.0	Not less than 21.0
5. P. Value	1.0–2.0	0.5–1.2	0.5–1.0
6. Moisture (%)		— Not more than 0.3 —	
7. Free fatty acid (% oleic)			
(a) *Special grade* Agmark Red Label		— Not more than 1.4 —	
(b) *General grade* Agmark Green Label		— Not more than 2.5 —	

* Where cotton seed is extensively fed to milch animals.

SOURCE: 'Ghee-making in the Tropical Countries and Possibilities of its Industrial Production' by M. R. Srinivasan: *Indian Dairyman*, 28(7), 279 (1976).

(h) *Progress of Agmarking ghee.* Although the Agmark ghee grading scheme has been in operation since 1938, barely 2 per cent of the total ghee production of the country is handled today under this scheme. The reasons for this slow progress are:

(i) Absence of quality consciousness on the part of producers and consumers;

(ii) absence of standards for organoleptic quality in the product;

(iii) difficulties experienced by Agmark packers in meeting all-India consumer acceptability due to natural variations in the quality of ghee produced in different regions of the country.

11.15.16　Judging and grading of ghee

A. *Score card.* A tentative score card of ghee is given in Table 11.33.

TABLE 11.33

Score card of ghee (tentative)

Items	Perfect score
Flavour	45
Texture	10
Acidity (oleic)	25
Colour	10
Freedom from suspended matter	5
Package	5
	100

B. *Procedure of examination*

(a) *Sampling.* After thoroughly mixing the lot of ghee, obtain a representative sample with the help of a spoon.

(b) *Sequence of observations.* Note the sanitary conditions of the package/container on the outside; if there are any tin containers, also observe whether there is any rust. On opening the package, examine the ghee for its colour, texture (size of grains) and proportion of liquid fat. Then thoroughly stir the ghee and take a representative sample, and after melting it note the amount and nature of sediment. Now briskly rub a small quantity of ghee with the index finger or other means on the back of one hand, and note the smell by inhaling. A few drops may also be taken inside the mouth and the taste noted. Determine the acidity (oleic) by the standard method. Finally, examine the package on the inside (after emptying the contents) for cleanliness; and in the case of tin-containers, note the presence of rust, etc.

C. *Requirements of high-grade ghee.*

Such ghee should have a natural sweet and pleasant odour, an agreeable taste and should be free from rancidity and any other objectionable flavour. A pleasant, nutty, slightly cooked or caramelized aroma is generally prized. A good texture requires large and uniform grains with very little liquid fat; a greasy texture is objectionable. When the ghee is melted, it should be clear, transparent and free from sediment or foreign colouring matter. The colour should be uniform throughout; it should be bright yellow for cow ghee and white, with or without a yellowish or greenish tint, for buffalo ghee (the intensity of colour depending on the method of preparation). The package should be clean inside and not soiled on the outside if tin containers are being used.

11.15.17   Defects in ghee, their causes and prevention.   Defects in ghee arise due to low quality raw material (milk/curd/butter/cream) and faulty methods in the production and handling of ghee. The defects in ghee, their causes and prevention are given in Table 11.34.

TABLE 11.34

Defects in ghee, their causes and prevention

Name of defects	Causes	Prevention
(a) *Flavour*		
Smoky	Smoky fire used for boiling milk or converting mak-khan into ghee in desi-method.	Using non-smoky fire for boiling milk or converting makkhan into ghee in desi-method.
Overcooked/burnt	Excessively high temperature of clarification of ghee.	Optimum temperature of clarification of ghee.
Undercooked	Excessively low temperature of clarification of ghee.	Optimum temperature of clarification of ghee.
Rancid	Fat hydrolysis due to lipase action in milk/cream/curd/butter/*kachcha* ghee.	(i) Inactivation of lipase by proper pasteurization/heating of milk/cream, etc. (ii) Using optimum clarification temperature (which ensures minimum moisture content in ghee) (iii) Packaging in small containers for retail sale.
Oxidized/Oily/Metallic/	Fat oxidation due to: direct contact of milk/curd/cream/butter/ghee with copper or iron. exposure of these products to sunlight, etc.	(i) Storage of milk/curd/cream/butter/ghee in properly tinned or aluminium alloy/stainless steel vessels (ii) Filling ghee up to the brim so as to avoid any headspace air (oxygen) (iii) Avoiding storage of ghee at high temperatures (above 21°C) (iv) Avoiding use of salted butter for ghee making

Name of defects	Causes	Prevention
		(v) Avoiding long storage of ghee
		(vi) Storage of ghee in opaque containers.
(b) Texture		
Greasy	(i) Rapid cooling of hot ghee after clarification	(i) Slow cooling of hot ghee after clarification
	(ii) Subjecting ghee to further heating and cooling treatment after preparation.	(ii) Avoiding further heating and cooling of ghee after preparation.
Colour		
Burnt	Excessively high temperature of clarification of ghee.	Optimum temperature of clarification of ghee.
Sediment		
High	Incorrect straining of ghee.	Correct straining of ghee.
Burnt	Excessively high temperature of clarification of ghee.	Optimum temperature of clarification of ghee.

11.15.18 Uses of ghee

(a) *Major uses*

 (i) As a cooking or frying medium;

 (ii) in confectionary;

 (iii) for direct consumption (with rice, chapaties, etc.)

(b) *Minor use.* In indigenous pharmaceutical preparations (mainly cow ghee).

11.16 Lassi

11.16.1 Definition. Lassi, also called *chhas* or *matha*, refers to desi buttermilk, which is the by-product obtained when churning curdled whole milk with crude indigenous devices for the production of desi butter (makkhan).

11.16.2 Statistics of production. It appears that 50–60 kg. (ave. 55 kg.) of lassi are produced for every kg. of ghee. Assuming that 90 per cent of India's total ghee production is obtained by the desi method, the total annual production of lassi may be estimated to be about 27,500 million kg. (1966).

11.16.3 Composition. The composition of lassi varies considerably, depending upon the composition of dahi, the extent to which the curd is diluted when churning and the efficiency of fat removal. An average composition of lassi is given in Table 11.35.

TABLE 11.35

Composition of lassi* (percentage)

Water	Total solids	Fat	Solids-not-fat	Protein	Lactose	Ash	Lactic acid
96.2	3.8	0.8	3.0	1.3	1.2	0.4	0.44

* *Adapted from*: Table 9.5 of *Indian Dairy Products* by Rangappa and Achaya (1974).

11.16.4   Food and nutritive value. Lassi contains appreciable amounts of milk proteins and phospholipids, and is an excellent beverage for quenching thirst by reason of its lactic acidity.

11.16.5   Yield. This will depend mainly on the extent to which the curd is diluted when churning—the greater the dilution, the greater the yield, and vice versa.

11.16.6   Uses

(i) As a beverage, usually after the addition of ice (in hot weather), sugar or salt, with or without additional flavours;

(ii) as a starter culture (optional);

(iii) as a coagulant (optional).

Note: In the northern region of the country, whole milk curd beaten up to be served as a beverage as above, is also called lassi.

11.17   Ghee Residue

11.17.1   Definition. This refers to the charred (burnt) light to dark brown residue which is obtained on the cloth strainer after the ghee, prepared by any of the methods given above, is filtered. It is a by-product of the ghee industry.

11.17.2   Composition. This is influenced by the composition of the non-fatty constituents in the raw material (butter or cream), the technique adopted for the production of ghee and that employed for the separation of the ghee-residue (by hand or mechanical pressing).

Essentially it contains heat-denatured milk-proteins, caramelized lactose and varying amounts of entrapped fat, besides some minerals and water. The composition of the ghee-residue together with its yield from the raw material used, is given in Table 11.36.

TABLE 11.36 (117)

Chemical composition and yield of hand-pressed ghee-residue (percentage)

Type of residue	Chemical composition					Ave. Yield (per 100 kg.) butter/ cream (kg.)
	Water	Fat	Protein	Lactose	Ash	
From desi butter:						
Cow	14.4	32.4	36.0	12.0	5.2	1.6
Buffalo	13.4	33.4	32.8	15.4	5.2	1.6
From creamery butter (unsalted):						
Cow	9.7	61.4	24.8	Traces	4.1	1.7
Buffalo	5.7	65.0	25.5	Traces	3.8	1.2
From cream (sweet-unwashed):						
Cow	3.0	62.5	24.1	8.2	2.2	12.0
Buffalo	4.1	63.2	18.0	12.3	2.4	7.7
From cream (sweet-washed):						
Cow	1.4	70.2	27.3	Traces	1.1	3.6
Buffalo	1.7	80.8	16.2	Traces	1.3	3.5

11.17.3 Food and nutritive value. Ghee-residue is a rich source of milk fat, proteins and minerals. The residue obtained from the desi butter ghee process is appreciably richer in proteins and minerals.

11.17.4 Yield. This is influenced by the percentage of solids-not-fat in the raw material, the method of ghee making and the technique used for the separation of the residue. The higher the solids-not-fat, the higher the outturn; the lower the final temperature of clarification, the higher the yield (due to the greater residual moisture content in the residue); the lower the pressure used in squeezing out surplus fat from the residue, as in hand pressing when compared to mechanical pressing, the higher the yield, and vice

(117) Adapted from S. N. Prahlad, M.Sc. Thesis: University of Bombay (1954).

versa. The comparative yields of residue by the different methods of ghee making are given in Table 11.36.

11.17.5 Colour. This normally varies from light-brown to deep-chocolate. The colour of the residue is chiefly influenced by the temperature-time of heating given; the higher the intensity of heat-treatment, the darker the colour, and vice versa.

11.17.6 Recovery of ghee from ghee-residue. Two methods have been developed, viz. the centrifugal and pressure techniques. The centrifugal method consists of transferring the occluded ghee to water by heating the ghee-residue in water and centrifuging the water-fat phase; the pressure method (hand-screw or hydraulic) consists of subjecting the heated ghee-residue to a limited pressure in a hand-screw or hydraulic press. The hand-screw method has been recommended for adoption by ghee manufacturers as it is simple, efficient, practical and economical (because it increases the amount of fat recovered) (118).

Note: In the dairy industry, a common procedure for the recovery of ghee from ghee-residue is to place the residue in milk cans, pour enough water to submerge the entire residue in it and then heat up the mixture with live-steam. Next, the level of water in the can is brought up to the neck (to make it easier to remove the ghee-layer on top at a later stage). The can with its contents is then moved to the cold store (5–10°C). The ghee-layer, which surfaces at the top, is then added towards the last stages of the next batch of ghee making. The process is continuous.

11.17.7 Uses

(i) For direct consumption, as such, with rice or chapati in producer's household (when made in small quantities);

(ii) for the preparation of ghee-toffees;*

(iii) for the preparation of pastes to be used as spreads in sandwiches and in dosa and samosa ;*

(iv) for the preparation of a burfi-type sweet (the method has recently been standardized)* (119).

---

* See 12.6.5.

(118) K. Viswanathan, S. D. T. Rao and B. R. Reddy: *Indian J. Dairy Sci.* **26**(4), 345 (1973).

(119) B. B. Verma and S. De: *Indian J. Dairy Sci.*, **31**(4), 370 (1978).

12 DAIRY BY-PRODUCTS

12.1 Introduction

During the manufacture of dairy products, there invariably arises the problem of the utilization of by-products. Because of their great and unique nutritional value, the most rational method of utilization from the standpoint of general welfare is in food products; usually this is the most profitable method as well. Conversion of edible substances into non-food items is not ordinarily justifiable especially in countries where there is an overall shortage of milk supplies. It has always been realized that economic disposal of by-products is an essential prerequisite to profitable dairying. In recent years there has been widespread and increasing interest throughout the world in creating newer channels of utilization for the by-products of the dairy industry.

12.2 Definition

A dairy by-product may be defined as a product of commercial value produced during the manufacture of a main product. (However, what is currently a by-product may become the main product in the future.)

12.3 Classification

(a) The important dairy by-products in developed dairying countries are given in Table 12.1.

TABLE 12.1

By-products of Western dairy industry

Main product	By-product
Cream	Skim milk
Butter	Buttermilk
Cheese ⎫ Casein ⎭	Whey

(b) The by-products of the Indian dairy industry are given in Table 12.2.

TABLE 12.2

By-products of Indian dairy industry

Main product	By-product
Cream	Skim milk
Butter	Buttermilk
Ghee	Lassi*
	Ghee residue
Chhana/Paneer Cheese Casein }	Whey

12.4 Composition

The average percentage composition of some by-products is given in Table 12.3.

TABLE 12.3

Composition of some by-products (percentage)

Name of by-product (from cow milk)	Composition				
	Water	Fat	Protein	Lactose	Ash
Skim milk	90.6	0.1	3.6	5.0	0.7
Buttermilk (sweet cream)	91.0	0.4	3.4	4.5	0.7
Lassi	96.2	0.8	1.4	1.2	0.4
Ghee residue (sweet-cream butter)	9.7	61.4	24.8	—	4.1
Chhana whey	93.6	0.5	0.4	5.1	0.4
Cheese whey	93.1	0.3	0.9	4.9	0.6
Acid-casein-whey	93.1	0.1	1.0	5.1	0.7

SOURCE: Miscellaneous.

* Produced in larger quantities than any other Indian by-product.

12.5 Principle of Utilization

The broad principles for the utilization of the various dairy by-products, both foreign and Indian, together with the names of commonly made food-products, is given in Table 12.4.

TABLE 12.4

By-products, their principle of utilization and names of food products made

By-product	Principle of utilization	Food products made
Skim milk	Pasteurization	Flavoured milks
	Sterilization	Sterilized flavoured milk
	Fermentation	Cultured buttermilk Acidophilus milk Bulgarian buttermilk
	Fermentation and concentration	Concentrated sour skim milk
	Concentration	Plain condensed skim milk Sweetened condensed skim milk Low-lactose condensed skim milks (Frozen condensed skim milk)
	Drying	Dried skim milk
	Coagulation	Cottage cheese Bakers' cheese Quarg Gammelost Sapsago Casein (edible)
Buttermilk	Fermentation and concentration	Condensed buttermilk
	Drying	Dried buttermilk
	Coagulation	Soft cheese
Whey	Fermentation	Whey beverage Yeast whey
	Concentration	Plain condensed whey Sweetened condensed whey Whey protein concentrate Whey paste Lactose

By-product	Principle of utilization	Food products made
	Drying	Dried whey
	Coagulation	Ricotta cheese
		Mysost ⎫ Gjetost ⎬ cheese Primost ⎭
Lassi	Icing and seasoning	Beverage
Ghee-residue	Processing	Toffee or paste or indigenous sweetmeat

12.6 Methods of Utilization

The utilization of the various by-products resulting from the manufacture of different products, has been described briefly as follows:

12.6.1 Skim milk. Its use in the standardization of milk, cream, etc. has already been discussed.

A. *Flavoured milks.* (See 2.4).

B. *Sterilized flavoured milks.* (See 2.4).

C. *Cultured buttermilk.* (See 2.7).

D. *Acidophilus milk.* (See 2.7).

E. *Bulgarian buttermilk.* (See 2.7).

F. *Concentrated sour skim milk.* Acid (lactic) is used as a preservative agent. The required acidity of about 2 per cent is produced by encouraging a lactic fermentation with *Lactobacillus bulgaricus* and an *Acetobacter* in the skim milk which is then concentrated to about one-third of its weight. In actual practice, fresh, sweet skim milk is pasteurized at 77–82°C (170–180°F), No Hold and cooled to 46°C (115°F). Now 2 per cent starter is added and properly mixed into it. It is incubated at the same temperature (46°C) for 1 ᵢ–18 hours after which the acidity should be between 1.7 to 2 per cent lactic acid. The curd is then thoroughly broken up and concentrated in a single effect evaporator; forewarming is unnecessary. The final concentrated product should have an acidity of 5–6 per cent (lactic) to ensure not only good keeping quality but also a smoother texture and a more stable product. It is used in developed dairying countries primarily as an animal feed for poultry and pigs.

G. *Plain condensed skim milk.* (See 8.13).

H. *Sweetened condensed skim milk.* Similar procedure as for condensed milk, except that the first standardization is not necessary. (See 8.7)

J. *Low-lactose condensed skim milks.* These are skim milk derivatives from which part of the lactose has been removed or hydrolysed. They were first developed to prevent sandiness in ice cream and to improve the body and texture.

K. *Frozen condensed skim milk.* (See 8.15)

L. *Dried skim milk.* (See 9.14 and 9.15)

M. *Cottage cheese.* (See 7.12)

N. *Baker's cheese.* This originated in the U.S.A. It is similar to cottage cheese but softer and finer-grained. It is acid in flavour and is drained without cooking or washing. The curd, which may or may not be salted, is marketed for commercial use for making cheese cakes, pies or pastries. Its keeping quality is as low as that of cottage cheese.

P. *Quarg cheese.* This is an European cheese made from fermented skim milk. It is similar to Baker's cheese. However, cream is usually blended into it before it is packaged, thereby producing a product containing as much as 10 per cent fat and 75 per cent moisture. It is generally consumed fresh.

Q. *Gammelost cheese.* This semi-soft blue-mould cheese originated in Norway. Pasteurized skim milk is ripened with 0.5 to 1.0 per cent lactic starter for 1 or 2 days at 18–24°C (65–75°F).

The sour mixture is heated to 63°C (145°F) for 30 minutes, the curd broken into pieces and packed into cloth-lined forms which are covered and placed in boiling whey for $3\frac{1}{2}$ hours. Following its removal from the hoops, it is air-dried and pierced with metal needles inoculated with *Penicillium roqueforte* and cured at 11°C (52°F). It develops a rather sharp aromatic flavour during its 4 weeks of curing.

R. *Sapsago cheese.* This originated in Switzerland. It is a very hard, cone-shaped, greenish grating cheese which derives its flavour and colour from the leaves of an aromatic clover mixed into it. It has a sharp pungent flavour and a pleasing aroma.

Slightly soured skim milk is boiled in a round kettle. Cold buttermilk is slowly added while it is being heated and stirred. The coagulum that appears on the surface is removed and set aside. Sufficient sour whey is then added to precipitate the casein and the stirring is stopped. The curd is dipped, mixed with the coagulum that had been set aside, and spread in boxes to cool and drain away. Lids are placed on the boxes and pressure is applied for at least 5 weeks at a temperature of 16°C (60°F). The ripened dry curd is ground and mixed with 5 kg. of salt and 2.5 kg. of powdered clover leaves for every 100 kg. of curd. The mixture is stirred into a homogeneous paste and packed into truncated cones and cured for 5 months.

S. *Casein-Industrial*

I. *Introduction.* An important utilization of skim milk is in the production of industrial casein which, however, is a non-food item. Because of its widespread demand, industrial casein is prepared extensively throughout the world. There are two types of industrial casein, viz. acid casein and rennet casein. The casein precipitated by various acids is called acid casein, free casein or (simply) casein; while that precipitated by rennet is called rennet casein. The two types of casein have different uses.

II. *Types of casein*

(a) *On the basis of the coagulating agent used:*

(i) Acid casein

(ii) Rennet casein.

(b) *On the basis of the particular acid used:*

(i) Hydrochloric acid casein

(ii) Sulfuric acid casein

(iii) Nitric acid casein

(iv) Lactic acid casein: 1. Direct precipitation 2. Self-soured.

(c) *On the basis of the texture of the curd:*

(i) Grain curd casein

(ii) Cooked curd casein

(iii) Pressed curd casein.

III. *General method of manufacture of acid casein*

(a) *Flow diagram of manufacture*

Receiving skim milk
|
Precipitating
|
Draining and washing
|
Pressing
|
Milling and spreading
|
Drying
|

(Contd. on next page)

Grinding
|
Packaging
|
Storage

(b) *Details*

(i) *Receiving skim milk.* Fresh, clean, sweet skim milk which is as fat-free as possible should be used.

(ii) *Precipitating.* Casein exists in milk as a calcium caseinate-calcium phosphate complex. When an acid is added to milk, this complex is dissociated. At about pH 5.3, the casein begins to precipitate from the solution; and at the iso-electric point of casein, about pH 4.7, maximum precipitation occurs. The casein coagulates as a watery, gel-like curd. The gel is broken to allow for the expulsion of the water from it. The precipitation of casein involves three considerations: acidity and pH, temperature, and the speed at which it is stirred. Once out of solution, casein does not dissolve appreciably in either a slightly more acid or alkaline solution. However, a little more acid is added after precipitation till a pH of 4.1 is reached in order to dissolve the calcium which flows out with the whey; the texture of the curd is thereby also improved (it becomes coarse). Washing, which is done so as to remove the impurities, viz. whey, proteins, lactose, salts and acid, also becomes easier.

The temperature should be carefully controlled during precipitation, since the casein curd is sensitive to heat. A jacketed vat is recommended for this purpose. The effect of temperature on the character of curd is shown in Table 12.5.

TABLE 12.5

Effect of temperature of precipitation on character of casein curd

Temperature of precipitation	Character of casein curd
Less than 35°C/95°F	Soft and fine; slow to settle and difficult to wash
35–38°C/95–100°F	Coarse, provided it is not stirred too quickly; quick to settle and easy to wash
More than 38°C/100 F	Chewing-gum texture (i.e. stringy, lumpy and coarse)

Stirring is essential to distribute the acid uniformly but it should always be done at slow speed. Rapid stirring at less than 38°C (100°F) produces so fine a curd that it settles very slowly when being drained and washed, and is likely to be partly lost in the whey and washings.

Note: When hydrochloric or sulfuric acids are used for precipitation, they are diluted with water to prevent any local injury to the curd (through the action of concentrated acid, even though agitation may be rapid). The proportion of acid and water is given in Table 12.6,

TABLE 12.6

Dilution of acids used for precipitation

Name of acid	Proportion (by weight)		Remarks
	Acid	Water	
Hydrochloric	1	3–9	—
Sulfuric	1	6–30	Add acid to water for dilution

(iii) *Draining and washing*. The longer the casein curd stands in the whey, the more difficult it becomes to remove the impurities (viz. whey proteins, lactose, salts and acid). Hence the whey is removed promptly. The first step in this regard is to allow the curd to settle and then push it back from the gate/outlet end of the vat. Next, the gate strainer is fixed in position and another cloth-lined strainer hung at the discharge end of the gate to recover small curd particles. Then the whey is drained off promptly.

As soon as the whey ceases to run freely, cold wash-water is added in quantities approximately equal to the amount of whey removed. The wash water is made very slightly acidic (pH 4.1), especially for the first washing. The curd is well-stirred in the wash-water, but care is taken not to break it into fine particles; it is then allowed to settle, and the wash water drained as above. It should be washed at least twice.

Note: Inadequately washed casein is less soluble than thoroughly washed casein, has less adhesive strength and develops more colour when dry.

(iv) *Pressing*. The wet curd is pressed to remove as much water as possible, so as to reduce the cost of drying. Normally it is not possible to reduce the moisture level in the pressed curd to less than 55 per cent.

(v) *Milling and spreading*. After being pressed, the curd is milled to produce particles of a uniform size and surface for drying. If it is not milled, it dries unevenly. Pressed curd should be promptly milled and dried, in order to prevent spoilage by mould and bacterial action. Milling should be of the shredding variety. The milled curd should be evenly spread over standard perforated trays with a fixed amount of curd to ensure adequate drying. The lowest tray should be of a finer mesh than the others and may be covered with a cloth to catch fine particles falling from above.

(vi) *Drying*. It is essential to control the temperature and humidity of the intake air correctly if the curd is to be efficiently dried. Once started, drying should not be interrupted till the moisture content has been reduced to less than 8 per cent. The intake air temperature may range from 71 to 77°C (160 to 170°F), while the outlet air temperature should be between 52 and 57°C (125 to 135°F) in order to avoid the risk of discolouring the casein and impairing its solubility.

(vii) *Grinding*. Before it is ground, casein should be properly cooled, since warm casein becomes plastic in a grinder and sticks to it. The fineness of grinding depends on the requirement of the user. Uniformity in size of ground casein is ensured by passing it through screens of a particular mesh size.

(viii) *Packaging*. The dried casein, whether ground or unground, is normally packaged either in gunny bags lined inside with closely woven cloth, or in heavy 3-ply paper bags with polythene liners.

(ix) *Storage*. The filled packages of casein should be closed air-tight and transferred to a clean, dry storage room maintained at a uniform temperature. Wide variations in storage temperature will cause the casein to 'sweat' and mould. If stored in a damp atmosphere, it will absorb water and deteriorate. For long storage, it is best to store casein in a basement, away from the sun.

IV. *Manufacturing particulars of some acid-caseins*

(a) *Grain-curd casein*. A high-grade acid-casein, low in ash and readily soluble, is made by the grain-curd process, provided the pH and temperature are closely controlled. A jacketed vat is essential for accurately controlling the temperature. The best product is obtained by using hydrochloric acid, but lactic or sulfuric acids can also be successfully used.

(i) *Direct precipitation.* Skim milk is held close to 38°C (100°F) for lactic, 37°C (98°F) for sulfuric and 35°C (95°F) for hydrochloric acids. The pH of 4.1 is obtained by slowly adding dilute acid while also gently stirring the milk. The curd is settled, drained, washed twice or thrice with water at 32°C (90°F) and pH 4.1, and finally, once with cold neutral water. The washed curd is pressed, dried, ground and packaged.

(ii) *Self-soured (lactic).* Skim milk is held at 38°C (100°F). An active, high-acid producing, lactic starter is added at 10 per cent of the skim milk and thoroughly mixed into it. Acidity is allowed to develop up to 0.55 per cent. Then the temperature of the curd is raised to 40–41°C (104–106°F), and the curd stirred until clear whey separates. The curd is now settled and the whey drained off as quickly as possible. The speed at which it is drained is more important than the thoroughness of the operation. Then lactic whey, containing about 2 per cent acid and previously heated to 38°C (100°F), is added and stirred until the pH is 4.1. The granular curd is settled, drained and washed twice or thrice with acidulated water of pH 4.1 and temperature 32°C (90°F), and finally once with cold neutral water. The washed curd is pressed, dried, ground and packaged.

(b) *Continuous process casein.* There are two processes which are used commercially, viz. the Sheffield process and the Universal process. Their principle of manufacture may be outlined as follows: the skim milk and precipitating acids are mixed and the mixture dropped into a riffle-trough. The slope of the trough may be altered to vary the size of the curd particles—the steeper the slope, the finer the particles obtained. From the riffle-trough, the curd and whey mixture drops to an inclined vibrating screen, which allows the whey to pass through but advances the curd to a 2-roll press where it enters a beater. Here it is broken up sufficiently to allow it to pass through the perforated bottom to a second inclined vibrating screen, where it is washed with sprays of water. The washed curd enters another 2-roll press and passes through another beater, after which it is ready for drying.

V. *Method of manufacture of rennet-casein.* High quality fresh, sweet skim milk is essential. This is heated in a jacketed vat up to 36–38°C (96–100°F). Sufficient rennet and calcium chloride are added to the skim milk to give a setting time of 20–30 minutes. The rennet should previously have been diluted with about 15–20 times its weight in water (by volume); calcium chloride is also used @ 1 per cent solution. The coagulum is agitated for 2–5 minutes after co-agulation begins but before the coagulum reaches a solid clot, so as to produce curd particles of an optimum size for further processing. Simultaneously with agitation, the temperature of the curd is raised to 54–66°C (130–150°F). The curd is cooked at this temperature for about 30 minutes. After cooking, the curd is processed in the same manner as acid caseins (wash-water being neutral).

VI. *Method of manufacture of buttermilk-casein* (120). The method for the isolation of casein from buttermilk/lassi may be briefly outlined as follows: the casein in the buttermilk is first dissolved by adding enough sodium hydroxide solution at 32°C (90°F) to raise the pH to 7.5. It is then precipitated by adding dilute hydrochloric acid to a pH of 4.6. The curd is settled, whey drained, curd washed and pressed, and then the wet curd dissolved once more, this time at 38°C (100°F) in dilute alkali. The solution is passed through a cream separator to remove fat. The casein from the separated por-tion is re-precipitated by dilute acid, the curd settled and whey drained; the curd now obtained is finally washed, pressed, dried, ground and packaged. Although a fairly acceptable casein is obtain-ed by this 'Double alkali treatment-cum-mechanical separation process', it has been found to be uneconomical.

Note: The buttermilk-casein tends to precipitate in a soft, finely divided condition, which makes it difficult to wash the curd without excessive loss. Moreover, it contains a greater quan-tity of fat and becomes highly coloured during drying.

VII. *Yield of acid-casein.* The yield is roughly equal to the per-centage of casein in the skim milk and may vary from 2.8 to 3.2 per cent, depending on whether it is cow or buffalo skim milk.

VIII. *Specifications for casein*

(a) *Acid casein.* This is normally yellowish white in colour for cow and chalky white for buffalo milk, has a faint pleasant odour, a slightly acid taste; a total acidity equivalent to not more than 10.5 ml and N/10 alkali per g., not more than 10 per cent moisture; not more than 1 per cent fat (on moisture-free basis), not more than

(120) M. C. Badami: M.Sc. Thesis, University of Bombay (1952).

4.0 per cent ash (on moisture-free basis) and not less than 14.25 per cent nitrogen (on a moisture-, fat- and ash-free basis).

(b) *Rennet casein.* This is normally light-yellowish in colour for cow and whitish for buffalo milk, has a faint agreeable odour, is tasteless, has a pH of about 7.0, not more than 10 per cent moisture and approximately 7.5 per cent ash.

IX. *Defects in casein, their causes and prevention.* Defects in casein arise from the use of low-grade raw material (skim milk), faulty methods of production and drying, etc. The important defects, their causes and prevention are given in Table 12.7.

TABLE 12.7

Defects in casein, their causes and prevention

Name of defects	Causes	Prevention
Browning	(i) Overheating of casein when drying	(i) Maintaining the optimum casein drying temperature
	(ii) Presence of excess fat in casein during drying	(ii) Using low-fat skim milk for casein manufacture
	(iii) Presence of sulphuric acid/sulfate in casein during drying.	(iii) Proper washing of curd.
Poor solubility	(i) Excessively high temperature of cooking curd	(i) Optimum temperature of cooking curd
	(ii) Overheating of casein during drying	(ii) Maintaining optimum casein drying temperature
	(iii) Moulding of curd before drying.	(iii) Proper drying of the wet curd.
Low adhesive strength	(i) High ash content in casein	(i) Adequate washing of curd
	(ii) Moulding of curd before drying.	(ii) Prompt drying of the wet curd.

X. *Uses of casein.* The two types of casein, viz. acid and rennet, have separate uses and one type cannot be used as a substitute for the other. The various uses of industrial casein are given below:

(a) *Rennet casein.* Plastics (such as buckles, brush-backs, buttons, costume jewellery, umbrella handles, etc.).

(b) *Acid casein*

(i) Adhesive (glue);

(ii) paper coating;

(iii) paint;
(iv) fibre;
(v) bristles;
(vi) films;
(vii) leather finish;
(viii) textile finish;
(ix) spreader for insecticide;
(x) medicine (silver and mercury caseinate).

Note: The food uses of casein are given under 'edible casein'.

T. *Casein* (*edible*)

I. *Definition*. Edible casein may be defined as casein which has been isolated from skim milk by taking special precautions to ensure its suitability for use in patented food and pharmaceutical preparations. These precautions are concerned chiefly with: (i) strict control of the quality of the raw material (skim milk); (ii) use of standard equipment and technique for production; (iii) maintenance of strict hygienic conditions of production, and (iv) packaging and storage under approved conditions.

II. *Specifications*. The Indian Standard Specifications for casein (edible quality) are given in Table 12.8.

TABLE 12.8

Indian Standard Specifications for casein
(edible quality) (IS: 1167, 1965)

Characteristics	Requirement
Moisture (% wt.) Max.	10.0
Total ash (% wt.) (On dry basis) Max.	2.5
Acid insoluble ash (% wt.) (On dry basis) Max.	0.1
Fat (% wt.) (On dry basis) Max.	1.5
Nitrogen (% wt.) (On dry basis) Max.	14.5
Total acidity in terms of ml. of 0.1N NaOH (per g.)	6.14
Free acidity in terms of ml. of 0.1N NaOH (per 10 g.) Max.	5.6
Bacterial count (per g.) Max.	50,000
Coliform count (per g.) Max.	10
Mould count (per g.) Max.	50
Rate of solubility	To conform to test

III. *Method of preparation.* On lines similar to those followed for acid casein (preferably grain-curd, hydrochloric), under the special precautions mentioned above. These include: (i) precipitation of the curd at pH 4.1–4.3; (ii) at least 3 separate washings of the curd in waters of proper pH and with a contact time of 15–20 minutes each; (iii) last but one washing with hot water at 71–77°C (160–170°F), which effects pasteurization of curd for reducing bacterial count; (iv) last washing with neutral water at 41°C (105°F); etc.

IV. *Uses.* In its original form or as sodium caseinate, edible casein is used in various food products such as: (i) ice cream; (ii) coffee whiteners; (iii) imitation milk; (iv) whipping powders: (v) instant breakfast; (vi) water binders in sausages, and (vii) protein hydrolysates.

12.6.2 Buttermilk

A. *Condensed buttermilk.* Also known as semi-solid buttermilk, this is usually sweet cream buttermilk which has been ripened and condensed (approx. 3:1) in much the same way as concentrated sour skim milk. Alternatively, sour-cream buttermilk may be used without ripening it, but the acidity (lactic) of the buttermilk prior to its being condensed should be greater than 1.6 per cent. This will ensure in the finished product a 5–6 per cent acidity, which is necessary for long keeping quality. Either sour whey or an organic acid (such as lactic, acetic, citric or tartaric) may be used to increase the acidity of buttermilk. While the older packages were air-tight wooden barrels, a modern package might consist of an acid-resistant, tight plastic film with a suitable fibre board container. Condensed buttermilk is also used for feeding pigs and poultry.

B. *Dried buttermilk* (See 10.2).

C. *Soft cheese from buttermilk* (121). The production of soft cheese from creamery buttermilk may be outlined as follows: fresh buttermilk, obtained by churning sweet-cream butter, is admixed with fresh skim milk in the proportion of 1:1. The mixture is pasteurized at 65°C for 20 minutes, cooled to 35°C, inoculated with lactic starter @ 10 per cent and allowed to set for 3 hours. The curd is cut with standard cheese knives and the curd cubes subjected to a cooking process during which a maximum of 40°C is reached in

(121) S. De, O. N. Mathur and G. Kumar: *Indian Dairyman*, **26**(9), 363 (1974).

15-20 minutes. The curd cubes are then collected in a muslin cloth and pressed overnight, preferably inside a cold store (5-10°C), to remove excess moisture. The pressed curd, which has a rather low keeping quality, can be utilized either for direct consumption after the addition of sugar @ 15 per cent, or in the manufacture of processed cheese up to 10 per cent of raw cheese.

Note: An Indian work on preservation of (creamery) buttermilk has been reported. (122)

12.6.3 Whey

A. *Whey beverages*: The whey obtained as a by-product of cheese industries has long since been employed in the production of fermented beverages, both alcoholic and non-alcoholic (acidic). The production technique of one such beverage of the acidic type is described below.

Whevit (123). Utilization of whey in the production of a soft drink called whevit may be outlined as follows: fresh whey obtained from chhana (or paneer) making is passed through a cream separator and the separated whey then steamed for 30 minutes in a double-jacketed vat. It is cooled to room temperature and kept overnight to allow the precipitated proteins to settle down, and then filtered through a muslin cloth. Now 50 per cent sugar syrup @ 22-23 per cent of whey, 10 per cent citric acid @ 2-2.1 per cent of whey and sugar mixture, and selected colour and flavours in requisite amounts are added. The above mixture is inoculated with a culture of *Saccharomyces Cerevisae* @ 1 per cent of yeast whey broth. (Whey broth is prepared by adding 1 per cent sugar in filtered whey and sterilizing it at 15 lb. pressure for 15 minutes; the inoculum is prepared by inoculating it with the yeast culture and incubating it for 48 hours at 25°C.) After mixing the inoculum in the whey, it is incubated at 22°C for 14-16 hours. The bottles with their contents are then crown-corked to retain the carbon dioxide and pasteurized at 75°C for 30 minutes in hot water, cooled and stored at a low temperature (5-10°C).

Alternatively, 'carbonated' whevit may be prepared. As in the

(122) J. L. Bhanumurthi and K. S. Trehan, *Indian J. Dairy Sci.*, 22(11), 275 (1976).

(123) P. P. Bhamba, V. K. N. Nambudripad and M. R. Srinivasan, NDRI Publication No. 136.

above, the manufacturing process consists of receiving the whey, separating and steaming it, cooling and precipitating proteins, filtering, adding sugar syrup, citric acid, colour and flavour. The mixture is then filled at 5–10°C into the carbonation-cum-bottling plant for carbonation and crown-corking. The bottles and their contents are subjected to pasteurization at 75°C for 10 minutes in hot water, then slowly cooled and stored at a low temperature (5–10°C) till marketed. Whevit bottles should be gently inverted 2 to 3 times, if required, to make the product homogeneous.

B. *Yeast-whey.* This is a newly developed product. A world-wide protein deficiency makes the production of yeast from whey particularly attractive, as a much needed food supplement rich in proteins and vitamins can be made from a substrate which is often used inefficiently or wasted.

The factors involved in its production are: (i) *type of whey*: a selection is made from wheys resulting from cottage, cheddar or similarly made cheese, or casein whey; the whey is separated if necessary, to remove the fat which makes drying of the finished product difficult; (ii) *supplementation of whey*: this is done by adding nutrients such as phosphorus, ammonium sulphate, etc., which help to maximize yields; (iii) *type of yeast*: yeast extract or brewer's yeast (preferably containing *Saccharomyces Fragilis*) is a necessary additive; (iv) *pH*: the optimum is 5.0 to 5.7 for maximum yeast production; (v) *temperature*: the optimum for the growth of yeast-whey is 31–32°C (89–91°F); (vi) *size of inoculum*: this is determined by the time required to obtain maximum yield, and (vii) *oxygen*: there should be sufficient oxygen to allow for the growth of yeast.

The yeast suspension is concentrated with a centrifuge so that a slurry of 15–18 per cent solids is produced. It may be washed at this point so that the final product is more bland in flavour. The yeast-slurry can be roller or spray-dried. The dried product can be used as a food supplement for proteins and vitamins.

C. *Plain condensed whey.* This is made by pasteurizing the separated whey and draining the hot liquid into the vacuum pan. The whey may be condensed to any degree up to 70 per cent total solids. Condensed whey is highly supersaturated with lactose, which may crystallize in the pan itself and prevent the viscous product from flowing. If crystallization in the pan can be avoided, a smooth-bodied paste will flow from the pan as a clear syrup. This must then be rapidly cooled to about 32°C (90°F), seeded with lactose and run into containers. It may be used in human and animal food products; it is valuable in confectionary, baked foods and cheese foods and makes excellent chicken feed.

D. *Sweetened condensed whey.* Separated, pasteurized, sweet, cheese whey (Cheddar or Swiss) with a quantity of sugar equal to the weight of the solids in the whey, is drawn into a vacuum pan and condensed to at least 75 per cent total solids. The concentrate is cooled to 35°C (95°F), seeded and stirred slowly for 1 to 3 hours to crystallize the lactose. It may be packed in barrels or cans. It has a salty taste and a characteristic whey flavour. It has good whipping properties (provided well-skimmed whey is used as the raw material); the whipped, sweetened, condensed whey may be used in fruit whips, certain candies and frozen dessert preparations.

E. *Whey protein concentrates.* These include soluble and coagulated whey proteins. Earlier soluble whey proteins were recovered from separated sweet cheese whey by partially neutralizing it, condensing it to 62 per cent total solids, holding it at 3°C (38°F) for 18 hours with occasional stirring, and then centrifuging the mother liquor. More recently, using the modern tools of electrodialysis, gel filtration, and reverse osmosis, commercial processes for concentrating undenatured whey proteins have been developed. Coagulated whey proteins may be recovered by their heat-denaturation and acid precipitation, followed by filtration or centrifuging. The whey proteins separated by any of the above processes may be used in baking, baby foods, ice cream mixes, whipping agents, emulsifying agents, etc.

F. *Whey paste.* This is manufactured in Russia by pre-concentrating a mixture of whey and skim milk in a vacuum evaporator, and adding sufficient sugar syrup, butter and cream so as to obtain 15 per cent sugar, 15 per cent fat and 65 per cent total solids in the finished product. After slowly cooling it to 48°C, vanillin is added and the product cooled rapidly to 18–20°C before packaging.

G. *Lactose*

I. *Introduction.* Lactose normally occurs in either one of its two crystalline forms or as a non-crystalline glass. The more common crystalline form is that of α-lactose hydrate, which is regarded as the lactose of commerce. By far the most important source of lactose in the major producing countries is cheese-whey, although hydrochloric-acid-casein-whey is still considered to be the best source for its production. In India, chhana-whey is produced in larger quantities than any other whey, and should, therefore, be the great-est source of lactose in the country. However, its collection from small-scale and scattered producers needs to be systematically orga-nized.

II. *Grades of lactose.* The common grades of lactose are: crude, edible and USP. Crude lactose is the product obtained in the first stage of the common process of manufacture and contains many impurities; it is ordinarily used for refining lactose to the USP grade. The edible grade contains less impurities than crude, but is below the standards for USP; it is suitable for use in infant foods. The USP grade is obtained by refining edible-grade lactose and meets the highest standards of purity; it is used in pharmaceutical prepara-tions and for infant feeding. The specifications for the above grades of lactose are given in Table 12.9.

TABLE 12.9

Specifications for various grades of lactose

Particulars	Requirements		
	Crude	Edible	USP
Lactose, percentage	98.4	99.0	98.85
Moisture, nonhydrate, percentage	0.3	0.5	0.1
Protein (N × 6.38), percentage	0.8	0.1	0.01
Ash, percentage	0.4	0.2	0.03
Lipids, percentage	0.1	0.1	0.01
Acidity, as lactic percentage	0.4	0.06	0.04
Standard Plate Count (per g.)	*	Less than 30	Less than 30
Coliforms, sporeformers, moulds, yeasts (per g.)	*	—ve	—ve

* Not determined routinely for this grade.
SOURCE: *By-Products from Milk* by Webb and Whittier (1970).

III. *Method of manufacture*

(a) *Principle.* The lactose is separated from the whey (rennet or acid) by the simple process of concentration and crystallization. The whey is pre-treated for the removal of impurities, viz., whey proteins, salts and acid, primarily for two reasons: (i) to reduce the viscosity of the concentrated whey so as to make separation of lactose crystals possible, and (ii) to increase the purity of the recovered lactose. The lactose crystals are then removed from the concentrate in a centrifuge, while most of the whey proteins and salts pass on to the remaining liquid called the mother liquor, which is used for animal feed or cooked food.

(b) *Flow diagram of manufacture*

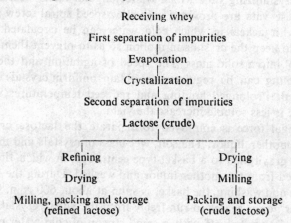

Receiving whey
|
First separation of impurities
|
Evaporation
|
Crystallization
|
Second separation of impurities
|
Lactose (crude)
|

Refining	Drying
Drying	Milling
Milling, packing and storage	Packing and storage
(refined lactose)	(crude lactose)

(c) *Details of manufacture.* (Adapted from Webb and Whittier).
The whey (rennet or acid) is run into an iron tank/vat and boiled by means of live steam supplied by perforated pipes set in the tank. During the heating, milk of lime may be added gradually in the case of acid-whey until the acidity has been reduced to about 0.05 per cent (pH 6.2). When the milk proteins have completely coagulated, the steam is stopped and the whey allowed to stand undisturbed for a few minutes to enable the impurities to settle as a sludge.

The clear whey is drawn to a storage vat that feeds it to a double or triple-effect evaporator, the sludge being left in the vat to be filtered later. The whey is concentrated to about 20° Baume (equivalent to a lactose content of 30 per cent). The impurities that separate from the whey during the first stage of concentration are removed by filtering the whey in a filter press. Subsequently the sludge from the coagulating vat is passed through the same press. The partially purified whey may be combined with the earlier whey before proceeding with the second stage of evaporation, while the press-cake may be used for poultry feeding.

The partially concentrated and filtered whey is drawn into a single-effect vacuum evaporator for the second stage of evaporation, which is generally done up to 40° Baume. Part of the lactose crystallizes during its concentration in the pan and the operator observes the progress of crystal formation by looking through the sight glass. When graining has progressed sufficiently, it is 'struck'.

The hot mass of crystals and syrup (51–60°C/125–140°F) is dropped into crystallizing vats, which are rectangular tanks with round bases. These vats are provided with slow-speed spiral screw agitators and with jackets in which cold water can be circulated. It is essential to keep the crystals in motion so as to prevent them from 'setting up' into a solid mass. The speed of agitation and the rate of the cooling can be regulated to obtain uniform crystals of the size desired. Prolonged holding and reduced temperatures where the lactose is less soluble increase the yield.

Centrifugal force is employed to separate the lactose crystals from the mother liquor. The soft, wet mass of crystals and mother liquor are gravity-fed to a basket-type centrifuge, in which the lactose is freed from the mother liquor and washed. During the initial separation and washing, the basket is spun at about 600 rpm. When the mother liquor ceases to run freely from the sugar crystals, the remainder is washed off with a small stream of cold water played on the crystals. The speed of the basket is then increased to 1200 rpm to remove as much of the wash water as possible. The crude sugar which emerges from the centrifuge is either refined promptly or dried at 79°C (175°F) in a rotary drum drier.

The refining of crude sugar to produce a sugar of USP grade requires that a solution of the lactose be treated to remove colour, protein and salts. The crude sugar is dissolved in water or washings from a previous batch, in a stainless steel tank, by means of live steam, the proportions of sugar and water being adjusted so that the Baume reading is 20° (which indicates an approximate 30 per cent lactose solution). For each 100 kg. of sugar in the batch, one-fourth kg. of a filtering aid and 1 kg. of decolorizing paste are added. The decolorizing paste consists of 3 parts bone black, 1 part activated carbon, 1 part 36 per cent hydrochloric acid and enough water to make a paste that is easy to handle. The treated solution is boiled and its acidity adjusted to 0.09 per cent (lactic) with hydrochloric acid. Before filtering, this acidity is lowered to 0.05 per cent with milk of lime. Over-neutralization should be avoided, as this will cause the sugar to caramelize and become discoloured. After the lime treatment, the solution is boiled vigorously for a few minutes and then allowed to stand until the flocculated mixture of carbon, protein and insoluble salts have settled. It is then filtered through cloth in a filter press, using first a filter aid such as diatomaceous earth and then some fine-textured rag paper. The clear solution is drawn into a single effect evaporator and concentrated to about 40° Be. This is followed by crystallization (initiated by seeding), centrifuging, washing, drying, milling, packaging and storage on similar lines as for crude sugar. However, particular attention must to paid to details so as to meet the standards for USP grade.

IV. *Yield.* The first crop of crude lactose should contain about 70 per cent of the sugar present in the whey and between 85 to 90 per cent lactose. (The second crop of crystals is difficult to separate and the yield is variable.) The conversion of crude to refined sugar gives an aproximately 90 per cent yield, but overall yields amount to nearly 100 per cent, depending upon the lactose content of the crude, since the mother liquor and washings are re-processed.

V. *Specifications.* The Indian Standard Specifications for lactose, commercial, are given in Table 12.10.

TABLE 12.10

Indian Standard Specification for lactose, commercial
(vide IS: 1000, 1959)

Characteristic	Requirement
Total ash (% weight), Max.	1.5
Acidity	To conform to test
Fat (% weight), Max.	2.5
Nitrogen (% weight), Max.	0.05
Lactose (% weight), Min.	90.0
Specific rotation	52.0–52.6
Lead (ppm), Max.	2.5
Arsenic (ppm), Max.	1.0

VI. *Uses*
  (i) In the preparation of humanized milk;
  (ii) in infant food;

(iii) in caramels or fudges;

(iv) in solid pharmaceutical preparations such as pills and tablets;

(v) in silvering mirrors;

(vi) in bakery products.

H. *Dried whey* (See 10.3).

J. *Ricotta cheese.* This is a product of Italian origin. It is made from cheese whey. Skim milk, buttermilk or whole milk are added to raise the milk-solids level and improve precipitation and flavour. The whey protein is coagulated by heating it to 85°C (185°F) or above, and adding sour whey, citric acid, or white vinegar. The precipitate, which rises to the surface, is dipped and drained, and after being cooled, is salted and packaged. It is sometimes pressed into forms, surface-salted and cured, and used for grating.

K. *Mysost, Gjetost and Primost cheese.* These are of Scandinavian origin. Mysost is made from cow-milk whey, Gjetost from goat-milk whey, and Primost from whey containing additional milk fat. All the whey-solids are utilized. Primost is light tan in colour with a sweet caramelized flavour and a smooth creamy body. Mysost and Gjetost are darker brown and have a coarser texture.

Sweet whey is condensed in a double effect evaporating pan to 60 per cent total solids and further concentrated in an open drying kettle to 84 per cent total solids. It is heated and constantly agitated, until it reaches a plastic condition with a definite brown colour. The plastic mass is transferred to a kneading box and stirred while it cools to prevent the formation of large lactose crystals. While still warm, it is packed in cubical boxes and cooled until it can be cut and packaged. If no evaporating equipment is available, the whey can be condensed by boiling it in open kettles. The coagulated protein is skimmed off during the operation, and later re-mixed into the concentrate when it reaches one-fourth of its original consistency. It is vigorously stirred until it attains the consistency of mortar and is transferred to a kneading box and handled as above.

12.6.4 Lassi. Also known as desi (indigenous) buttermilk, this is largely consumed by the producer's household after seasoning it with salt or sugar, or fed to his cattle. In view of its very small-scale and scattered production, it would be a highly uneconomical proposition to attempt to collect and utilize it.

12.6.5 Ghee-residue. This is a nutritious food containing fat, denatured protein, burnt lactose and minerals. Although usually consumed with sugar in the producer's household, it is generally wasted in the large ghee manufacturing/blending concerns. Indian research so far has shown that it can be utilized in the preparation of candy and chocolate; and can be used as a paste as sandwich-spread and with Indian foods such as idli, dosa and samosa.

Before its utilization, it is desirable to remove the excess fat from the ghee-residue. This can be done by enclosing the material in a piece of muslin cloth and keeping the bundle suspended in a boiling waterbath for 30–40 minutes. The bundle is then taken out and the water allowed to drain out first by itself, and then gently squeezed when partially cool. After this, the residue is given a pre-treatment by boiling it in a similar manner in 10 per cent sodium bicarbonate solution, which should be constantly stirred during cooking.

The processed cooked ghee-residue can be made into candy and chocolate as follows: (i) *Candy*. A 50 per cent sugar syrup is first prepared. The cooked residue is thoroughly mixed into the syrup in a karahi by means of a khunti. The mixture is heated on a low fire until a good deal of water has evaporated. To this sticky mass, powdered dry coconut may be added and the candy evenly spread on a plate (5–10°C) for an hour or so to allow it to cool. It is then cut into small cubes and wrapped in parchment paper for storage at room temperature till marketed. (*Note*: For every 1 kg. of cooked residue, the sugar required is 500 to 625 g. and dry coconut powder 125 to 250 g.). (ii) *Chocolate*. The cooked residue is mixed with 50 per cent sugar syrup as above. To the sticky mass, cocoa powder and skim milk powder are added and stirred vigorously till a pat is formed. The finished product is spread on a plate and allowed to cool (5–10°C) overnight. It is then cut into slabs or cubes and wrapped in parchment paper for storage at room temperature before being marketed as above. (*Note*: For every 1 kg. of cooked residue, the sugar required is 500 to 625 g., cocoa powder 60 to 90 g. and skim milk powder 250 g.)

For making the paste, the procedure is as follows: the cooked residue is first mixed with salt @ 2.5–3 per cent, then with marmite (a yeast product) @ 0.1–0.5 per cent, and heated on a low fire for about 5 minutes till a paste is formed. This can be used in sand-wiches. Alternatively, the salted residue is mixed with chutney powder @ 2–4 per cent, ground thoroughly and then heated as above to yield a paste for use with idli, dosa and samosa.

For making a burfi-type sweet, the recently-developed method is as follows: the processed (sweet) ghee-residue is mixed with standard-quality khoa (prepared from 5 per cent standardized buffalo milk with a moisture content of 30 per cent in khoa) in the proportion of 1 : 1 of total solids content. This mixture is heated in a steam-jacketed kettle, and thoroughly agitated with a khunti to ensure proper mixing. All the crystal sugar to be used (calculated @ 45 per cent of total solids in the khoa and 75 per cent of total solids in the processed residue) is now added to the mixture, which is then worked rigorously for 10–15 minutes, so as to dissolve the sugar completely. Approximately one-third of the sweetened mass is separated and chocolate (@ 8 per cent of the total solids content of the processed residue khoa) well-mixed into it. This portion, containing the dissolved chocolate, is applied as a thin layer over the remaining two-thirds of the mixture, which has already been spread out as a thick layer on a well-greased tray. This combined mass is allowed to cool and set and then cut into pieces of a uniform size and shape for packaging and sale. The product has been called 'chocsidu' burfi (119).

APPENDIX I

PACKAGING OF MILK AND MILK PRODUCTS

1. Introduction

Packaging is the technique of using the most appropriate containers and components to protect, carry, identify and merchandise any product. It constitutes a vital link between the manufacturer and eventual consumer for the safe delivery of the product through the various stages of manufacture, storage, transport, distribution and marketing.

In spite of all the efforts taken to produce high-grade processed milks or manufactured dairy products, unless they are delivered in a fresh, sound and convenient form to the consumer, they are likely to be rejected, thus causing enormous wastage. This loss can be minimized to a great extent by adequate protective packaging to withstand the hazards of climatic changes, transportation, handling, etc.

As a result of socio-economic changes, packaging has become increasingly important in the scheme of distribution. The criteria by which a package is judged are usually the following: it must protect and preserve the commodity from the time it is packed to the point of consumption; it must be suitable for the chosen selling and distribution system; it must be attractive to the consumer, easy to open, store and dispose; and it must cost no more than the market can bear.

The importance of packaging as a means of promoting exports has been well recognized in recent times. Packaging is today an essential part of any industrial activity and an integral part of the modern marketing complex.

2. Definition

Packaging means placing a commodity into a protective wrapper or container for transport or storage.

3. Functions

A package must perform the three-fold functions of containing, protecting and merchandising:

(a) *To contain the product.* The package/container should be adequately large to hold the product. It should have proper constructional features so as not to allow leakage and spillage. It should have enough strength to withstand handling, transportation and storage hazards. Finally, it should also be as compatible as possible with the product.

(b) *To protect the product.* The package should safeguard the product against contamination or loss and damage or degradation due to microbial action, exposure to heat, light, moisture and oxygen, accidental spillage, evaporation, pilferage, etc.

(c) *To help in selling the product.* The shape of the package should be favourable to dispensation and reclosure, and to its disposal or re-use.

Note: Apart from the above, the package should lend itself to operation on whatever machines are available; be economical; be printable on the exterior surface (with regard to type and quantity of product, manufacturer's brand and quality/grade, instruction for purchaser on how to use the product, etc.), and have sales appeal.

4. Present Status of the Packaging Industry

(a) *In developed countries.* The packaging industry in developed countries has made tremendous advances. The consumer is extremely package conscious. With newer marketing systems like supermarkets, self-service stores, etc., packaging technology in these countries has risen to great heights. Newer and better packaging materials, development of packaging machinery and appliances, improved system of packaging, etc., have all advanced in an integrated manner. In fact, Western packaging technology is undergoing a revolution.

(b) *In developing countries.* In contrast, the packaging industry in many developing countries (such as India) is still in its infancy. The benefits of adequate and functional packaging seem to have touched only the fringe of the population. In such countries, there was no attempt, until recently, to establish industries. After World War II, many countries which had been under colonial rule became independent, one by one. Political change in turn brought about the need for rapid industrialization and an improvement in their economy. The requirement of foreign exchange, it was realized, could be met only through exports. Instead of traditional goods, manufactured items now had to be exported to the highly sophisticated markets abroad. This required the use of better packaging materials and improved packaging techniques.

Note: The estimated per capita expenditure on packaging in 1972 was: U.S.A., Rs 460; U.K., Rs 280; Japan, Rs 217; and India, Rs 6.

5. Packing Materials and Forms

(a) *Materials*. These include: paper and paper-based products (coated or lined), glass, tin-plate, aluminium foil, timber (wood), plastics and laminates.

(i) *Paper and paper-based products*. These may be kraft paper (bleached or unbleached); grease-proof paper; vegetable-parchment paper (butterpaper); glassine paper; wax-coated paper; plastic-coated paper; paper boards (straight or corrugated); solid-fibre boards; liner boards; box-boards; etc. The papers are used commonly in the form of wrappers, cartons, boxes, bags, cups, etc.; while boards are used as cartons, boxes, etc. The merits of paper are: its relative weightlessness, its printability, low cost and easy disposal; on the other hand, it has the demerits of low tear and wet-strength (unless treated or coated).

(ii) *Glass*. May be transparent or opaque (coloured). Transparency may be an advantage or disadvantage. (Thus, while the customer would prefer direct vision of the milk in the bottle, ultraviolet light may degrade the milk.) Used in the form of bottles, jars, jugs, tumblers, etc. Glass has the merits of strength, rigidity, chemical inertness, an excellent gas and water vapour barrier; and the demerits of heavy weight and fragility.

(iii) *Tinplate*. This consists of a thin sheet (0.025 mm thick) of mild steel coated on both sides with a layer of pure tin. (The tinning may be carried out either by the hot-dipping or electrolytic process.)

For packing certain products, it is desirable to use an internally lacquered can which provides greater resistance to corrosion. Tin-plate has the merits of good strength, excellent barrier properties, etc.; and the demerits of high cost, heavy weight, difficult reclosure and disposal, etc. Used mostly in the form of cans.

(iv) *Aluminium foil*. The common thickness of this medium for use in food products is 0.012–0.015 mm. To increase corrosion resistance, it may be coated with lacquer or plastic. It has good barrier properties, is grease-proof, non-sorptive, shrink-proof, odourless and tasteless, hygienic, non-toxic, opaque to light, bright in appearance, etc. On the other hand, it has low tear strength, is attacked by certain strong alkalis and acids, does not heat-seal by itself, etc. Used in the form of wrapper, carton, box, etc.

(v) *Timber*. Should be free from odour, have an attractive appearance and necessary mechanical strength. May be treated with casein-formalin, or sprayed with paraffin-wax or plastics, to make it more water-resistant and prevent the passage of the timber-taint to butter. Used in the form of a box, tub, cask or barrel.

(vi) *Plastics*. The use of plastics in packaging has made tremendous advances in recent years throughout the world. A wide variety of rigid plastics can be used as thermoformed, injection-moulded or blow-moulded containers, such as bottles, cartons, cups, boxes, etc. The merits of rigid plastic containers are its low cost and ease of fabrication; and its demerits are lack of product compatibility, low barrier properties, plastic deterioration, lack of resistance to high heat and fragility at low temperatures.

Flexible plastic packaging films are used as wrappers or sachets/bags/pouches. These are of two types, viz., low polymers and high polymers. *Low polymers*—These include cellophane (coated with plain or nitrocellulose/saran/polyethylene (polythene), treated cellulose, etc. *High polymers*—These include polyethylene*, polypropylene, polystyrene, polyvinyl chloride, polyvinyledene chloride (cryovac), rubber hydrochloride (pliofilm), polyester, polyamide (nylon), saran (a mixed polymer), etc. Many new films have already been developed

---

*Polyethylene, abbreviated as polythene is obtained in two different forms, viz., low density polytehylene (LDPE) and high density polyethylene (HDPE). LDPE is a low cost film with moderate tensile strength. It is a good moisture but poor oxygen barrier. It gives excellent liquid-tight seals. HDPE offers excellent moisture protection and increased stability to heat. Polythene is the largest single film and high-polymer product to be used in the flexible packaging industry.

and others are in various stages of development.

The merits of flexible packaging films are: they can be easily applied and the packaging-process can be readily mechanized; loss of moisture in dairy products is practically nil; it protects food from attack by micro-organisms, insects etc; it is a cheap and convenient method of packaging; humidity control of the surrounding air is not necessary during storage; etc. Its demerits are: not all technical problems in film packaging have been solved; failure to obtain a perfect seal and remove all air before packaging may lead to spoilage; the most careful attention to detail is necessary, else faulty production will result; etc.

Note. Only 'Food-grade' plastics should be used for packaging milk and milk products, since this will prevent the transfer of any toxicity (if present) from the package material to the product.

(vii) *Laminates.* These are formed by combining the complete surfaces of 2 or more webs of different films, with the primary object of overcoming the defects of single films. Laminations are made for the following reasons: to further strengthen the film material (i.e., toughness, tear resistance, etc.); to improve barrier properties; to improve grease-resistance; to provide a surface that will heat-seal; etc. Some typical laminates are: paper-polythene; cellophane-polythene; aluminium foil-polythene; paper-aluminium foil-polythene; polyester-polythene; etc. Used as sachet/bag/pouch or cartons.

(viii) *Others.* These include textiles (such as cloth, jute, hessian) for use in the form of bags, sacks, etc.

B. *Forms.* These consist mainly of: bottles, cartons, sachets/bags/ pouches, boxes/tubs, casks/barrels, cups and collapsible tubes. Also in use are jars, jugs, tumblers and sacks.

(i) *Bottle.* The glass bottle still continues to be the most frequently used package for milk in the world. However, in several developed countries, it has already lost ground to single service containers. The merits and demerits of the glass bottle have already been discussed (See p. 71).

Rigid plastic bottles are also in use for milk and liquid milk products. The plastic bottle systems in common use are:

Beku } W. Germany
Humba }

Mecaplast } Switzerland
Bottle pack }

(ii) *Carton.* This is a common package for milk; also used for liquid, frozen and coagulated milk products. Cartons are commonly made of 'food' grade paper coated on the inside with wax or plastics; or lined with paper, plastic films or aluminium foil; or made of laminates. Its merits are: maximum space utilization in vehicles and storage; ability to carry attractive printing, and convenience as a means for stacking milk on supermarket shelves. Retailers in developed countries consider it the best available package for self-service selling. Cartons (paper and board) also play a significant role in the bulk packaging of milk.

Cartons are commonly available either as preformed containers or as precut blanks ready to be formed into containers. The carton systems in common use are:

Perga (preformed)	—	U.K.
Pure Pak (precut)	—	U.S.A.
Zupack ⎱ (precut) Blockpak ⎰	—	W. Germany
Tetra Pak (precut)	—	Sweden

(iii) *Sachet/bag/pouch.* Flexible water-proof plastic bags are commonly used for packaging milk and liquid milk products. Since it is difficult to pour from these, a jug is usually also provided. The popular laminate for such bags is black or dark brown (to exclude ultra-violet light) or white. The bags may be formed from either a reeled or flat film. Generally it is a form/fill/seal system. Ultra-violet light may be used to sterilize the film. The bags are heat-sealed and cut, the common sequence being to bottom-seal, fill, move down on sachet length, top seal and cut off.

(iv) *Can.* This is commonly used for all types of solid, semi-solid and powdered products. Cans are traditionally made of soldered tinplate steel, generally lacquered on the inner surface to prevent corrosion. Recently aluminium cans have been introduced. Cans are the most convenient for gas packing.

Note: Can coatings (lacquer or plastics) are now considered essential for food products. Coatings, especially in the interior of cans, must be non-toxic and free from off-flavours; they must not deteriorate, or come loose from the can-wall during processing or storage.

(v) *Box/tub.* May be made of wood or paper board. While wooden boxes/tubs are used for the bulk packing of butter and butteroil with butterpaper/plastic liners, paper board boxes are generally used as over-wraps.

(vi) *Barrel/cask*. Commonly made of wood and coated with wax on the inner surface. Used for bulk packaging of sweetened condensed milk, semi-solid buttermilk/whey, butteroil, etc.

(vii) *Cup*. Made of paper with wax or plastic coating on the inside. Used for frozen and coagulated products.

(viii) *Collapsible tube*. Generally made of aluminium and lacquered on the inside. Its merits are: low cost; light-weightedness; ease of handling and dispensing; product protection; etc. Used for semi-fluid products such as sweetened condensed milk, processed cheese spread, etc.

6. Packaging Machinery

In developed countries all types of packaging machinery are available, including those for the production of basic packaging materials and for converting these into finished packages, for filling and sealing, handling and storage, printing, testing, etc. Developing countries, on the other hand, are largely dependent upon imported machinery. It is in this field that there is an urgent need of improvement, as lack of suitable packaging machinery is impeding the productivity of industrial and consumer goods.

7. Standardization in Packaging

The adoption of standard packaging materials and techniques, both with regard to testing and usage, would go a long way to improving productivity, as well as national and international trade. The Indian Standards Institution is already engaged in the development of standards both for packaging materials and filled packages for use in this country. With rapid industrialization and the improvement in transportation methods, packaging standards would have to be reviewed periodically so as to effect an economy in packaging—which is so vital, particularly in international trade.

8. Package Disposal

After product use, the empty packages have necessarily to be discarded. These constitute a fair proportion of the solid waste produced by the community, especially in big cities. The collection and proper disposal of these empty packages should be a concern of the Municipal/Public Health Authorities. The common disposal methods include land-in-fill, incineration and bio-deterioration; and care should be taken, when selecting them, to avoid subsequent atmospheric or land pollution.

APPENDIX II

PROBLEMS IN THE USE OF BUFFALO MILK DURING MANUFACTURE AND STORAGE OF VARIOUS PRODUCTS

1. Introduction

Over 50 per cent of the total milk production in India consists of buffalo milk (see Table 1.4). As it has a higher fat and total solids content, buffalo milk gives greater outturn of milk products than cow milk. However, due to some basic differences in its physico-chemical properties, the use of buffalo milk creates a few special problems during product manufacture and storage. A review published over a decade ago highlighted this aspect. (124)

Considerable research on the physico-chemical make-up and standardization of techniques in the manufacture of several products from buffalo milk has been carried out in this country over the past two decades by various scientific and industrial workers. These have been briefly summarized in a recent publication (125) from which Tables A-1 to A-3 in this appendix have been adapted.

2. Basic Differences in the Physico-Chemical Properties of Cow and Buffalo Milks

(a) *Compositional differences.* Buffalo milk, in general, contains higher amounts of milk solids, viz., fat, proteins, lactose, minerals, SNF and TS than cow milk, as shown in Table A-1.

---

(124) S. Parkash, *Indian Dairyman*, **17** (4), 137 (1965).
(125) N. C. Ganguli, *NDRI Publication No. 143* (1976).

TABLE A-1

Compositional differences between cow and buffalo milks (percentage)

Type of milk	Country	Composition						
		Water	Total solids	Fat	Solids-not-fat	Pro-tein	Lac-tose	Ash
Buffalo	USSR	82.00	18.00	8.00	10.00	4.32	4.96	0.84
–do–	Egypt	83.60	16.40	6.37	10.03	3.87	5.00	0.79
–do–	Italy	83.14	16.86	7.22	9.64	3.95	4.88	0.81
–do–	India	82.98	17.02	7.06	9.96	3.90	5.28	0.78
Cow	USA	86.61	13.39	4.14	9.25	3.58	4.96	0.71
–do–	*India	86.07	13.93	4.90	9.43	3.42	4.91	0.70

Note: Buffalo milk has a higher casein content (3.00 per cent) than cow milk (2.65 per cent).

(b) *Physico-chemical differences.* Buffalo milk normally has a higher pH, acidity, buffer value, density, viscosity, and fat globule size than cow milk, as shown in Table A-2.

TABLE A-2

Physico-chemical characteristics of cow and buffalo milks

Characteristics	Buffalo milk	Cow milk
pH	6.7	6.6
Buffer value (at pH 5.1)	0.0417	0.0359
Density at 20°C	1.0310	1.0287
Viscosity (cp)	2.04	1.86
Specific Refr. Index	0.2061	0.2059
Surface tension	55.4	55.9
Acidity	0.15	0.14
Fat globule size (mm.)	5.01	3.85
Phosphatase (units)	28	83
Ultra-violet fluorescence	Greenish-yellow	Pale bluish

(c) *Casein differences.* It has been established that there exist distinct differences in the physico-chemical make-up of casein from buffalo milk as compared with that of cow milk. The proportion of miscellar casein is greater in buffalo milk, while that of soluble casein is very low. The particle size of the buffalo miscellar casein is larger (135 μM) than that of the cow micellar casein (90 μM). The buffalo micelle is more opaque (when suspended in a different medium) than the cow micelle. Turbidity studies with the casein micelle in different buffer systems, and also in the presence of rennet, show that turbidity develops more quickly in buffalo casein, due perhaps to its higher proportion of calcium.

(d) *Whey-protein differences.* Certain differences have been noticed in the whey-proteins of buffalo milk as compared with those of cow milk.

(e) *Milk fat differences*

(i) *Analytical constants.* Buffalo milk fat has a higher Reichert value, Saponification value, Kirschner value and melting point, but a lower Polenske value, Iodine value and butyro refractometer index than cow milk fat.

(ii) *Fatty acid composition.* Buffalo milk fat is higher than cow milk fat in butyric, palmitic, stearic and oleic acids, but lower in caproic, caprylic, capric, lauric and myristic acids, as shown in Table A-3.

TABLE A-3

Major fatty acid composition of buffalo and cow milk fats

Fatty acid	Buffalo milk fat	Cow milk fat
Butyric	4.4	3.2
Caproic	1.5	2.1
Caprylic	0.8	1.2
Capric	1.3	2.6
Decinoic	Trace	0.3
Lauric	1.8	2.8
Myristic	10.8	11.9
Palmitic	33.1	30.6
Stearic	12.0	10.1
Oleic	27.2	27.4
Linoleic	1.5	1.5
Linolenic	0.5	0.6

(f) *Mineral-salt differences.* Buffalo milk contains more calcium and phosphorus (0.22 per cent and 0.13 per cent respectively) than cow milk (0.12 per cent and 0.09 per cent respectively). The calcium/ phosphorus ratio is higher in buffalo milk (2.26) than cow milk (1.96). There are more cations (calcium and magnesium) in buffalo milk, but fewer anions (phosphate and citrate). Lastly, the soluble forms of calcium, magnesium and citrate are lower in buffalo milk than cow milk.

Note: Due to a high salt-balance ratio, i.e. a high ratio of calcium →+ magnesium/citrate + phosphate, buffalo milk has a low heat-stability.

3. Problems in Product Manufacture and Storage

The problems arising out of the compositional and physico-chemical characteristics of buffalo milk in the manufacture and storage of various products from this raw material, together with their speci- fic causes and suggested preventive measures, viz., modified techniques, have been summarized below:

(a) *Cheese.* Due to differences in the micellar composition of milk-protein, especially casein, and in the fatty-acid make-up of milk fat, and in its higher buffer value, calcium, casein and fat levels, buffalo milk behaves quite differently from cow milk both during the manufacture and curing of cheese.

The major problems faced by cheese-makers and suggested modified techniques are: (i) slow ripening (i.e. acidity develop- ment) in milk; (ii) faster rennet action (i.e. low rennetting time; (iii) excessive syneresis (i.e. lower retention of moisture); (iv) slow cheddaring (i.e. mellowing of curd); (v) slow curing of cheese (slow proteolysis and lipolysis causes a delay in the development of the characteristic cheese flavour and body and texture); (vi) slightly bitter taste in cured cheese (quite often), and (vii) hard body and texture in cured cheese.

The modified technique includes, among other things: (i) adjust- ment of casein/fat ratio to 0.70 (same as for cow milk); (ii) addition of more starter culture (for proper acidity development); (iii) addi- tion of less rennet (to ensure proper rennetting time and prevent the development of a bitter taste in cured cheese); (iv) lower temperature and a longer cooking period (to ensure proper develop- ment of acidity and greater retention of moisture); (v) piling cheese

3-high during cheddaring (for greater retention of moisture), and (vi) curing cheese first at a high temperature (10–12°C) for 2 months for rapid flavour development, and then at a low temperature (2°C) for desirable body and texture changes (126).

(b) *Condensed milks* (sweetened and unsweetened). Due to: (i) differences in micellar composition of milk-proteins, especially casein; (ii) higher levels of milk proteins (both casein and serum-proteins), milk fat and milk-sugar; (iii) higher calcium content and lower heat-stability of milk. Buffalo milk behaves quite differently from cow milk not only during production but also during the storage of condensed and evaporated milks.

The major problems faced by condensed milk manufacturers are: (i) greater likelihood of undesirable gel formation during production of both condensed and evaporated milks; (ii) greater incidence of age-thickening during storage of both condensed and evaporated milks; (iii) greater possibility of sandiness defect in sweetened condensed milk, and (iv) greater incidence of browning discolouration and cooked flavour development during storage of both condensed and evaporated milks.

The modified technique includes, amongst other things: (i) adjustment of the fat : SNF ratio to 1 : 2.44 (same as for cow milk); (ii) addition of stabilizer (trisodium citrate or disodium phosphate) to correct the salt-balance ratio; (iii) pre-heating of milk to 115–118°C/No hold, to ensure freedom from gelation in the resulting product; (iv) addition of sugar in the form of a 65–71 per cent syrup to milk in the correct concentration (43–44 parts sugar for every 31 parts milk solids) in the standardized milk and at the right stage (towards the end of the condensing period) for SCM only; (v) cooling and crystallization of the product at the proper stage and in the correct manner (viz., when total solids reach about 75 per cent, condensing is stopped, the product cooled to 27.5–29.5°C and seeded with lactose by the standard technique as for cow milk) for condensed milk; (vi) storage at 5–8°C to ensure maximum shelf-life and minimum browning-discolouration and cooked flavour development, and (vii) regular inversion of the canned product during storage to prevent sedimentation (127).

(126) Adapted from M. R. Srinivasan and S. D. Burde: *NDRI Publication No. 85* (1972).

(127) Adapted from J. L. Bhanumurthi, B. N. Mathur, K. S. Trehan, M. R. Srinivasan and O. Samlik: *Food Ind. J.*, 4(1), 3 (1971).

Note: The heat-stability of buffalo milk has recently been studied. An empirical formula to assess approximate heat-stability (expressed as the time taken by milk to coagulate at 120°C), of a given sample of milk from the knowledge of its fat and total calcium contents has been suggested (128). It has been observed that exchange of calcium by sodium in the caseinate-complex enhances the heat-stability of milk; this effect increases with increase in the extent of the exchange, but as the sodium to calcium ratio in the complex exceeds 1 : 2, there is a marked destabilization of milk (129).

(c) *Milk powder* (*whole and skim*). The chief differences of buffalo milk as compared to cow milk which come into play seem to be: (i) higher level of milk proteins (both casein and serum-proteins); (ii) high calcium content, and (iii) micellar differences in milk proteins, especially casein.

The major problems noticed during manufacture and storage are: (i) low heat-stability, and (ii) low solubility of the resultant dried product.

The modified technique should include: (i) adjustment of the fat: SNF ratio to approximately 1 : 2.7 (same as for cow milk); (ii) addition of stabilizers to correct the salt-balance ratio; (iii) the use of correct pre-heating drying temperatures (air inlet and outlet), and (iv) gas packing.

Note: (i) Amul Dairy, Anand, has been successfully manufacturing milk powder (whole and skim) by the spray process on a commercial scale from buffalo milk since 1956.

 (ii) Buffalo milk powder shows less resistance towards oxidation, a higher free fat content, lower wettability and dispersability, and a higher solubility index as compared to cow milk powder under identical conditions of production, packaging and storage (130).

(d) *Infant milk food.* The causes, the problems and the modified

(128) B. R. Puri, H. Narain, U. Joshi and S. K. Verma: *Indian J. Dairy Sci.*, **30**(1), 24 (1977).

(129) B. R. Puri, H. Narain and S. K. Verma: *Indian J. Dairy Sci.*, **30**(1), 27 (1977).

(130) U. M. Ingle: Ph.D. Thesis, Mahatma Phule Agricultural University (1971).

technique are much the same as for milk powder. Amul Dairy, Anand, has been a pioneer in the successful manufacture of infant milk food, using the formula evolved under the joint collaboration of the Central Food Technological Research Institute, Mysore, and Amul (see 10.9). Amul baby food (roller dried) came into commercial production in 1960 and Amul spray baby food in 1967. Several other Indian manufacturers have also gradually become successful in the production and marketing of their brands of infant milk food from buffalo milk.

(e) *Butter.* It has been pointed out earlier that buffalo milk contains a higher level of fat, larger-sized fat globules and a differential fatty-acid make-up in its milk fat as compared to cow milk. In Table A-3, it will be seen that buffalo milk fat contains larger amounts of fatty acids with a high melting point, such as palmitic and stearic, which contribute towards its hardness. Buffalo milk fat has been reported to be distinctly harder than cow milk fat (131). Due to this difference, the triglycerides are expected to crystallize much earlier in buffalo milk fat than in cow milk fat; and at a given temperature, the amount of crystallized or solid fat should be higher in buffalo cream than cow cream. This is bound to have a practical significance in butter-making, as for instance in the conditions of cooling and ageing of cream, in the churning process and in the rheological properties of butter (132). Two Indian studies carried out support this conclusion: in one (133), it was observed that to obtain the lowest fat loss in buttermilk when churning cream into butter, buffalo cream needed a fat level of 35 per cent, while cow cream required a fat level of 40 per cent under identical conditions; in another (134), buffalo butter was observed to show greater hardness value (about twice as much) than cow butter under identical conditions of production and testing.

(f) *Ghee.* The differential fatty acid make-up of buffalo milk fat plays an important role in the granulation and shelf-life of buffalo ghee as compared to cow ghee. It will be observed in Table A-3 that buffalo milk fat is richer than cow milk fat in butyric, palmitic and stearic acid contents. The higher content of higher melting

(131) M. K. Rama Murthy: *Indian Dairyman,* **28**(9), 415 (1976).

(132) A. B. Nabar, M. R. Srinivasan and K. K. Iya: *Indian J. Dairy Sci.,* **22**(4) 237 (1969).

(133) S. De and B. N. Mathur: *Indian Dairyman,* **20**(12), 351 (1968).

(134) P. K. Gupta and S. De *Indian J. Dairy Sci.,* **23**(1), 67 (1970).

glycerides of palmitic and stearic acids are responsible for larger grains in buffalo ghee.

Further, since a fat in the solid state is hydrolysed more slowly, the rate of hydrolysis of buffalo ghee is slower; that is why buffalo ghee is less vulnerable to the development of a rancid flavour than cow ghee. Further, probably due to its higher content of highly unsaturated tetraenoic and pentaenoic fatty acids, buffalo milk fat is less stable to autoxidation than cow milk fat. These are reflected in the common observation that buffalo ghee has a poorer shelf-life than cow ghee (135).

(g) *Chhana.* Due to: (i) higher level of milk fat; (ii) higher calcium and milk protein contents (especially casein), and (iii) micellar differences in milk proteins, buffalo milk shows differences from cow milk in the physico-chemical properties of chhana. Buffalo chhana is normally greasy, hard in body and coarse in texture and does not produce the best sweets (viz. rossogolla and sandesh).

The modified technique adopted by the trade for obtaining a better chhana from buffalo milk consists of: (i) partially defatting the milk (by skimming off the top layer of cream after boiling and simmering the defatted milk), and (ii) adopting coagulation-cum-straining procedures which help to retain a higher moisture level. The technique of using buffalo milk for the production of chhana, which will be suitable for the preparation of high quality rossogolla, for adoption in organized dairies has been standardized.*

(h) *Khoa.* Although khoa made from buffalo milk is different in its physico-chemical properties from its counterpart made from cow milk, it is not considered inferior. Rather, buffalo milk khoa is well known to produce better sweets, such as barfi, kalakand, gulabjamun, etc. than cow milk khoa.

Concluding remarks. It has already been pointed out that the low heat-stability of buffalo milk is due to its high calcium content and that heat-stability can be improved by the partial replacement of calcium with sodium and potassium. The attention of Indian scientists has already been drawn to this problem. This modification of mineral composition by ion-exchange treatment by electrometathesis has been studied (136). Such treated buffalo milk has been

(135) M. K. Rama Murthy: *Indian Dairyman*, 28(9), 415 (1976).
*See footnote (68) in Chapter 11.
(136) R. Balachandran: Ph.D. Thesis, submitted to Punjab University.

observed to behave more or less like cow milk. This course of action seems to be indicated for adoption in the future by manufacturing dairies engaged in the routine production of cheese, condensed milks, dried milks, chhana, etc., from buffalo milk both in this country and abroad.

4. Manufacture of Gouda Cheese from Buffalo Milk*

On the basis of an ICAR Scheme carried out at the Central Dairy of Aarey Milk Colony, Bombay, in the nineteen sixties, the method of manufacture of Gouda cheese from buffalo milk has been standardized.† A step-by-step comparison has been made in the table below of the production technique of Gouda cheese from foreign cow and Indian buffalo milk.

Table A-4 Gouda Cheese from Foreign Cow and Indian Buffalo Milk

Steps in manufacture	Cow milk (foreign)	Buffalo milk (Indian)	Remarks (regarding buffalo cheese)
Receiving milk	Of high quality.	Of reasonably good quality.	Desirable to have a min. MBR time of 1 hr 30 mts and acidity (lactic) of not more than 0.15%.
Standardization of milk	Clarified and then standardized to 2.8% fat and C/F ratio of 0.70.	C/F ratio of 0.65–0.70.	A lower C/F ratio results in greater fat loss in whey, and cured cheese has an oily texture accompanied by fat leakage from cut surface; a higher ratio results in a crumbly body.

(Continued on next page)

*Gouda cheese is a hard-pressed variety of cheese of Dutch origin. It is made from cow's milk and is exported as orange or red waxed wheels with parallel flat sides, and weighs between 4.5 to 5.5 kg. It is a sweet-curd renneted cheese made from partly defatted milk. The curd is cooked with little acid development. The presence of some shiny 'eyes' (of less than 12.5 mm. diam.) is considered normal in this cheese.

†*Indian Farming*, March 1966, p. 18.

Steps in manufacture	Cow milk (foreign)	Buffalo milk (Indian)	Remarks (regarding buffalo cheese)
Pasteurization of milk	72°C to 15 sec. and cooled to 30°C.	72°C for 15 sec. and cooled to 31°C.	—
Addition of starter	Usually 1.5% of milk with no ripening.	Usually 1% of milk with 1 hr ripening at 31°C.	Desirable to have an acidity (lactic) of 0.7–0.85% in starter.
Addition of potassium nitrate (to both types of milk)	Usually 15 g. per 100 kg milk.	Usually 12 g. per 100 kg milk.	To check the growth of gas-forming bacteria, which causes cheese to blow.
Addition of colour	Usually 9–18 ml. per 100 kg. milk.	Usually 7–8 ml. of standard (Danish) colour per 100 kg. milk.	—
Addition of rennet	Usually 28 ml. of single-strength rennet (1 : 15,000) pre-diluted in at least 20 times water per 100 kg. milk.	Usually 3 g. of standard (Danish) rennet powder pre-diluted in 40 times water per 100 kg. milk.	Desirable to have coagulation in 35 mts at 31°C.
Cutting of curd (as for cheddar cheese)	When coagulum is firm (softer than cheddar).	When coagulum is slightly more firm than cow's.	Curd more fragile than cow's.
Cooking of curd	(1) Stir gently till acidity rises by 0.02% at 30°C.	(1) Stir gently till acidity rises by 0.005% in 35 mts.	—
	(2) Drain off one-third whey and replace with water (15% of remainder) at 55–60°C.	(2) Drain off one-third whey and replace with water (15% of remainder) at 60–70°C.	Higher temp. of added water yields dry curd.
	(3) Hold at 37–38°C with gentle stirring for 30 mts till curd cubes firm.	(3) Stir gently for 15 mts at 36°C.	Higher cooking temp. yields dry curd.

Steps in manufacture	Cow milk (foreign)	Buffalo milk (Indian)	Remarks (regarding buffalo cheese)
Drainage of whey	Introduce wooden drainboards, slitted and cloth-lined (on inside) and press curd under whey; when all whey removed, cut curd into large blocks.	Same as for cow.	—
Hooping of curd	Cut portions of curd (at 30° or above) into suitable sizes as required to fill (circular) hoops.	Same as for cow.	—
Pressing of curd	Final pressure same as for cheddar.	Same as for cow.	Desirable to press curd while warm.
Brine salting of cheese	Brine of conc. 18–20% and pH 4.8–4.9%; brining time is 3 days for 4 kg. cheese block, which is inverted a few times daily.	Brine at 18°C and of conc. 21–22%; brining time is 2 days for 3 kg. block, which is inverted a few times daily.	Higher brine conc. yields lower moisture in cheese.
Drying of cheese	Same as for cheddar.	See under 'curing' below.	
Paraffining of cheese	–do–, but using orange or red-coloured wax.	Same as for cheddar.	—
Curing of cheese	Same as for cheddar; a max. period of 3–4 mths. at 15°C is required.	*I Stage*: First 4 weeks under 95% humidity; cheese has to be washed and turned daily. After rind formation (in 4 weeks), cheese ready for paraffining	(1) For washing, mixture of 75% whey + 25% starter is satisfactory (2) Optimum temp. of curing is 18°C

(Continued)

Steps in manufacture	Cow milk (foreign)	Buffalo milk (Indian)	Remarks (regarding buffalo (cheese)
		II *Stage*: Paraffined cheese kept for 6–8 weeks under 80–85% humidity for curing at 18°C.	(3) During curing cheese inverted 3 times per week.

Note: 1. Cheese curd from buffalo milk undergoes excessive syneresis (due to a high concentration of calcium-ions in the milk) and has a low moisture-retaining capacity. Hence a longer curing period is required and the desired body and texture develop more slowly in the finished product.

2. Cheese made from milk diluted with 15% water has been found to be of satisfactory quality.

APPENDIX III

RHEOLOGY OF DAIRY PRODUCTS*

The word 'rheology' is derived from the Greek verb meaning 'to flow'. In 1928, Professor Bingham of the U.S.A. defined rheology as the science of deformation and flow of matter. Rheology is a branch of knowledge with direct application not only to butter and cheese making but to many other dairy products like ice cream, evaporated and condensed milk, etc. It should also be applicable to Indian dairy products such as khoa, chhana, rabri, etc.

1. Scope of Rheology

The term 'Rheological Properties' of dairy products includes such physical properties as hardness, elasticity, plasticity, viscosity, cohesiveness, adhesiveness, spreadability and standing-up qualities. These properties are to a considerable extent mutually interdependent. They are also clearly important from a practical point of view. Thus, the standing-up property or resistance to deformation under its own weight is an essential quality of butter, which normally has to stand on the grocer's counter for some time. Its spreadability, i.e. the ease with which it can be cut, spread or kneaded, is a question of everyday importance to the housewife.

In the grading of several dairy products, considerable importance is given to body and texture. The exact meaning of body and texture has not yet been clearly defined. Certain properties such as hardness and softness obviously refer to 'body', while others such as openness obviously refer to 'texture'. The assessment of the body and texture of dairy products by the grader is carried out by subjective tests which are dependent on the accuracy and consistency of

*Adapted from S. De and P. K. Gupta: 'Rheology of Dairy Products', *Indian Dairyman*, 23(1), 12 (1971).

human observation, and are subject to certain psycho-physical errors, including adaptation and contrast effects. The terms used by the grader to describe the various qualities of body and texture do not always correspond to the qualities expected by the consumer. There have been, therefore, many endeavours in the past to evolve objective tests, which are attempts to apply mechanical or instrumental methods to measure the physical properties referred to above.

2. Rheology of Butter

The body and texture of butter are both influenced by the composition of the milk fat and the conditions under which the cream is processed/pre-treated before churning. The cream should be kept at a low temperature long enough for the fat to partially solidify. Texture can be spoilt by rough handling or overworking. These characteristics and the consequent spreadability of butter may be influenced by a variety of factors such as seasonal variation in the fat composition, size and clumping of the fat globule, the fat content of cream at churning, heat-treatment and cold storage of cream, the method of churning (including temperature, size of butter grains and washing process), the working, the moisture and salt content, and final blending of butter.

For quite a long time, investigations have been under way to measure instrumentally some of the rheological properties of finished butter. In fact, the earliest investigations on butter were reported at the end of the last century and were concerned with the penetrability of the material. The relationships between these measurements and the various factors in the making process, such as chemical composition, salting and working of butter, and more fundamentally the structural properties of the raw materials, have been investigated. The different methods of measurement include the penetrometer method, sectility method, extrusion method, single beam method, spreadability method and others. It is obvious that no single method can supply all the desired information about these structural properties of a sample of butter.

3. Rheology of Cheese

Largely as a result of the work done by Scott Blair and his collea-

gues at Reading in the United Kingdom, several methods for studying the rheological behaviour of cheese, milk and curd have been
evolved. Of the various tests which have been developed in that
count y, the plastic bowl and new torsiometer for measuring the
firmness of the coagulum before cutting, the curd pitching tester for
assessing the condition of the curd on pitching, and the ball compressor or hardness tester have been developed to the stage where
they can be usefully employed in cheese making. Other tests may
be of help to the research worker but are not yet suited or sufficiently understood to be of practical use. Methods for the control of
the rheological properties and structure of processed cheese have
also been described by several investigators.

4. Rheology of Other Products

Manufacturers' viscosity measurements of condensed and evaporated milks are now included in the routine tests for assessing their
consistency to meet consumer acceptance. It would be in the fitness
of things if rheological studies were to be taken up on Indian milk
products like khoa, chhana, rabri, etc.

APPENDIX IV
RECIPES FOR A FEW INDIAN MILK-SWEETS*

A. Khoa Sweets

1. PEDA

Ingredients

Khoa (Mawa)	225 g.
Sugar	75 g.
Pista (optional)	A few pieces
Silver paper (optional)	1 leaf
Cardamom (optional)	A few sticks

Method

Break freshly made khoa (mawa) into bits. Mix (preferably ground) sugar into it. Put into a karahi and cook over a very slow non-smoky fire, stirring all the while with a khunti. Add crushed cardamom if desired. When mixture is ready (mixture forms balls when tested), pour into a tray and leave to cool and set. Peda is now ready. Decorate, if desired, with silver paper and sliced pista. Cut into required size and shape to serve.

2. KALAKAND

Ingredients

Milk	1 kg.
Sugar	60 g.
Citric acid	1/2 g.
Pista (optional)	A few pieces
Silver paper (optional)	1 leaf
Cardamom	A few sticks

Method

Boil the specific quantity of milk in a karahi placed over a brisk

* Adapted from L. K. Gill and S. De: 'Sweets from Milk—Recipes', *NDRI Publication No. 119* (1974).

and non-smoky fire. Stir continuously with a khunti with a circular motion. After 10–15 minutes, add to it the required amount of citric acid as a dilute solution in water. This will partially coagulate the milk. At this time vigorous stirring is required to obtain a product of good quality. When a semi-solid stage is reached, add sugar and stir well. Add crushed cardamom if desired. Remove after five minutes. This finished product is set in a greasy tray or plate and allowed to cool at room temperature. Kalakand is now ready. Decorate, if desired, with silver paper and sliced pista. Cut into required size and shape to serve.

3. GULABJAMUN

Ingredients

Khoa	300 g.
Maida	35 g.
Baking powder	1/2 tsp. (teaspoonful)
Sugar	1 kg.
Water	1 kg.
Ghee	500 g.

Method

Break the entire (freshly made) khoa into bits. Mix baking powder into the maida separately. Add this mixture to the broken khoa and mix again. Now start kneading by adding small quantities of water until uniform dough is obtained. While kneading, there should be no oozing of fat. To avoid this, especially in summer, keep the vessel in which the kneading is done upon a tray in which ice or chilled water is kept. The consistency of the dough should be such that when made into small balls it has a smooth uncracked surface.

Meanwhile dissolve all the sugar in water, and boil the solution till a 2-string-consistency-syrup is obtained. During this process, add 4 tablespoonfuls of milk and ladle out the scum to obtain a clear syrup. Keep this in a container so that a minimum depth of about 10 cm. of syrup is obtained.

Now make the balls and test-fry in sufficient ghee or dalda (vegetable ghee) in a shallow karahi, so as to immerse the balls completely during frying. The balls should be neither over- nor underfried. They should be deep brown in colour. Cut one fried ball into two and examine the inside for porosity. If found satisfactory, then fry the whole lot. If insufficiently porous, add a minute quantity of baking soda solution, sprinkling and mixing it well into the dough, and repeat the process of test-frying, etc. If it is too porous and the ball bursts when fried, add small lots of maida instead and repeat the testing process.

Remove the balls and put them into syrup immediately, pressing them down in the sugar syrup for some time so that it soaks in. Keep gulabjamun at room temperature for at least 10–12 hours before serving.

5. BURFI (Plain and Chocolate)

Ingredients

Khoa (fresh and hot)	250 g.
Sugar (crystal)	75 g.
Chocolate	10 g.

Method

Break khoa into bits and spread it in a karahi. Add (preferably crystal) sugar to it and mix well by working vigorously with a wooden ladle. Collect the mixture into a compact mass when all the sugar has dissolved. This is Plain Burfi. Now separate one-third of the mixture and mix chocolate into it. Take a well-greased plate and spread plain burfi (two-thirds of the mixture) as a thick layer. Apply the chocolate-mixed portion all over it as a thin layer. Allow to cool and set at room temperature. This is Chocolate Burfi. Cut into desired size and shape to serve.

BURFI (Coconut)

Ingredients

Khoa	275 g.
Sugar	135 g.
Coconut (grated, fine and dried)	35 g.
Silver paper (optional)	1 leaf
Colour (optional)	A few drops

Method

Mix sugar with broken khoa, put into a karahi over gentle heat and stir with a khunti. When the mixture is ready (mixture forms balls when tested) remove it from the fire. Add coconut with the fingers and stir well. Spread on a greased tray, keeping aside a little. Mix colour, light pink or green, in the portion set aside. Put back on the fire. Cook till it becomes creamy. Spread on top of the first layer. Allow to cool. Decorate with silver paper, if desired. Cut into desired size and shape to serve.

B. Chhana Sweets

1. SANDESH

Ingredients

Chhana	250 g.
Sugar	75 g.
Flavour (optional)	A few drops
Cardamom (optional)	A few sticks

Method

Break freshly-made chhana into bits. Mix (preferably ground) sugar into it. Put the mixture in a karahi and heat on a slow fire stirring all the time with a khunti. (Add crushed cardamom, if desired, towards the end.) When the mixture is ready (mixture forms balls when tested) pour it into a tray and leave it to cool and set. Sandesh is now ready. It is cut or moulded into the desired size and shape. (A popular flavour-cum-colour is saffron, which is admixed with the finished product before it is cut or moulded.)

2. ROSSOGOLLA

Ingredients

Chhana (soft)	200 g.
Maida (optional)	8 g.
Sugar	250 g.
Water	1 kg.
Elaichidana	A few pieces
Flavour (Rose)	A few drops

Method

Break the above quantity of chhana into bits and start kneading. There should be no oozing of fat during this operation. To avoid this, especially during summer, keep the vessel in which the kneading is done, upon a tray in which ice or chilled water is kept. If required, a small quantity (as above) of maida may be added to avoid cracks in the finished rossogollas. The consistency of the kneaded mass should be such that when made into small balls, it has a smooth surface without signs of cracks.

Meanwhile, dissolve all the sugar in water and boil the solution. During this process, add 2 tablespoonfuls of milk and ladle out the scum to obtain a clear syrup. Keep this in a suitable-sized degchi in which the chhana balls are to be cooked, such that a minimum depth of 10–15 cm. of syrup is obtained.

Now make the balls of chhana. While doing this, one sugar-coated elaichidana may be put in the centre of each ball. After all the balls (10–15) have been made, put them gently in the boiling sugar syrup for the cooking process. See that the balls do not over-crowd the degchi and that there is enough space for them to move freely, especially after they swell. Close the lid of the vessel. The heating should be so controlled that the balls are constantly covered with foam. Keep a watch from time to time. After 5–10 minutes, the balls will swell. If the chhana has been well-made and properly kneaded, the balls will not crack or break. After 5–10 minutes, the colour of the balls will darken slightly. The finished rossogollas should normally be ready after 20–25 minutes. During the last stage, the lid should be removed so that the sugar syrup finally attains 1-string consistency. After cooling, sprinkle flavour (rose) to serve.

Note: In the trade, the cooking process is usually carried out in large karahis. The sugar syrup has a 1-string consistency right at the beginning, and this is maintained throughout by sprinkling cold water regularly from time to time during the entire cooking period.

3. CHHANA-KHEER (Kheer-Paneer)

Ingredients

Milk	1 kg.
Chhana	150 g.
Sugar	40 g.
Flavour (optional)	A few drops
Dry nuts (optional)	A few pieces

Method

Cut the chhana into small cubes. Boil the milk and reduce it to one-half of its original volume. Add sugar to it and boil further till its original volume is reduced to one-third. Then add the pieces of chhana and continue heating gently until the sugar has penetrated into chhana cubes. (When cool, sprinkle flavour on the chhana kheer. If desired, decorate with dry nuts.)

4. CHHANA-MURKI

Ingredients

Chhana	250 g.
Sugar	125 g.
Water	45 g.

Flavour (optional)	A few drops
Dry nuts (optional)	A few pieces

Method

Dissolve sugar in water and boil the mixture until it has a 3-string consistency. Add to it 4 tablespoonfuls of milk to clear the sugar solution of suspended dirt, etc.

Cut the chhana into small cubes and put them into the prepared syrup in a karahi. Boil the mixture for 5 minutes, stirring gently to ensure that the cubes do not break. Remove karahi from the fire and allow the contents to cool. Stir the cubes further till the entire sugar is uniformly coated around them. Chhana-murki is ready (When cool, sprinkle flavour (kewra) on it. If desired, serve multi-coloured and decorate with dry nut flakes.)

C. (Khoa + Chhana) Sweet

1. PANTOOA

Ingredients

Khoa	300 g.
Chhana	300 g.
Baking powder	1/2 tsp.
Maida	35 g.
Sugar	1 kg.
Water	1 kg.
Ghee	500 g.

Method

Break all the khoa and chhana into bits. Mix baking powder with the maida separately. Add this mixture to the broken khoa and chhana and mix again. Now start kneading, adding small quantities of water until a uniform dough is obtained. Thereafter proceed as for gulabjamun.

APPENDIX V
CONVERSION TABLES

1. *Units*

Base units	Metric system	British system
Length	Metre (m.)	Foot (ft.)
Mass (weight)	Kilogram (kg.)	Pound (lb.)
Time	Second (s.)	Second (s.)

2. *Prefixes and symbols*

1,000,000	$= 10^6$	Mega	(M)
1,000	$= 10^3$	Kilo	(k)
100	$= 10^2$	Hecto	(h)
10	$= 10^1$	Deca	(da)
0.1	$= 10^{-1}$	Deci	(d)
0.01	$= 10^{-2}$	Centi	(c)
0.001	$= 10^{-3}$	Milli	(m)
0.000,001	$= 10^{-6}$	Micro	(μ)

3. *Conversion: Units of length*

Conversion→To ↓ From	Metre	Centimetre	Feet	Inch
Metre	1	100	0.281	39.37
Centimetre	0.01	1	0.328	0.393
Feet	0.3048	30.48	1	12
Inch	0.0254	2.54	0.0833	1

1 metre = 10 decimetres = 100 centimetres = 1000 millimetres
1 kilometre = 10 hectometres = 100 decametres = 1000 metres
1 micron = 10^{-3} millimetres = 10^{-6} micrometres
1 km = 0.6214 mile; 1 mile = 1.609 kms
1 mile = 8 furlongs = 1760 yards
1 yard = 0.9144 metre; 1 metre = 1.0936 yards

Appendix V

4. *Conversion: Units of area*

Conversion→To ↓ From	Square metre	Square yard	Square feet	Square inch
Square metre	1	1.196	10.764	1550.00
Square yard	0.836	1	9	1296
Square feet	0.0929	0.1111	1	144
Square inch	0.000645	0.00077	0.0069	1

1 sq. in. = 6.452 sq. cm.; 1 sq. cm. = 0.1550 sq. in.
1 hectare = 10,000 sq. metres = 2.471 acres
1 acre = 4848 sq. yds. = 4046.8 sq. metres = 0.4047 hectare
1 sq. mile = 640 acres

5. *Conversion: Units of volume*

Conversion→To ↓ From	Cubic feet	U.S. gallon	British gallon	Litre	Cubic metre
Cubic feet	1	7.48	6.229	28.316	0.0283
US gallon	0.1337	1	0.833	3.785	0.0038
British gallon	0.1605	1.201	1	4.546	0.0045
Litre	0.0353	0.2642	0.220	1	0.001
Cubic metre	35.314	264.173	220.0	1000.0	1

1 Br. gallon = 4 quarts = 8 pints
1 pint = 20 oz. (fluid)
1 cu. in. = 16.387 c.c.; 1 c.c. = 0.061 cu. in.
1 fl. oz. = 29.5737 c.c. = 1.8047 cu. in.

6. *Conversion: Units of mass (weight)*

Conversion→To ↓ From	Seer	Maund	Pound (Avoir.)	Kilogram	Tonne (Metric)
Seer	1	0.025	2.057	0.933	—
Maund	40	1	82.286	37.324	0 0373
Pound (Avoir.)	0.486	—	1	0.4535	—
Kilogram	1.0717	0.0268	2.2046	1	0.001
Tonne (Metric)	1071.7	26.792	2204.6	1000	1

1 long ton = 20 cwt. = 27.22 maunds = 2240 lb. (avoir.)
    = 1016.05 kg. = 1.016 tonne
1 cwt. = 112 lb. (avoir.) = 50.80 kg. = 1.3611 md.
1 seer = 16 chataks = 80 tolas
1 quintal = 100 kg. = 220.46 lb.
1 maund = 0.37 quintal = 0.7347 cwt.
1 oz. = 2.45 tolas; 1 tola = 11.664 g.
1 lb. (avoir.) = 16 oz. = 453.59 g.
1 oz. = 28.35 g.; 1 g. = 0.03527 oz.

7. *Conversion: Temperature*

$$\frac{C}{5} = \frac{F - 32}{9}$$

$1°C = 1.8°F; 1°F = 0.555°C$

where C = Centigrade and F = Fahrenheit

8. *Formulae*

Area of a circle = πr^2
Circumference of a circle = $2\pi r$
Surface of a sphere = $4\pi r$
Volume of a sphere = $\frac{4}{3}\pi r^3$

where r = radius and π = 22/7

9. *Pressure*

1 kg./sq. cm. = 14.223 psi; 1 psi = 0.07 kg./sq. cm..

BOOKS RECOMMENDED

General

1. Davis, J. G.: *A Dictionary of Dairying*, Leonard Hill Ltd., London (1955); Supplement (1965).
2. Farrall, A. W.: *Engineering for Dairy and Food Products*, John Wiley and Sons Inc., New York (1963).
3. Foster, E. M., Nelson, F. E., Speck, M. L., Doetsch, R. N. and Olson, J. C.: *Dairy Microbiology*, Prentice-Hall Inc., Englewood Cliffs, New Jersey (1957).
4. *Indian Standard Specifications*, Indian Standards Institution, Manak Bhavan, New Delhi.
5. Jenness, R. and Patton, S.: *Principles of Dairy Chemistry*, Wiley Eastern Pvt. Ltd., New Delhi (1969).
6. Lampert, L. M.: *Modern Dairy Products*, Eurasia Publishing House (P) Ltd., New Delhi (1970).
7. Nelson, J. A. and Trout, G. M.: *Judging Dairy Products*, The Olsen Publishing Co., Milwaukee, Wisconsin (1964).

Market Milk and Special Milks

1. Hall, C. W. and Trout, G. M.: *Milk Pasteurization*, The A.V.I. Publ. Co. Inc., Westport, Connecticut (1968).
2. Henderson, J. L.: *The Fluid-milk Industry*, The A.V.I. Publ. Co. Inc., Westport, Connecticut (1971).
3. Kay, H. D. and others: *Milk Pasteurization, Planning, Plant Operation and Control*, F.A.O. Agricultural Studies No. 23, F.A.O., Rome (1953).
4. *Manual for Milk Plant Operators*, Milk Industry Foundation, Washington D.C. (1957).
5. Sommer, H. H.: *Market Milk and Related Products*, The Author, Madison, Wisconsin (1952).

Cream, Butter, Butteroil

1. Hunziker, O. F.: *The Butter Industry*, The Author, La Grange, Illinois (1940).
2. McDowall, F. H.: *The Buttermaker's Manual*, Vols. I & II, New Zealand University Press, Wellington (1953).

Ice Cream

1. Arbuckle, W. S.: *Ice Cream*, The A.V.I. Publ. Co. Inc., Westport, Connecticut (1972).

2. Sommer, H. H.: *The Theory and Practice of Ice Cream Making*, The Author, Madison, Wisconsin (1952).

Cheese

1. Davis, J. G.: *Cheese*, Vols. I & III, J & A Churchill Ltd., London (1965 and 1976).
2. Van Slyke, L. L. and Price, W. V.: *Cheese*, The Orange Judd Publ. Co. Inc., New York (1952).

Condensed and Dried Milk Products

1. Hall, C. W. and Hedrick, T. I.: *Drying of Milk and Milk Products*, The A.V.I. Publishing Co. Inc., Westport, Connecticut (1971).
2. Hunziker, O. F.: *Condensed Milk and Milk Powder*, The Author, La Grange, Illinois (1949).

Indian Dairy Products

1. Rangappa, K. S. and Achaya, K. T.: *Indian Dairy Products*, Asia Publishing House, Bombay (1974).
2. Srinivasan, M. R. and Anantakrishnan, C. P.: *Milk Products of India*, ICAR Animal Husbandry Series No. 4, New Delhi (1964).
3. *Report on the Marketing of Ghee and Other Milk Products in India*, Marketing Series No. 85, Manager of Publications, Delhi (1957).

By-products

1. Webb, B. H. and Whittier, E. O.: *By-products from Milks*, The A.V.I. Publ. Co. Inc., Westport, Connecticut (1970).

INDEX